11.25 ERR 74G1

HORSES
AND
HORSEMANSHIP

(Animal Agriculture Series)

M. E. Ensminger, B.S., M.A., Ph.D.

Formerly: Assistant Professor in Animal Science
University of Massachusetts

Chairman, Department of Animal Science
Washington State University

Consultant, General Electric Company
Nucleonics Department (Atomic Energy Commission)

Currently: President
Consultants-Agriservices
Clovis, California

President
Agriservices Foundation

Collaborator
U.S. Department of Agriculture

Distinguished Professor
Wisconsin State University

HORSES
AND
HORSEMANSHIP

THE INTERSTATE
PRINTERS & PUBLISHERS, INC.

Danville, Illinois

First Edition, 1951
Second Edition, 1956
Third Edition, 1963
Fourth Edition, 1969

Library of Congress
Catalog Card No. 68-24651

To Rex C. Ellsworth, who, through rare ability and sheer determination, has carved a large niche in any horseman's Hall of Fame. It all began on his father's Arizona ranch, where Rex first acquired basic knowledge of horses astride a cow pony. In 1933, he attended his first Thoroughbred sale in Kentucky, from which he returned with three mares, all acquired for a total of $300. Many obstacles were strewn along the way between that unpretentious, three-mare beginning in 1933 and the winning of the Kentucky Derby in 1955. His staunch Mormon parents frowned upon his horse enterprise; there was the depression with which to cope; and it almost seemed that a Swaps would never come along. Anyone less resolute than Rex Ellsworth wouldn't have made it.

To Rex C. Ellsworth—because he is a man of character and determination, because his success story is an inspiration to every boy and girl in America, and because he is a master breeder and racer of Thoroughbreds.

Preface to the Fourth Edition

This generation has more money to spend and more leisure time in which to spend it than any population in history. In 1968, leisure time spending consumed an average of 10 percent of personal income, or an amount equal to 47 billion dollars.

Today, draft horses and mules are of negligible economic importance, having become the victims of mechanization and automation. But the light horse business has continued to increase in importance. In 1969, there were an estimated 6,865,000 horses in the United States; and it is predicted that we shall have 5 million more by 1980.

Horse racing continues to be America's leading spectator sport. In 1968, 68,899,989 people went to horse races (Thoroughbred and harness races)—27.9 million more than went to automobile racing, the second ranking spectator sport; 31.8 million more than went to football (pro and college), the third-ranking sport; and 35.4 million more than witnessed baseball (including both major and minor leagues), which ranked fourth.

In 1968, 825 horse shows sanctioned by the American Horse Shows Association (AHSA) offered premium money totalling $2,879,280.

Currently, United States horses make for a gross business—from vitamins to saddlery—of about 5 billion dollars per year. Additionally, horses inventory out at approximately $5.3 billion.

In 1966, for the first time in history, 4-H club horse and pony projects took the lead over 4-H beef cattle projects, 165,510 to 157,949, respectively. Subsequently, this lead has been widened further—in 1969, there were 207,000 horse and pony projects to 154,742 beef projects.

But a really big horse boom lies ahead—provided horsemen are geared for it. A shorter work week, increased automation, more suburban and rural living, and the continued recreation and sports surge, with emphasis on physical fitness and the out-of-doors, will require more horses and support more racetracks, shows, and other horse events. Yet, it is inevitable that there will be greater competition for the recreation and sports dollar in the years ahead. To meet this competition, horsemen must accept and use scientific, technological, and business methods similar to those employed by (1) successful livestock operators with other classes of animals, and (2) their competitors. Their pocketbooks can no longer stand the luxury of fads, foibles, and trade secrets.

This revision of *Horses and Horsemanship* was prepared to assist those progressive horsemen who want to improve their lot—those who wish to move ahead rather than follow two paces to the rear, and those students, teachers, and researchers who have need for an up-to-date and authoritative book on horses.

Grateful appreciation is expressed to all those who, through their reviews, imparted authoritativeness and confidence to this book.

M. E. ENSMINGER

Clovis, California
September, 1969

The following books are by the same author and the same publisher as *Horses and Horsemanship*:

ANIMAL SCIENCE

BEEF CATTLE SCIENCE

SHEEP AND WOOL SCIENCE

SWINE SCIENCE

THE STOCKMAN'S HANDBOOK

Animal Science presents a perspective or panorama of the far-flung livestock industry; whereas each of the specific class-of-livestock books presents specialized material pertaining to a specific class of farm animals.

The Stockman's Handbook is a modern "how to do it" book which contains, under one cover, the pertinent things that a stockman needs to know in the daily operation of a farm or ranch. It covers the broad field of animal agriculture, concisely and completely, and, whenever possible, in tabular and outline form.

Other Selected General References

Title of Publication	Author(s)	Publisher
Anatomy of the Horse, The	Robert F. Way Donald G. Lee	J. B. Lippincott Company, Philadelphia and Montreal, 1965.
Horse Care	Frederick Harper	Popular Library, New York, N. Y., 1966.
Horse, The	D. J. Kays	Rinehart and Company, New York, N. Y., 1953.
Horseman's Encyclopedia, The	Margaret Cabell Self	A. S. Barnes and Company, Inc., London and Toronto, 1963.
Horseman's Handbook on Practical Breeding, The	Col. J. F. Wall	Thoroughbred Bloodlines, Camden, S. C., 1950.
Horsemanship & Horsemastership	Gordon Wright	Doubleday & Company, Inc., Garden City, N. Y., 1962.
Horses and Horsemanship 4-H Horse Program	Federal and State Extension Services	National 4-H Service Comm., Inc., Chicago, Ill., 1965.
Horse Science 4-H Horse Program	Federal and State Extension Services	National 4-H Service Comm., Inc., Chicago, Ill., 1965.
Horse Science Handbook Vol. 1—1963 Vol. 2—1964 Vol. 3—1966	Edited by Dr. M. E. Ensminger	Agriservices Foundation, Clovis, Calif.
Horses: Their Selection, Care and Handling	M. C. Self	A. S. Barnes & Co., Inc., New York, N. Y., 1943.
Horses of Today	H. H. Reese	Wood & Jones, Pasadena, Calif., 1956.
Light Horse Breeds, The	J. W. Patten	A. S. Barnes & Co., Inc., New York, N. Y., 1960.
Light Horses; Farmers' Bulletin 2127, USDA	M. E. Ensminger	Supt. of Documents, Govt. Printing Office, Washington, D. C.
Practical Horse Breeding and Training	Jack Widmer	Charles Scribner's Sons, New York, N. Y.
Practical Light Horse Breeding	J. F. Wall	The Monumental Printing Co., Baltimore, Md., 1936.
Shetland Pony, The	L. Frank Bedell	The Iowa State University Press, Ames, Ia., 1959.

Title of Publication	Author(s)	Publisher
Stud Managers' Handbook Annual, beginning with Vol. 1 in 1965.	Edited by Dr. M. E. Ensminger	Agriservices Foundation, Clovis, Calif.
Summerhays' Encyclopedia for Horsemen	R. S. Summerhays	Frederick Warne and Co., Ltd., London and New York, 1966
Western Horse, The Its Types and Training	J. A. Gorman	The Interstate Printers & Publishers, Inc., Danville, Ill., 1967.

Contents

APPENDIX

1

In this chapter . . .

1

History and Development of
the Horse Industry[1]

THE EVOLUTION AND TRANSFORMATION of the horse from the early-day wild forms, its subsequent domestication, and the overlapping uses made of it in both war and peace is a fascinating story.

EVOLUTION OF THE HORSE

Fossil remains prove that members of the horse family roamed the plains of America (especially what is now the Great Plains area of the United States) during most of Tertiary time, beginning about 58 million years ago. Yet no horses were present on this continent when Columbus discovered America in 1492. Why they perished, only a few thousand years before, is still one of the unexplained mysteries of evolution. As the disappearance was so complete and so sudden, many scientists believe that it must have been caused by some contagious disease or some fatal parasite. Others feel that perhaps it was due to multiple causes; including (1) climatic changes, (2) competition, and/or (3) failure to adapt. Regardless of why horses disappeared, it is known that conditions in America were favorable for them at the time of their re-establishment by the Spanish conquistadores, less than 500 years ago.

Through fossil remains, it is possible to reconstruct the evolution of the horse (see Table 1-1), beginning with the ancient four-toed

[1]In the preparation of Chapter I, the author was especially fortunate in having the valued counsel and suggestions of Mr. Karl P. Schmidt, formerly Chief Curator of the Department of Zoology, Chicago Natural History Museum, Chicago, Illinois, who so patiently and thoroughly reviewed this historical material.

ancestor, the *Eohippus* (meaning "dawn horse"). This was a small animal, scarcely more than a foot high, with four toes on the front feet and three toes on the hind feet, and with slender legs, a short neck, and even teeth. It was well adapted to traveling in and feeding on the herbage of swamp lands. Gradually, the descendants of *Eohippus* grew in size and changed in form, evolving into a three-toed animal known as *Mesohippus*, which was about 24 inches in height or about the size of a collie dog. Further changes continued, transforming the animal from a denizen of the swamp to a creature capable of surviving in the forest and finally to one adapted to the prairie. In terms of conformation, the animal grew taller. The teeth grew longer, stronger, and more roughened to suit the gradual changes to grazing on the prairie. The cannon bones—metacarpals and metatarsals—lengthened; the middle toe (or third toe) grew longer and stronger, forming a hoof; and the other toes (second and fourth toes) gradually disappeared except for vestiges, the slender bones known as splints, under the skin. The transformation in length and structure of foot made for greater speed over prairie type of terrain, thus enabling the animal to feed farther and farther from water, and providing for greater safety in its struggle to survive. The horse is an excellent example, therefore, of the slow adaptation of animal life to changing conditions in environment, climate, food, and soil. The animal was transformed from one adapted to a swamp type environment to one adapted to the prairie.

Though all horses eventually perished in the New World and none were present on the continent when America was discovered, fortunately some of these animals had long before emigrated to Asia and Europe at a time when there was a land bridge connecting Alaska and Siberia (now the Bering Strait). These emigrants formed the sturdy wild European stock from which the horse family of today descended, and this stock also populated Africa with its asses and zebras.

From Table 1-1, it can be seen that the evolution of the horse covered a period of approximately 58,000,000 years; but that man hunted him as recently as 25,000 years ago and domesticated him a mere 5,000 years ago, and that the Spanish conquistadores returned him to the New World less than 500 years ago.

ORIGIN AND DOMESTICATION OF THE HORSE

The horse was probably the last of present-day farm animals to be domesticated by man. According to early records, after subduing the ox, the sheep, and the goat, man domesticated the ass and then the camel; and, finally, the horse became his servant.

Horses appear to have been domesticated first in Central Asia or Persia more than 3,000 years B. C., for they spread westward through southern Europe in the time of the Lake Dwellers. They were reported in Babylonia as early as 2000 B. C., perhaps coming into the country via neighboring Persia.

Although the Egyptians—the most advanced civilization of the day—had domesticated and used the ass from the earliest times, horses were wholly unknown to them until the dynasty of the Shepherd Kings, who entered Egypt from Asia in 1680 B. C. It is reported that, thereafter, the horse was much favored in Egypt.

Presence of the horse seems to have prompted the invention of the chariot, a type of vehicle drawn by horses that the Egyptians used in war and other pursuits. The Bible also relates that when Joseph took his father's remains from Egypt back to Canaan "there went up with him both chariots and horsemen."[2] It is probable that the Egyptians were largely responsible for the spread of domesticated horses to other countries.

Certainly, Greece was not even peopled, and there were no horses in Arabia during the early period when they were flourishing in Egypt. But horses and chariots were used in Greece at least a thousand years before Christ, to judge from the account of their use in the siege of Troy. It is also interesting to note that the first and most expert horsemen of Greece, the Thessalians, were colonists from Egypt. As evidence that the Greeks were accomplished horsemen, it might be pointed out that they developed the snaffle bit at an early period. Also, one of their number is said to have originated the axiom "No foot, no horse." Yet the use of the saddle and stirrups appears to have been unknown at this time.

From Greece, the horse was later taken to Rome and from there to other parts of Europe. The Romans proved to be master horsemen. It was they who invented the curb bit. According to historians, when Caesar invaded Britain, about 55 B. C., he took horses with him. Although there were other horses in Britain at the time of the Roman occupation, Eastern breeding was probably greatly infused at this time—thus laying the foundation for the Blood Horse of today.

---

[2]Genesis 50:9.

Eras	Periods	Epochs	Approximate Duration in Years	Approximate Number of Years Since Beginning	General Characteristics
Cenozoic (Recent life) Age of Mammals and Angiosperms	Quaternary	Recent	12,000±	12,000±	Post Glacial Age. Rise of Modern Man, *Homo sapiens*. Development of complex cultures and civilizations. Domestication of animals.
		Pleistocene (Gr. *pleistos*, most+*kainos*, recent)	1,000,000	1,000,000	Ice Age: Four major advances Evolution of primitive man, Neanderthal, Heidelberg, Peking, Java, etc. Mammoth, mastodon, great slot, saber-tooth tiger, etc. 90-100% modern species. Rise of Alps and Himalayas.
	Tertiary	Pliocene (Gr. *pleion*, more+*kainos*)	11,000,000	12,000,000	Mammals increase in size. 50-90% modern species.
		Miocene (Gr. *meion*, less *kainos*)	16,000,000	28,000,000	The "Golden Age" of mammals. Luxuriant grasses; culmination of plains-dwelling mammals. 20-40% modern species.
		Oligocene (Gr. *oligos*, little+*kainos*)	10,000,000	38,000,000	Modern mammals predominate over primitive ones. 10-15% modern species.
		Eocene (Gr. *eos*, dawn+*kainos*)	20,000,000	58,000,000	Archaic mammals, the advent of the horse. 1-5% modern species.
		Paleocene	17,000,000	75,000,000	The beginning of the age of mammals. Great development of the angiosperms. 1% modern species.

[1]Grateful acknowledgement is made to the following eminent authorities for their help in the preparation of this table: Dr. Frank Scott, Department of Geology, Washington State University, and Mr. Karl P. Schmidt, formerly Chief Curator, Department of Zoology, Chicago Natural History Museum, Chicago, Illinois. (Drawings by R. F. Johnson)

DECIPHERED FROM THE FOSSIL RECORD[1]

The Horse[2]

Equus (Modern Horse. *Equus*, is Latin for horse). Beginning about 25,000 years ago, during the Paleolithic (Old Stone Age), man hunted horses and used them as a source of food. They were probably the last of the common domestic animals to be domesticated. This domestication is thought to have occurred toward the end of the Neolithic (New Stone Age) about 5,000 years ago. The horse was returned to the "New World" by the Spanish conquistadores less than 500 years ago.

Equus (Modern Horse). One large functional toe on each foot with the two side toes reduced to mere splint bones and entirely non-functional. The horse reached the climax of his evolutionary development with *Equus*. Several known species in North America. Most of these were the size of small ponies but one fully equaled the greatest of modern draft horses. However, in the Americas he died out toward the end of the Pleistocene Epoch; perhaps due to multiple causes, including: (1) climatic changes, (2) competition, (3) epidemic, and/or (4) failure to adapt. Fortunately, however, horses had found a land bridge (probably via Alaska and Siberia) into the Old World, where they survived to become a servant and friend to man. They had entered the Old World by this same route at other times in the Tertiary past.

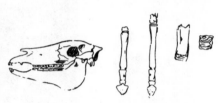

Pliohippus (Gr. *pleion*, more+*hippos*, horse). First one toed horse, the side toes being reduced to splints. High-crowned grazing type teeth. Pony size. This was the immediate and virtually fullgrown forerunner of *Equus*. Also *Hipparion* (Gr. dim. of *hippos;* a pony), a three toed grazer, and several other genera.

Merychippus (Rudimentary horse. Gr. *Meryx*, ruminant+*hippos*, horse.) Three toes on each foot with the middle much heavier than the others which failed to touch the ground. A slim, graceful animal about the size of a Shetland pony. His teeth were high-crowned and hard-surfaced, suitable for eating grass. Thus *Merychippus* was thoroughly adapted to life on the prairie. Also *Protohippus* (Gr. *Protos*, first, primordial+*hippos*) generally similar to *Merychippus; Miohippus* (Gr. *meion*, less+*hippos*) with foot structure like *Merychippus* but with short-crowned, browsing, teeth; *Parahippus* (Almost, nearly *hippos*) and others.

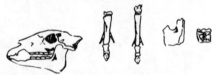

Mesohippus (Gr. *meso*, in the middle, intermediate-*hippos*). Three toes on each foot with the middle toe distinctly larger and a fourth toe on the front foot reduced to a splint, all touched the ground and shared in carrying the animal's weight. Teeth low-crowned, probably for browsing. *Mesohippus* was about the size of a collie dog with longer legs and a straighter back than his tiny Eocene forerunner. Also his intelligence and agility increased.

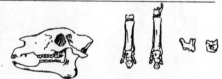

Eohippus (Gr. *eos*, dawn—*hippos*). Four functional toes on the front foot, one larger than the others, with a fifth reduced to a splint; the hind foot had three functional toes and a splint. *Eohippus* was a small graceful animal, scarcely more than a foot high with a slender face, an arched back, short neck, slender legs and a long tail. He was adapted for living in swamps. Also *Orohippus* (Gr. *oros*, mountain—*hippos*), having foot structure like *Eohippus* but without vestigial splints, and *Epihippus* (Gr. *epi*, upon, among—*hippos*).

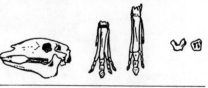

Pre-horse. The five toes (one a splint) on the forefeet of *Eohippus* indicate that its ancestor probably had five toes all around, but no five toed horse has yet been found. The ancestors of the horse were probably primitive five toed ungulates, perhaps similar to some primitive Condylarth.

[2]In some cases, other genera might well be listed, but the leading ones of the respective epochs are here given.

The Arabs, strangely enough, did not use horses to any extent until after the time of Mohammed (570 to 632 A. D.), depending on camels before that time. As evidence of this fact, it is noted that in the seventh century after Christ, when Mohammed attacked the

Fig. 1-1. Joseph using horses in his move to Egypt (about 1500 B.C.), from a miniature painting in the Bible of the Counts of Toggenburg, 16th century. (Courtesy, The Bettmann Archive)

Fig. 1-2. Distinguished young Greek in fashionable riding habit. Bowl painting, 500 B.C. Though the Greeks were accomplished horsemen, at this time the use of the saddle and stirrups appears to have been unknown. (Courtesy, The Bettmann Archive)

Koreish near Mecca, he had but two horses in his whole army; and at the close of his murderous campaign, although he drove off 24,000 camels and 40,000 sheep and carried away 24,000 ounces of silver, not one horse appeared in his list of plunder. This would seem to indicate rather conclusively that Arabia, the country whose horses have done so much to improve the horses of the world, was not the native home of the horse and that the Arabs did not use horses until after the time of Christ.

Of course, it seems incredible that all the various breeds, colors, and types of draft, light, and pony horses should have descended from a common, wild ancestor. Rather, there were probably many different wild stocks giving descent to domestic horses.

Fig. 1-3. Horses vary in size and use. The Shetland Pony foal (left) is thought to have descended from the small, shaggy, wild stock of northern Europe; whereas the draft horse (right) is thought to have descended primarily from the ponderous, wild black horse of Flanders. (Courtesy, Iowa State University)

The Wild Horse of Asia

The wild horses of Asia, which are sometimes referred to as the Oriental light-legged horses, were of Asiatic origin, tracing to a wild horse (now extinct) of the Asiatic deserts. Historic evidence indicates that this group of horses gave rise to most of the swift and slenderly built breeds of modern times. The Arabian, the Barb, and the Turk are all descendants of these animals; and, in turn, the Throughbred was originated from these stocks.

The Wild Horse of Europe

The European wild horse, sometimes referred to as the European forest type, continued to live in the forests of Germany and Scandinavia until historic times; and wild horses are believed to have lived in the Vosges Mountains on the western border of Alsace until the year of 1600. One of the pagan practices of the ancient German tribes was the sacrifice of horses and the eating of their meat at religious feasts. To this day one may find a relic of horse worship in the horse skulls set on the gables of houses and barns in southern Germany.

The European wild horse was the wild black horse of Flanders. This was a stocky animal that possessed considerably more size and scale than the Oriental type. This draft type was native to Western Europe at the time of the Roman invasion. It was the forerunner of the Great War Horse of the Middle Ages. The latter, in turn, fathered the modern draft breeds.

Not all wild horses of Europe were large, however, for small, shaggy animals were native to northern Europe. They were strong and hardy and required less feed than other types of horses. These animals are thought to be the progenitors of the Shetland Pony.

The Tarpan

Though now extinct, the Tarpan—a small dun-colored, genuine wild species of horse—was formerly abundant everywhere in southern Russia and Central Asia. These animals were hated by the farmers because they devoured their crops and especially because the Tarpan stallions constantly recruited domestic mares for their wild bands. For these reasons, they were killed off by the Russians, finally being completely exterminated by the year 1870.[3]

Przewalsky's Horse

The only surviving species of original wild horses—not feral or escaped from domestication—known to exist at the present time is Przewalsky's horse (or the Asiatic wild horse). This is the wild horse discovered by the Russian explorer, Przewalsky, in 1879, in the northwestern corner of Mongolia. It is a small, stockily built, and distinctly yellowish

---

[3]Some authors believe the Tarpan to have been a feral type; i.e., a horse escaped from domestication, and not a distinct wild form. Certainty as to this point can now scarcely be determined.

horse, with an erect mane and no forelock. There is usually a dark stripe on the shoulders and down the middle of the back. Like the wild mustang or feral horses of the frontier days, Przewalsky's horses separate into bands, seldom more than forty in number, with a stallion leader in each group. At the present time, it is reported that only three wild bands remain. Fortunately, however, live specimens have been

Fig. 1-4. Przewalsky's horse. This is the only surviving species of original wild horses—not feral or escaped from domestication—known to exist at the present time. Note that the animal is small and stockily built, with an erect mane and no forelock. (Courtesy, New York Zoological Society, New York)

brought to Europe and America where they are being preserved and propagated successfully in captivity. When crossed on domestic horses, the hybrids are fertile, which proves that Przewalsky's horse is very closely related to the domestic horse.

It is not intended to imply that Przewalsky's horse was the foundation stock of any or all of the present-day improved breeds throughout the world. Rather, this wild horse of Asia is extremely interesting because it is the only one known to have survived the vicissitudes of time.

Fig. 1-5. A Mongolian wild ass in the Gobi desert in Asia. (Courtesy, American Museum of Natural History, New York)

ORIGIN AND DOMESTICATION OF THE DONKEY

The two species of the horse family that have been tamed by man are *Equus caballus,* the horse, and *Equus asinus,* the ass or donkey. The history of the domestic donkey is as clear as that of the horse is obscure. Donkeys were first domesticated in Egypt, where they served man from earliest times. Good figures of them appear on slates of the First Dynasty, about 3400 B. C. Domestic donkeys are descended from the wild donkey (the Nubian wild ass) of North Africa, a species which is now almost extinct. Because of the frequent tendency to stripes on the legs, however, some zoologists also think that the domestic donkey is related to the Somali wild ass of Africa.

From Egypt, the use of the domestic donkey spread into southwestern Asia sometime prior to the year 1000 B. C. The Bible first refers to the ass in relating how Abraham, the patriarch of the Old Testament, rode one of these animals from Beersheba to Mount Mordah. Every child is familiar with the fact that Jesus rode into Jerusalem on an ass. This mode of transportation was not unusual at the time of Christ, for donkeys were then the common saddle animals throughout the Near East.

As is generally known, the donkey is commonly used in this country in the production of mules.[4] Mules have been known from very ancient times, as we learn from the accounts of the Trojan War.

POSITION OF THE HORSE IN THE ZOOLOGICAL SCHEME

The following outline shows the basic position of the domesticated horse in the zoological scheme:

Kingdom *Animalia:* Animals collectively; the Animal Kingdom.

Phylum *Chordata:* One of approximately 21 phyla of the animal kingdom, in which there is either a backbone (in the vertebrates) or the rudiment of a backbone, the chorda.

Class *Mammalia:* Mammals, or warm-blooded, hairy animals that produce their young alive and suckle them for a variable period on a secretion from the mammary glands.

Order *Perissodactyla:* Nonruminant hoofed mammals, usually with an odd number of toes, the third digit the largest and in line with the axis of the limb. This suborder includes the horse, tapir, and rhinoceros.

Family *Equidae:* The members of the horse family may be distinguished from the other existing perissodactyla (rhinoceros and tapir) by their comparatively more slender and agile build.

Genus *Equus:* Includes horses, asses, and zebras.

Species *Equus caballus:* The horse is distinguished from asses and zebras by the longer hair of the mane and tail, the presence of the "chestnut" on the inside of the hind leg, and by other less constant characters such as larger size, larger hoofs, more arched neck, smaller head, and shorter ears.

MAN'S USE OF THE HORSE

The name "horse" is derived from the Anglo-Saxon, *hors,* meaning swiftness; and the word horseman comes from the Hebrew root "to

---

[4]In recent years, some miniature donkeys are being used as children's pets in the United States.

prick or spur."[5] These early characterizations of the horse, within themselves, tell somewhat of a story. Perhaps the very survival of the wild species was somewhat dependent upon its swiftness, which provided escape from both beast and man. The Hebrew description of a horseman was obviously assigned after the horse had been domesticated and ridden by man.

The various uses that man has made of the horse down through the ages, in order of period of time, are: (1) as a source of food, (2) for military purposes, (3) in the pastimes and sports of the nations, (4) in agricultural and commercial pursuits, and (5) for recreation and sport.

The Horse as a Source of Food

Man's first use of the horse was as a source of food, these animals being hunted by Paleolithhic (Old Stone Age) man. This was prior to their domestication. These earliest records date back to some 25,000 years ago. Perhaps the best preserved record of this type consists of the cracked and dismembered bones of horses, mostly young animals, found around old camp sites. One bone heap of this sort is at Solutre, in the Rhone Valley in southern France. It is estimated that this one camp site contains the remains of 100,000 horses.

Following domestication, which is thought to have occurred some time toward the end of the New Stone Age, it is reasonable to surmise that mares were milked for human food—a practice still followed in certain parts of the world. Mares may give up to four and one-half gallons of milk per day.[6]

The Horse for Military Purposes

Unfortunately, not long after domestication of the horse, man used him for waging war. About 1500 B. C., Pharaoh pursued the Israelites to the Red Sea, using chariots and horses.[7] This would seem to imply that the Egyptian army used horses, both as cavalry and to draw vehicles.

During the glamorous days of the knight in armor, horses of size, strength, and endurance were essential. The Great Horse of medieval times was the knight's steed. Usually stallions were used. Often the

---

[5]The Jews were forbidden by divine authority to use horses. In fact, they were required to hamstring horses captured in war.
[6]Mares of mature weights of 600, 800, 1,000, and 1,200 pounds may produce 36, 42, 44, and 49 pounds of milk daily, respectively.
[7]Exodus 14:7.

knight and his armor weighed 350 to 425 pounds. During the Crusades and for several centuries after, the clad-in-armor type of warrior relied upon sheer weight to beat down the enemy.

The deeds of great warriors, mounted on their favorite chargers, were long perpetuated in marble or bronze. Every school boy vividly associates Alexander the Great with his charger, Bucephalus; Napoleon with his famous horse, Marengo; the Duke of Wellington with his favorite mount, Copenhagen; George Washington, receiving the surrender of Cornwallis' army at Yorktown, with his handsome mount, Nelson; and General Grant with his horse, Jack.

Many people are under the erroneous impression that no horses were used in World War II. Nothing could be further from the truth. But this is another story, to be related at the end of the present chapter.

The Horse in the Pastimes and Sports of Nations

As early as 1450 B. C., the sports-loving Greeks introduced the horse in the Olympic games, in both chariot and horse races. The most celebrated of these events was held at Olympia every fourth year in honor of Jupiter. However, because of the scarcity of horses, very few were used in early contests. Classes were divided according

Fig. 1-6. Chariot driven through Pompeii. The horse-drawn chariot was used by the sports-loving Greeks in chariot races, as well as in war and other pursuits. (Courtesy, The Bettmann Archive)

to age—and sometimes sex—and the distance of the course was approximately four miles.

For these important events, the Greeks trained both themselves and their horses. The chariot races were even provided with settings to tempt the charioteers to daring deeds. The chariots in use were a low, two-wheeled, narrow-track type of vehicle.

The Horse in Agricultural and Commercial Pursuits

For many years following domestication, horses were used for purposes of war and sport. Their use in pulling loads and tilling the soil is a comparatively recent development.

There is no evidence to indicate that the horse was used in Europe to draw the plow prior to the tenth century, and oxen remained the common plow animal in England until the end of the eighteenth century. Remains of ancient art show conclusively that, long after domestication of the horse, the ox and the camel continued as the main source of agricultural power and transportation, respectively.

It is interesting to note that heavier draft-type animals had their development primarily in those countries in which Caesar campaigned in western Europe, including England. Without doubt, the improved roads that the Romans constructed during their long occupation were largely instrumental in encouraging the breeding of heavier horses capable of drawing heavier loads. The Great Horse served as the progenitor of the draft horse of agriculture.

The Horse for Recreation and Sport

The present generation has more money to spend and more leisure time in which to spend it than any population in history. In 1968, leisure time spending consumed an average of 10 percent of personal income, or an amount equal to 47 billion dollars. The combination of available money, leisure time, and emphasis on the out-of-doors has created great interest in light horses for recreation and sport. As a result, the race crowds are bigger than ever, the bridle paths in the city parks are being lengthened each year, the game of polo is expanding, riding to hounds is sharing its glamour with greater numbers, people of all walks of life enjoy the great horse shows throughout the land, and saddle clubs are springing up everywhere. This trend will continue.

INTRODUCTION OF HORSES AND MULES
TO, AND EARLY HISTORY IN,
THE UNITED STATES

It has been established that most of the evolution of the horse took place in the Americas, but this animal was extinct in the Western World at the time of Columbus' discovery, and apparently extinct even before the arrival of the Red Man some thousands of years earlier.

Columbus first brought horses to the West Indies on his second voyage in 1493. Cortez brought Spanish horses with him to the New World in 1519 when he landed in Mexico (16 animals were in the initial contingent, but approximately 1,000 head more were subsequently imported during the two-year conquest of Mexico). Horses were first brought directly to what is now the United States by DeSoto in the year 1539. Upon his vessels, he had 237 horses. These animals traveled with the army of the explorer in the hazardous journey from the Everglades of Florida to the Ozarks of Missouri. Following DeSoto's death and burial in the upper Mississippi three years later, his followers returned by boats down the Mississippi, abandoning many of their horses.

One year following DeSoto's landing in what is now Florida, in 1540, another Spanish explorer, Coronado, started an expedition with an armed band of horsemen from Mexico, penetrating to a point near the boundary of Kansas and Nebraska.

Beginning about 1600, the Spaniards established a chain of Christian missions among the Indians in the New World. The chain of missions extended from the eastern coast of Mexico up the Rio Grande, thence across the mountains to the Pacific Coast. Each mission brought animals, including horses, from the mother country.

There are two schools of thought relative to the source of the foundation stock of the first horses of the American Indians, and the hardy bands of Mustangs—the feral horses of the Great Plains. Most historians agree that both groups were descended from animals of Spanish (Arabian) extraction. However, some contend that their foundation stock came from the abandoned and stray horses of the expeditions of DeSoto and Coronado, whereas others claim that they were obtained chiefly from Santa Fe, ancient Spanish mission founded in 1606. It is noteworthy that Santa Fe and other early Spanish missions were the source of Spanish Longhorn cattle, thus lending credence to the theory that the missions were the source of foundation horses for the Indian and the wild bands of Mustangs.

Much romance and adventure is connected with the Mustang, and each band of wild horses was credited with leadership by the most wonderful stallion ever beheld by man. Many were captured, but the real leaders were always alleged to have escaped by reason of speed, such as not possessed by a domesticated horse. The Mustang multiplied at a prodigious rate. In one high luxuriant bunch grass region in the state of Washington, wild horses thrived so well that the region became known as "Horse Heaven," a name it bears even today.

The coming of the horse among the Indians increased the strife and wars between tribes. Following the buffalo on horseback led to greater infringement upon each other's hunting grounds, which had ever been a cause for war. From the time the Indians came into possession of horses until the country was taken over by the white man, there was no peace among the tribes.

Later, animals of both light- and draft-horse breeding were introduced from Europe by the colonist. For many years, however, sturdy oxen continued to draw the plows for turning the sod on many a rugged New England hillside. Horses were largely used as pack animals, for riding, and later for pulling wagons and stagecoaches. It was not until about 1840 that the buggy first made its appearance.

Six mares and two stallions were brought to Jamestown in 1609, these being the first European importations. Some of these animals may have been eaten during the period of near starvation at Jamestown, but importations continued; and it was reported in 1611 that a total of seventeen horses had been brought to this colony.

The horse seems to have been much neglected in early New England, as compared with cattle and sheep. This is not surprising, inasmuch as oxen were universally used for draft purposes. Roads were few in number; speed was not essential; and the horse had no meat value like that of cattle. Because of the great difficulty in herding horses on the commons, they were usually hobbled. Despite the limited early-day use of the horse, the colonists must have loved them, because, very early, the indiscriminate running of stallions among the mares upon the commons was recognized as undesirable. Massachusetts, before 1700, excluded from town commons all stallions "under fourteen hands high and not of comely proportion."[8]

Even before horses found much use in New England, they became valuable for export purposes to the West Indies for work in the

---

[8]Thompson, James Westfall, *History of Livestock Raising in the United States, 1607-1860,* USDA, Agricultural History Series No. 5, Nov., 1942.

Fig. 1-7. A covered wagon, drawn by horses. This was a common method of transportation in this country prior to the advent of the railroad and the motor vehicle. (Photo by Ewing Galloway, New York)

sugar mills. In fact, this business became so lucrative that horse stealing became a common offense in New England in the eighteenth century. Confiscation of property, public whippings, and banishment from the colony constituted the common punishments for a horse thief.

As plantations materialized in Virginia, the need for easy-riding saddle horses developed, so that the owners might survey their broad estates. Racing also became a popular sport among the Cavaliers in Virginia, Maryland, and the Carolinas—with the heat races up to four miles being common events. The plantation owners took considerable pride in having animals worthy of wearing their colors. So great was the desire to win that by 1730 the importation of English racehorses began.

George Washington maintained an extensive horse- and mule-breeding establishment at Mount Vernon. The President was also an ardent race fan, and riding to hounds was a favorite sport with him. As soon as Washington's views on the subject of mules became known abroad, he received some valuable breeding stock through gifts. In 1787, the Marquis de Lafayette presented him with a jack and some jennets of the Maltese breed. The jack, named Knight of Malta, was described as a superb animal, of a black color, with the form of a stag and the ferocity of a tiger. In 1795, the King of Spain

Fig. 1-8. Conestoga freight wagon drawn by six Conestoga horses, in front of a country inn. These improved horses and large wagons were both given the name Conestoga, after the Conestoga Valley, a German settlement in Pennsylvania. The advent of the railroads drove the Conestoga horses into oblivion, and the Conestoga wagon was succeeded by the prairie schooner. (Courtesy, The Bettmann Archive)

gave Washington a jack and two jennets that were selected from the royal stud at Madrid. The Spanish jack, known as Royal Gift, was 16 hands high, of a gray color, heavily made, and of a sluggish disposition. It was said that Washington was able to combine the best qualities of the two gift jacks, especially through one of the descendants named Compound. General Washington was the first to produce mules of quality in this country, and soon the fame of these hardy hybrids spread throughout the South.

The Dutch, Puritan, and Quaker colonists to the north adhered strictly to agricultural pursuits, frowning upon horse races. They imported heavier types of horses. In Pennsylvania, under the guidance of William Penn, the farmers prospered. Soon their horses began to improve, even as the appearance and fertility of their farms had done. Eventually, their large horses were hitched to enormous wagons and used to transport freight overland to and from river flatboats and barges along the Ohio, Cumberland, Tennessee, and Mississippi rivers. Both horses and wagons were given the name Conestoga, after the

Conestoga Valley, a German settlement in Pennsylvania. The Conestoga wagon[9] was the forerunner of the prairie schooner, and before the advent of the railroad it was the freight vehicle of the time. It was usually drawn by a team of six magnificent Conestoga horses, which were well groomed and expensively harnessed. At one time, the Conestoga horses bid to become a new breed—a truly American creation. However, the railroads replaced them, eventually driving them into permanent oblivion. Other breeds were developed later, but this is another story.

GROWTH AND DECLINE OF UNITED STATES HORSE AND MULE PRODUCTION

The golden age of the horse extended from the Gay Nineties to the mechanization of agriculture; to the advent of the automobile, truck, and tractor. During this era, everybody loved the horse. The town livery stable, watering trough, and hitching post were trademarks of each town and village. People wept when the horse fell on the icy street, and jailed men who beat or mistreated him. The oat-bag, carriage, wagon, buggy-whip, axle-grease, horseshoe, and horseshoe-nail industries were thriving and essential parts of the national economy. Every school boy knew and respected the village blacksmith.

Bob-tailed hackneys attached to high-seated rigs made a dashing picture as they pranced down the avenue; they were a mark of social prestige. A few memorable dinner parties of the era were even staged on horseback; with the guests lining up in exclusive restaurants astride their favorite mounts (see Figure 1-9).

In 1900, the automobile was still the plutocrat's plaything, and the truck and tractor were unknown. Most of the expensive 8,000 cars in the country at the time were either imported or custom built. Tires cost about $40.00 each, and lasted only 2,000 miles. Few really loved the auto. Complaints were made of the noise autos made; laws were enacted against their going through the city parks; and people

---

[9]It is noteworthy that the American custom of driving to the right on the road, instead of to the left as is the practice in most of the world, is said to have originated among the Conestoga wagon drivers of the 1750's. The drivers of these four- and six-horse teams either sat on the left wheel horse or on the left side of the seat, the better to wield their whip hand (the right hand) over the other horses in the team. Also, when two Conestoga drivers met, they pulled over to the right so that, sitting on the left wheel horse or on the left side of the seat, they could see that the left wheels of their wagons cleared each other. Lighter vehicles naturally followed the tracks of the big Conestoga wagons.

Fig. 1-9. A horseback dinner staged in Louis Sherry's restaurant, corner of Fifth Avenue and 44th Street, New York City, on March 28, 1903, with Cornelius K. G. Billings—racing enthusiast, Chicago utilities heir, and self-styled "American Horse King"—as host. To publicize his newly opened $200,000 stable at 196th Street and Fort Washington Road (now Fort Tryon Park), Mr. Billings converted the grand ballroom of Sherry's into a woodland paradise by means of $10,000 worth of full-scale scenic props, artificial foliage, potted palms, and a tanbark floor covering—borrowed, at Mr. Sherry's insistence, from the Barnum and Bailey Circus. Thirty-six mystified horses were conveyed up to the ballroom by freight elevators, and the guests—members of the New York Riding Club—attired in white ties and tails, and gingerly astride their favorite mounts, drank and ate to the merriment of music, while their steeds munched oats, and costumed lackeys cleaned up behind them. (Photo by Byron, The Byron Collection, Museum of the City of New York)

split their sides with laughter when autos had to be pushed uphill or got stuck in the mud.

Then, in 1908, Henry Ford produced a car to sell at $825. The truck, the tractor, and improved highways followed closely in period of time. Old dobbin did not know it at the time, but his days were numbered. As shown in Table 1-2 and Figure 1-10 the passing of the horse age and the coming of the machine age went hand in hand; as automobile, truck, and tractor numbers increased, horse and mule numbers declined.

The number of horses in the United States increased up to 1915, at which time there was a record number of 21,431,000 head. Horse production expanded with the growth and development of farms.

Table 1-2

U.S. FARM AND RANCH (1) HORSE AND MULE POPULATION, (2) TRACTOR NUMBERS, (3) TRUCK NUMBERS, AND (4) AUTOMOBILE NUMBERS, FROM 1900 to 1960

Year	Horses and Mules	Tractors Nos. (excluding garden)	Trucks Nos.	Automobiles Nos.
1900	21,531,635[1]			
1905	22,077,000[2]			
1910	24,042,882[1]	1,000[3]	0[3]	50,000[3]
1915	26,493,000[2]	25,000[3]	25,000[3]	472,000[3]
1920	25,199,552[1]	246,083[4]	139,169[4]	2,146,362[4]
1925	22,081,520[1]	505,933[4]	459,000[3]	3,283,000[3]
1930	18,885,856[1]	920,021[4]	900,385[4]	4,134,675[4]
1935	16,676,000[5]	1,048,000[3]	890,000[3]	3,642,000[3]
1940	13,931,531[5]	1,567,430[4]	1,047,084[4]	4,144,136[4]
1945	11,629,000[6]	2,422,000[7]	1,490,000[7]	4,148,000[7]
1950	7,604,000[6]	3,394,000[7]	2,207,000[7]	4,199,000[7]
1955	4,309,000[6]	4,692,000[7]	2,701,000[7]	4,258,000[7]
1960	3,089,000[6]	4,770,000[7]	3,110,000[7]	4,260,000[7]
1961 (Horses only)	5,625,008[8]	4,700,000[9]	2,850,000[9]	3,587,000[9]
1965	6,150,000[8]	4,625,000[9]	2,925,000[9]	
1968	6,675,000[8]	4,820,000[9]	3,125,000[9]	

[1]1950 Census of Agriculture, pp. 385, 387.
[2]Agricultural Statistics, 1952, p. 455.
[3]Agricultural Statistics, 1952, p. 631.
[4]1950 Census of Agriculture, p. 204.
[5]1950 Census of Agriculture, p. 398.
[6]Agricultural Statistics, 1960, p. 370.
[7]Agricultural Statistics, 1960, p. 449.
[8]See Table 2-1, Chapter 2, this book.
[9]Agricultural Statistics, 1968, p. 441.

On the other hand, mules on farms slowly but steadily increased in numbers for ten years after horses began their decline, reaching a peak in 1925 at 5,918,000 head. Mule numbers decreased proportionally less than horses because of their great use in the deep South where labor was cheaper and more abundant and the farms smaller in size.

On January 1, 1968, there were an estimated 6,675,000 head of horses, mostly light horses, in the United States.[10] Draft animals have been the victims of mechanization; farming has changed. Between 1940 and 1968,[11] the number of tractors on U.S. farms more than tripled to 4,820,000; trucks on farms nearly tripled to 3,125,000; combines increased from 190,000 to 870,000; and corn pickers increased from 110,000 to 640,000.

[10]Ensminger, M.E., Fact Sheet Relative to U.S. Horse Population, August, 1968.
[11]Agricultural Statistics, USDA, 1954 and 1968.

Millions

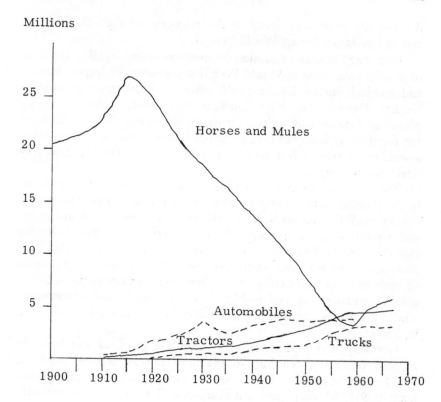

Horses and Mules

Automobiles

Tractors

Trucks

Fig. 1-10. United States horse and mule numbers. Horse numbers reached a peak in 1915, whereas mule numbers reached a peak in 1925. The period of decline in horse and mule numbers coincided closely with the advent of mechanized power, especially the tractor, truck, and automobile. Tractor, truck, automobile, and horse and mule numbers to 1960 were secured from *Agricultural Statistics*, published by USDA. Data, beginning in 1961, on which this chart is based, was secured from Table 1-2 of this book. The rise in horse numbers since 1960 (and it is light horses only; draft horses and mules were eliminated because of their negligible importance) is due to (1) increased numbers of horses for recreation and sport, and (2) suburban-owned horses being included in estimates, rather than the estimates being limited to horses on farms over 10 acres in size. (Drawing by Dennis Gadberry)

THE STORY OF HORSES AND MULES IN WORLD WAR II; THE REMOUNT SERVICE

Though declining in numbers and considered "old fashioned" by those persons who are enthralled by the speed of the machine age, the horse—man's good friend and stout companion through the ages—

dramatically proved his worth again and again on the field of battle and on our farms during World War II.

Once the bulwark of armies—its numbers often deciding the issue of conflict—the horse in World War II was practically jeeped, tanked, and trucked out of his long-held place of importance in military history. Despite the unparalleled mechanization, however, horses played an indispensable role on many fronts during the great struggle for freedom. It is an old cavalry axiom that a horse can go wherever a man can travel, a feat which even the Army's famous little jeep could not accomplish.

The use of horses in World War II reached its greatest proportions in the Russian Army. Long famous for its Cossacks and centuries of cavalry tradition, Russia had, in 1940, about 200,000 horses in cavalry and 800,000 more in artillery, draft, and pack. It is also estimated that the U.S.S.R. had two mounted armies available for combat. The Russian cavalry is credited with playing a decisive role in the defense of both Moscow and Stalingrad—striking swift, devasting blows, then quickly withdrawing and melting into the forests and countryside. The full story of the role played by the Russian Cossacks may never be known.

Germany and Japan also recognized the place of the horse in modern warfare. According to the most reliable sources available, the Germans at one time had 50,000 horses for cavalry use and approximately 910,000 draft and pack animals. The Japanese—constantly building up their horse units in China, where large areas were prohibitive to motor vehicles—probably had a cavalry force of 50,000 horses with an additional 300,000 in use for draft and pack purposes.

The United States Army had relatively few horses during World War II—only about 25,000 for cavalry use and 12,000 for draft and pack—but these units performed magnificently in combat. The 26th Cavalry fought a brilliant delaying action on Luzon; and both horses and mules were used in the Burma and Italian campaigns, which were conducted through jungles and over mountains where no vehicle of any sort could go.

On the civilian front, the contributions of horses and mules, though less spectacular than on the field of battle, were nonetheless substantial. Though statistics show a continued gradual but steady decline in horse and mule numbers throughout the war years, perhaps figures alone do not tell the true story. With the rationing of critical rubber and gasoline, the diverting of iron and steel to war production, and the consequent shortage of equipment—all resulting in a scarcity

Fig. 1-11. Pack mules and "mule skinners" in service during World War II. Horses and mules dramatically proved their worth again and again on the field of battle and on our farms during World War II. (U. S. Army Photo)

of mechanized power—there is little doubt that the horses and mules on farms in the United States were utilized to the maximum to help carry the major load of farm production.

During the five war years, 1941 to 1945, the total number of horses on farms declined 13.5 percent below the average of 1936 to 1940.

The Remount Service, which was established by Act of Congress in 1921, was transferred to the United States Department of Agriculture on July 1, 1948, following which the program was liquidated. At the time of the transfer, approximately 700 remount stallions were in service throughout the country.

In summary, it may be said that the relentless wheels of progress lifted from the horse—that faithful beast of burden—his role in both agriculture and war. But the horse is not being relegated to permanent oblivion. Instead, he is rising to a more happy position in contributing to the fields of recreation and sport.

Selected References

Title of Publication	Author(s)	Publisher
Appaloosa Horse, The	Francis Haines G. B. Hatley Robert Peckinpah	R. G. Bailey Printing Co., Lewiston, Ida., 1957.
Changes in Horse Numbers As Related to Farm Mechanization, Recreation, and Sport	B. G. Stark	Thesis, Washington State University, Pullman, Wash., 1960.
Encyclopaedia Britannica		Encyclopaedia Britannica, Inc., Chicago, Ill.
Evolution of the Horse	W. D. Matthew and S. H. Chubb	American Museum of Natural History, New York, N. Y., 1921.
History of Domesticated Animals, A	F. E. Zuener	Harper & Row, Publishers, Inc., Great Britain
History of Thoroughbred Racing in America	Wm. H. P. Robertson	Prentice-Hall, Inc., Englewood Cliffs, N. J., 1965.
Horse, The	D. J. Kays	Rinehart & Company, New York, N. Y., 1953.
Horses	G. G. Simpson	Oxford University Press, New York, N. Y., 1951.
Horses and Americans	P. D. Strong	Frederick A. Stokes Company, New York, N. Y., 1939.
Horses of Today	H. H. Reese	Wood & Jones, Pasadena, Calif., 1956.
Our Friendly Animals and Whence They Came	K. P. Schmidt	M. A. Donohue & Co., Chicago, Illinois, 1938.
Power to Produce	Yearbook of Agriculture, 1960	U. S. Department of Agriculture, Washington, D. C., 1960.
Principles of Classification and a Classification of Mammals, The	G. G. Simpson	Bulletin of the American Museum of Natural History, Vol. 85, New York, N. Y., 1945.
Thoroughbred Racing Stock	Lady Wentworth	Charles Scribner's Sons, New York, N. Y., 1938.

2

In this chapter . . .

2

Distribution, Adaptation, and the Future of the Horse Industry

SINCE PREHISTORIC TIMES, there has been nearly world wide distribution of the horse. Moreover, man's effective use of the horse has constantly progressed, especially from the standpoint of improvement in the equipment to which the horse was attached for the purpose of drawing loads. But horsemen recognize the passing of the horse as a source of power. For the most part, his future is in the fields of recreation and sport and as the cow pony of the West.

WORLD DISTRIBUTION OF HORSES AND MULES

After the horse was domesticated and no longer hunted down and killed for meat, he was used to carry riders and support goods upon his strong back. In an effort to provide transportation for a longer load than could be fastened directly to the back of the horse, ingenious man devised a basket-like arrangement which was fitted between two long poles. One end of these poles rested on the back of the horse and the other end dragged on the ground to the rear. In an effort to reduce the resistance of this vehicle and permit the carrying of still heavier loads, man supported the poles on a wooden axle and two wheels made of wood, thus inventing a two-wheeled cart. Next, leather harness was developed, transferring the pull from the back of the horse to the better-adapted shoulders. Finally, man developed the four-wheeled, self-supporting vehicle with improved axles made of iron instead of wood; and eventually he replaced steel wheels with pneumatic tires mounted on ball bearings.

31

At a very early date and throughout the world, the versatility
and adaption of the horse were recognized. He was unexcelled in
carrying a rider comfortably and swiftly on a long journey; he
possessed a long life of usefulness; and, above all, he was intelligent.
Despite all these virtues, in some areas the horse has been unable
to replace the patient "roughage-burning" ox. To this day, oxen are
still the main source of power on farms in such densely populated
countries as India, Pakistan, and Mainland China, in many Near
Eastern and African countries, and in some countries of Latin America;
and water buffalo are the main source of power in rice-producing
areas, because of their ability to work in muddy paddy fields. In the
more isolated portions of the New England states, oxen are still used,
and stone boat pulling contests are a great attraction at the New
England fairs.

Members of the ass family (mules and donkeys) are distributed
in the warmer regions of the world, where they still occupy a rather
important place among the animals used for both pack and draft
purposes.

Table 2-1 shows the size and density of horse population of the
important horse countries of the world. According to the best available data, world horse numbers in 1961-62 totaled 64.7 million head.
This was far below the 1934-38 prewar average of 96.4 million head.
The decline in horse numbers since 1938 can be attributed chiefly
to mechanization of agriculture in certain areas. For example, the
number of tractors in use in agriculture in the world (exclusive of
the U.S.S.R. and Mainland China) in early 1954 was estimated at 6.7
million units, compared with fewer than 2 million in 1939.

UNITED STATES HORSE POPULATION

The sharp decrease in the number of horses and mules in the United
States during the last four decades has had a serious and far-reaching
effect upon American agriculture—and indirectly upon all industry. In
1920, there were 25,199,552 horses and mules on farms and ranches in
the United States and about an additional 2,000,000 head in cities, but
by January 1, 1960, there were only 3,089,000 head on the nation's
farms and ranches (not counting suburban-owned horses on parcels
under 10 acres in size). Thus, despite expansion in light horse numbers
since World War II, until recent years there has been a steady decrease
in the total number of horses and mules since the 1920's. Naturally, the
explanation of this marked decrease is the invasion of the automobile,

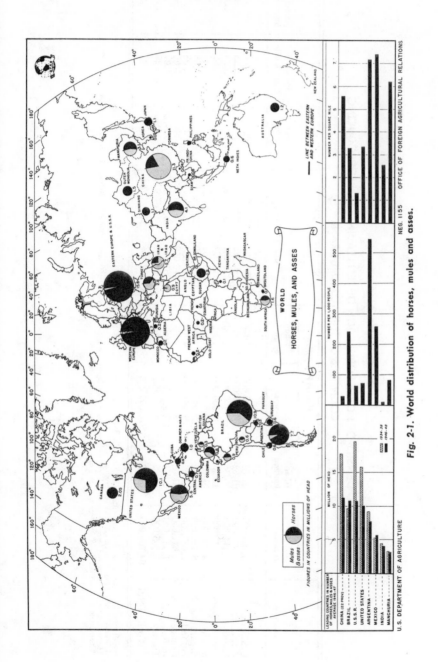

Fig. 2-1. World distribution of horses, mules and asses.

Table 2-1

SIZE AND DENSITY OF HORSE POPULATION OF TEN LEADING HORSE-PRODUCING COUNTRIES OF THE WORLD, BY RANK

Country	Horses[1]		Human Population[2]		Size of Country		Horses per Capita[3]	Horses per Square Mile	Horses per Square Km
	Number	When Estimated	Number	When Estimated	(sq. mile)	(sq. km)			
U.S.S.R.	9,400,000	61/62	229,100,000	1964	8,655,890	22,418,755	.027	1.09	.41
Brazil	8,374,000	61/62	78,809,000	1964	3,286,270	8,511,439	.11	2.55	.98
China	7,411,000	55/56	686,400,000	1960	2,279,134	5,902,957	.01	3.25	1.25
United States	6,675,000[4]	1968	200,000,000	1968	3,548,974	9,191,843	.03	1.88	.73
Mexico	4,169,000	61/62	39,643,000	1964	758,259	1,963,891	.11	5.50	2.12
Argentina	3,930,000	61/62	22,045,000	1964	1,072,700	2,778,293	.18	3.66	1.41
Poland	2,657,000	61/62	31,161,000	1964	120,359	311,730	.09	22.08	8.52
France	1,617,000	61/62	48,492,000	1965	212,659	550,787	.03	7.60	2.93
India	1,351,000	60/61	471,627,000	1964	1,261,597	3,267,536	.003	1.07	.41
Turkey	1,305,000	61/62	31,118,000	1964	296,500	767,935	.04	4.40	1.69
World Total	64,700,000	61/62	3,220,000,000	1965	52,403,746	138,725,702	.02	1.23	.47

[1]*Production Yearbook*, Food and Agriculture Organization, Volume 17, Table 71, 1963.
[2]*World Almanac*, 1966, New York World-Telegram.
[3]Horses per capita computed from most recent horse and human census figures reported; in some cases use of data for different years necessitated.
[4]Ensminger, M. E., *Fact Sheet Relative to U.S. Horse Population*, April, 1968.

Fig. 2-2. Horse-drawn covered wagons. This photograph was taken when making the film for the "Covered Wagon," founded on Emerson Hough's novel of the same name. When the news was spread that gold had been discovered in California, the Oregon Trail split in half, one part branching off to the south while the other part turned north toward Oregon. Improved roads and the advent of the motor vehicle have practically eliminated horses from the highways and city streets. (From Ewing Galloway)

tractor, truck, and improved heavy farm machinery; and in point of time, the decrease in horses has closely followed the introduction of such machinery.

This decrease in the work stock of the country was a considerable factor in the overproduction problem which confronted American agriculture, except during and immediately following World War II. It has been estimated that about 100,000,000 acres of land that formerly had produced feed for draft horses and mules was released for other purposes. This surplus production represents an area two and one-half times the size of the state of Illinois.

Today, there is much disagreement relative to the U.S. horse population. Part of the confusion stems from the fact that the

Census Bureau figures of horses have always been limited to those on farms (and ranches), with no consideration given to those owned by suburbanites. Most population figures fail to reflect the shift in the horse population from farm to town.

To complicate matters still further, there is little unanimity of opinion on the definition of a farm; on the dividing line between farm and non-farm. Then the *coup de grâce* was administered when the census takers discontinued counting horses in 1960; they counted Old Dobbin out with the passing of the draft horse. But they failed to recognize that the light horse was coming up fast; indeed, that the horse was rising to a new and more important position in the fields of recreation and sport.

Thus, some definitions are necessary if horse population figures are to be meaningful. Hence, the author presents the following:

1. *Farm.*—The definition of a farm varies from source to source, and from time to time. Webster defines a farm as "any tract devoted to agricultural purposes." The U.S. Census Bureau has changed its definition from time to time. As recently as 1954, it drew the line at 3 acres; units under 3 acres being classed as non-farm, and over 3 acres as farm. In 1960, the figure was changed to 10 acres. In addition to acreage, the Census Bureau has certain stipulations relative to income. Using its definitions, there were 3.2 million farms in 1967.

   By common usage, a farm is a parcel of land used for agricultural purposes from which the operator derives most of his income.

2. *Rural population.*—The words "rural" and "farm" are frequently, but erroneously, used interchangeably. At one time, this was essentially correct, for most rural residents lived on farms. But with the rise of "rural living," this was no longer true. Today, there are about 54 million rural residents,[1] with a distribution between farms and "other rural, but non-farm" as follows:

   a. *Farm*—11.5 million people (using the Census Bureau definition of a farm).[2]

   b. *Other rural, but non-farm*—42.5 million people live in the open country,[3] but not on farms; they live in small, unincorporated

---

[1] *The World Almanac 1966*, p. 324 (from Bureau of the Census—Census 1960).
[2] *Agricultural Statistics 1967*, p. 526, Table 649.
[3] 54 million (rural) — 11.5 million (farm) = 42.5 million "other rural, but non-farm."

places, along highways and streams, and in suburban areas. They're craftsmen, foremen, and operators; white-collar workers; manufacturers; and other commuters. They moved to the country to recapture a romantic ideal, to escape the hustle and bustle of city life, to cut the cost of living, or to find a better place for their children. Others moved to the country to acquire a status symbol, for prestige, or for gracious living. Many of them have rural backgrounds or are only a generation or two removed from the land. Among these non-farm rural people are many ardent horsemen.

3. *U.S. horse population.*—By using as guideposts (a) the census figure of horses on farms in 1960 and (b) Cornell's survey estimate of total U.S. horses in 1964,[4] and by making certain arbitrary assumptions and computations, the author arrived at the following estimates of U.S. horse population:

	1968 horse numbers
Farm horses (using the Census Bureau definition of a farm)	2,605,000
Non-farm horses	4,070,000
Total U.S. horses	6,675,000

The computations out of which the 6,675,000 figure evolved are shown in Table 2-2.

The leading states in horse numbers, by rank, are: Texas, California, Kentucky, Tennessee, Missouri, and Florida.

HORSES VERSUS MECHANICAL POWER

Ironical as it may seem, the development of manufacturing and commerce has been responsible for both the rise and fall of the horse and mule industry of the United States. The early growth of American industry created a large need for horses to transport the raw and manufactured goods and to produce needed agricultural products for those people who lived in the cities and villages. With further scientific developments—especially the invention of the tractor, truck,

---

[4] *New York Equine Survey*, by Prof. Harold A. Willman, Department of Animal Husbandry, Cornell University, Ithaca, New York, February 15, 1965; with national estimate of "over six million horses" projected therefrom by Dr. David L. Call, Graduate School of Nutrition, Cornell University, in a paper entitled "Looking Ahead at the Pet Food Market." Latter paper was given at 1964 Cornell Nutrition Conference for Feed Manufacturers, Buffalo, New York.

and automobile—the horse was replaced, first ever so slowly but then rapidly and drastically.

Over a period of time, mechanical power has been perfected from the standpoint of durability, versatility, and ease and economy of operation. No doubt further progress along these lines lies ahead.

Today, very few horses are found on city streets. The old-time livery stable has long since passed out of existence; draft horses are seldom hitched to large dray wagons; and horses hitched to a delivery wagon or to a plow are almost a novelty.

THE FUTURE OF THE HORSE INDUSTRY

Horse numbers will continue to increase. In 1969, there were an estimated 6,865,000 horses. It is predicted that we shall have 5 million more by 1980.

It is expected that the estimated 500,000 horses in the 17 western range states will continue to hold their own. Even the Jeep is not sufficiently versatile for use in roping a steer on the range. It is reasonable to assume, therefore, that the cow pony will continue to furnish needed assistance to man in the West.

Horse racing now outdraws automobile racing by 27.9 million people; and it outdraws football (pro and college) by 31.8 million people, and baseball (including both major and minor leagues) by more than 35.4 million. It will continue to be America's leading spectator sport, although there will be increased competition for the recreation and sports dollar in the years ahead.

Nationally, in 1966, for the first time, 4-H Club horse and pony projects exceeded 4-H beef projects—165,510 to 157,949, respectively. Subsequently, this lead has been widened further—in 1969, there were 207,000 horse and pony projects to 154,742 beef projects.

In total, U.S. horses make for an industry, ranging from vitamins to saddlery, of 5 billion dollars per year. Additionally, horses inventory out at approximately $5.3 billion.

But a really big horse boom lies ahead! A shorter work week, increased automation, more suburban and rural living, and the continued recreation and sports surge—with emphasis on physical fitness and the out-of-doors, will require more horses and support more racetracks, shows, and other horse events.

In the final analysis, the dominant factors that will determine the future of the horse situation are: (1) the need for the cow pony and (2) the use of horses for recreation and sport.

Table 2-2

U.S. HORSE POPULATION

Year	Estimated No. Mares Bred[1]	Estimated No. Foals Produced[1]	Estimated Death Losses[1]	Horses on Farms	Horses on Non-farms	Total U.S. Horses
1960	275,000	137,500	50,000	2,125,000[2]	3,400,000	5,525,000
1961	300,000	150,000	50,000			5,625,000
1962	325,000	162,500	50,000			5,737,500
1963	350,000	175,000	50,000			5,862,500
1964	375,000	187,500	50,000			6,000,000 (Cornell survey estimate)
1965	400,000	200,000	50,000	2,400,000	3,750,000	6,150,000
1966	425,000	212,500	50,000	2,470,000	3,850,500	6,312,000
1967	450,000	225,000	50,000	2,530,000	3,957,500	6,487,500
1968	475,000	237,500	50,000	2,605,000	4,070,000	6,675,000

[1]Estimates by Dr. M. E. Ensminger.
[2]M. E. Ensminger, *Horses and Horsemanship*, 3rd Ed., 1963, p. 33. The 2,125,000 figure was for 1958-59, which is arbitrarily estimated by the author to be the same for 1960.

Fig. 2-3. The way it used to be done. (Courtesy, USDA)

Horse Research

The Age of Research was ushered in with World War II, the most notable accomplishment of which was the developing and unleashing of the atom bomb. Now we are in a space age, and all industry, big and little—including the horse business—must be geared to it. Other animal industries have long been cognizant of new frontiers possible through research. But horse research has lagged. In 1967, the scientific man years (a man year is defined as one person devoting full time to research for one year) devoted to research on each class of livestock by USDA and college personnel was as follows:

Class of Animal	Scientific Man Years Devoted to Research, in 1967
Dairy Cattle	587.0
Beef Cattle	542.1
Poultry	488.0
Swine	236.2

(*continued*)

Fig. 2-4. The cow pony of the West will continue to furnish needed assistance in han-dling the range herds. (Courtesy, The Quarter Horse Journal)

Sheep and Wool 208.8
Horses 12.0
Other 74.7

There is every reason to believe that today's research will be reflected in a host of tomorrow's advances; that many of today's horse problems will be solved through research. Indeed, horse research should be expanded. More specifically, and among other things, we need to know the following in the light horse business:

1. We need to know how to modernize rations and effect savings in costs.

2. We need to know how to rectify appalling and costly sterility and reproductive failures; forty to sixty percent of all mares that are bred fail to foal.

3. We need to know how (a) to bring mares in heat at will, and (b) to transplant fertilized eggs (on an experimental basis, ova trans-plantation has been achieved extensively in rabbits).

4. We need to improve artificial insemination.

5. We need to know more about the relationship between soil fertility, plant nutrients, and horses.

6. We need to know how to provide labor-saving buildings and equipment. Seventy-five percent of horse work is still hand labor, one-third of which could be eliminated by mechanization and modernization.

Fig. 2-5. White Lipizzan stallion literally flying through the air with perfectly-seated stirrupless rider. The horse is decorated with gold trappings and the rider is smartly dressed in an old-time Napoleonic military uniform. The stallion is pictured doing the Capriole, one of several intricate movements resembling the leaping, twisting, fighting, and frolicking of high-spirited horses in pasture.

The Lipizzan breed—named after the town of Lipizza, one time site of the old Hapsburg stud farm—was founded back in 1565 by Emperor Maximilian of Austria. The emperor assembled white animals of Arabian and Spanish breeding, and established the Spanish Riding School in Vienna, Austria. Foals of the Lipizzan breed are brown or gray at birth, but turn completely white at four to six years of age.

Toward the close of World War II, the Spanish Riding School and the Lipizzan breed were threatened with extinction by both the German and Russian armies. In desperation, the school heads appealed to excavalryman George S. Patton whose tanks were dashing across Austria in the spring of 1945. After observing a special exhibition of the historic white horses, the horse fancier General agreed to preserve and protect the entire herd as a part of European culture. To this end, the Spanish Riding School and its horses were moved to Wels, Austria, near Salzburg. (Courtesy, Colonel Alois Podhajsky, Spanish Riding School, Wels, Austria)

7. We need to know more about automation and integration; how to reap the rewards therefrom.

8. We need to know how to control more diseases and parasites.

9. We need to know how to increase the durability and useful life of a horse—in racing, in showing, and in breeding.

We must remember, however, (1) that horse research is both slow and costly, and (2) that other industries have long liberally supported research costs with no assistance from the taxpayer, simply including them as a normal part of their operating costs. In addition to individual owners contributing to the support of research programs, the time has arrived when horsemen should review where racing dollars go. Perhaps a liberal proportion of racing revenue which now goes into the treasuries of the 30 states having pari-mutuel betting should be earmarked for horse research, teaching, and extension. Otherwise, there is grave danger of starving "the goose that laid the golden egg."

Finally, it should be emphasized that research can make the information available, but it is still up to each individual—each horseman —to secure and apply the results; "you can lead a horse to water but you can't make him drink."

What's Ahead

We have just begun to apply science, automation, and technology to light horses, an industry in which the following developments appear to lie ahead:

1. *Light horse numbers will increase.*—The light horse business will continue to expand, especially in the area of recreation and sport.

2. *The biological sciences will arrive.*—In the present space age, the physical sciences—physics, mathematics, and chemistry—are having their day. In the next fifty years, the greatest advances will be in the biological sciences—and many of these will come via the animal route, for living material will be used in these studies. Now that the physical sciences have discovered how to destroy mankind, the biological sciences will unlock many of the secrets of the living organism.

3. *Those adhering to status quo will lose.*—In a democracy, change is up to the individual; but in the future, sheer survival in the competitive horse industry will be dependent on the use of science and technology. Horsemen will not be able to cling to horse-and-buggy methods while the rest of industry forges ahead.

4. *Increasing competition.*—Horse production will, in common with

most businesses, encounter increasing competition in the years ahead. Competition will be keen for land, labor, and capital; and from other sports.

5. *More chemicals.*—More chemicals will be used (a) to control diseases and parasites, and (b) as feed additives.

6. *Skilled management; producing for the market.*—Skilled management and production programs geared to produce horses that meet more exacting market demands will be the two essential ingredients for success.

It will require greater skill and understanding of fundamental relationships to take care of highly bred, sensitive animals in forced production.

7. *There is reason for confidence and optimism.*—Never has there been so much reason to have confidence in, and to be optimistic about, the future. The years ahead will be the most rewarding in the history of the horse industry.

Selected References

Title of Publication	Author(s)	Publisher
Changes in Horse Numbers As Related to Farm Mechanization, Recreation, and Sport	B. G. Stark	Thesis, Washington State University, Pullman, Wash., 1960.
Horse, The	D. J. Kays	Rinehart & Company, New York, N. Y., 1953.
Light Horses	M. E. Ensminger	Farmers' Bul. No. 2127, U. S. Department of Agriculture, Supt. of Documents, U. S. Govt. Printing Office, Washington, D. C.
Power to Produce	Yearbook of Agriculture	U. S. Department of Agriculture, Washington, D. C., 1960.
Use of Horses and Mules on Farms, The	J. J. Csorba	ARS 43-94, March 1959, U. S. Department of Agriculture, Washington, D. C.

3

In this chapter . . .

3

Functional Anatomy
of the Horse

THIS CHAPTER IS NOT DESIGNED to cover the structure of the horse purely from an anatomical standpoint. Rather, its purpose is to relate the structure to desired function and usefulness. Broadly speaking, one type of animal is required for slow, heavy, draft purposes, and quite another for recreation and sport. This is really the distinction between draft and light horse breeds. However, further and very fundamental differences in structure fit the respective types and breeds for more specific purposes. Thus, the Thoroughbred running horse possesses certain hereditary structural characteristics which better fit him for speed and endurance than for usage as a five-gaited saddle horse. For the same reason, hunters are seldom obtained from among American Saddle Horses. In general, these structural differences between different types of horses are as marked as the fundamental differences between beef-type and dairy-type cattle. Yet, it must be pointed out that, regardless of the usage to which the animal is put, horsemen universally emphasize the importance of good heads and necks, short couplings, strong loins, and good feet and legs.

SKELETON OF THE HORSE

The skeleton of the horse consists of 205 bones, as follows:

Vertebral column 54
Ribs 36
Sternum 1
Skull (including auditory ossicles) 34
Thoracic limbs 40
Pelvic limbs 40

        Total 205

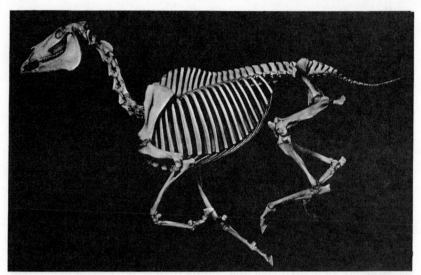

Fig. 3-1. Skeleton of the famous American racehorse Sysonby, showing action at the run. This illustration shows how the bones act as levers as (1) the hind legs are drawn up beneath the body, then moved forward preparatory to straightening out and propelling the horse forward with a long stride typical of great running horses, and (2) the front legs sustain a tremendous jar as the horse lands. The run is a four-beat gait where the feet strike the ground separately; first one hind foot, then the other hind foot, then the front foot on the same side as the first hind foot, then the other front foot which decides the lead. (Courtesy, The American Museum of Natural History, New York, N. Y.)

Vertebral Column

In the preceding summary, it is considered that there is an average of 18 coccygeal (tail) vertebrae. In addition, the vertebral column consists of 7 cervical (neck) vertebrae, 18 dorsal (back), 6 lumbar (loin), and 5 sacral (croup) vertebrae.

In horses of the correct conformation, the lower line of the dorsal vertebrae (commonly referred to as the backbone) is arched slightly upward. The degree to which the backbone is arched in different horses varies greatly. If the arch is extreme, the animal is referred to as "roach backed"; whereas if the backbone sags very markedly, the animal is known as "sway backed." Either of these conditions represents a weakness in conformation and is objectionable.

Desired height at the withers and proper topline are obtained through variation in the length of the spinous processes which project upward from the vertebrae. Thus, the structure at this point is of especial importance in the saddle horse, determining the desirableness of the seat.

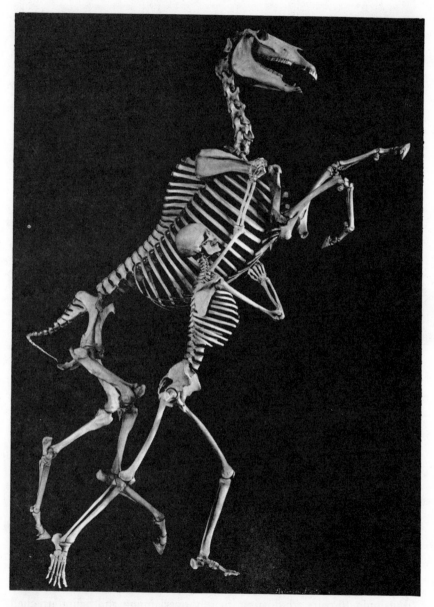

Fig. 3-2. Skeleton of horse and man. It can be seen that: (1) the knee joint in the horse is the counterpart of the wrist joint in man; (2) the stifle joint in the horse is the counterpart of the knee joint in man; and (3) the hock joint in the horse is the counterpart of the ankle joint in man. (Courtesy, The American Museum of Natural History, New York, N. Y.)

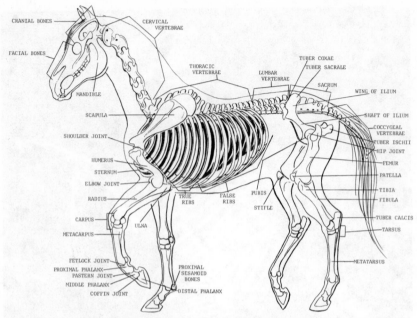

Fig. 3-3. Skeleton of horse. (Drawing by Ethel Gadberry)

There is a close correlation between the length of the individual vertebrae and the length of the component parts of the entire animal. Thus, an animal with long vertebrae has a long neck, back, loin, croup, and tail. Within limits, length is desired. For example, the longer neck on a saddle horse gives the desired effect of "much horse in front of the rider." On the other hand, a very long back and loin are objectionable, denoting lack of strength. Apparent length of back may be alleviated by having a sloping shoulder, with the upper end joining the back at the rear part of the withers.

Ribs

There are usually eighteen pairs of ribs in the horse, but a nineteenth rib on one side or both is not at all rare. Eight pairs are known as true ribs, joining the segments of the sternum or breastbone; whereas the remaining 10 pairs are floating, merely overlapping and being attached to each other. The seventh and eighth ribs are longest, with the back ribs much shorter.

A capacious chest and middle, which is desirable in all horses, is obtained through long, well-sprung ribs. Such a structural condition allows for more room for the vital internal organs, and experienced horsemen know that such horses eat better and stand up under more hard work.

Sternum

The sternum or breastbone of the horse is composed of eight segments, the whole of which is shaped somewhat like a canoe. There are indentures in the sides for the reception of the cartilages extending from the ribs.

Skull

The skull encloses the brain and the most important organs of sense. It consists of 34 bones, mostly flat, which yield and overlap at points of union at the time of birth, thus making for greater ease of parturition.

The size of the head should be proportionate to the size of the horse, and the shape true to the characteristics of the breed or type represented. Thus, the Thoroughbred possesses a broad forehead, with the face gradually tapering from the forehead to the muzzle, giving the animal an intelligent and alert expression.

The lower jaw should always be strong and well defined, with good width between the branches so as not to compress the larynx when the neck is flexed.

The mature male horse has 40 teeth, and the female 36. Animals of each sex possess 24 molars or grinders and 12 incisors or front teeth. In addition, the male has 4 tushes or pointed teeth, and sometimes these occur in females.

The young animal, whether male or female, has 24 temporary or milk teeth. These include 12 incisors and 12 molars.

Thoracic Limbs

This includes all the bones of the foreleg; namely, the scapula, humerus, radius and ulna, seven or eight carpal bones, cannon bone and two splint bones, two sesamoid bones, large pastern bone, small pastern bone, navicular bone, and coffin bone. The correctness of these bones determines the action and consequent usefulness and value of the animal. Since the front feet maintain about 60 percent of the horse's weight and are subject to great concussion, they should receive careful attention.

The scapula, humerus, radius, and ulna are enclosed in heavy muscles which move them; whereas the parts of the leg below the knee are motivated by long tendons.

The carpal bones collectively comprise the knee of the horse, which corresponds to the wrist in man. The knee should be broad, deep, straight, clean-cut, strongly supported, and free from soft fluctuating swellings. The cannons should be wide, flat, and clean with large, sharply defined, cord-like tendons.

The degree of slope of the pasterns is closely associated with that of the shoulders, and moderate slope (about 45°) to these parts of the anatomy—the scapula and large and small pastern bones—is desirable. Oblique shoulders and pasterns aid in producing elastic springy action and absorb concussions or jars much better than short, straight pasterns and straight shoulders—thereby lessening the possibility of an unsoundness.

The set to the front legs should also be true. When viewed from the front, a vertical line dropped from the point of the shoulder should fall upon the center of the knee, cannon, pastern, and foot. When viewed from the side, a vertical line dropped from the center of the elbow joint should fall upon the center of the knee and fetlock and strike the ground just back of the hoof.

Pelvic Limbs

The pelvic limbs, embracing 40 bones, are the horse's chief means of propulsion forward. The stifle and hock joints will be discussed separately under this heading.

The stifle joint of the horse corresponds to the knee in the human. Excepting for an occasional dislocation of the patella (a condition known as stifled), this joint is not subject to much trouble.

The hock is the most important single joint of the horse, probably being the seat of more serious unsoundnesses than any other part of the body—among them bone spavins, bog spavins, curbs, and thoroughpins. The hock should be wide, deep, flat, clean, hard, strong, well supported, and correctly set with prominent points.

The rear pasterns should be similar to the front ones, although they may be slightly less sloping (a 50° angle being satisfactory for the hind foot).

The set to the hind legs should be such that, when viewed from the rear, a vertical line dropped from the point of the buttock will fall upon the center of the hock, cannon, and foot. When viewed from the side, this vertical line should touch the point of the hock and run parallel with the back of the cannon.

ANATOMY OF THE FOOT[1]

When it is realized that the horse has been transplanted from his natural roving environment and soft, mother earth footing to be used

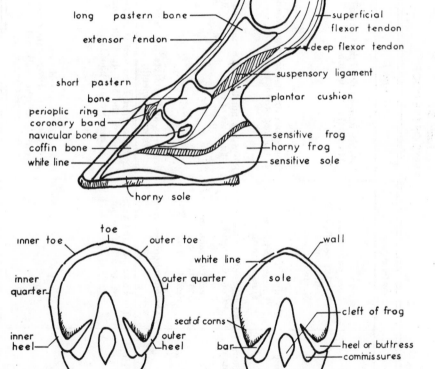

long pastern bone — extensor tendon — cannon bone — superficial flexor tendon — deep flexor tendon — suspensory ligament — short pastern bone — plantar cushion — perioplic ring — coronary band — navicular bone — coffin bone — white line — sensitive frog — horny frog — sensitive sole — horny sole

inner toe — toe — outer toe — wall — white line — inner quarter — outer quarter — sole — seat of corns — cleft of frog — inner heel — outer heel — bar — heel or buttress — commissures

FORE FOOT   HIND FOOT

Fig. 3-4. Parts of the foot. From the *Horse Science Handbook,* 2nd Annual, 1964, published by Agriservices Foundation, Clovis, California.

---

[1] This section was authoritatively reviewed by Mr. Don Canfield, the Horse Science School farrier-instructor.

Table 3-1
PARTS OF THE HOOF

The Parts	Description	Functions	Comments
The Four Major Parts: The bones	They are: Long pastern bone Short pastern bone Coffin bone Navicular bone	Provide framework of the foot and facilitate locomotion.	Long pastern bone lies entirely above the hoof. Only lower end of short pastern bone is within hoof.
The elastic structure	Consists of: Lateral cartilages Planter cushion	Overcomes concussion or jar when the foot strikes the ground.	Normally, heel expands about 1/16 in. on each side of foot.
The sensitive structure, called the corium or pododerm	Consists of: Coronary band Perioplic ring Sensitive laminae Sensitive sole Sensitive frog	Furnishes nutrition to corresponding part of hoof.	All five parts are highly sensitive and vascular.
The horny wall	The outer horny covering	Encloses and protects the sensitive parts beneath.	
The Exterior of the Hoof: The horny wall	The basic shell and wearing surface of the foot.	Protects; there is no feeling in the wall of the foot until the area of the coronary band is reached.	The horny wall extends vertically from the edge of the hair around the front and sides of the foot, then turns in upon itself at the heel, forming the bar which extends forward toward the center.
The perioplic ring	The seat where periople is produced.	Produces periople, the varnish-like substance that covers the outer surface of the wall and seals it from excess drying.	The wall of a normal foot consists of about one-fourth water, by weight.

(Continued on next page)

Table 3-1 (Continued)

The Parts	Description	Functions	Comments
The white line	The juncture of the wall and horny sole. It is about ⅛ in. wide.	Serves as the horseman's "red light," beyond (toward the inside of the foot) which nails should not go.	A nail past the white line may either enter the sensitive structure or produce pressure, with resulting lameness.
The horny frog	The V-shaped pad in the middle of the sole.	Compresses under weight, and transmits pressure to the elastic structures. Aids blood circulation, absorbs concussion, and prevents slippage.	Without this normal pressure, the hoof has a tendency to shrink and become dormant, with contracted feet and unsoundness resulting.
The commissures	The deep grooves on both sides of the frog.	Give elasticity.	Thrush is often found in the commissures.
The horny sole	The bottom of the foot. It is a thick (about ⅜ in.) plate or horn which grows out from the fleshy sole.	Protects the foot from the bottom. Nature didn't intend that the horny sole should carry weight, for it is convex in shape so that most of the weight rests on the wall and frog area.	The sensitive sole is directly under the horny sole. Pressure on the horny sole area will usually produce lameness.
The bars	The horny protrusions that lie along the frog between the commissures and the sole.	Help support the foot and keep it open at the heels.	
The Perimeter Sections: Inside and outside toe The quarters The heel		(See above)	

in carrying and drawing loads over hard, dry-surfaced topography by day and then stabled on hard, dry floors at night, it is not surprising that foot troubles are commonplace. Nor are these troubles new. The Greeks alluded to them in the age-old axiom, "No foot, no horse."

In order to lessen foot troubles, and to permit intelligent shoeing, knowledge of the anatomy of a horse's foot, pasterns, and legs is necessary.

Parts of the Foot

Figure 3-4 shows the parts of the foot, and Table 3-1 gives the pertinent facts about each part.

How the Hoof Grows

The hoof grows downward and forward. A complex system of arteries, veins, and nerves inside the outer structure provides for its growth. The average rate of growth of the horny portions of the hoof (wall, sole, and frog) is ⅛ to ¼ inch per month.

Selected References

Title of Publication	Author	Publisher
Anatomy of the Domestic Animals	Septimus Sisson	W. B. Saunders Company, Philadelphia, Pa., 1953
Anatomy and Physiology of Farm Animals	R. D. Frandson	Lea & Febiger, Philadelphia, Pa., 1965
Lameness in Horses	O. R. Adams	Lea & Febiger, Philadelphia, Pa., 1966

4

In this chapter . . .

4

Selecting and Judging Horses

THE GREAT HORSE SHOWS throughout the land have exerted a powerful influence in molding the types of certain breeds of horses. Other
breeds have been affected primarily through selections based on performance, such as the racetrack. It is realized, however, that only
a comparatively few animals are subjected annually to the scrutiny
of experienced judges or to trial on the racetrack. Rather, the vast
majority of them are evaluated—bought and sold—by persons who lack
experience in judging, but who have a practical need for an animal
and take pride in selecting and owning a good horse. Before buying
a horse, the amateur should enlist the help of a competent horseman.

PARTS OF A HORSE

In selecting and judging horses, we usually refer to parts rather
than to the individual as a whole. It is important, therefore, to master
the language that describes and locates the different parts of a horse.
In addition, it is necessary to know which of these parts are of major
importance; that is, what comparative evaluation to give the different
parts. Nothing so quickly sets a real horseman apart from a novice as a
thorough knowledge of the parts and the language commonly used in
describing them. Figure 4-1 shows the parts of a horse.

HOW TO SELECT A HORSE

As with other classes of farm animals, any one or a combination
of all four of the following methods may serve as bases for selecting
horses: (1) individuality, (2) pedigree, (3) show-ring winnings, and/or
(4) Performance Testing. One must also be aware of the fact that

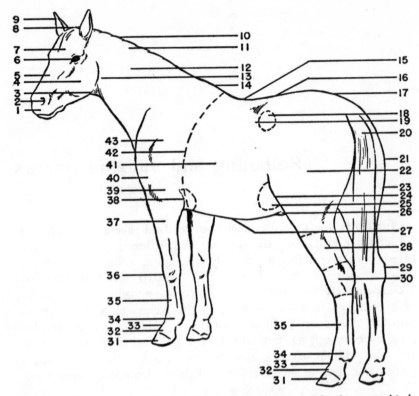

Fig. 4-1. Parts of a horse. The first step in preparation for judging horses consists in mastering the language that describes and locates the different parts of the animal.

1. Muzzle	12. Neck	23. Quarter	34. Fetlock
2. Nostril	13. Throatlatch	24. Stifle	35. Cannon
3. Jaw	14. Wither	25. Rear flank	36. Knee
4. Cheek	15. Back	26. Sheath	37. Forearm
5. Face	16. Loin	27. Underline	38. Point of
6. Eye	17. Croup	28. Gaskin	elbow
7. Forehead	18. Hip	29. Point of hock	39. Arm
8. Poll	19. Coupling	30. Hock	40. Point of
9. Ear	20. Tail	31. Foot	shoulder
10. Mane	21. Point of	32. Coronet	41. Ribs
11. Crest	buttocks	33. Pastern	42. Heart girth
	22. Thigh		43. Shoulder

environment, including feeding and training, plays a tremendously important part in the individuality and performance of a horse.

Selection Based on Individuality

In addition to obtaining a sound horse of desirable conformation, consideration should be given to the following points:

1. The mount should be purchased within a price range that the rider can afford.

2. The amateur or child should have a quiet, gentle, well-broken horse that is neither headstrong nor unmanageable. The horse should never be too spirited for the rider's skill.

3. The size of the horse should be in keeping with the size and weight of the rider. A very small child should have a small horse or pony, whereas a heavy man should have a horse of the weight-carrying type. An exceedingly tall man or woman also looks out of place if not mounted on a horse with considerable height.

4. Usually the novice will do best to start with a three-gaited horse and first master the three natural gaits before attempting to ride a horse executing the more complicated five gaits, should a five-gaited horse be desired.

5. Other conditions being equal, the breed and color of horse may be decided on the basis of preference.

6. The mount should be well suited to the type of work to be performed.

ALL-BREED HORSE SCORE CARD

First, a horse must conform to the specific type which fits him for the function he is to perform. Second, he should be true to the characteristics of the breed that he represents. The use of a score card is a good way in which to make sure that (1) no part is overlooked, and (2) proper weight or value is assigned to each part.

A score card is a listing of the different parts of an animal, with a numerical value assigned to each according to its relative importance. Figure 4-2 shows an All-breed Horse Score Card, developed by the author. Breed characteristics may be, and are, considered in this score card.

Selection on the basis of individuality and performance alone is still the best single method for obtaining suitable using horses, whether they be used for heavy-harness, light-harness, saddle, or pony purposes. In other words, the individuality of the horse, its phenotype, is closely correlated with its performance. However, if the animals are selected for breeding purposes, additional criteria—pedigree, record of both the individual and near relatives, progeny if the animal is old enough and has produced, family name, etc.—should be taken into consideration. Also, show-ring winnings may be helpful.

	POINTS OR %	(name and/or no. of horse)	(name and/or no. of horse)	(name and/or no. of horse)	(name and/or no. of horse)
BREED TYPE .... The breed is distinguished by its unique combination of style and beauty, with ruggedness. COLOR: In keeping with the breed. HEIGHT AT MATURITY: Proper height; extremes undesirable. WEIGHT AT MATURITY: Proper weight; extremes undesirable.	15				
FORM .... STYLE AND BEAUTY: Attractive, good carriage, alert, refined, symmetrical, and all parts nicely blended together. BODY: Nicely turned; long, well-sprung ribs; heavily muscled. BACK AND LOIN: Short and strong, wide, well muscled, and short coupled. CROUP: Long, level, wide, muscular, with a high-set tail. REAR QUARTERS: Deep and muscular. GASKIN: Heavily muscled. WITHERS: Prominent, and of the same height as the high point of the croup. SHOULDERS: Deep, well laid in, and sloping (about a 45° angle). CHEST: Fairly wide, deep, and full. ARM AND FOREARM: Well muscled.	35				
FEET AND LEGS: .... LEGS: Correct position and set (when viewed from front, side, and rear). PASTERNS: Long, and sloping (about a 45° angle). FEET: In proportion to size of horse, good shape, wide and deep at heels, dense texture of hoof. HOCKS: Deep, clean-cut, and well supported. KNEES: Broad, tapering gradually into cannon. CANNONS: Clean, flat, with tendons well defined.	15				
HEAD AND NECK .... Alertly carried, showing style and character. HEAD: Well proportioned to rest of body, refined, clean-cut, with chiseled appearance; broad, full forehead with great width between eyes; ears medium sized, well carried and attractive; eyes large and prominent.	10				

(*continued*)

	POINTS OR %	(name and/or no. of horse)	(name and/or no. of horse)	(name and/or no. of horse)	(name and/or no. of horse)
(*continued*) NECK: Long, nicely arched, clean-cut about the throatlatch; with head well set on, gracefully carried.					
QUALITY . . . . Clean, flat bone; well defined and clean joints and tendons, and fine skin and hair.	10				
ACTION . . . . WALK: Easy, springy, prompt, balanced, a long step, with each foot carried forward in a straight line; feet lifted clear of the ground. TROT: Prompt, straight, elastic, balanced, with hocks carried closely, and high flexion of knees and hocks.	15				
DISCRIMINATION: Any abnormality that affects the serviceability of the horse.					
DISQUALIFICATION: Blindness (except by injury), bone spavin, stifled, stringhalt, cryptorchid.					
TOTAL SCORE	100				

Fig. 4-2. All-breed horse score card.

Selection Based on Pedigree

The Arabians were the first livestock breeders to trace the lineage of their animals, often memorizing many generations of the pedigree. Moreover, they accorded particular importance to the dam's side of the heritage, a condition that still prevails in certain breeds of live-stock today as evidenced by the family names tracing to certain great females many generations removed.

If the pedigree is relatively complete in terms of records of per-formance (speed, show winnings, etc.) of the ancestors, particularly those close up, it can be of very great usefulness in providing a safer basis for selection. A pedigree of this type is of value in predicting (1) the usefulness of the individual (whether it be for racing under the saddle or jumping, etc.) and (2) the probable prepotency as a breeding animal.

Pedigree selection is of special importance where animals are either too thin or so young that their individual merit cannot be ascertained with any degree of certainty. Then, too, where selection is being made between animals of comparable individual merit, the pedigree may be the determining factor.

Selection Based on Show-Ring Winnings

Breeders of pleasure horses have long used show-ring records as a basis of selection. Because training plays such an important part in the performance and show-ring winnings of pleasure horses, however, it is likely that this basis of selection is less valuable from a breeding standpoint than with any other class of animals. At the same time, the show record may be a most valuable criterion in indicating the utility value of the horse.

Selection Based on Performance Testing

Although selection on the basis of Progeny Testing is the most infallible tool available to the horse breeder, it must be pointed out that the following limitations exist:

1. Because of relatively few offspring, it is difficult to apply it to females.

2. Even with males, a Progeny Testing rating cannot be obtained until late in life, after sufficient offspring have been born and have reached an age when they can be tested.

3. There is the hazard that the stallion being tested will be bred to only a few select mares and that only the top offspring will be tested.

4. Training and feeding play such a major part in the development of horses that it is always difficult to separate out environmental from hereditary influences.

Performance Testing is easier to apply because it is an individual matter. In fact, most race horses used for breeding purposes are first Performance Tested on the track.

Perhaps it might be added that the progressive breeder will continue to use all four methods of selection—individuality, pedigree, show-ring winnings, and Production Testing—but with increasing emphasis upon the latter method.

JUDGING HORSES

The discussion that follows represents a further elucidation of the first point discussed under selection—individuality. But, in addition to individual merit, the word judging implies the comparative appraisal or placing of several animals.

Judging horses, like all livestock judging, is an art, the rudiments of which must be obtained through patient study and long practice. Successful horsemen are usually competent judges. Likewise, shrewd traders are usually masters of the art, even to the point of deception.

Accomplished stockmen generally agree that horses are the most difficult to judge of all classes of farm animals. In addition to considering conformation—which is the main criterion in judging other farm animals—action and numerous unsoundnesses are of paramount importance.

Qualifications of a Good Horse Judge

The essential qualifications that a good horse judge must possess, and the recommended procedure to follow in the judging assignment, are as follows:

1. *Knowledge of the parts of a horse.*—This consists of mastering the language that describes and locates the different parts of a horse (see Figure 4-1). In addition, it is necessary to know which of these parts are of major importance; that is, what comparative evaluation to give to the different parts.

2. *A clearly defined ideal or standard of perfection.*—The successful horse judge must know for what he is looking. That is, he must have in mind an ideal or standard of perfection.

3. *Keen observation and sound judgment.*—The good horse judge possesses the ability to observe both good conformation and performance, and defects, and to weigh and evaluate the relative importance of the various good and bad features.

4. *Honesty and courage.*—The good horse judge must possess honesty and courage, whether it be in making a show-ring placing or in conducting a breeding and selling program. For example, it often requires considerable courage to place a class of animals without regard to (a) winnings in previous shows, (b) ownership, and (c) public applause. It may take even greater courage and honesty within oneself to discard a costly stallion or mare whose progeny have failed to measure up.

5. *Logical procedure in examining.*—There is always great danger of the beginner making too close an inspection; he often gets "so close to the trees that he fails to see the forest."

Good judging procedure consists of the following three steps: (a) observing at a distance and securing a panoramic view where several horses are involved, (b) seeing the animals in action, and (c) inspecting close up. Also, it is important that a logical method be used in viewing an animal from all directions (front view, rear view, and side view), and in judging its action and soundness—thus avoiding overlooking anything and making it easier to retain the observations that are made.

6. *Tact.*—In discussing either (a) a show-ring class or (b) horses on a farm or ranch, it is important that the judge be tactful. The owner is likely to resent any remarks which indicate that his animal is inferior.

Do's and Don'ts for Contest Horse Judges

F.F.A. students, 4-H club members, college judging classes, and other prospective horse judges should first become thoroughly familiar with the six qualifications of a good judge as outlined in the previous section. Next, they should observe the following do's and don'ts:

1. *Do's:*

a. Make certain how the class is numbered, and keep the numbers straight.

b. Get a clear picture of the class and of each individual animal in mind, so that they will be remembered.

c. Keep in a position of vantage, where the class can be seen at all times; usually this means some distance away rather than too close.

d. Make placings on the basis of the big things.

e. Make certain that the card is filled out completely and correctly, and that the correct numbers are kept in mind.

f. If permissible, make concise notes that will assist in recalling each individual in the class; record such things as distinctive color markings, outstanding faults, etc.

g. When giving reasons, use good poise and look the judge in the eye.

h. State reasons clearly, and with conviction and confidence.

i. Give reasons in a logical sequence; give the major reasons first.

j. Use terms appropriate to the class of animals; for example, use breeding terms in a breeding class.

k. Use comparative and descriptive terms in giving reasons. Avoid such vague terms as "good," "better," and "best."

l. Concede or grant good points and faults, regardless of the placing of the animal.

2. *Don'ts*:

a. Don't act on hunches; if the first placing is arrived at after due consideration and in a logical manner, stick to it.

b. Don't place animals on the basis of small, relatively unimportant characters.

c. Don't destroy self-confidence and self-respect by discussing the class with others before giving reasons.

d. Don't pay attention to what you overhear others say about a class; be an independent judge.

e. Don't give wordy and meaningless reasons.

f. Don't bluff; if you don't know the answer to a question, say so.

Judging Procedure for Breeding or Halter Classes

It is suggested that the beginner proceed as follows:

1. Master the nomenclature of the animal—the parts (see Fig. 4-1).

2. Have an ideal in mind, and be able to recognize both desirable characteristics and common faults (see Fig. 4-3).

3. Follow a procedure in examining, such as is indicated in Table 4-1; namely (a) front view, (b) rear view, (c) side view, (d) action, and (e) soundness. This applies to breeding or halter classes in particular.

4. Rank or place animals of each class on each of the points listed under "what to look for," keeping in mind the "ideal type" and "common faults" (see Table 4-1).

5. Rank or place the animals according to their consistent rating on all points, especially the most important ones (Table 4-1).

What to Look For

A horse must first conform to the specific type which fits him for the function he is to perform. Secondly, he should be true to the characteristics of the breed that he represents. Regardless of type or breed, however, Figure 4-3 shows certain desirable and undesirable characteristics in horses, and Table 4-1 is a handy judging guide.

GOOD HEAD, NECK, AND SHOULDERS

The head should be well proportioned to the rest of the body, refined and clean-cut, with a chiseled appearance. A broad, full fore-

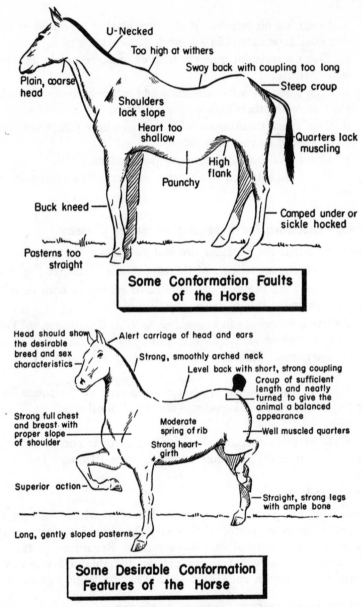

U-Necked

Too high at withers

Sway back with coupling too long

Plain, coarse head

Steep croup

Shoulders lack slope

Heart too shallow

Quarters lack muscling

High flank

Paunchy

Buck kneed

Camped under or sickle hocked

Pasterns too straight

Some Conformation Faults of the Horse

Head should show the desirable breed and sex characteristics

Alert carriage of head and ears

Strong, smoothly arched neck

Level back with short, strong coupling

Croup of sufficient length and neatly turned to give the animal a balanced appearance

Strong full chest and breast with proper slope of shoulder

Moderate spring of rib

Well muscled quarters

Strong heart-girth

Superior action

Straight, strong legs with ample bone

Long, gently sloped pasterns

Some Desirable Conformation Features of the Horse

Fig. 4-3. Ideal type versus common faults. Regardless of type or breed, certain desirable characteristics should be present in all horses. The successful horse judge must be able to recognize both the desirable characteristics and the common faults, and the relative importance of each. (Drawing by R. F. Johnson)

Table 4-1

HANDY JUDGING GUIDE FOR LIGHT HORSES[1]

Procedure for Examining, and What to Look for	Ideal Type	Common Faults
Front View:		
Fig. 4-4	Fig. 4-5	Fig. 4-6
1. Head	1. Head well proportioned to rest of body, refined, clean-cut, with chiseled appearance; broad, full forehead with great width between the eyes; jaw broad and strongly muscled; ears medium sized, well carried and attractive	1. Plain headed
2. Sex character	2. Refinement and femininity in the broodmare; boldness and masculinity in the stallion	2. Mares lacking femininity; stallions lacking masculinity
3. Chest capacity	3. A deep, wide chest	3. A narrow chest
4. Set to the front legs	4. Straight, true, and squarely set	4. Crooked front legs
Rear View:		
Fig. 4-7	Fig. 4-8	Fig. 4-9
1. Width of croup and through rear quarters	1. Wide and muscular over the croup and through the rear quarters	1. Lacking width over the croup and muscling through the rear quarters
2. Set to the hind legs	2. Straight, true, and squarely set	2. Crooked hind legs

(Continued on next page)

Table 4-1 (Continued)

Procedure for Examining, and What to Look for	Ideal Type	Common Faults
Side View:		

Fig. 4-10	*Fig. 4-11*	*Fig. 4-12*
1. Style and beauty	1. High carriage of head, active ears, alert disposition and beauty of conformation	1. Lacking style and beauty
2. Balance and symmetry	2. All parts well developed and nicely blended together	2. Lacking in balance and symmetry
3. Neck	3. Fairly long neck, carried high; clean-cut about the throatlatch; with head well set on	3. A short, thick neck; ewe-necked
4. Shoulders	4. Sloping shoulders (about a 45° angle)	4. Straight in the shoulders
5. Topline	5. A short, strong back and loin, with a long, nicely turned and heavily muscled croup, and a high, well-set tail; withers clearly defined and of the same height as the high point of croup	5. Swaybacked; steep croup
6. Coupling	6. A short coupling as denoted by the last rib being close to the hip	6. Long in the coupling
7. Middle	7. Ample middle due to long, well-sprung ribs	7. Lacking middle
8. Rear flank	8. Well let down in the rear flank	8. High cut rear flank or "wasp waisted"
9. Arm, forearm, and gaskin	9. Well-muscled arm, forearm, and gaskin	9. Light-muscled arm, forearm, and gaskin
10. Legs, feet, and pasterns	10. Straight, true, and squarely set legs; pasterns sloping about 45°; hoofs large, dense, and wide at the heels	10. Crooked legs; straight pasterns, hoofs small, contracted at the heels, and shelly
11. Quality	11. Plenty of quality, as denoted by clean, flat bone, well-defined joints and tendons, refined head and ears, and fine skin and hair	11. Lacking quality
12. Breed type (size, color, shape of body and head, and action true to the breed represented)	12. Showing plenty of breed type	12. Lacking breed type

(Continued on next page)

Table 4-1 (Continued)

Procedure for Examining, and What to Look for	Ideal Type	Common Faults
Soundness:		
1. Soundness, and freedom from defects in conformation that may predispose unsoundness	1. Sound, and free from blemishes	1. Unsound; blemished (wire cuts, capped hocks, etc.)
Action[2]		
 1. At the walk	1. Easy, prompt, balanced; a long step, with each foot carried forward in a straight line; feet lifted clear of the ground	1. A short step, with feet not lifted clear of the ground

Fig. 4-13

 2. At the trot	2. Rapid, straight, elastic trot, with the joints well flexed	2. Winging, forging, and interfering

Fig. 4-14

3. At the canter	3. Slow collected canter, which is readily executed on either lead	3. Fast and extended canter

[1]The illustrations for this table were prepared by R. F. Johnson.
[2]The three most common gaits are given here. Five-gaited horses must perform two additional gaits. In selecting for gait, (1) observe horse at each intended gait, and (2) examine trained horses while performing at use for which they are intended.

head with great width between the eyes indicates intelligence. A straight face is usually preferable to a concave profile or a convex one (Roman nose), the former suggesting a timid disposition and the latter strong will power. The jaw should be broad and strongly muscled. There should be great width between large, clear eyes; and the ears should be of medium size, well carried and active. The neck should be fairly long. It should be carried high, slightly arched, lean and muscular, and clean-cut about the throatlatch, with the head well set on. Also, the neck should neatly join long, oblique, smooth shoulders. The head and neck of the animal should show sex character —boldness and masculinity in the stallion and refinement and femininity in the broodmare.

A STRONG, HEAVILY MUSCLED TOPLINE, WITH A SHORT BACK AND LOIN AND A LONG LEVEL CROUP

The topline should include a short, strong back and loin, with a long, nicely turned and heavily muscled croup, and a high, well-set tail. The withers should be rather clearly defined and of the same height as the hips. Good withers and oblique shoulders make for a better seat in riding horses. Moreover, a sloping shoulder is usually associated with sloping pasterns and more springy, elastic action. The back and loin muscles help sustain the weight of the rider, lift the forequarters of the horse, and strengthen the arch of the back of the horse in motion. A desirable short coupling is obtained when the last rib is close to the hip.

AMPLE CHEST AND MIDDLE

Ample chest and middle due to long, well-sprung ribs is desired. A deep, wide chest and large, full heart-girth—together with a good middle—provide needed space for the vital organs and indicate a strong constitution and good feeding and staying qualities. All horses should be fairly well let-down in the hind flank, though racehorses in training may show much less depth at this point than other types of horses. Even with racehorses, however, the extremely high-cut, so-called "wasp-waisted" ones will not endure heavy racing. Moreover, racehorses usually deepen materially in the rear flank with age or higher condition.

WELL-MUSCLED ARM, FOREARM, AND GASKIN

The muscles of the arm, forearm, and gaskin should be well developed. Since little or no fat can be placed upon the forearm and gaskin, these areas are a good indication of the muscular development of the entire animal, even when horses are in high condition. The powerful muscles of the croup, thigh, and gaskin give the animal ability to pull, jump, or run.

CORRECT LEGS, FEET, AND PASTERNS

There has long been a saying "no foot, no horse." After all, the value of a horse lies chiefly in his ability to move, hence the necessity of good underpinning. The legs should be straight, true, and squarely

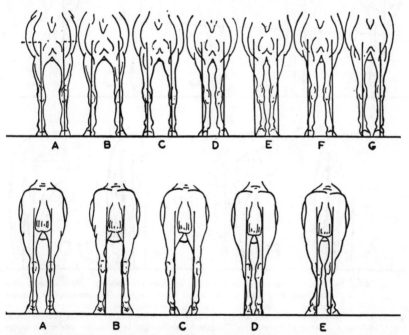

Fig. 4-15. The proper and faulty conformation of the forelegs (top) when viewed from the front, and the hind legs (bottom) when viewed from the rear. The forelegs: A, represents correct conformation; B, splay-footed or base narrow-forefeet, toes cut out, heels in; C, bowed legs; D, knock-kneed, knees set close together with toes pointing outward; E, conformation predisposing to interfering; F, knees set close together; G, pigeon-toed or toe narrow—a conformation which will cause the animal to wing or throw out the feet as they are elevated. The hind legs: A, represents correct conformation; B, hind legs set too far apart; C, bandy-legged—wide at the hocks and hind feet toe in; D, hind legs set too close together; E, cow-hocked. The direction of the leg and the form of the foot are very important in the horse. (Courtesy, USDA)

set; the bone should be well placed and clearly defined. The pasterns should be sloping; the feet large and wide at the heels and tough in conformation.

The hock should be large, clean, wide from front to back, deep, clean-cut, and correctly set. The knee should be deep from front to rear, should be wide when viewed from the front, should be straight, and should taper gradually into the leg. Since the hock and knee joints of the horse are subject to great wear and are the seat of many unsoundnesses, they should receive every attention.

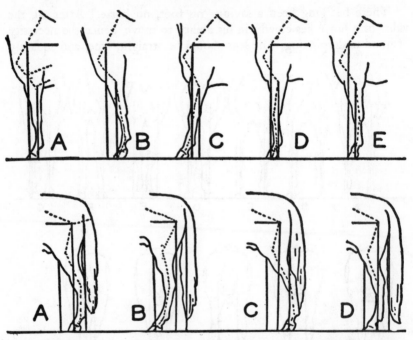

Fig. 4-16. The proper and faulty conformation of (top) the forelegs when viewed from the side, and (bottom) the hind legs when viewed from the side. The forelegs; A, correct conformation; B, forelegs too far under the body; C, forelegs too far advanced; D, knee-sprung or buck-kneed—over in the knees; E, calf-kneed—standing with knees too far back. The hind legs; A, correct conformation; B, sickle hocked—hind legs too far under the body; C, legs set too far back; D, hock joint is too straight. The direction of the legs and the form of the foot are very important in the horse. (Courtesy, USDA)

GOOD ACTION

Although the degree of action of the horse will vary somewhat with the type (speed, show, and saddle), the usefulness of all horses is dependent upon their action and their ability to move in various types of racing, driving, hunting, riding, polo, etc. In all types and breeds, the motion should be straight and true with a long, swift, and elastic stride.

SOUNDNESS

The horse should be serviceably sound, and in the young animal there should be no indication of defects in conformation that may predispose unsoundnesses. The horseman must first know and recognize the normal structure and function before attempting to determine unsoundnesses. Practically speaking, *an unsoundness is any deviation in form or function that interferes with the usefulness of the individual; whereas, a blemish is an abnormality which may detract from the appearance of the animal but which does not affect his serviceability.* The latter includes wire-cut scars, capped hocks, etc.

OTHER CONSIDERATIONS IN BUYING A HORSE

In addition to the desirable qualities in conformation already enumerated, there should be style and beauty, balance and symmetry, an abundance of quality, an energetic yet manageable disposition, freedom from vices, good wind, suitable age, freedom from disease, and proper condition. The buyer should also be on the alert for possible misrepresentations. As each of these factors should receive careful consideration when buying a horse, they will be discussed separately.

Style and Beauty

This has reference to the attractiveness with which the horse displays himself at all times. Good carriage of the head, active ears, an alert, active disposition, and beauty of conformation are factors contributing to the style of the horse. This quality is especially important in heavy harness, fine harness, and saddle horses.

Balance and Symmetry

Balance and symmetry refers to the harmonious development of all parts. With the full development of all important parts, which are nicely blended together, the horse will present an attractive appearance.

Quality

Quality is denoted by clean, flat bone, well-defined joints and tendons, refined head and ears, and fine skin and hair. Good quality in the horse indicates easy keeping and good endurance.

An Energetic Yet Manageable Disposition

Both sexes and all types of horses should at all times display energetic yet manageable dispositions. The disposition of a horse, whether good or bad, is usually considered as being a product of both inheritance and environment. Regardless of the cause of a nasty disposition, one should avoid purchasing such an animal. Superb manners and disposition are especially important in all types of pleasure horses.

Freedom from Vices

Although not considered as unsoundnesses, such stable vices as cribbing, weaving, tail rubbing, kicking, stall-walking and stall-trotting, and halter-pulling do detract from the value of a horse. But vices are not confined to actions in the stall. Some horses object to taking a bit in their mouths; others are touchy about the ears; still others jump when an attempt is made to place a saddle or harness on their backs. Any of these traits is objectionable.

Good Wind

Good wind is imperative. Defects of wind may be easily detected by first moving the animal at a rapid gait for some distance, then suddenly bringing him to a stop and listening in near proximity to the head. Unsound animals are usually noisy in breathing.

Suitable Age

The horse is usually considered as being in his prime between the ages of three and eight. Since younger horses are still growing and becoming hardened, many two- and three-year-olds do not stand up under heavy racing or other use. Although a horse's market value begins to depreciate when he reaches his eighth year, he may be useful in performing certain services until he is well over 20 years old.

Freedom from Diseases

In transporting a horse, there is always a possible exposure to the many ills to which he is subject. Sometimes these prove to be of sufficiently serious nature as to make working impossible at a time when the animal is most needed; and occasionally they even prove fatal. It must also be remembered that such diseases as contracted may very likely spread to the other horses on the farm and even in the community, thus exposing them to the same risk.

Condition

Both productive ability and endurance are lowered by either a thin, run-down condition or an overfat and highly fitted condition. A good, vigorous, thrifty condition is conducive to the best work and breeding ability, and horses so fitted attract the eye of the prospective buyer. However, extremes in feeding and lack of exercise are to be avoided in purchasing a horse for either work or breeding. It must be remembered that fat will cover up a multitude of defects. In buying valuable mares or stallions, the purchaser should insist on having a health certificate signed by a licensed veterinarian. Such examination should also show that the reproductive organs are normal and healthy.

Misrepresentations

The inexperienced man is especially likely to encounter misrepresentations as to age, soundness, vices, and the training and working ability of the horse. Perhaps knowing the seller as well as the horse is the best preventative of this sort of thing.

COLORS AND MARKINGS OF HORSES

Izaak Walton, in *The Compleat Angler*, says, "There is no good horse of a bad color." Yet, within certain breeds, some colors are preferred, or even required, whereas others are undesirable or even constitute disqualifications for registry. Also, a good horseman needs a working knowledge of horse colors and patterns because it is the most conspicuous feature by which a horse can be described or identified.

Body Colors

The five basic horse body colors and their descriptions follow:

1. *Bay.*—Bay is a mixture of red and yellow. It includes many shades, from a light yellowish tan (light bay) to a dark, rich shade which is almost brown (dark bay); a bay horse usually has a black mane and tail and black points.

2. *Black.*—A black horse is completely black, including the muzzle and flanks. If there is doubt as to whether a horse is dark brown or black, one should note the color of the fine hairs on the muzzle and the hair on the flanks; tan or brown hairs at these points indicate that the horse is not a true black, but a seal brown.

3. *Brown.*—A brown horse is almost black but can be distinguished by the fine tan or brown hairs on the muzzle or flanks.

4. *Chestnut (sorrel).*—A chestnut horse is basically red. The shades vary from light washy yellow (light chestnut) to a dark liver color (dark chestnut), between which come the brilliant red gold and copper shades. Normally, the mane and tail of a chestnut horse are the same shade as the body, although they may be lighter in color; these are termed a flaxen mane and tail. Chestnut color is never accompanied by a black mane and tail.

5. *White.*—A true white horse is born white and remains white throughout its life. A white horse has snow-white hair, pink skin, and brown eyes (rarely blue).

In addition to the five basic horse colors given, there are five major variations to these coat colors; namely:

1. *Dun (Buckskin).*—A dun horse has a yellowish color of variable shading from pale yellow to a dirty canvas color; the horse also has a stripe down its back.

2. *Gray.*— A gray horse has a mixture of white and black hairs. Sometimes gray is difficult to distinguish from black at birth, but grays get lighter with age.

3. *Palomino.*—A palomino is a golden color (the color of a newly minted gold coin, or three shades lighter or darker), with a light colored mane and tail (white, silver, or ivory).

4. *Pinto (Calico or Paint).*—Pinto is a Spanish word, meaning "painted." The Pinto horse is characterized by irregular colored and white areas; as (a) piebald (white and black), and (b) skewbald (white and any color other than black).

5. *Roan.*—A roan horse has a mixture of white hairs intermingled with one or more base colors; as (a) white with bay (red roan), (b) white with chestnut (strawberry roan), and (c) white with black (blue roan).

Head Marks

When identifying an individual horse, it is generally necessary for one to be more explicit than to refer to body color only; for example, it may be necessary further to identify the dark sorrel as the one with the blaze face. The most common head marks are shown in Figures 4-17 through 4-23.

Fig. 4-17

Star.—Any white mark on the forehead located above a line running from eye to eye.

Fig. 4-18

Stripe.—A narrow white marking that extends from about the line of the eyes to the nostrils.

Fig. 4-19

Blaze.—A broad white marking covering almost all the forehead, but not including the eyes or nostrils.

Fig. 4-20

Star, stripe, and snip.—Includes all three— a star, a stripe, and a snip.

Fig. 4-21

Snip.—A white mark between the nostrils or on the lips.

Fig. 4-22

Bald face.—A white face, including the eyes and the nostrils, or a portion thereof.

Fig. 4-23

Star and stripe.—Includes both a star and a stripe.

(Head drawings by Dennis Gadberry)

Leg Marks

Leg marks are usually used, along with head marks, to describe a horse. The most common leg marks are shown in Figures 4-24 through 4-31.

Coronet.—A white strip covering the coronet band.

Fig. 4-24

Pastern.—White extends from the coronet to and including the pastern.

Fig. 4-25

Ankle.—White extends from the coronet to and including the fetlock.

Fig. 4-26

Half stocking.—White extends from the coronet to the middle of the cannon.

Fig. 4-27

Fig. 4-28

Stocking.—White extends from the coronet to the knee. When the white includes the knee, it is known as a full stocking.

Fig. 4-29

White outside heels.—Both heels are white.

Fig. 4-30

White outside heel.—Outside heel only is white.

Fig. 4-31

White inside heel.—Inside heel only is white.

(Leg drawings by Dennis Gadberry)

Fig. 4-32. Diagram showing the customary procedure in examining a three-gaited Saddle Horse in the show-ring. The animal herein shown (1) walking, (2) trotting, (3) cantering, and (4) lined up. Traditionally, the judge or judges work from the center of the ring while the ringmaster requests the riders to execute the different gaits. (Continued on next page.)

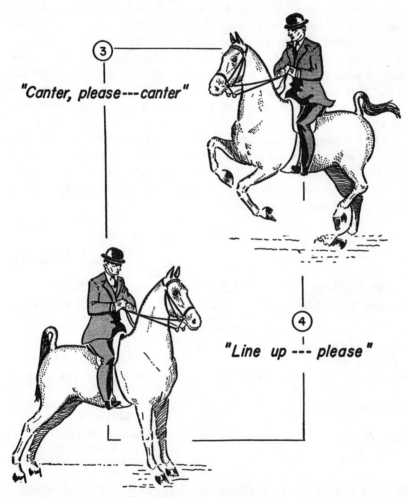

Fig. 4-32 (Continued). Three-gaited horses are expected to walk, trot, and canter. Five-gaited horses must perform two additional gaits; namely, (a) slow gait (which is the stepping pace in the show-ring), and (b) the rack. In addition to performing the gaits with perfection, both three- and five-gaited horses should possess desirable conformation, perfect manners, and superior style and animation. (Drawings by R. F. Johnson)

JUDGING PROCEDURE FOR PERFORMANCE CLASSES

Custom decrees somewhat different show-ring procedure in judging different classes. Halter classes are first examined while lined up side by side, or while being led in a circle and later inspected while moved one at a time; whereas performance classes are first examined with the entire class in action, and later lined up for close inspection. In judging performance classes, the officials should be thoroughly familiar with, and follow, the show rules; either local or the American Horse Shows Association, Inc., whichever applies. If the judge is in doubt as to what is expected of a performance class, he should seek the advice of the steward.

After a judge has inspected a light horse performance class, both in action and when lined up, it is considered entirely proper to request that certain animals be pulled out and again put through their gaits. Figure 4-32 shows the common method of examining a three-gaited Saddle Horse performance class.

Selected References

Title of Publication	Author(s)	Publisher
Breeding Better Livestock	V. A. Rice F. W. Andrews E. J. Warwick	McGraw-Hill Book Co., New York, N. Y., 1953.
Elements of Livestock Judging, The	W. W. Smith	J. B. Lippincott Co., Philadelphia, Pa., 1933.
Horses	M. C. Self	A. S. Barnes and Company, New York, N. Y., 1953.
Horses of Today	H. H. Reese	Wood & Jones, Pasadena, Calif., 1956.
Light Horses	M. E. Ensminger	Farmers' Bulletin No. 2127, U. S. Department of Agriculture, Washington, D. C.
Livestock Judging Handbook	J. E. Nordby W. M. Beeson D. L. Fourt	The Interstate Printers & Publishers, Inc., Danville, Ill., 1962.
Selecting, Fitting, and Showing Horses	J. E. Nordby H. E. Lattig	The Interstate Printers & Publishers, Inc., Danville, Ill., 1963.
Stockman's Handbook, The	M. E. Ensminger	The Interstate Printers & Publishers, Inc., Danville, Ill., 1970.

5

In this chapter . . .

5

Determining the Age and
Height of Horses

ESTABLISHING THE AGE OF HORSES through the appearance of the
teeth is not new. Apparently this technique was known in ancient days.
It is not surprising, therefore, to find that the old saying, "Do not
look a gift horse in the mouth," is attributed to Saint Jerome, a Father
of the Latin Church and papal secretary in the fifth century, who used
this expression in one of his commentaries.

Physical changes within the body are constant. As they affect the
general outward appearance and disposition of the horse within certain limits, it is possible by mere general appearance to estimate the
age of the animal. Changes in the teeth, however, afford a much more
accurate method.

There is nothing mysterious about the determination of the age
by the teeth. In horses up to five years of age, it is simply a matter
of noting the number of permanent and milk teeth present. From
six to twelve years, the number of cups or indentations in the incisor
teeth is used; whereas the age of horses beyond twelve years may
be estimated by studying the cross section and slant of the incisor
teeth. It must be realized, however, that theoretical knowledge is not
sufficient and that anyone who would become proficient must also
have practical experience. The best way to learn how to recognize
age is to examine the teeth in horses of known ages.

THE IMPORTANCE OF AGE

As the productive life of the horse is comparatively brief and the
height of his usefulness is even more limited, the market value of the

89

animal increases rather sharply with maturity and then decreases beyond eight years of age. On the other hand, for many purposes horses are quite useful up to twelve years of age or longer.

Fig. 5-1. How to look a horse in the mouth. With the tongue held in one hand and the lower jaw grasped with the other hand, you can look at the teeth for as long as you like. (Drawing by R. F. Johnson)

NUMBER AND TYPES OF TEETH

The mature male horse has a total of 40[1] teeth; whereas the young animal, whether male or female, has 24. These are listed in Table 5-1.

Table 5-1

NUMBER AND TYPES OF TEETH

Number of Teeth of Mature Animal	Number of Teeth of Young Animal	Types of Teeth
24	12	Molars or grinders.
12	12	Incisors or front teeth (the two central incisors are known as middle incisors, centrals, pinchers, or nippers; the next two—one on each side of the nippers—are called intermediates; and the last—or outer pair—the corners).
4	None	Tushes or pointed teeth. These are located between the incisors and the molars in the male.

[1] Quite commonly, a small pointed tooth, known as a "wolf tooth," may appear in front of each first molar tooth in the upper jaw, thus increasing the total number of teeth to 42 in the male and 38 in the female. Less frequently, two more wolf teeth in the lower jaw increase the total number of teeth in the male and female to 44 and 40, respectively.

As the tushes are usually not present in the mare, the mature female may be considered as having a total of 36 teeth rather than 40 as in the male.

The good horseman is also aware of the difference between permanent and temporary teeth. The temporary or milk teeth are smaller, much whiter, and have a distinct neck at the junction of the crown and fang, which is at the gum line. After their eruption, the permanent teeth may be distinguished from the temporary teeth by their greater size, darker color, a broader neck showing no constriction, and greater width from side to side.

The permanent incisor teeth of young horses five to seven years of age are elliptical or long from side to side; whereas when the animal becomes older, these teeth become triangular, with the apex of the triangle pointed upward. As the animal advances still more in age, the teeth become more slanting. Instead of curving to approach a right angle with the jaws, they slant outward.

From five to twelve years of age the wearing surface of the cups is the most reliable indication of age. At fairly regular intervals, according to age, the cups disappear with wear.

STRUCTURE OF THE TOOTH

The tooth consists of an outside cement and a second layer of a very hard enamel followed by the dentine and a dark center known as the pulp. The enamel passes up over the surface of the teeth and extends inward, forming a pit. The inside and bottom of the pit, which is blackened by feed, constitutes the "mark" or "cup." As the rims of these cups disappear through wear, two distinct rings of enamel remain, one around the margin of the tooth and the other around the cup. With wear, the cups become smaller —first more oval or rounding in shape, then triangular and more shallow, and they finally disappear completely. Further wear on the table or grinding surface of the tooth exposes the tip of the pulp canal or cavity in the center of the tooth. The exposed tip of this canal, which appears between what is left of the cup and the front of the tooth, is known as the "dental star." The gradual wearing and disappearance of the cups according to a rather definite pattern in period of time enables the experienced horseman to judge the age of an animal with a fair degree of accuracy up to twelve years.

A summary showing the changes in teeth according to usual age intervals is given in Table 5-2.

After twelve years of age, even the most experienced horseman cannot determine accurately the age of an animal. It is known,

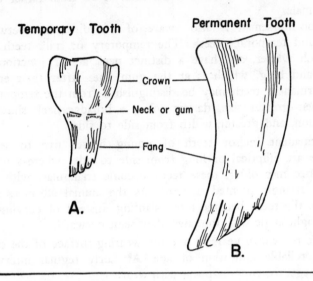

Temporary Tooth   **Permanent Tooth**

Crown

Neck or gum

Fang

A.

B.

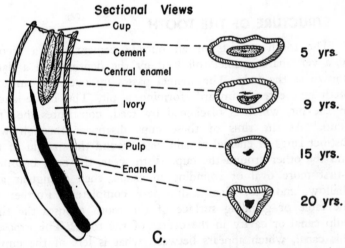

Sectional Views

Cup

Cement

Central enamel

Ivory

Pulp

Enamel

5 yrs.

9 yrs.

15 yrs.

20 yrs.

C.

Fig. 5-2. The horse's tooth. A, temporary lower pincher tooth; B, permanent lower
pincher tooth. Temporary or milk teeth are smaller and much whiter than permanent teeth,
and constricted at the gum line (neck). C, longitudinal section of a permanent lower middle
pincher tooth; and cross-sections of permanent lower middle pincher teeth at different age
levels. These drawings show why, with advancing age, the teeth of a horse (1) slant out
toward the front, (2) change in wearing surface as noted in the cross sectional shape, (3)
change in shape of cups and in the time of disappearance of the cups, and (4) change in
appearance and shape of the dental star. (Drawing by R. F. Johnson)

Table 5-2

HANDY GUIDE TO DETERMINING THE AGE OF HORSES
BY THE TEETH[1]

Drawing of Teeth	Age of Animal	Description of Teeth	
 Fig. 5-3	At birth or be-fore ten days of age	First or central upper and lower incisors appear.	Appearance of temporary teeth
 Fig. 5-4	4 to 6 weeks of age	Second or intermediate upper and lower incisors appear.	
 Fig. 5-5	6 to 10 months	Third or corner upper and lower incisors appear.	
 Fig. 5-6	1 year of age	Crowns of central incisors show wear.	Wear of temporary teeth
 Fig. 5-7	1½ years of age	Intermediate incisors show wear.	
 Fig. 5-8	2 years of age	All temporary incisors show wear.	

(Continued on next page)

Table 5-2 (Continued)

Drawing of Teeth	Age of Animal	Description of Teeth	
Fig. 5-9	2½ years of age	First or central incisors appear.	Appearance of permanent teeth
Fig. 5-10	3½ years of age	Second or intermediate incisors appear.	
Fig. 5-11	4½ years of age	Third or corner incisors appear.	
Fig. 5-12	4 to 5 years of age (in male)	Canines appear.	
Fig. 5-13	5 years of age	Cups in all incisors.	Wear of permanent teeth
Fig. 5-14	6 years of age	Cups worn out of lower central incisors.	

(Continued on next page)

Table 5-2 (Continued)

Drawing of Teeth	Age of Animal	Description of Teeth	
Fig. 5-15	7 years of age	Cups also worn out of lower intermediate incisors.	
Fig. 5-16	8 years of age	Cups worn out of all lower incisors, and dental "star" appears on lower central and intermediate pairs.	
Fig. 5-17	9 years of age	Cups also worn out of upper central incisors, and dental "star" appears on upper central and intermediate pairs.	Wear of permanent teeth
Fig. 5-18	10 years of age	Cups also worn out of upper intermediate incisors, and dental "star" is present on all incisors both upper and lower.	
Fig. 5-19	11 years of age	Cups worn out of all upper and lower incisors, and dental "star" approaches center of cups.	
Fig. 5-20	12 years of age	No cups. "Smooth mouthed."	

¹The illustrations for this table were prepared by R. F. Johnson.

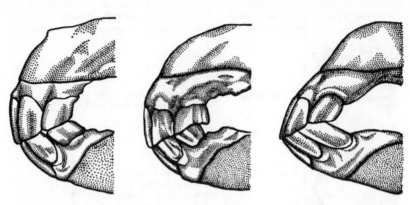

Fig. 5-21. Side view of horse's mouth at five, seven, and twenty years. Note that as the horse advances in age, the teeth change from nearly perpendicular to slanting sharply toward the front. (Drawing by R. F. Johnson)

however, that with more advanced age the teeth change from oval to triangular and that they project or slant forward more and more each year.

It must also be realized that the environment of the animal can very materially affect the wear on the teeth, often making it impossible to determine accurately the age of animals. For example, the teeth of horses raised in a dry, sandy area will show more than normal wear. Thus, the five-year-old western horse may have a six- or even eight-year-old mouth. The unnatural wear resulting in the teeth of cribbers, or animals with parrot mouth or undershot jaw, also makes it difficult to estimate age.

TAMPERED OR "BISHOPED" TEETH

Occasionally, unscrupulous horsemen endeavor to make the amateur a victim of their trade tricks, especially through tampering with the teeth. As very young horses increase in value to a certain stage, the milk teeth are sometimes pulled a few months before they would normally fall out. This hastens the appearance of the permanent teeth and makes the animal appear older.

"Bishoping" is the practice of artificially drilling, burning, or staining cups in the teeth of older horses in an attempt to make them sell as young horses. The experienced horseman can detect such deception because the ring of enamel that is always present around the natural cup cannot be reproduced. This makes the practice more difficult than counterfeiting money. Moreover, the slanting position and triangular shape of the teeth of an older animal cannot be changed. An experienced horseman should always be called upon to make an examination if there is any suspicion that the teeth have been tampered with.

MEASURING HORSES

The normal measurements pertinent to a horse are his (1) height, (2) weight, (3) girth, and (4) bone.

Height

The height of a horse is determined by standing him squarely on a level area and measuring the vertical distance from the highest point of his withers to the ground. The unit of measurement used in expressing height is the "hand," each hand being 4 inches. Thus, a horse measuring 62 inches is said to be 15-2 hands (15 hands and 2 inches) high. Animals standing less than 14-2 (meaning 14 hands and 2 inches) are classed as ponies.

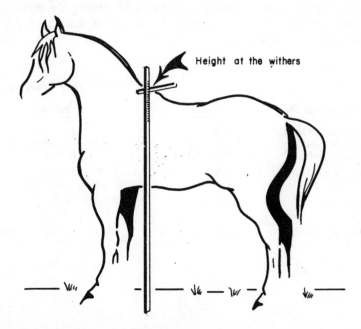

Height at the withers

Fig. 5-22. The height of a horse is measured from the highest point of the withers to the ground. The experienced horseman deftly estimates the height of a horse in relation to his own stature, and does not use any measuring device. (Drawing by R. F. Johnson)

Instead of actually measuring by calipers or tape, the experienced horseman deftly estimates the height of a horse in relation to his own stature. Thus, by knowing the exact height from the ground to the level of his eyes, the horseman can stand opposite the front limbs of the horse, look to the highest point of the withers, and estimate the height very quickly and accurately.

Weight

The weight of a horse is best determined by placing the animal on a properly balanced scale. The weight is recorded in pounds.

Girth

The girth is a measure of the circumference of the chest behind the withers and in front of the back. A large girth is desired because it indicates ample space for such vital organs as the heart and lungs.

Bone

The size of the bone is usually determined by placing a tape measure around the cannon bone halfway between the knee and fetlock joints. The reading is recorded in inches.

Selected References

Title of Publication	Author(s)	Publisher
Determining the Age of Farm Animals by Their Teeth	G. W. Pope Farmers' Bul. No. 1721	U. S. Department of Agriculture, Washington, D. C., 1934.
Elements of Live Stock Judging, The	W. W. Smett	J. B. Lippincott, Philadelphia, Pa., 1930.
Horse, The	D. J. Kays	Rinehart & Co., New York, N. Y., 1953.
Horses of Today	H. H. Reese	Wood & Jones, Pasadena, Calif., 1956.

6

In this chapter . . .

6

Unsoundnesses and Stable Vices

AN INTEGRAL PART of selecting and judging horses is the ability to recognize the common blemishes and unsoundnesses and to rate the importance of each.

DISTINCTION BETWEEN BLEMISHES AND UNSOUNDNESSES

Technically speaking, *any abnormal deviation in structure or function constitutes an unsoundness.* From a practical standpoint, however, a differentiation is made between those abnormalities that do and those that do not affect the serviceability of a horse. Thus, the following definitions usually apply:

1. *Blemishes include those abnormalities that do not affect the serviceability of the horse.* Such unsightly things as wire cuts, rope burns, nail punctures, shoe boils, capped hocks, etc., are generally placed under this category.

2. *Unsoundnesses include those more serious abnormalities that affect the serviceability of the horse.*

CAUSES OF UNSOUNDNESSES

Unsoundnesses may be caused by any one or various combinations of the following:

1. An inherent or predisposing weakness.
2. Subjection of the horse to strain and stress far beyond the capability of even the best structure and tissue.
3. Accident and injury.
4. Nutritional deficiencies, particularly minerals.

101

Unsoundnesses that can be definitely traced to the latter three causes should not be considered as hereditary. Unless one is very positive, however, serious unsoundnesses should always be regarded with suspicion in the breeding animal. Probably no unsoundness is actually inherited, but the fact that individuals may inherit a predisposition to an unsoundness through faulty conformation cannot be questioned.

LOCATION OF COMMON BLEMISHES AND UNSOUNDNESSES

Figure 6-1 and the accompanying outline give the body location of the common blemishes and unsoundnesses. As would be suspected, the great preponderance of troubles affect the limbs.

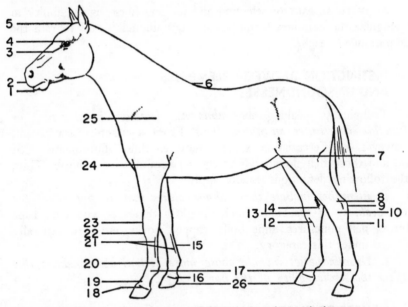

Fig. 6-1. Location of points of common unsoundnesses in horses.

1. Undershot jaw
2. Parrot mouth
3. Blindness
4. Moon blindness
5. Poll evil
6. Fistulous withers
7. Stifled
8. Thoroughpin
9. Capped hock
10. Stringhalt
11. Curb
12. Bone spavin or jack
13. Bog spavin
14. Blood spavin
15. Bowed tendons
16. Sidebones
17. Cocked ankles
18. Quittor
19. Ringbone
20. Wind-puffs
21. Splints
22. Knee-sprung
23. Calf-kneed
24. Capped elbow
25. Sweeney
26. Contracted feet, corns, founder, thrush, quarter crack or sand crack, scratches or grease heel.

General: heaves, hernia, roaring, thick wind.

I. Head:
    1. Blindness
    2. Moon blindness
       (periodic ophthalmia)
    3. Parrot mouth and under-
       shot jaw
    4. Poll evil

II. Withers and shoulders:
    1. Fistulous withers
    2. Sweeney

III. Front limbs:
    1. Bowed tendons
    2. Calf-kneed
    3. Cocked ankles
    4. Knee-sprung
    5. Ringbone
    6. Shoe boil
    7. Splints
    8. Wind-puffs

    9. Contracted feet ⎫
   10. Corns
   12. Navicular disease
   11. Founder or laminitis
   13. Quarter crack or
      sand crack   ⎬ Front
   14. Quittor   Feet
   15. Scratches or grease
      heel
   16. Sidebones
   17. Thrush   ⎭

IV. Rear limbs:
    1. Cocked ankles
    2. Ringbone
    3. Stifled
    4. Stringhalt
    5. Wind-puffs

    6. Blood spavin   ⎫
    7. Bog spavin
    8. Bone spavin or jack ⎬ Hocks
    9. Capped hock
   10. Curb
   11. Thoroughpin   ⎭

   12. Contracted feet ⎫
   13. Corn
   14. Founder or laminitis
   15. Quarter crack or
      sand crack   ⎬ Hind
   16. Quittor   Feet
   17. Scratches or
      grease heel
   18. Thrush   ⎭

V. General:
    1. Heaves
    2. Hernia or rupture
    3. Roaring
    4. Thick wind

DESCRIPTION AND TREATMENT OF COMMON BLEMISHES AND UNSOUNDNESSES

The following brief description and treatment pertain to the common blemishes and unsoundnesses of different body areas.

Unsoundnesses of the Head

The most serious unsoundnesses of the head are those that affect the sight of the animal; namely, blindness and moon blindness. In addition, poll evil is very serious, and the parrot mouthed and under-shot jaw conditions are most undesirable.

BLINDNESS

Partial or complete loss of vision is known as blindness. Either or both eyes may be affected. A blind horse usually has very erect ears and a hesitant gait. Frequently, blindness also can be detected by the discoloration of the eye. Further and more certain verification can be obtained by moving the hand gently in close proximity to the eye.

MOON BLINDNESS (OR PERIODIC OPHTHALMIA)

Moon blindness (or periodic ophthalmia) is a cloudy or inflamed condition of the eye which disappears and returns in cycles that are often completed in about a month. Because many people formerly believed the cycle to be related to changes of the moon, it was given the name of "moon blindness."

It appears that moon blindness may result from several conditions. Experiments initiated at the Front Royal Remount Depot, beginning in 1943, showed that, in some cases, it is a nutritional deficiency disease, caused by a lack of riboflavin.[1] Today, much evidence exists that leptospirosis may cause periodic ophthalmia. Also, some cases appear to be caused by the presence of the parasite *Filaria equina* within the eye, or from a reaction to systemic parasitism elsewhere in the body. Other investigations have suggested that periodic ophthalmia is a reaction of the eye to antigens from repeated streptococcal infections.

PARROT MOUTH AND UNDERSHOT JAW

Both parrot mouth and undershot jaw are hereditary imperfections in the way in which the teeth come together. In parrot mouth or overshot jaw, the lower jaw is shorter than the upper jaw. The reverse condition is known as undershot jaw.

POLL EVIL

This is an inflamed condition in the region of the poll (the area on top of the neck and immediately behind the ears). It is usually caused by bruising the top of the head. The swelling, which may be on one or both sides, usually contains pus or a straw-colored fluid. At first the affected area is hot and painful, but later the acute symptoms of inflammation subside. Treatment, which should be handled by a veterinarian, consists of establishing proper drainage and removing all dead tissue. In addition to surgery,

---

[1] In the Front Royal experiments, when crystalline riboflavin was added to the ration at the rate of 40 milligrams per horse per day, no new cases of periodic ophthalmia developed.

some veterinarians claim that recovery is hastened by injections of a specially prepared bacterin. Poll evil is slow to yield to treatment, and it may break out again after it is thought to be cured.

Unsoundnesses of the Withers and Shoulders

Though less frequent in occurrence than the unsoundnesses of the feet, the conditions of the shoulders known as fistulous withers and sweeney are very injurious to animals which are affected.

FISTULOUS WITHERS

Fistulous withers is an inflamed condition in the region of the withers, commonly thought to be caused by bruising. Fistula and poll evil are very similar except for location. As in poll evil, therefore, treatment for fistulous withers, which should be handled by a veterinarian, consists of establishing proper drainage and removing all dead tissue. Caustic applications to destroy the diseased tissues should be used only on the advice of a veterinarian.

Fig. 6-2. An average case of shoulder fistula on a horse. This is an inflamed condition caused by bruising. (Courtesy, J. W. McManigal, Agricultural Photographs, Horton, Kansas)

SWEENEY

A depression in the shoulder due to atrophied muscles is known as sweeney. Sweeney is caused by nerve injury. No known treatment will restore the nerve, but it is possible to fill in the depression by injecting irritants into the affected area.

Unsoundnesses of the Limbs

Although they are confined to a relatively small proportion of the anatomy of the horse, there appears to be hardly any limit to the number of unsoundnesses that may affect the front limbs. The major unsoundnesses of this type will be discussed briefly.

BLOOD SPAVIN

Blood spavin is a varicose vein enlargement which appears on the inside of the hock but immediately above the location of bog spavin. No successful treatment for blood spavin is known.

BOG SPAVIN

Bog spavin is a filling of the natural depression on the inside and front of the hock. A bog spavin is much larger than a blood spavin. Treatments usually include some combination of cold packs, antiphlogistic applications (clay, mud, cooling lotions, etc.), stimulating

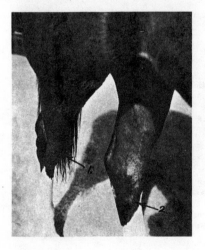

Fig. 6-3. Bog spavin on right hock (No. 1) and bone spavin on left hock (No. 2). Bog spavin is a filling of the natural depression on the inside and front of the hock. Bone spavin is a bony enlargement that appears on the inside and the front of the hock at the point where the base of the hock tapers into the cannon part of the leg. (Courtesy, Major C. B. Team, USDA)

liniments, mild to severe blisters, the aspiration or withdrawal of the fluid from the joint, and injections of hydrocortisone. Some equine veterinarians prefer patient daily massage with an absorbent type liniment for two to three weeks. Treatment consists of applying a special bog spavin truss or of applying tincture of iodine. Blistering or firing is seldom successful.

BONE SPAVIN (OR JACK SPAVIN)

Bone spavin (or jack spavin) is a bony enlargement that appears on the inside and front of the hock at the point where the base of the hock tapers into the cannon part of the leg. It is one of the most destructive conditions affecting the usefulness of a horse. The lameness is most evident when the animal is used following

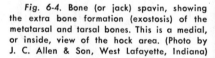
Fig. 6-4. Bone (or jack) spavin, showing the extra bone formation (exostosis) of the metatarsal and tarsal bones. This is a medial, or inside, view of the hock area. (Photo by J. C. Allen & Son, West Lafayette, Indiana)

rest. A hereditary weakness—together with such things as bruises, strains, and sprains—appears to cause bone spavin. Rest seems to be the most important treatment. Counterirritants, iodine, liniments, and blistering agents have all been used with varying degrees of success. Surgery or firing by a qualified veterinarian may be in order.

BOWED TENDONS

Enlarged tendons behind the cannon bones, in both the front

and hind legs, are called bowed tendons. Descriptive terms of "high" or "low" bow are used by horsemen to denote the location of the injury; the high bow appears just under the knee and the low bow just above the fetlock. This condition is often brought about by severe strains, such as heavy training or racing. When bowed tendons are pronounced, more or less swelling, soreness, and lameness are present. Treatment consists of blistering or firing. The object of blistering and firing is to convert a chronic into an acute inflammation. This hastens nature's processes by bringing more blood to the part, thus inducing a reparative process which renders the animal suitable for work sooner than would otherwise be the case.

Blisters consist of such irritating substances as Spanish fly and iodide of mercury (one common preparation consists of 15 parts

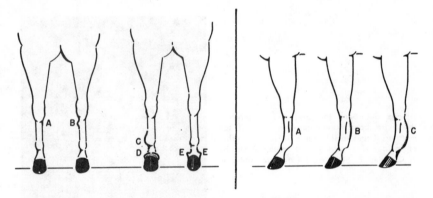

Fig. 6-5. Unsoundnesses of the front limbs: Left—Front legs of the horse, as viewed from the front; A—sound leg, B—splint, C—wind puffs, D—ring-bone, and E—side-bone. Right—Front legs of the horse, as viewed from the side; A—sound leg, B—bowed tendon, and C—filled tendon.

Spanish fly, 8 parts iodide of mercury, and 120 parts of lard). Before applying a blister, the hair should be closely clipped from the affected area, the scurf brushed from the skin, and the animal tied so that it cannot rub, lick, or bite the treated area. The blistering agent is then applied by rubbing it into the pores of the skin with the palm of the hand. Three days later the blistered area should be bathed with warm water and soap, dried and treated with sweet oil or vaseline to prevent cracking of the skin. Firing, which is used for about the same purposes as blistering, consists of the application of a hot iron or the use of thermocautery to the affected area.

Recently, there has been a growing interest in the surgical treatment of bowed tendons, which has been tried on a limited scale with varying degrees of success.

BUCKED SHINS

Bucked shins refers to a temporary racing unsoundness. For the most part, it is peculiar to two-year-olds, although occasionally a three-year-old that did little campaigning at two will fall victim to the condition. It usually strikes early in the final stages of preparation to race or early in the racing career. It is a very painful inflammation of the periosteum (bone covering) along the greater part of the front surface of the cannon bone, caused by constant pressure from concussion during fast works or races. Afflicted horses become very lame and are very sensitive when the slighest pressure is applied about the shins; many horses will almost lie down to keep a person from touching the sore area.

When a horse starts to "buck," most experienced trainers feel that it is wise to continue rather vigorous exercise until the acute form is produced; following which the routine treatment consists in cooling the shins out with antiphlogistic treatment (and time) and applying a good blister. When a pronounced case of shin-buck is treated in this manner, the condition will not likely return. However, if exercise is discontinued at the first indication that the horse is about to "buck" and treatment is given, he will often develop the condition again about the time he is ready to start racing. It is not uncommon for a two-year-old to buck two or three times before he can race successfully.

CALF-KNEED

Standing with knees too far back, directly opposite to buck-kneed or knee-sprung, is called calf-kneed.

CAPPED HOCK

Capped hock is an enlargement at the point of the hock; it is usually caused by bruising. Daily painting of the enlargement with tincture of iodine may help to diminish it. Though it may be unsightly, capped hock need not be considered serious unless it interferes with the work of the horse. Successful reduction of the

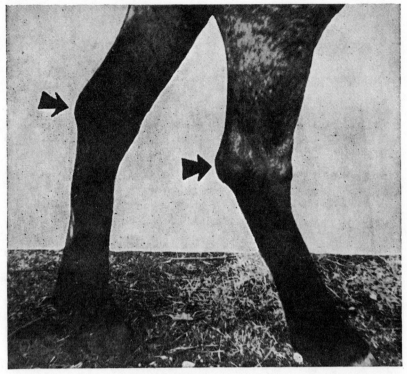

Fig. 6-6. Unsightly capped hocks.

swelling depends on prompt and persistent treatment, with anti-phlogistic applications, before the fluid has a chance to form the fibrinous tissue in the sheath or bursa. Once the "cap" has set or become fibrinous, all that can be done is to remove any inflammation present, and then, by a series of blisters, attempt to cause resorption (reduction in size).

COCKED ANKLES

Cocked ankles refers to horses that stand bent forward on the fetlocks in a cocked position. This condition can be corrected by proper trimming, allowing the toes to grow out while keeping the heels trimmed. However, where cocked ankles are of nutritional origin (as a result of the rickets syndrome), they should be treated by correcting the causative nutritional deficiency or imbalance.

CONTRACTED FEET

This condition, known as contracted, most often occurs in the forefeet and is characterized by a drawing in or contracting at the heels (see Fig. 6-7). A tendency toward contracted feet may be inherited, but improper shoeing usually aggravates the condition. Paring, removal of shoes, or use of special shoes constitutes the best treatment.

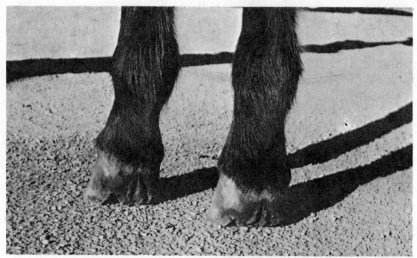

Fig. 6-7. Contracted heels on forefeet. (Courtesy, Western Horseman, Colorado Springs, Colo.)

CORNS

A bruise to the soft tissue underlying the horny sole of the foot—which manifests itself in a reddish discoloration of the sole immediately below the affected area—is known as a corn. Fast work on hard and rough roads, flat soles, weakened bars, and poor shoeing may cause corns. Paring, special shoeing, poulticing, sanitation, and rest constitute the best treatment.

CURB

Curb is the name given to the condition in which there is a fullness at the rear of the leg and below the point of the hock. This fullness is due to enlargement of the ligament or tendon. The condition is caused by anything that brings about a thicken-

ing in the ligament, tendon, or skin of this region so as to cause
a deviation in the straight line that normally extends from the
point of the hock to the fetlock. Firing and blistering are the usual
treatments.

Fig. 6-8. Curb. (Courtesy, Michigan State University)

FOUNDER (OR LAMINITIS)

Founder (or laminitis) is a serious ailment of the fleshy laminae.
Founder may be caused by: (1) overeating (grain, or lush legume or
grass, known as "grass founder"), (2) overwork, (3) giving
animals too much cold water when they are hot, or (4) inflammation
of the uterus following foaling. All feet may be affected, but the front
feet are more susceptible. Prompt treatment by a competent veterinarian will usually prevent permanent injury. Until the veterinarian
arrives, the horse may be given great relief by applying cold applications to the feet. This may be accomplished by wrapping the feet
with burlap bags saturated with cold water or by standing the horse
in a foot bath. If the condition is neglected, chronic laminitis will
develop and will cause dropping of the hoof soles and a turning up
of the toe walls.

Fig. 6-9. Hoof of a foundered horse. In founder, the foot undergoes structural changes. As it grows down, successive rings appear and it becomes deformed through a bulging or "dropped" sole, and the horse walks on the heels with a shortened stride. (Drawing by R. F. Johnson)

FRACTURED FIBULA

Most cases of acute or chronic lameness due to fibula fractures are found on the racetrack.

The fibula is a small, long bone extending along the back side of the tibia from the stifle downward. The upper end articulates with the end of the tibia and the lower end eventually becomes fused with this same bone. In young horses, only the upper third is visible on X-ray plates, because the long, thin shaft has not changed from cartilage to bone. In older horses, the entire length is easily seen on X-ray plates.

The fracture of the fibula causes lameness of the stifle, hip, and back. Horses in training are able to negotiate turns well, but they tend to turn sideways (away from the injured leg) on the straight. An X-ray examination is the only conclusive way to arrive at a diagnosis.

Fibular fracture is caused by undue stress, a strain, or a blow— from (1) sudden starts from off-balanced positions at the starting gate, (2) sudden stops or propping, (3) bad racetracks, (4) sudden shifting of weight in rearing or shying, (5) being cast in the stall, or (6) kicks or collisions. Also, faulty nutrition may be a causative factor in some cases.

Rest is the only effective treatment at the present time. Counter-irritant injections and blisters, anti-inflammatory drugs (corticosteroids) and drugs which tend to relieve muscle spasms, and improved nutrition may be used along with rest.

GRAVEL

Gravel is usually caused by penetration of the protective covering of the hoof by small bits of gravel or dirt. Access to the sensitive tissue is usually gained at the "white line" or junction of the sole and wall, where the horn is somewhat softer. Once in the soft tissue inside the wall or sole, bacterial infection carried by the foreign material develops rapidly, producing pus and gas that create pressure and intense pain in the foot. In untreated cases, it breaks out at the top of the coronary band and the pus and gas are forced out through this opening.

Treatment consists in (1) opening the pathway used by the gravel or dirt going into the foot, thus draining the pus at the bottom and relieving the pressure, (2) administering antitoxin, and (3) protecting the opening from further infection.

KNEE-SPRUNG

A condition of over in the knees, or with the knees protruding too far forward, is known as knee-sprung or buck-kneed.

NAVICULAR DISEASE

Navicular disease is an inflammation of the small navicular bone and bursa of the front foot. It is often impossible to determine the exact cause of the disease. Affected animals go lame; have a short stubby stride; and usually point the affected foot when standing. Few animals completely recover from the disease. Treatment consists of special shoeing. In cases of persistent and severe lameness, unnerving may be performed by a veterinarian, who can destroy sensation in the foot.

OSSELETS

Osselets, like bucked shins, are primarily an affliction of younger horses and the result of more strain or pressure from training or racing than the immature bone structure can stand. However, osselets are not so common among two-year-olds as bucked shins.

Osselets is a rather inclusive term used to refer to a number of inflammatory conditions around the ankle joints. Generally it denotes a swelling that is fairly well defined and located slightly above or below the actual center of the joint, and, ordinarily, a little to the inside or outside of the exact front of the leg. When touched, it imparts the feeling of putty or mush, and it may be warm to hot. The pain will be in keeping with the degree of inflammation as evidenced by swelling and fever. Afflicted horses travel with a short, choppy stride and show evidence of pain when the ankle is flexed.

Standard treatment consists in (1) stopping training at the first sign that the condition is developing, (2) "cooling out," and (3) resting. Firing, or firing followed by blistering, gives very satisfactory results.

POPPED KNEE

Popped knee (so named because of the sudden swelling that accompanies it) is a general term describing inflammatory conditions affecting the knees. It is due either to (1) sprain or strain of one or more of the extensive group of small but important ligaments that hold the bones of the knee in position, or (2) damage to a joint capsule, followed by an increase in the amount of fluid within the capsule and a distention or bulging-out between overlying structure. Of course, faulty conformation of the knees contributes largely to the breaking down of some individuals.

Horses suffering severe popped knees rarely are able to regain a degree of soundness that will allow them to return to the racing form shown before the injury. Thus, the usual cooling applications followed by counter-irritant (blistering and firing) treatment are used with varying degrees of effectiveness in the treatment of knee troubles.

QUARTER CRACK (OR SAND CRACK)

A vertical split in the horny wall of the inside of the hoof (in the region of the quarter), which extends from the coronet or hoof head downward, is known as quarter crack or sand crack. It is seldom found in the hind legs. When the crack is on the fore part of the toe, it is termed toe crack. This condition usually results from the hoof's being allowed to become too dry and brittle or from improper shoeing. Special shoeing or clamping together of the cracks is the usual treatment. Also, the coronet may be blistered; or a

crescent may be burned through the hoof wall over the crack with
a hot iron.

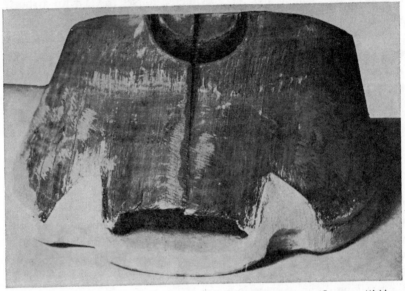

*Fig. 6-10. Hoof showing sand crack and the method of treatment. (Courtesy, Michigan
State University)*

QUITTOR

Quittor is a deep-seated running sore at the coronet or hoof
head caused by necrosis of the cartilage of the third phalanx. It results
in severe lameness. The infection may arise from a puncture wound,
corns, and sand-cracks; or it may be carried in the bloodstream.
Quittor is usually confined to the forefeet, but it sometimes occurs
in the hind feet. Drainage and antiseptics may relieve the condition,
although surgery by a veterinarian may be necessary.

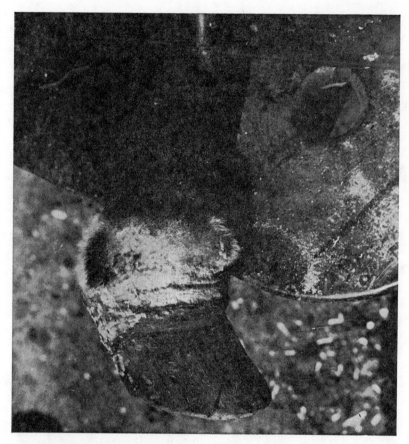

Fig. 6-11. Quittor on right hind foot. This is a deep-seated running sore at the coronet or hoof head. It causes severe lameness. (Courtesy, Major C. B. Team, USDA)

RINGBONE

Ringbone is a bony growth on the pastern bone generally of the forefoot, although occasionally the hind foot is affected. The

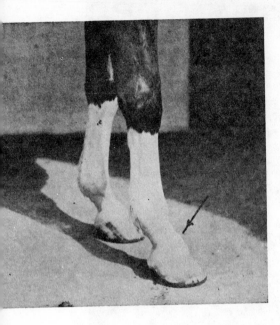

Fig. 6-12. Ringbone on the right foot. This is a bony growth on the pastern bone, generally of the forefoot, although occasionally the hind foot is affected. (Courtesy, Major C. B. Team, USDA)

Fig. 6-13. Ringbone on the pastern, showing the extra bone formation, in coral-like masses, on the surface of the first and second phalanges. (Photo by J. C. Allen & Sons, West Lafayette, Ind.)

condition usually causes a lameness, accompanied by a stiff ankle. This condition generally follows severe straining, blows, sprains, or improper shoeing. Treatment consists of the application of cold water bandages for temporary relief. For more permanent relief, veterinarians sometimes resort to blistering, firing, or severing of the nerve leading to the area. The condition is thought to be heredi- tary.

SCRATCHES (OR GREASE HEEL)

Scratches or grease heel is a mange-like inflammation of the posterior surfaces of the fetlocks, most frequently confined to the hind legs. Treatment consists of placing the affected animal in clean quarters, clipping closely all hair on the affected areas, cleaning with mild soap and water, and applying astringent, antiseptic sub- stances at regular intervals.

SESAMOID FRACTURES

The sesamoids are two pyramid-like bones that form a part of the fetlock or ankle joints (on both front and rear legs) and articulate with the posterior part of the lower end of the cannon bone. They lie imbedded in ligaments and cartilage which form a bearing surface over which the flexor tendons glide.

The fracture of these fragile little bones is more frequent than has been supposed.

SHOE BOIL (OR CAPPED ELBOW)

Shoe boil is a soft, flabby swelling caused by an irritation at the point of the elbow, hence the common name "capped elbow." The two most common causes of this unsoundness are injury from the heel calk of the shoe and injury from contact with the floor. Affected animals may or may not go lame, depending upon the degree of inflammation and the size of the swelling. If dis- covered while yet small, shoe boil may be successfully treated by daily applications of tincture of iodine and the use of the shoe boil boot or roll. The latter is strapped about the pastern in such manner as to keep the heel from pressing upon the elbow while the horse is in a recumbent position. For treatment of large shoe boils, surgery by a veterinarian may be necessary, but such treatment is not always successful. Some horsemen report good results from the use of ligature which is passed around the neck of the swelling and tightened each day until circulation is stopped and the whole mass sloughs off.

SIDEBONES

Sidebones are ossified lateral cartilages immediately above and toward the rear quarter of the hoof head. They occur most commonly in the forefeet. Lameness may or may not be present. The condition may occur on one or both sides of the foot, or on one or both front feet. This is perhaps the most common unsoundness of the feet of horses.

Sidebones may be partially or entirely of genetic origin; or the condition may result from running or working horses on pavement or other hard surface. Sidebones may also develop following sprains, cracks, quittor, or other injuries. Treatments vary and are not always successful. Temporary relief from fever and soreness can usually be obtained through the application of cold-water bandages. Veterinarians sometimes apply blistering agents, fire, or sever the nerve leading to the area; but the "nerving" operation has fallen into disfavor among most horsemen and racing officials.

SPLINTS

Splints are abnormal bony growths found on the cannon bone,

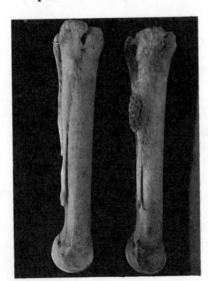

Fig. 6-14. Two common (forelimb) bones. The left one is normal. The right one shows a splint on the median, or inside, involving the second and third metacarpal bones. (Photo by J. C. Allen & Son, West Lafayette, Ind.)

usually on the inside surface, but occasionally on the outside. They are most common on the front legs. When found on the hind cannon, they are generally on the outside. Splints may enlarge and interfere with a ligament and cause irritation and lameness. Their presence detracts from the appearance of the animal, even when there is no lameness. When found on young horses, they often disappear. Point firing, blistering agents, and tincture of iodine have been employed with variable success in treating splints.

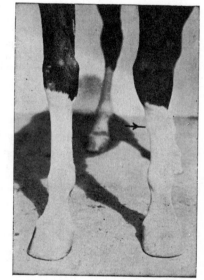

Fig. 6-15. Splints on left front leg. (Courtesy, Major C. B. Team, USDA)

STIFLED

The stifle corresponds to the knee in man. A horse is said to be stifled when the patella (or kneecap) slips out of place and temporarily locks in a location above and to the inside of its normal location. Technically, this condition is known as dorsal patellar fixation. Sometimes it is possible to place the patella back in normal position manually. However, the most effective treatment is surgery, known as medical patellar desmotomy, which consists of the removal of one of the ligaments which attach to the patella.

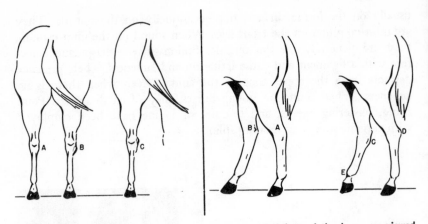

Fig. 6-16. Unsoundnesses of the rear limbs: Left—Hind legs of the horse, as viewed from the rear; A—sound leg, B—bog spavin, C—bone spavin. Right—Hind legs of the horse, as viewed from the side; A—sound legs, B—thoroughpin, C—curb, D—capped hock, and E—cocked ankle.

STRINGHALT

Stringhalt is characterized by excessive flexing of the hind legs. It is most easily detected when backing a horse. The condition may be cured or greatly relieved by a surgical operation on the lateral extensor tendon. An incision is made over the tendon on the outside of the leg just below the hock, and about two inches of the tendon is removed.

SUSPENSORY LIGAMENT SPRAIN

The suspensory ligament is situated over the back of the leg and passes over the fetlock or ankle joint, both in the fore and hind legs. Its principal function is to support the fetlock. This ligament is frequently the object of severe strain; the swelling begins just above the ankle and extends obliquely downward and forward over the sides of the ankle. Should the injury be further up on the leg, the exact location at first may appear obscure as the ligament is covered by the flexor tendons.

When the suspensory ligament is affected, the swelling will be found right up against the bone. If it is the flexor tendons that are involved, the swelling will be farther back near the surface on the back of the leg.

The front legs are more frequently affected than the hind legs;

except in the Standardbred breed, where suspensory ligament injury most commonly occurs in the hind legs.

THOROUGHPIN

Thoroughpin is a puffy condition in the web of the hock. It can be determined by movement of the puff, when pressed, to the opposite side of the leg. Treatment consists of applying pressure and massaging, but these may not always be successful.

THRUSH

Thrush is a disease of the frog. It is most commonly found in the hind feet and is caused by unsanitary conditions in the animal's stall. Most cases will respond to trimming away of the affected frog, sanitation, and the use of an antiseptic. Every horseman has his favorite thrush remedy; among them are calomel, creolin, iodine, bichloride of mercury, formalin, and carbolic acid.

WIND-PUFFS (OR WINDGALL)

Windgalls or "puffs" are an enlargement of the fluid sac (bursa) located immediately above the pastern joints on the fore and rear legs. They are usually the result of too fast or hard road work, especially on hard surfaces. Treatment consists of applying cold packs followed by liniments or sharp blistering agents. Firing or draining by a veterinarian may be in order, but experienced horsemen report that in many cases no permanent benefit results from such treatment.

General Unsoundnesses of the Horse

Hernia and certain abnormal respiratory conditions are classed as general unsoundnesses. These unsoundnesses greatly lower the usefulness and value of affected animals.

HEAVES

Heaves is a difficulty in forcing air out of the lungs. It is characterized by a jerking of the flanks (double-flank action) and coughing after drinking cold water. There is no satisfactory treatment, although affected animals are less bothered if turned to pasture, if used only at light work, if the hay is sprinkled lightly with water at the time of feeding, or if the entire ration is pelleted.

HERNIA (OR RUPTURE)

Hernia (or rupture) refers to the protrusion of any internal organ through the wall of its containing cavity, but it usually means the passage of a portion of the intestine through an opening in the abdominal muscle. Umbilical, scrotal, and inguinal hernias are fairly common in young foals.

An umbilical hernia may be present at birth or may develop soon thereafter. In the majority of cases, the condition corrects itself. If surgery becomes necessary, it is usually postponed until after weaning.

A scrotal hernia, which may be noticed at birth or shortly thereafter, will usually correct itself also, although such natural correction may require several weeks' time. Nevertheless, it is well to advise the veterinarian of the trouble.

ROARING

An animal that whistles or wheezes when respiration is speeded up with exercise is said to be a "roarer." Within recent years a surgical operation has been perfected which when properly performed is successful in about 70 percent of the cases so treated.

THICK WIND

Difficulty in breathing is known as thick wind.

Racing Unsoundnesses

In 1961, the author surveyed a select group of Thoroughbred, Standardbred, and Quarter Horse breeders.[2] This study revealed the following reasons, by rank and percentages, for retiring horses from racing:

Rank	Thoroughbred	Standardbred	Quarter Horse	Three Breeds Combined
1	Bowed tendons (23%)	Bowed tendons (34%)	Bowed tendons (27%)	Bowed tendons (25%)
2	Osselets (21%)	Splint (14%)	Bucked shin (18%)	Knee injury (16%)
3	Knee injury (20%)	Fractured fibula (12%)	Knee injury (12%)	Osselets (16%)
4	Splint (6%)	Curb (5%)	Fractured sesamoid (9%)	Bucked shin (7%)
5	Bucked shin (5%)	Knee injury (5%)	Osselets (8%)	Splint (7%)
6	Fractured sesamoid (4%)	Suspensory ligament (4%)	Splint (5%)	Fractured sesamoid (5%)
7	Sand crack (3%)	Osselets (3%)	Suspensory ligament (2%)	Fractured fibula (3%)

[2]*The Thoroughbred of California*, March, 1961, p. 258.

Rank	Thoroughbred	Standardbred	Quarter Horse	Three Breeds Combined
8	Fractured fibula (2%)	Ringbone (2%) Parasites (2%)	Sand crack (2%)	Sand crack (2%)
9	Suspensory ligament (1%)	Sidebone (2%)	Shoulder injury (2%)	
10	Other (15%)	Other (11%)	Arthritis (2%) Other (13%)	Suspensory ligament (2%) Other (17%)

Experienced trainers estimate that one-third of the horses in training require treatment in one form or another.

UNSOUNDNESS, INJURY OR DISEASE FOR ALL THREE BREEDS
(RANKED ORDER)

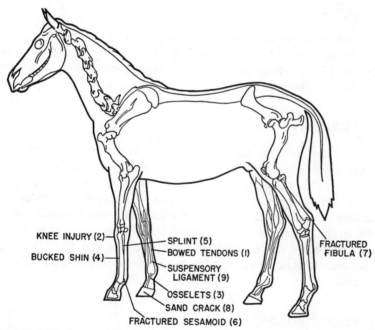

KNEE INJURY (2)

BUCKED SHIN (4)

SPLINT (5)

BOWED TENDONS (I)

SUSPENSORY LIGAMENT (9)

FRACTURED FIBULA (7)

OSSELETS (3)

SAND CRACK (8)

FRACTURED SESAMOID (6)

Fig. 6-17. Most common causes, by rank, for retiring horses (composite of Thoroughbred, Standardbred, and Quarter Horse breeds) from racing. (Courtesy, Washington State University)

VICES

Vices are difficult to suspect for they are often present in the most handsome and lovable creature. Some vices are vicious and dangerous to man and other animals; others inflict punishment upon the offender himself; and still others merely use energy wastefully. Regardless of the type of vice, it is undesirable and to be avoided. In general, vices may be divided into two classifications: stable vices and other vices.

Common Stable Vices

As the name would indicate, stable vices are those which are observed in confinement. Perhaps many of these have arisen because of the unnaturalness of stable conditions.

BOLTING

Bolting is the name given to the habit that ravenous horses have of eating too fast. This condition may be controlled by adding chopped hay to the grain ration or by placing some large, round stones, as big or bigger than baseballs, in the feed box.

CRIBBER

A horse that has the vice of biting or setting the teeth against some object, such as the manger, while sucking air is known as a cribber. This causes a bloated appearance and hard keeping; and such horses are more subject to colic. The common remedy for a cribber is a strap buckled around the neck in a way that will compress the larynx when the head is flexed, but that will not cause any discomfort when the horse is not indulging in the vice. A surgical operation to relieve cribbing has been developed and used with some success.

HALTER PULLING

Halter pulling refers to pulling back on the halter rope when tied in the stable.

KICKING

Occasionally, unusual excitement or injury will cause the so-called gentle horse to kick. However, a true stable kicker appears to have no other excuse than the satisfaction of striking something or somebody with his hind feet.

TAIL RUBBING

Persistent rubbing of the tail against the side of the stall or other objects is objectionable. The presence of parasites may cause animals to acquire this vice. Installation of a tail board or electric wire may be necessary in breaking animals of this habit. A tail board is a board projecting from the wall of the stall high enough to strike just below the point of the buttock, instead of the tail, of the rubbing horse.

WEAVING

A rhythmical swaying back and forth while standing in the stall is called weaving.

Other Vices

Other vices that are often difficult to cope with and which detract from the value of the animal are: balking, backing, rearing, shying, striking with the front feet, a tendency to run away, and objection to harnessing, saddling, and grooming. Many of these vices originate with incompetent handling; nevertheless, they may be difficult to cope with or to correct. This is especially true in older animals, thus lending credence to the statement, "You can't teach an old horse new tricks."

Selected References

Title of Publication	Author(s)	Publisher
Anatomy and Physiology of Farm Animals	R. D. Frandsen	Lea & Febiger, Philadelphia, Pa., 1965.
Equine Medicine and Surgery	Edited by J. F. Bone, et al.	American Veterinary Publications, Inc., 114 N.W. Street, Wheaton, Ill., 1963
Guide to Lameness and Unsoundness in Horses, A		Troy Chemical Co., 110 East 42nd St., New York, N. Y.
Horse, The	D. J. Kays	Rinehart & Co., New York, N. Y., 1953.
Horses of Today	H. H. Reese	Wood & Jones, Pasadena, Calif., 1956.

Title of Publication	Author(s)	Publisher
How to Select a Sound Horse	H. H. Reese Farmer's Bul. No. 779	U. S. Department of Agriculture, Washington, D. C., 1949.
Lameness in Horses	O. R. Adams	Lea & Febiger, Philadelphia, Pa., 1967.
Progress in Equine Practice	Edited by E. J. Catcott J. M. Smithcors	American Veterinary Publications, Inc., 114 N.W. Street, Wheaton, Ill., 1966.
Sound Horse, The	H. F. Moxley B. H. Good	Extension Bul. 330, Michigan State University, East Lansing, Mich., 1960.
Soundness and Nutrition In Stable and Kennel		Radiol Chemicals Limited, 78 Upper Richmond Road, London S.W. 15, England.
Veterinary Notebook	Wm. R. McGee	*The Blood Horse,* Lexington, Ky., 1958.

7

In this chapter . . .

The Horse in Action

IN THE WILD STATE, the horse executed four natural gaits—the walk, trot, pace, and gallop or run. Under domestication, these gaits have been variously modified, and additions have been made through (1) type, (2) breeding and selection, and (3) schooling.

RELATION OF TYPE TO ACTION

Regardless of the use to which horses are put, certain points in conformation are stressed—for example, a shapely, clean-cut head with a large, clear eye; a strong, heavily muscled topline; heavy muscling in the forearm and gaskin; and correct set to the feet and legs. Yet, certain differences in conformation better adapt the animal for use in specific types of work—as draft animals, gaited saddle horses, running horses, heavy harness horses, or hunters, etc. These differences are often as marked as those in the build of the ten-second track man and the champion wrestler. The thickness, massiveness, and low-station of the draft horse are points of conformation that adapt him to power at the walk; whereas the angular form, relatively long legs, well-muscled hind quarters, and close-to-the-ground action of the Thoroughbred constitute form conducive to great speed at the run. But many less exaggerated differences exist. Thus, a horse with straight shoulders and short, straight pasterns is almost certain to be short and choppy in his action, and a very wide-fronted conformation often predisposes paddling.

RELATION OF BREEDING AND SELECTION TO ACTION

The relation of breeding and selection to action becomes especially obvious in a group of weanlings of mixed breeding.

131

Upon starting across a field, some amble off in a rhythmic running-walk, nodding their heads as they go; others travel high enough to clear the tops of the daisies; still others break away in an easy gallop. Each of these three types of action is executed with equal ease and naturalness. The first weanlings described are Tennessee Walking Horses, the second are Hackneys, and the third are Thoroughbreds. In each of these breeds, the distinctive way of going has been accomplished through years of breeding and selection.

RELATION OF SCHOOLING TO ACTION

If the offspring of Man-o'-War and six of the fastest mares to grace the tracks had merely worked on laundry trucks until six years old and if they then suddenly—without training or other preparation—had been placed upon a racetrack, the immediate results would have been disappointing. Their natural aptitude in conformation and breeding would not have been enough. Schooling and training would still have been necessary in order to bring out their inherent ability. No horse—whether he be used for saddle, race, or other purposes—reaches a high degree of proficiency without an education.

On the other hand, it must be emphasized that it is equally disappointing to spend time and money in educating a colt for purposes to which he is not adapted. It is difficult, for example, to train a Hackney as a five-gaited park hack, and it is equally unsatisfactory to school a born Standardbred to the high action of the heavy harness horse.

It should also be pointed out that horses, like people, are likely to revert to an untrained status if placed in an improper environment—despite type, breeding, and early schooling. Thus, an inexperienced rider may, through ignorance, allow the most beautifully trained five-gaited park hack to revert to a very ordinary mount. Proper and frequent handling is necessary if a horse of this training is to retain the five distinct gaits which are executed in a proud and collected manner. For this reason, the less experienced rider often rightfully prefers and will pay more for a three-gaited saddle horse than for a five-gaited one.

THE GAITS

A gait is a particular way of going, either natural or acquired, which is characterized by a distinctive rhythmic movement of the feet and legs. In proper show-ring procedure, horses are brought back to a walk each time before being called upon to execute a different gait. An exception is made in five-gaited classes, where the rack may be executed from the slow gait.

The Walk

The walk is a natural, slow, flatfooted, four-beat gait; the latter meaning that each foot takes off from and strikes the ground at a separate interval. It should be springy, regular, and true.

On the draft horse, in which class of animals it constitutes the most important gait, the walk should be executed as a powerful stride; whereas the American Saddle Horse displays what is known as a proud walk, which calls for high action and attractiveness in contrast to power.

The Trot

The trot is a natural, rapid, two-beat, diagonal gait in which the front foot and the opposite hind foot take off at the same split second and strike the ground simultaneously. There is a brief moment when all four feet are off the ground and the horse seemingly floats through the air.

This gait varies considerably according to breed and training. The trot of the Standardbred is characterized by the length and rapidity of the individual strides; whereas the trot of the Hackney shows extreme flexion of the knees and hocks that produces a very high-stepping show gait.

The Canter; Lope

The canter is a slow, restrained, three-beat gait in which the two diagonal legs are paired, thereby producing a single beat which falls between the successive beats of the other unpaired legs. The canter imposes a special wear on the leading forefoot and its diagonal hindfoot. It is important, therefore, that the lead should be changed frequently; and in a well-trained horse, this shift is easily made at the will of the rider. In the show-ring, the lead should be toward the inside of the ring. It is changed by reversing the direction of travel (when the ringmaster calls for "reverse and canter").

It is a common saying among saddle horse enthusiasts that "a horse should canter all day in the shade of an apple tree." This is but another way of emphasizing that this gait should be executed in such a slow, collected manner that the animal may perform in a relatively small circle.

The lope is the western adaptation of a very slow canter. It is a smooth, slow gait in which the head is carried low.

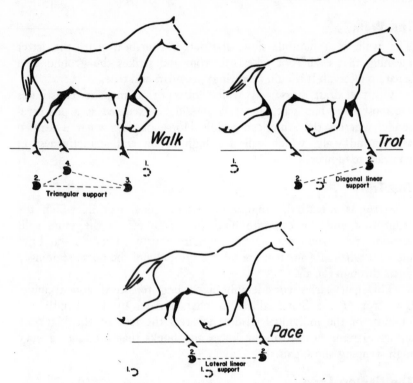

Fig. 7-1. Diagrams showing the features of five gaits: walk, trot, pace, canter (3 stages), and gallop (4 stages). Note the movement of the feet and legs of each gait (above), and the support base and beat of the feet (below). (Drawing by R. F. Johnson)

The Run or Gallop

The run or gallop is a fast, four-beat gait where the feet strike the ground separately; first one hind foot, then the other hind foot, then the front foot on the same side as the first hind foot, then the other front foot which decides the lead. There is a brief interval in which all four feet are off the ground. In executing the gallop, the propulsion is chiefly in the hindquarters, although the forequarters sustain a tremendous jar as the horse lands. The gallop is the fast natural gait of both the wild horse and the Thoroughbred racehorse.

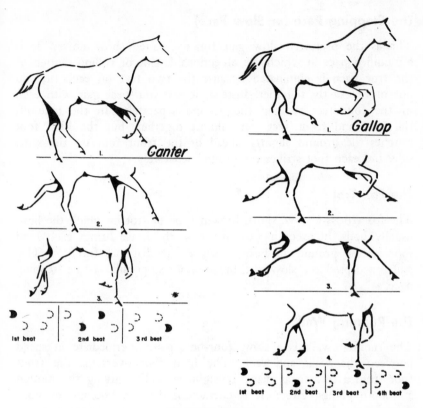

Fig. 7-1 (Continued).

The Pace

The pace is a fast, two-beat gait in which the front and hind feet on the same side start and stop simultaneously. The feet rise very little above the ground level. There is a split second when all four feet are off the ground and the horse floats forward through the air.

The pace is faster than the trot but not so fast as the run or gallop. It was a popular gait in the early history of England, but it lost in favor soon after the development of the Thoroughbred. The pace allows for a quick getaway with a burst of speed, but it produces an objectionable side or rolling type of motion. The pace is not suited to travel in mud or snow, as a smooth, hard footing and easy draft are necessary for its best execution.

The Stepping Pace (or Slow Pace)

This is the preferred slow gait for five-gaited show horses. It is a modified pace in which the objectionable side or rolling motion of the true pace is eliminated because the two feet on each side do not move exactly together. Instead, it is a four-beat gait with each of the four feet striking the ground separately. In the take-off, the hind and front feet start almost together, but the hind foot touches the ground slightly ahead of the front foot on the same side, and each foot strikes the ground separately.

The Fox Trot

The fox trot is a slow, short, broken type of trot in which the head usually nods. In executing the fox trot, the horse brings each hind foot to the ground an instant before the diagonal forefoot. This gait is accepted as a slow gait, but it is not so popular as the stepping pace.

The Running Walk

The running walk is a slow, four-beat gait, intermediate in speed between the walk and rack. The hind foot oversteps the front foot from a few to as many as eighteen inches, giving the motion a smooth gliding effect. It is characterized by a bobbing or nodding of the head, a flopping of the ears, and a snapping of the teeth in rhythm with the movement of the legs. The running walk is easy on both horse and rider. It is the all-day business gait of the South and is executed at a speed of six to eight miles per hour. This is a necessary gait in Plantation Walking Horses.

The Rack

The rack (formerly, but now incorrectly, called single-foot) is a fast, flashy, unnatural, four-beat gait in which each foot meets the ground separately at equal intervals; hence, it was originally known as the "single-foot," a designation now largely discarded. The rack is easy on the rider but hard on the horse. However, it is without doubt the most popular gait in the American show-ring; being fast, brilliant, and flashy. On the tanbark, great speed at the rack is requested by giving the command to "rack on."

The Traverse or Side Step

The traverse or side step is simply a lateral movement of the animal to the right or left as desired, without moving forward or backward. This trick will often assist in (1) lining up horses in the show-ring, (2) opening and closing gates, and (3) taking position in a mounted drill or a posse.

COMMON DEFECTS IN WAY OF GOING

The feet of an animal should move straight ahead and parallel to a center line drawn in the direction of travel. Any deviations from this way of going constitute defects.

Cross-Firing

Cross-firing, a defect in the way of going, is generally confined to pacers and consists of a scuffing on the inside of the diagonal fore and hind feet.

Dwelling

Dwelling, most noticeable in trick-trained horses, consists of a noticeable pause in the flight of the foot, as though the stride were completed before the foot reaches the ground.

Forging

The striking of the forefoot by the toe of the hind foot is known as forging.

Interfering

The striking of the fetlock or cannon by the opposite foot that is in motion is known as interfering. This condition is predisposed in horses with base-narrow, toe-wide, or splay-footed standing positions.

Lameness

Lameness is a defect that can be detected when the affected foot is favored when standing. In action, the load on the ailing foot is eased, and there is characteristic bobbing of the head of the horse as the affected foot strikes the ground.

Paddling

Throwing the front feet outward as they are picked up is known as paddling. This condition is predisposed in horses with toe-narrow or pigeon-toed standing positions.

Pointing

Perceptible extension of the stride with little flexion is called pointing. This condition is likely to occur in the Thoroughbred and Standardbred breeds—animals bred and trained for great speed with a long stride.

Pounding

Pounding is a condition in which there is heavy contact with the ground in contrast to the desired light, springy movement.

Rolling

Excessive lateral shoulder motion, characteristic of horses with protruding shoulders, is known as rolling.

Scalping

Scalping is that condition in which the hairline at the top of the hind foot hits the toe of the forefoot as it breaks over.

Speedy Cutting

Speedy cutting is a condition of a horse at speed in which a hind leg above the scalping mark hits against the shoe of a breaking-over forefoot. In trotters, legs on the same side are involved. In pacers, diagonal legs are involved.

Stringhalt

Stringhalt is characterized by excessive flexing of the hind legs. It is most easily detected when backing a horse.

Trappy

A short, quick, choppy stride is known as trappy. This condition is predisposed in horses with short, straight pasterns and straight shoulders.

Winding or Rope-Walking

A twisting of the striding leg around in front of the supporting leg so as to make contact in the manner of a "rope-walking" artist is known as winding or rope-walking. This condition most often occurs in horses with very wide fronts.

Winging

Winging is an exaggerated paddling, particularly noticeable in high-going horses.

Selected References

Title of Publication	Author(s)	Publisher
Horse, The	D. J. Kays	Rinehart & Co., New York, N. Y., 1953.
Lameness in Horses	O. R. Adams	Lea & Febiger, Philadelphia, Pa., 1966.

8

In this chapter . . .

8

Types and Classes of Light Horses
According to Use

HORSES MAY BE CLASSIFIED as light horses, draft horses, or ponies, according to size, build, and use.

Light horses stand 14-2 to 17 hands high, weigh 900 to 1,400 pounds, and are used primarily for riding, driving, or racing, or for utility purposes on the farm. Light horses generally are more rangy and are capable of more action and greater speed than draft horses.

Draft horses stand 14-2 to 17-2 hands high, weigh 1,400 pounds or more, and are used primarily for drawing loads and other heavy work.

Ponies stand under 14-2 hands high and weigh 500 to 900 pounds. Not every small horse is a pony, however. Some small horses are merely small animals of established light horse breeds; others are nondescript runts. In ponies, there is a distinct conformation; in miniature, they are either of draft horse, heavy harness horse, or saddle or harness horse type. The breeding, feeding, care, and management are essentially the same for ponies as for larger light horses; the only differences result from their diminutive size. The discussion which follows in this chapter will be limited to light horses and ponies.

In no class of animals have so many diverse and distinct types been developed as in the horse. The descendants of the Oriental light-legged horse have, for generations, been bred and used for riding and driving purposes—first as the chariot and riding horses of Egypt, Greece, and Arabia; later as the running horse of England; and finally for purposes of recreation and sport in the United States and throughout the world. In due time, further refinements in breeding light horses were made, and these animals were adapted for more specific purposes. In this manner, light horses specifically adapted to the purposes enumerated in Table 8-1 have evolved.

In attempting to produce animals to meet these specific purposes, new breeds of light horses have been developed. In certain cases, however, the particular use or performance is so exacting that only one breed appears to be sufficiently specialized; for example, in running races the Thoroughbred is used almost exclusively,[1] and harness races are now synonymous with the Standardbred breed.

RIDING HORSES

Riding horses have many and varied uses, but, as the name indicates, they are all ridden. They may have a very definite utility value, as is true of stock horses, or they may be used chiefly for purposes of recreation and sport. For the latter use, training, manners, and style are of paramount importance, although durability and efficiency are not to be overlooked in any horse.

Three- and Five-Gaited Saddle Horses

Long after the development of the New England town, the opening up of roads along the eastern seaboard, and the development of the buggy and the popularity of the roadster type of horse, the states of Virginia, West Virginia, Kentucky, Tennessee, and Missouri still consisted of large plantations under the ownership of southern gentlemen. Roads were few and far between, and travel was largely on horseback over the most natural paths that could be found. Thus, there was need for a horse that would carry the plantation owners with dignity befitting their station in life and with the least distress possible to both rider and horse. As the plantation owners rode over their broad estates, easy gaits were a necessity. Such was the need, and out of this need arose the beautiful American Saddle Horse.

Animals qualifying as either three- or five-gaited saddle horses in the leading American horse shows are generally of American Saddle Horse breeding, a truly American creation.[2] Occasionally, however, animals of the other light horse breeds are trained to execute the five gaits. It must also be remembered that the vast majority of American horses of all breeds are of the three-gaited variety and that only a

---

[1] Except for Quarter Horse races, and races limited to certain other breeds.
[2] Herein reference is made to the Saddle Horse Division as described by The American Horse Shows Association, and not to the several performance classes in which three-gaited horses of various breeds compete.

relatively small proportion of these animals are ever exhibited. Instead, most of the three-gaited horses are used for utility purposes and pleasure riding.

Fig. 8-1. Wing Commander, among whose notable winnings were: (1) six times World's Grand Champion five-gaited Saddle horse at the Kentucky State Fair, and (2) eight-time winner of the World's Championship Stake at the Chicago International. Shown and owned by Mrs. F. L. Van Lennep, Dodge Stables, Castleton Farm, Lexington, Kentucky. Wing Commander, presented here in the trot, was 15-2 hands in height and weighed 1,100 pounds. Note his superb style and type. True to custom for five-gaited horses, Wing Commander is shown with flowing mane and full-length tail. (Courtesy, *The National Horseman*, Louisville, Kentucky)

The gaits of the three-gaited horses are: the walk, the trot, and the canter. In addition to performing these same gaits, the five-gaited horse must possess a slow gait and the rack. The slow gait may be either the running-walk, fox trot, or stepping pace (slow pace); but for show purposes only the stepping pace is accepted. In the show-ring, generally the judge requests that five-gaited horses execute the gaits in the following order: the walk, the trot, the slow gait, the rack, and the canter.

Whether an animal is three-gaited or five-gaited is primarily a matter of training. Custom decrees that three-gaited horses be shown with their manes roached or clipped short and their tails clipped or sheared for a short distance from the base; whereas five-gaited horses are shown with flowing manes and full-length tails. Also, because of the speed at which five-gaited horses are expected to perform at the trot and the rack, they are permitted to wear quarter boots to protect the heels of the front feet, a practice which is forbidden in three-gaited classes.

Both three- and five-gaited horses are shown under saddle; and each may be shown in combination classes, in which they must perform both in harness and under saddle. Also, five-gaited horses (but

Table

LIGHT HORSE

Type	Use	Breeds
Riding Horses	Three-gaited saddle horses	American Albino Horse American Saddle Horse Arabian Appaloosa Missouri Fox Trotting Horse Morgan Palomino Pinto Thoroughbred
	Five-gaited saddle horses Walking horses	American Saddle Horse Tennessee Walking Horse
	Stock horses	Grades, crossbreds, or following purebreds: American Paint Horse Appaloosa[1] Arabian[1] Buckskin Hungarian Horse Morgan Palomino Pinto Quarter Horse Spanish Mustang Thoroughbred
	Polo mounts	Grades, crossbreds, and purebreds of all breeds, but predominantly of Thoroughbred breeding.
	Hunters and Jumpers	Grades, crossbreds, and purebreds of all breeds, but predominantly of Thoroughbred breeding.
	Ponies for riding	American Gotland Connemara Pony Pony of the Americas Shetland Welsh
Racehorses[1]	Running racehorses	Thoroughbred
	Harness racehorses (trotters and pacers)	Standardbred
	Quarter racehorses	Quarter Horse
Driving Horses	Heavy harness horses	Cleveland Bay Hackney
	Fine harness horses	American Saddle Horses (predominantly, although other breeds are so used)
	Roadsters	Morgan Standardbred
	Ponies for driving: 1. Harness show ponies 2. Heavy harness ponies	Hackney Shetland Welsh

[1]On a limited basis, and in a few states, Appaloosa and Arabian horses are also being raced under saddle.

-1

UMMARY

Height	Weight		Place of Origin
(hands)	(pounds)	(kg)	
			United States
			United States
			Arabia
14-2 to 17	900-1,400	409-636	United States
			United States
			United States
			United States
			United States
			England
14-2 to 17	900-1,400	409-636	United States
15 to 16	1,000-1,200	454-545	United States
			United States
			United States
			Arabia
			United States
			Hungary
15 to 15-1	1,000-1,100	454-499	United States
			United States
			United States
			United States
			United States
			England
14-2 to 15-2	1,000-1,250	454-568	
15-2 to 16-2	1,000-1,250	454-568	
			Sweden
9 to 14-2	500-900	227-409	Ireland
			United States
			Shetland Isles
			England
15-1 to 16-2	900-1,150	409-522	England
14-2 to 15-2	900-1,200	409-545	United States
14-2 to 15-2	1,000-1,200	454-545	United States
14-2 to 16-1	900-1,300	409-590	England
			England
14-2 to 17	900-1,400	409-636	United States
14-2 to 15-2	900-1,200	409-545	United States
			United States
9 to 14-2	500-900	227-409	England
			Shetland Isles
			England

not three-gaited horses) may be shown in a third division; namely, in fine harness classes.

In combination classes, the entries enter the ring hitched to an appropriate four-wheeled vehicle, with the saddle and bridle hidden in the back of the rig. The judge works the class both ways of the ring, then lines them up in the center for inspection and backs each horse in order to test his manners. Next the judge orders that the entries be unhitched, unharnessed, saddled, bridled and worked under saddle both ways of the ring. Finally, the horses are again lined up in the center of the ring, and each animal is backed under saddle.

Fig. 8-2. Dixie Haines, a weanling American Saddle Horse filly. Whether an animal of American Saddle Horse breeding is three-gaited or five-gaited is primarily a matter of training. (Courtesy, American Saddle Horse Breeders Association)

A fine harness horse is exactly what the name implies—a fine horse presented in fine harness. The entire ensemble is elegant, and represents the ultimate in grace and charm.

Fine harness horses are penalized if driven at excessive speed. Combination horses, especially five-gaited ones, should be driven at a more speedy trot than fine harness horses.

In addition to executing the gaits with perfection, both three- and five-gaited animals should possess the following characteristics:

1. *Superior conformation,* in which the principal requirements are:
    (a) Graceful lines obtained through a fairly long, arched neck; short, strong back and loin with a good seat; a nicely turned croup; a smartly carried, flowing tail; and a relatively long underline.
    (b) A shapely and smart head.
    (c) Nicely sloping shoulders and pasterns.
    (d) Symmetry and blending of all parts.
    (e) Quality, as evidenced by a clean-cut, chiseled appearance throughout, and soundness.
    (f) Style, alertness, and animation, sometimes said to be comparable to that of a "peacock."

2. *Perfect manners,* which include form, training, and obedience—those qualities that make for a most finished performance.

3. *Superior action,* including an elastic step, high action, and evidence of spirit and dash.

Walking Horses

This particular class of horses is largely comprised of one breed: the Tennessee Walking Horse.[3]

Horses of this type were first introduced into Tennessee by the early settlers from Virginia and the Carolinas. For many years, the plantation owners of middle Tennessee—men who spent long hours daily in supervising labor from the saddle—selected and bred animals for their easy, springy gaits, good dispositions, and intelligence. Particular stress was placed upon the natural gait known as the running-walk and upon the elimination of the trot. Thus, the three gaits that evolved in the walking horse (also called Plantation Walking Horse) were: the walk, the running-walk, and the canter.

---

[3]A more detailed description of this and other breeds may be found in Chapter 10.

In animals of this type, the head is somewhat low in carriage, and at the running-walk there is a characteristic nodding of the head. Sometimes there is also a flopping of the ears and a snapping of the teeth while the animal is in this rhythmic movement. Walking horses

Fig. 8-3. The Plantation Walking Horse, Setting Sun. World's Grand Champion Walking Horse. Owned by M. M. Bullard, Newport, Tenn.; shown by Sam Paschal. (Courtesy, Paschal)

are also noted for their wonderful dispositions. Their easy gaits and a superb disposition make them an ideal type of horse for the amateur rider or the professional or society person who rides infrequently.

Stock Horses

Stock horses constitute the largest single class of light horses of this country; there are approximately 500,000 of them in use in the seventeen range states. They are the cow ponies of the West.

Usually, stock horses are of mixed breeding. Most generally they are descended from the Mustang—the feral horse of the United States. Subsequently, Mustang mares were mated to sires of practically every known light horse breed—especially Thoroughbreds and Quarter

Fig. 8-4. A stock horse in action. Stock horses constitute the largest single class of light horses in this country. (Courtesy, Quarter Horse Journal)

Horses. Stallions of the Palomino, Morgan, Arabian, and other breeds have also been used. Such grading-up has improved the size, speed, and perhaps the appearance of the cow pony, but most horsemen will concede that no amount of improved breeding will ever produce a gamer, hardier, and more durable animal than the Mustang. In addition to being game and hardy, the stock horse must be agile, sure-footed, fast, short coupled, deep, powerfully muscled, durable, and must possess good feet and legs. Above all, the cowboy insists that his pony be a good companion and that he possess "cow sense."

Polo Mounts

As the name would indicate, polo mounts include that type and class of horses particularly adapted for use in playing the game of polo. This game, which was first introduced into this country in 1876, is played by four mounted men on each team. The object is to drive a wooden ball between goal posts at either end of a playing field 300 yards long and 120 to 150 yards wide. Long-handled regulation mallets are used to drive the ball.

At the time the game was first introduced into the United States, there was a decided preference for ponies under 13-2 hands in height.

Fig. 8-5. Belle of All, one of the most famous polo mounts that ever played at Meadow-brook, Long Island. Note the pronounced Thoroughbred type. Polo ponies must be quick and clever in turning, and they must be able to dodge, swerve, or wheel while on a dead run. (Courtesy, Horse Association of America)

Later, horses up to 14-2 hands were accepted, and more recently horses up to 15-2 and over have been used.

Although very similar to the hunter in type, the polo mount is smaller in size. He must be quick and clever in turning, and he must be able to dodge, swerve, or wheel while on a dead run. He must like the game and be able to follow the ball.

The polo mount is trained to respond to the pressure of the reins on the neck, so that the rider may be free to guide him with only one hand. Up to five or six years is required to complete the schooling of a polo horse, and as many as four to six mounts may be used by each player in a single game—all of which contributes to the expensiveness of the sport.

Polo ponies are usually of mixed breeding, but most of them are predominantly Thoroughbred. Type and training, together with native ability and intelligence, are the primary requisites.

The American Horse Shows Association has developed show classi-

Fig. 8-6. Hunters and fox hounds at Southern Acres Farm, Shelburne, Vermont. The sport is traditional in England, and each year it is sharing its glamour with greater numbers in the United States. (Courtesy, J. Watson Webb, former President, Masters of Fox Hounds Association of America, 99 John Street, New York City, New York)

Fig. 8-7. A hunter in action, and well ridden. (Courtesy, A. Mackay-Smith, Editor, *The Chronicle*)

fications for polo ponies. For information relative to same, the reader is referred to the A.H.S.A. Rule Rook.

Hunters and Jumpers

The hunter is that type of horse used in following the hounds in fox hunting. The sport is traditional in England, and each year it is sharing its glamour with greater numbers in the United States.

Again, the hunter is not necessarily of any particular breeding, but Thoroughbred blood predominates. The infusion of some cold blood (draft breeding) is often relied upon in order to secure greater size and a more tractable disposition.

Hunters are classified as *small* (those under 15-2½ hands in height); *lightweight* (those expected to carry a rider weighing under 165

Fig. 8-8. Miss Betty MacLane up on Wampus Kitty, champion jumper in the Open Horse Show at Washington State University. (Courtesy, Washington State University)

pounds); *middleweight* (those expected to carry weights ranging from 165 to 185 pounds); and *heavyweight* (those expected to carry over 185 pounds but under 205 pounds). As many folks who ride to hounds do so in order to keep down their weight, their need for a sizeable mount can be fully appreciated. It must also be realized that a 5-foot object is 4 inches lower for a 16-hand horse than for one only 15 hands in height. Hunters are further classified as "green" or "qualified," the latter having hunted one season with a pack recognized by the United Hunts and Steeple Chase Association.

In addition to being of ample size and height, the hunter must possess the necessary stamina and conformation to keep up with the pack. He must be able to hurdle with safety such common field obstacles as fences and ditches. The good hunter, therefore, is rugged, short coupled, and heavily muscled throughout.

All hunters are jumpers to some degree, but a high jumper is not necessarily a good hunter. To qualify as a hunter, the horse must do more. He must execute many and varied jumps over a long period of time.

Fig. 8-9. Pony ridden by Olivia and Anastasia Musgrave of Co. Dublin, Ireland. (Courtesy, Sir Richard Musgrave)

Jumpers are a nondescript group; consisting of all breeds and types. The only requisite is that they can jump.

Ponies for Riding

These are children's mounts. In addition to their miniature size, they should possess the following characteristics: (1) gentleness, (2) sound feet and legs, (3) symmetry, (4) good eyes, (5) endurance, (6) intelligence, (7) patience, (8) faithfulness, and (9) hardiness. Above all, they must be kind and gentle in disposition.

RACEHORSES

According to some historians, the Greeks introduced horse racing in the Olympic games in 1450 B. C. Also, it is reported that a planned horse race of consequence was run in 1377 between animals owned by Richard II and the Earl of Arundel. The sporting instinct of man being what it is, it is reasonable to surmise, however, that a bit of a contest was staged the first time that two proud mounted horsemen chanced to meet. Today, three types of horse races are run: (1) running races, (2) harness races, and (3) quarter races. For the most part, each type of race is dominated by one breed. Thus, in running races, it's Thoroughbreds; in harness races, it's Standardbreds; and in quarter races, it's Quarter Horses. However, on a limited basis, and in a few states, Appaloosa and Arabian horses are now being raced under saddle.

In 1967, 68,231,089 people went to horse races.[4] This was 28 million more than went to automobile races, the second-ranking spectator sport; 32.3 million more than went to football games (pro and college), the third-ranking sport; and 33.5 million more than witnessed baseball (including both major and minor leagues).[5] As further evidence of the magnitude of horse racing, the following figures for 1967 are noteworthy: (1) $4,921,518,485 was wagered through the mutuel windows, (2) $167,087,846 in purses was collected by horsemen, and (3) $393,873,251 in revenue was turned into the treasuries of the 30

---

[4]38,526,589 to Thoroughbred races (personal communication from The National Association of State Racing Commissioners); 27,201,833 to harness races (personal communication from The United States Trotting Association); and 2,502,667 to Quarter Horse races and fairs (personal communication from The National Association of State Racing Commissioners).

[5]Triangle Publications, Inc., reported the following attendance figures for 1967: Automobile racing, 40,177,800; football, 35,955,219; baseball, 34,699,590.

Fig. 8-10. Citation, sensational Thoroughbred, bred and owned by Warren Wright, Calumet Farm, shown as a two-year-old. Citation was the first million dollar winner of the Thoroughbred breed, with total earnings of $1,085,760. Running races under saddle are now confined almost exclusively to the Thoroughbred breed. (New York Racing Association Photo)

states having legalized pari-mutuel wagering and used to build and operate schools, hospitals, fairs, and other things of benefit to old and young alike.[6]

Running Racehorses

Racehorses used for running (an extended gallop) under the saddle are now confined almost exclusively to one breed, the Thoroughbred. On the other hand, the Thoroughbred breed (including both purebreds and crossbreds) has been used widely for other purposes; especially as a stock horse, polo mount, hunter, and cavalry horse.

Although trials of speed had taken place between horses from the

---

[6]Personal communication from The National Association of State Racing Commissioners.

earliest recorded history, the true and unmistakable foundation of the Thoroughbred breed as such traces back only to the reign of Charles II, known as the "father of the British turf."

Although the length of race, weight carried, and type of track have undergone considerable variation in recent years, the running horse always has been selected for speed and more speed at the run. The distinguishing characteristics of the running horse, as represented by the Thoroughbred, are the extreme refinement, oblique shoulders, well-made withers, heavily muscled rear quarters, straight hind legs, and close travel to the ground.

Harness Racehorses (Trotters and Pacers)

Prior to the advent of improved roads and the automobile, but following the invention of the buggy, there was need for a fast, light-harness type of horse. This horse was used to draw vehicles varying in type from the light roadster of the young gallant to the dignified family carriage. In the process of meeting this need, two truly American breeds of horses evolved: the Morgan and the Standardbred. The first breed traces to the foundation sire, Justin Morgan; and the latter to Hambletonian 10, an animal which was line bred to imported Messenger.

As horse and buggy travel passed into permanent oblivion, except for recreation and sport, the Standardbred breeders wisely placed greater emphasis upon the sport of racing; whereas the Morgan enthusiasts directed their breeding programs toward transforming their animals into a saddle breed.

The early descendants of Messenger were sent over the track, trotting (not galloping) under the saddle; but eventually the jockey races in this country came to be restricted to a running type of race in which the Thoroughbred was used. With this shift, qualifying standards—a mile in 2:30 at the trot and 2:25 at the pace when hitched to the sulky—were set up for light harness races; and those animals so qualifying were registered.[7] The pneumatic-tire racing vehicles, known as sulkies, were first introduced in 1892. With their use that year, the time was reduced nearly four seconds below the record of the previous year. Thus were developed harness racing and the Standardbred breed of horses, which today is the exclusive breed used for this purpose.

---

[7]On January 1, 1933, registration on performance alone was no longer granted, and registration of both sire and dam was required. The qualifying standards were initiated in 1879.

Fig. 8-11. The fabulous Dan Patch, flawless early-day performer and great attraction on tracks throughout the U. S. He was foaled in 1896, and in 1903 he was sold at private treaty for $60,000. The official record for the great horse was 1:55¼, which stood as a world record until 1938 when Billy Direct paced the mile in 1:55 (unofficially, Dan Patch ran the mile in 1:55 with the aid of a windshield. But this form of assistance had been ruled out previously, with the result that this record was not accepted). Dan Patch lived to the age of twenty. (Courtesy, United States Trotting Association, Columbus, Ohio)

Trotters and pacers are of similar breeding and type, the particular gaits being largely a matter of training. In fact, many individuals show speed at both the trot and the pace. It is generally recognized, however, that pacers are handicapped in the mud, in the sand, or over a rough surface.

The Standardbred breed—like the Thoroughbred—also finds other uses, as driving horses in roadster classes, delivery horses, and general utility horses. By way of comparison with the Thoroughbred, the Standardbred possesses a more tractable disposition; is smaller, longer bodied, closer to the ground, heavier-limbed, and sturdier in build. The latter characteristic is very necessary because harness races are usually "heat races"—for example, the best two out of three races.

In the beginning, horses of this type found their principal use in harness races at county and state fairs. However, in recent years pari-

Fig. 8-12. A rare "triple dead heat" of Quarter Horses, which occurred at the Alameda County Fair Grounds, Pleasanton, Calif. (Photo by Photo-Patrol, Inc., San Mateo, Calif.; courtesy, American Quarter Racing Association, Tucson, Ariz.)

mutuel harness racing has been established at a number of tracks. Today, harness racehorses are almost exclusively of the Standardbred breed.

Quarter Racehorses

Quarter racing has become an increasingly popular sport. For the most part, races of this type are confined to animals of the Quarter Horse breed, which animals derived their name and initial fame for their extraordinary speed at distances up to a quarter of a mile. Although the great majority of Quarter Horses are used to work cattle and never appear on the racetrack, the proponents of quarter racing advocate the racetrack as a means of proving animals. Performance, so they argue, is the proof of whether or not a horse can do the job for which he is bred. Thus, quarter racing is used as a breed proving ground for the Quarter Horse, for in this racing the fundamental quality of speed can be accurately measured and recorded in such a way that the performance of horses in all parts of the country can be compared.

DRIVING HORSES

At the present time, driving horses are used chiefly for purposes of recreation. According to the specific use made of them, driving horses are classified as heavy harness horses, fine harness horses, roadsters, or ponies.

Heavy Harness Horses

These are also known as carriage horses. At the present time, this type of horse has very little place in the utility field, its use being largely confined to the show-ring. As the name implies, the heavy harness horse of the show-ring wears heavier leather than the fine harness horse or the roadster, though it in no way approaches draft harness. The heavy leather used on these animals was first decreed by fashion in England, the idea being that to drive handsomely one must drive heavily. The vehicles drawn were of heavy construction and elegant design and logically and artistically the harness had to be in proportion thereto.

Heavy harness horses were especially popular during the Victorian

Fig. 8-13. Creation King, heavy harness horse in action. Creation King was national champion Hackney stallion for two years and winner of many stake championship classes. Bred and owned by Miss Iona and Mr. Harley Heyle, Washington, Illinois. At the present time, the use of heavy harness horses is largely confined to the show-ring. (Courtesy, *The National Horseman*, Louisville, Kentucky)

era, and the ownership of a handsome pair was an indication of social prestige. In this country during the gay nineties, bob-tailed hackneys attached to high-seated rigs made a dashing picture as they pranced down the avenue.

At one time, there were several heavy harness breeds, but at present all except the Hackney have practically ceased to exist in America. In this country, therefore, the Hackney is now the heavy harness breed; and the American Horse Shows Association officially refers to show classifications as Hackneys rather than as Heavy Harness Horses.

The heavy harness horse should possess the following distinguishing characteristics:

1. *Beauty.*—Beauty is obtained through graceful, curved lines; full-made form; and high carriage. Show-ring style decrees that heavy harness horses be docked and have their manes pulled.

2. *High action.*—Animals of this type are bred for high hock and knee action, but skilled training, bitting, and shoeing are necessary for their development. In the show-ring, heavy harness horses must be able to fold their knees, flex their hocks, and set their chins. "Wooden-legged" horses cannot take competition.

3. *Manners and temperament.*—Perfection in the manners and disposition of pleasure horses of this type is a requisite of first rank.

4. *Color.*—Seal brown, brown, bay, and black colors are preferred in heavy harness horses. White stockings are desired for the purpose of accentuating high action.

5. *Height.*—For horse show purposes, the maximum height of Hackney ponies shall be 14-2 hands.

Fine Harness Horses

A fine harness horse is exactly what the name implies—a fine horse presented in fine harness. The entire ensemble is elegant and represents the ultimate in grace and charm.

In the show-ring, fine harness horses are, according to the rules of the American Horse Shows Association, limited to the American Saddle Horse breed. In some shows, however, other breeds are exhibited in fine harness classes. Fashion decrees that fine harness horses shall be shown wearing long mane and tail and drawing a four-wheeled road show wagon without top, or with top drawn. Light harness with a snaffle bit is required. Fine harness horses are shown at an animated park trot and at an animated walk.

Fig. 8-14. Saint Nick, Standardbred shown here as a roadster to buggy. (Courtesy, Saddle and Bridle)

Roadsters

The sport of showing a roadster originated in the horse and buggy era. It was founded upon the desire to own an attractive horse that possessed the necessary speed to pass any of its rivals encountered upon the city or country thoroughfares.

In the show-ring, roadsters are generally shown in either or both (1) roadster to bike, or (2) roadster to buggy classes.[8] The latter are hitched singly or in pairs. Some shows also provide a class or classes for roadsters under saddle. In all divisions—whether shown to bike or buggy, or under saddle—entries must trot; pacing is barred.

Originally, roadster classes included animals of both Standardbred and Morgan extraction. In recent years, however, the Morgan has developed more in the direction of a saddler, leaving the roadster classification almost exclusively to the Standardbred.

In addition to possessing the usual Standardbred characteristics, particular stress is placed in roadster show classes upon the manners, style, and beauty of conformation, combined with speed. In striking contrast

---

[8]In many of the larger shows, a roadster appointment class is provided. Appointments are listed in the A.H.S.A. Rule Book.

to heavy-harness classes, the roadster is shown hitched to very light vehicles permitting fast travel.

Custom decrees that roadsters shall enter the ring at a jog, and work the wrong way (clockwise) of the track first. After jogging for a brief time, usually the judge asks that they perform at the road gait, then jog again (all clockwise of the ring). Then, in succession, the judge asks them to reverse, jog, road gait, and turn on or trot at speed. Lastly, they are called to the center of the ring for inspection in a standing position; at which time the judge usually tests their manners by asking each driver to back his horse.

Ponies for Driving

Ponies for driving are of two kinds; namely, (1) harness show ponies, and (2) heavy harness ponies.

The best harness show ponies are vest-pocket editions of fine harness horses; that is, they possess the same desirable characteristics, except that they are in miniature. According to the rules of the American Horse Shows Association, harness show ponies may be of

Fig. 8-15. Bolgoed Mighty Atom, Champion Harness Show Pony. This imported grey Welsh Pony stallion stands 46½ inches high. Owned by Hawthorn Farms, Libertyville, Illinois. (Courtesy, American Shetland Pony Journal)

any breed or combination of breeds; the only requisite is that they must be under 12-2 hands in height. Three breeds produce animals that qualify under this category; namely, the Shetland, Welsh, and Hackney breeds.

Heavy harness ponies are, as the name indicates, miniature heavy harness horses—they're under 14-2 hands. Generally they are either purebred Hackneys, or predominantly of Hackney breeding.

Three breeds produce animals that qualify as ponies; namely, the Hackney, Welsh, and Shetland breeds. The Hackney is generally exclusively of the harness type, but the Welsh and Shetland breeds are used either under saddle or in harness. In the major horse shows of the land, the latter two breeds may be exhibited in harness, but in practical use they are children's mounts.

Selected References

Title of Publication	Author(s)	Publisher
History of Thoroughbred Racing in America, The	W. H. P. Robertson	Prentice-Hall, Inc., Englewood Cliffs, N. J., 1965.
Horse, The	D. J. Kays	Rinehart & Company, New York, N. Y., 1953.
Light Horse Breeds, The	John W. Patten	A. S. Barnes and Company, Inc., New York, N. Y., 1960.
Light Horses	M. E. Ensminger	Farmers' Bul. No. 2127, U. S. Department of Agriculture, Washington, D. C.
Rule Book, Annual	American Horse Shows Assn.	The American Horse Shows Assn., Inc., 527 Madison Avenue, New York, N. Y.
Western Horse, The	J. A. Gorman	The Interstate Printers & Publishers, Inc., Danville, Ill., 1967.

9

In this chapter . . .

Types and Classes of Work Horses and Mules

AS WITH LIGHT HORSES, similar distinct types—though smaller in number—evolved in the draft horse. From the ponderous beast of Flanders, used as foundation stock, the Great War Horse of the Middle Ages was developed; the Great War Horse, in turn, served as the forerunner of the draft horse of commerce and agriculture. Further and eventual refinement through breeding and selection adapted the draft animals to many and diverse uses, most of which have subsequently passed into oblivion with mechanization. For example, expressers—fast-stepping, delivery-type horses in great demand during the early part of the present century—are seldom seen in the United States at the present time.

During their heyday, certain distinct types of mules were also bred. The type of mule desired was largely controlled through the selection of certain types of mares for breeding purposes. Today, draft horses and mules are of negligible importance, and types, classes, and market terms are primarily of historic interest.[1]

---

[1]After 1957, the USDA discontinued publishing horse and mule receipts and dispositions at public markets. In 1957, the nation's leading horse and mule market—Salt Lake City—received a mere 6,364 head, and all U. S. markets received only 32,555 horses and 2,322 mules, for a total of 34,877 head.

WORK HORSES

Work horses are classified according to use as: (1) draft horses, (2) wagon horses, (3) farm chunks, and (4) southerners. Originally, classes for loggers and artillery horses were included, but except for a few loggers, these have been the victims of mechanization.

Although marked differences in size and weight exist between these various classes, all possess a deep, broad, compact, muscular form suited to the pulling of a heavy load at the walk. A detailed description of a draft type of animal is as follows: He should have plenty of size, draftiness, and substance. The head should be shapely and clean-cut, the eyes large and clear, and the ears active. The chest should be especially deep and of ample width. The topline should include a short, strong back and loin, with a long, nicely turned, and well-muscled croup, and a well-set tail. The middle should be wide and deep, and there should be good depth in both fore and rear flanks. Muscling should be heavy throughout, especially in the forearm and gaskin; the shoulder should be sloping; the legs should be straight, true, and squarely set; the bone should be strong and flat and show plenty of quality. The pasterns should be sloping and the feet should be large and have adequate width at the heels and toughness in conformation. With this splendid draft type, there should be style, balance, and symmetry; an abundance of quality; an energetic yet manageable disposition; soundness; and freedom from disease. The action should be straight and true, with a long, swift, and elastic stride both at the walk and the trot.

The market classification of work horses according to the use to which they are put and their range in height and weight is shown in Table 9-1.

Table 9-1

MARKET CLASSIFICATION OF WORK HORSES

Class	Range in Height	Range in Weight	
	(hands)	*(lbs.)*	*(kg)*
Draft horses-----------------------	16 to 17-2	1,600 upward	726 upward
Wagon horses-----------------------	15-2 to 16-2	1,300 to 1,600	590-726
Farm chunks-----------------------	15 to 16	1,300 to 1,400	590-635
Southerners-----------------------	14-2 to 15-2	600 to 1,100	272-499

Draft Horses

Draft horses stand from 16 to 17-2 hands in height and weigh from

Fig. 9-1. The magnificent eight-horse hitch of champion Clydesdale horses, exhibited by Anheuser-Busch, Inc. (Through the courtesy of Anheuser-Busch, Inc., St. Louis, Mo.)

1,600 pounds upward. They represent the ultimate in power type. Formerly, draft-type horses of quality and style were used on city streets, but these have long since been replaced by trucks. Industry's most glamorous use of draft horses today consists of the six- and eight-horse hitches used for exhibition—a type of advertising.

Fig. 9-2. High quality draft horses drawing a plow. (Courtesy, Horse Association of America)

Wagon Horses

Wagon horses are intermediate in weight and height between the drafter and chunk but have more action than either. They weigh from 1,300 to 1,600 pounds and stand from 15-2 to 16-2 hands in height. They usually have less depth of body and longer legs than draft horses and thus are better able to jog along at the trot. Occasionally, animals of this type still find limited use for delivery purposes, mostly on milk and laundry wagons. In addition to possessing suitable conformation, wagon horses should have an attractive appearance to provide advertising value for the service in which they are used.

Farm Chunks

The term "chunk" is descriptive of the farm-chunk type of animals. They are "small-sized" drafters standing 15 to 16 hands in height and weighing from 1,300 to 1,400 pounds.

Southerners

Southerners are a smaller, plainer type of animal formerly used in the South. Many of them were obtained from the western range states. A few of them are still used by southern planters as a utility type of animal for tilling lands and for riding and driving. They usually stand from 14-2 to 15-2 hands and weigh from 600 to 1,100 pounds.

MULES

It has been correctly said that the mule is without pride of ancestry or hope of posterity. He is a hybrid, being a cross between two species of the family *Equidae*—the *caballus* or horse and the *asinus* or ass.[2] Like most hybrids, the mule is seldom fertile.

The use of the mule in the United States was first popularized by two early American statesmen, George Washington and Henry Clay. The first jack to enter this country, of which there is authentic record, was presented by the King of Spain to General Washington in 1787, shortly after the close of the Revolutionary War. Other importations followed; and from that day until mechanization, the hardy mule furnished the main source of animal power for the South. In comparison with the horse, the mule can (1) withstand higher temper-

---

[2]The cross between a jennet and a stallion is known as a hinny. The mule and the hinny are indistinguishable.

atures; (2) endure less experienced labor; (3) better adapt his eating habits to either irregularity or self-feeding with little danger of founder or digestive disturbances; (4) work or stable in lower areas without head injury (the mule lowers his head when the ears touch an object, whereas a horse will throw his head upward under similar conditions); (5) encounter less foot trouble, wire cuts, etc.; and (6) generally maneuver about without harm to himself.

Fig. 9-3. A near perfect model of a young jack. Note his heavy bone, well set legs, and good head and ears.

Although the mule resembles his sire, the jack, more than the mare, the desired conformation is identical to that described for the horse; perhaps the one exception is that more stress is placed upon the size, set, and quality of the ear. The most desirable mules must be of good size and draftiness, compact and heavily muscled; must show evidence of plenty of quality; must stand on correct feet and legs; and must be sound. As the natural tendency of the mule is to be lazy and obstinate, an active, energetic disposition is sought.

The market classification of mules according to the use to which they are put, including range in height and weight, is shown in Table 9-2.

Naturally, there is considerable spread in value between the animals within each class—depending upon weight, conformation, quality, temperament, condition, action, age, and soundness. Mare mules usually outsell horse mules. The most desirable age is between four and eight years, and well-matched spans of sorrel mules are most popular.

Table 9-2

MARKET CLASSIFICATION OF MULES

Class	Range in Height	Range in Weight	
	(hands)	*(lbs.)*	*(kg)*
Draft	16 to 17-2	1,200 to 1,600	545-726
Sugar	16 to 17	1,150 to 1,300	522-590
Farm	15-2 to 16	900 to 1,250	409-568
Cotton	13-2 to 15-2	750 to 1,100	341-499
Pack and Mining	12 to 16	600 to 1,350	272-613

Draft Mules

Draft mules are the finest mules in type and quality, weighing from 1,200 to 1,600 pounds and standing 16 to 17-2 hands in height. Limited numbers are still exhibited in livestock shows.

Fig. 9-4. A draft mule. Height 16-1 hands, weight 1,600 pounds. Note the thickness and draftiness of this mule, and the excellent feet and legs. (Courtesy, Horse Association of America)

Sugar Mules

Sugar mules are the sugar plantation mules of the South. They are intermediate in size and have a weight somewhere between that of draft and farm mules. Sugar mules weigh 1,150 to 1,300 pounds and are 16 to 17 hands tall. Mules of this class must show considerable quality and finish.

Farm Mules

Farm mules are those purchased for use on farms. These mules are often plainer looking, thinner in flesh, and show less evidence of quality than draft mules. The most desirable farm mules stand 15-2 to 16 hands in height and weigh from 900 to 1,250 pounds.

Cotton Mules

As the name would indicate, mules of this type are used primarily by cotton growers in the South to plant, cultivate, and harvest the cotton

Fig. 9-5. A farm mule. These mules are often more plain looking, thinner in flesh, and show less evidence of quality than draft mules. (Courtesy, Horse Association of America)

Fig. 9-6. A cotton mule. This is a smooth, well-finished type of excellent quality and with an unusually good set of legs and pasterns. (Courtesy, Horse Association of America)

Fig. 9-7. A pack mule. This mule is a very deep chested, thick-made animal, with powerful back and loin, and with excellent slope of pasterns. However, he is crooked on the hind legs, being sickle hocked. (Courtesy, Horse Association of America)

crop. They weigh from 750 to 1,100 pounds and stand from 13-2 to 15-2 hands high. Cotton mules are somewhat lighter and more angular than sugar mules. They also possess less quality.

Pack and Mine Mules

Pack mules are used for transport work—carrying heavy loads on their backs—in very rough or wooded country not accessible to vehicles. The Forest Service uses some animals of this type. A limited number of mining mules are still used to haul cars of ore or coal to the hoisting shafts.

Both pack and mining mules are of similar size and type. They must be close to the ground, thick and blocky, and possess a strong back and loin. They range in weight from 600 to 1,350 pounds and in height from 12 to 16 hands. Horse mules are often preferred to mare mules for this class.

Fig. 9-8. Pack mules in use in rough country not accessible to motor vehicles. (Courtesy, Horse Association of America)

Selected References

Title of Publication	Author(s)	Publisher
Horse, The	D. J. Kays	Rinehart & Company, New York, N. Y., 1953.

10

In this chapter . . .

10

Breeds of Light Horses[1]

A BREED OF HORSES *may be defined as a group of horses having a common origin and possessing certain well-fixed, distinctive, uniformly transmitted characteristics that are not common to other horses.*

There is scarcely a breed of horses that does not possess one or more distinctive breed characteristics in which it excels all others. Moreover, any one of several breeds is often well adapted to the same use. To the amateur, this is most confusing, and he is prone to inquire as to the best breed. Certainly, if any strong preference exists, it should be an important factor, though it is recognized that certain breeds are better adapted to specific purposes.

It is noteworthy that most of the breeds of light horses are American creations. There are two primary reasons for this; namely, (1) the diverse needs and uses for which light horses have been produced, and (2) the fact that many men of wealth have bred light horses.

RELATIVE POPULARITY OF BREEDS OF LIGHT HORSES

Table 10-1 shows the 1968 and total registrations to date of the various breeds of light horses.

---

[1] Sometimes people construe the write-up of a breed of livestock in a book or in a U. S. Department of Agriculture bulletin as an official recognition of the breed. Nothing could be further from the truth, for no person or office has authority to approve a breed. The only legal basis for recognizing a breed is contained in the Tariff Act of 1930, which provides for the duty-free admission of purebred breeding stock provided they are registered in the country of origin. But the latter stipulation applies to imported animals only.

In this book, no *official* recognition of any breed is intended or implied. Rather, the author has tried earnestly, and without favoritism, to present the factual story of the breeds in narrative and picture. In particular, such information relative to the new and/or less widely distributed breeds is needed, and often difficult to come by.

Table 10-1

1968 AND TOTAL REGISTRATIONS OF LIGHT HORSES IN UNITED STATES BREED ASSOCIATIONS

Breed	1968 Registrations	Total Registrations (since Breed Registry started)
Quarter Horse	65,321	586,356
Thoroughbred	23,000	500,000
Half-Breds	383[1]	39,791[1]
Appaloosa	12,389	106,299
Standardbred	10,232	333,229
Tennessee Walking Horse	8,500	100,000
Arabian		
Purebreds	7,000	54,000
Half Arabians and Anglo Arabs[2]	10,331	72,561
American Saddle Horse	3,589	219,726
Pinto	3,429	12,373
Shetland Pony	3,192	124,115
Welsh Pony	2,500	22,000
American Paint Horse	2,390	10,560
Morgan	2,134	37,461
Pony of the Americas	1,467	9,484
Palomino	1,369[3]	32,972[3]
Missouri Fox Trotting Horse	686	4,500
Hackney	649	16,185
Paso Fino	503	793
National Appaloosa Pony	407	3,460
American Buckskin	394	1,322
Connemara Pony	303	2,064
Peruvian Paso	300	176
Galiceno	201	1,584
American Albino	78	2,604
Ysabella Saddle Horse	28	2,112
Andalusian	27[4]	27[4]
Chickasaw Horse	25	625
Gotland Horse	14[1]	155[1]
Spanish Mustang	9	190
Hungarian Horse	—	209

[1]1965 figures.
[2]Registered in the International Arabian Horse Association, 224 East Olive Avenue, Burbank, California
[3]Includes registrations in both the Palomino Horse Association, Inc., and the Palomino Horse Breeders of America.
[4]1967 figures.

AMERICAN SADDLE HORSE

The American Saddle Horse is distinctly an American creation. With at least passable roads in the East, the breeding of harness horses was centered in this area, particularly in the vicinity of New York and Philadelphia. Farther inland, however, roads were few and far between, and horses' backs afforded the chief means of transportation. The early residents of Kentucky, Tennessee, Virginia, and West Virginia selected animals with easy, lateral, ambling gaits, finding these to be most desirable to ride over plantations and hilly and rolling grazing areas, especially on long journeys.

Origin and Native Home

The creation of the American Saddle Horse had its unplanned beginning with the settlement of the plantations of the states mentioned above. Later, Missouri took up the breeding of easy-gaited saddle horses. These southern pioneers, who never rode with short stirrups and who regarded posting as a heathenish invention of the English, very early selected and imported ambling types of horses from Canada and the New England states. Canada at that time had a sturdy little horse which paced, known as the Canadian pacer. Animals of the Thoroughbred breed and what later proved to be the forerunners of the Morgan and Standardbred breeds were also infused. The type of horse demanded was one that could travel long distances without distress to either the horse or the rider and which possessed beauty, speed, tractability, intelligence, courage, durability, longevity, and versatility (adapted to harness use if desired). Conditions calling for horses of this type prevailed throughout the states mentioned, beginning with the earliest settlement. It is not surprising, therefore, that the men, women, and children of this area became equestrians.

The amalgamation of diverse blood continued and with it constant selection for the desired qualities, particularly adaptability to easy riding gaits. Eventually, the plantation owners fixed a definite and beautiful type, even though it was not to be known as a breed until many years later, since no breed registry association was formed until 1891.

The modern American Saddle Horse now traces most of its origin to a four-mile Thoroughbred race stallion, Denmark (foaled in 1839). Although this horse did not achieve great fame on the track, his races were said to be characterized by unusual stamina and gameness. Denmark left numerous progeny, but his most notable offspring was Gaine's Denmark, out of a natural ambler of native stock, known as the Stevenson mare. Many have credited this mare with being of greater foundation importance than Denmark himself. Certainly the Stevenson mare supplied the genetic basis for the gaits so easily attained by her descendants. To Denmark, however, credit must be given for the courage, breediness, shoulders, fineness of head and neck, clean dense bone, and quality of the sons and daughters of many subsequent generations. In considering the diverse breeding of the native stock from which the breed sprung, including the Stevenson mare—and without in any way minimizing the influence of the Thoroughbred—one might even conclude that the American

Saddle Horse is indebted to the Canadian Pacer for his easy riding gaits; to the Morgan for his docility, beauty, and animation; and to the Standardbred for a good trot.

In 1901, the American Saddle Horse Breeders' Association approved a list of ten stallions entitled to rank as the great foundation sires of the breed. There can be little question, however, that Denmark, largely through his illustrious son, Gaine's Denmark, was the greatest of all.

American Saddle Horse Characteristics

The chief distinguishing characteristic of horses of this breed is their ability to furnish an easy ride with great style and animation. Park hacks may be either three- or five-gaited, the choice being largely a matter of preference and training. Walk-trot-canter horses are known as three-gaited; whereas animals possessing the rack, and, in addition, a slow gait (running walk, fox trot, or slow pace) are known as five-gaited.

Members of the breed are usually bay, brown, chestnut, gray, black, or golden in color. Most of them stand from 15 to 16 hands in height and weigh from 1,000 to 1,200 pounds.

The American Saddle Horse is noted for a beautiful head carried on a long graceful neck, short rounded back, level croup, high-set tail, and proud action. The entire ensemble is without a peer when it comes to style, spirit, and animation. At the same time, members of the breed are docile, intelligent, and tractable.

Adaptation and Use

The American Saddle Horse is now used almost exclusively as a three- or five-gaited saddle horse. Many of these horses are still used for business purposes, but by far the greater number of the top animals are used as pleasure horses—either on the bridle paths or in the show-ring.

Fine harness show horses come from the American Saddle Horse, and it has been said that horses of this breed meet the demand for combination horses better than any other group. Animals of American Saddle Horse extraction are occasionally used as stock horses, jumpers, and for other light horse purposes; but their versatility does not approach that of the Thoroughbred. They are primarily a park hack, for which use they are preeminent.

Fig. 10-1. The American Saddle Horse mare, Plainview's Julia, by Genius of Kentucky; twice winner of the $10,000 Five-gaited Grand Championship at the Kentucky State Fair. (Courtesy, C. J. Cronan, Jr., American Saddle Horse Breeders Association)

Present Status of the Breed

Well-trained American Saddle Horses of good type have enjoyed a broad demand at good prices for many years. This demand has come mostly from city people who use the saddle horse for purposes of pleasure, recreation, and exercise. Although representatives of the breed are found in every state, Kentucky and Missouri continue as the great breeding centers.

APPALOOSA

The Appaloosa is of particular interest in northwestern United States because it played a major role in the Indian Wars and in the development of the early-day livestock industry.

Origin and Native Home

Ancient art attests to the fact that spotted horses are as old as recorded

Fig. 10-2. Appaloosa stallion, Pete McCue, owned by Dr. W. R. Jacobs, M.D., Lewiston, Idaho; and ridden by Jesse Redheart, a full-blooded Nez Perce Indian. Note (1) that the horse is wearing a war bridle (Him-paiein), a type of "chin rein"; (2) that the Indian rider is wearing a bonnet of Golden Eagle feathers, of a type denoting the rank of warrior; and (3) that the rider is seated on a blanket, for the Nez Perces did not use saddles. Other standard equipment of the Nez Perce included a buffalo-hide shield, a bow and arrows. This entry won first in the Appaloosa Mounted Costume Class (a horse show class originated by the author of this book) in the Washington State University Horse Show. (Courtesy, Washington State University)

history. Without doubt, the ancestors of the Appaloosa were introduced into Mexico by the early Spanish explorers. Eventually (about 1730), through trading, wars, and capturing strays, the Nez Perce tribe of American Indians came into possession of some of these spotted horses. The Indians were pleased with these colorful mounts and greatly increased their numbers on their fertile ranges in northeastern Oregon, southeastern Washington, and the bordering area in Idaho. Eventually, these horses came to be known as the Appaloosa, which name is said to be derived from the word Palouse, which in turn came from the French word "peluse," meaning grassy sward. The rolling Palouse country was formerly covered by virgin prairie, but it is now a world famous wheat and pea country.

For many years, most of the Appaloosa horses were owned by the Nez Perce tribe, but the War of 1877 resulted in their being scattered throughout the West. Finally, on December 30, 1938, the Appaloosa Horse Club was organized for the purpose of preserving and promoting the breed.

Appaloosa Characteristics

Appaloosas may show many variations and combinations of unusual coat patterns, but the colorful spots are characteristic. Most members of the breed are white over the loin and hips, with dark, round, or egg-shaped spots varying in size from specks up to three or four inches in diameter. The eye is encircled by white, the same as the human eye; the skin is mottled; and the hoofs are striped vertically black and white.

Animals not having Appaloosa characteristics; animals of draft horse, pony, albino, or Pinto breeding; cryptorchids; and animals under 14 hands at maturity (five years of age) are not eligible for registry.

Adaptation and Use

Though once used for war, racing, and buffalo hunting, Appaloosas are now used for stock horses, pleasure horses, parade mounts, and racehorses.

Present Status of the Breed

In recent years, the Appaloosa has made great strides—increasing in both quality and numbers.

Fig. 10-3. Appalossa stallion, Chief of Four Mile. All performance horse and first in class, National Appaloosa Show. Note the flashy spots over the loin and croup; a characteristic of the breed. In 1960, this horse was sold at auction to C. D. Leon, Abilene, Tex., for $10,000. (Courtesy, the Oettermanns, Indian Lake Ranch, Boerne, Tex.)

The Appaloosa Horse Club, Inc., maintains the following types of registries:

Permanent Registration: For animals sired by and out of permanently registered and/or foundation-registered parents. Also, geldings and spayed mares are permanently registered.

Tentative Stud Book: For outstanding Appaloosas not out of registered sire and dam. A stallion may pass from Tentative Book to Permanent Registration after siring twelve progeny registered in the Tentative Book, and a mare in like manner after producing three qualifying offspring; such progeny must pass inspection and meet the standards of type and conformation.

Breeding Stock only: For horses having Appaloosa breeding and

Appaloosa characteristics such as the white sclera encircling the eye, striped hooves, and parti-colored skin, but which do not have a typical Appaloosa coat pattern making them "easily recognizable" as Appaloosas. They have full registration status as a breeding animal, but they are not eligible for show, race, or exhibition.

ARABIAN

Many writers have credited the Arabs with having first domesticated the horse, but this is not the case. The preponderance of evidence favors the belief that the foundation stock of the Arabian horse was obtained many centuries following their domestication from either the Egyptians or the Libyan tribes of northern Africa.

Origin and Native Home

The Arabian, oldest breed of horses and the fountainhead of all the other light horse breeds, was developed in the desert country of Arabia, from which it derives its name. Regardless of the clouded

Fig. 10-4. Earl Craig, formerly of Woodsbrook Stables, Tacoma, Wash., shown mounted on an Arabian and dressed as a Bedouin of the desert, in the Washington State University Horse Show. (Courtesy, Washington State University)

obscurity that surrounds the early origin of the breed, it is generally recognized that, through long and careful mating, the Arabs produced a superior type of horse which would carry them swiftly and safely over long stretches of sandy soil and at the same time withstand deprivations in feed and water to a remarkable degree. As the Bedouins of the desert were a warring, pilfering tribe, the very safety of their lives often depended upon a swift escape. Such was the need, and out of this need was developed the Arabian horse. Legend has it that the Arabs at night would often steal semen from a highly prized stallion owned by an enemy tribe and inseminate their mares therefrom. This was the first artificial insemination of farm animals.

It is easy to understand how the environmental conditions surrounding the development of the Arabian breed could and did give rise to myth and exaggerated statements as to the speed, endurance, docility, and beauty of the breed. At one moment, the Arab was cruel to his mount; then again he would shower him with kindness. During the latter moments, he was wont to remark, "Go and wash the feet of your mare and drink the water thereof."

Early American Importations

The Arabian stallion, Ranger, was imported into Connecticut in 1765. Ranger was the sire of the gray charger ridden by General Washington in the Revolutionary War. Throughout the nineteenth century many other notable importations followed, all of which gave a good account of the breed and encouraged other purchases.

Arabian Characteristics

The distinctive characteristics of the Arabian breed are: medium to small in size, a beautiful head, short coupling, docility, and great endurance. The usual height is from 14 to 15-1 hands and the weight from 850 to 1,100 pounds. A typical Arabian has a beautiful head, broad at the forehead and tapering toward the nose; a dished face; short alert ears; large clear eyes that are set wide apart; large nostrils; and deep, wide jaws. The Arabian also possesses an anatomical difference in comparison with other breeds, having one less lumbar (back) vertebra and one or two fewer vertebrae in the tail. In conformation, the Arabian breed is further noted for proud carriage of the head on a long and graceful neck; well-sloped shoulders and pasterns; a short back and loin; well-sprung ribs, a high, well-set tail; deep

Fig. 10-5. The Arabian mare, Dornaba, owned by Dr. Howard F. Kale, Bellevue, Washington; Canadian and U.S. National Champion Mare of 1966. (Courtesy, International Arabian Horse Association)

quarters; and superior quality of underpinning without any tendency to appear leggy.

The predominating colors are bay, gray, and chestnut, with an occasional white or black. According to an old Arab proverb, "The fleetest of horses is the chestnut; the most enduring the bay, the most spirited the black, and most blessed the white." White marks on the head and legs are common, but purebred Arabians are never piebald, skewbald, or spotted—circus and movie information to the contrary. The skin is always black, no matter what the coat color.

The better horses in Arabia, consisting of a relatively small number of animals owned by the tribes in the interior desert, have always been bred and raised in close contact with the families of their masters and are renowned for affection, gentleness, and tractability.

Adaptation and Use

The Arabian horse was primarily developed as a saddle horse, a use which still predominates among the breed today. Generally animals of this breed are trained and used at the three gaits—the walk, trot, and canter. Occasionally, however, purebred Arabians are trained to execute five gaits to perfection. Animals of this breed are easily broken to make a safe, although not a fast, driver in light harness.

The Arabian has made an invaluable contribution in the development of most all breeds; adding to their courage, endurance, quality, intelligence, docility, and beauty. It is no exaggeration to say that the prepotent blood of the Arabian has refined and improved all those breeds with which it has been infused.

Present Status of the Breed

At the present time, no great number of high-class Arabians remain in the country of their origin. In addition, World Wars I and II have devastated most of the better breeding establishments of Europe. Thus, the future preservation of the breed would appear to rest primarily with American breeders.

HACKNEY

The Hackney is the most prominent of the five breeds of heavy harness or carriage horses. In fact, except for the Hackney, the other breeds of this type are now practically extinct in the United States and are of historic interest primarily.

Origin and Native Home

The very name Hackney, and its abbreviated derivative "Hack," is suggestive of the type and adaptation of this breed, denoting both a general purpose horse and the vehicle which it draws.

The breed originated in Norfolk and adjoining counties on the eastern coast of England. Here, in the first half of the eighteenth century, was developed a trotting type of horse that was fast and that would go a distance, known as the Norfolk Trotter. It was this native stock with Thoroughbred infusion from which the Hackney was later derived. In this period, roads and vehicles were few and primitive, so that these Norfolk Trotters were used chiefly under saddle. Well authenticated records exist of travel at the rate of 17 miles per hour over ordinary roads.

The real beginning of the Hackney breed is traced to a stallion known as Blaze,[2] a Thoroughbred foaled in 1733 and a grandson of the immortal Darley Arabian, the latter being the most noted of the foundation sires of the Thoroughbred breed. Blaze and his noted son, Old Shales (foaled in 1755), produced a remarkably valuable riding and driving horse when crossed on the native stock of Norfolk.

The early formative period of the Hackney was before the advent of either the carriage or the railroad. Thus, these sturdy foundation animals were first used under saddle and were even employed for some light agricultural purposes. It was not uncommon in that era to see a farmer riding to market with his spouse behind him on a pillion.[3] Such use called for attractive animals with adequate size and substance and the ability to trot long distances at a fair speed.

With the development and use of the British hackney coaches of the eighteenth century, the Hackney became specialized for driving purposes. It soon became the leading heavy harness horse of the world, which position it still retains. With this specialized use and its increased popularity with the aristocracy of England, the Hackney's naturally high, trappy action was cultivated. As many of the vehicles were heavy, animals with size and a robust conformation were demanded. With it all, graceful, curved form, beauty, and style were emphasized. In brief, the quality and performance of the heavy harness horse became an indication of social prestige.

Early American Importations

One of the earliest, if not the first, Hackneys to be brought to America was a stallion named Pretender, a great grandson of Old Shales, imported to Virginia in 1801. Subsequent importations followed, but it was not until the era of the Gay Nineties that any great numbers were brought over. At this time, a boom in Hackneys developed in this country as prancing carriage horses became characteristic of the avenues traversed by the wealthy in the eastern cities.

Hackney Characteristics

Chestnut, bay, and brown are the most common colors found in the Hackney breed, although roans and blacks are seen. Regular

---

[2] The same Blaze from whom imported Messenger, the foundation sire of the Standardbred, was descended. Thus, on the sire's side the Hackney and Standardbred were of similar origin, but the native mares which served as foundation stock for the respective breeds and the objectives sought were very different.

[3] A seat or cushion which was put behind the gentleman's saddle.

white marks are rather common and are even desired for purposes
of accentuating high action. In the show-ring, custom decrees that
heavy harness horses and ponies be docked and have their manes pulled.

In size, the Hackney varies more than any other breed, ranging
from 12 to 16 hands. The small Hackney pony, under 14-2 hands in
height, and the larger animals are registered in the same stud book.
When used in a pair for a lady's phaeton, smaller animals are preferred. Because of the weight of the vehicle, however, a larger animal
is necessary when driven single. As would be expected with the wide
range in height of the breed, Hackneys vary considerably in weight,
from 800 to 1,200 pounds.

Typical Hackneys are relatively short-legged horses, rather robust
in conformation; heavy in proportion to their height; smooth and

*Fig. 10-6. Hackney stallion, Creation's King, six times All American Hackney stallion.
(Courtesy, Mr. A. Mackay-Smith, White Post, Va.)*

gracefully curved in form, with symmetry and balance; and up-headed, clean-cut, alert, and stylish to a high degree. High natural action—which is accentuated by skilled training, bitting and shoeing—is perhaps their most distinguishing feature.

Animals of piebald or skewbald color are not eligible for registry.

Adaptation and Use

The Hackney is the heavy harness horse *par excellence* for both the show-ring and park driving. Many hunters and jumpers are half-bred Hackneys, and they get their desired size from this breed.

Today, the Hackney is essentially a show animal, noted for superb quality, beautiful condition, and spirited high action. When drawing a proper vehicle devoid of shiny parts (which serve to blind the spectators), the well-trained Hackney is a wonderful spectacle to behold.

Present Status of the Breed

The nearer the street surfaces approach perfection for automobile traffic, the less satisfactory they are for use by horses. Thus, at the present time, the use of the Hackney is almost exclusively confined to the show-ring. On the tanbark, these high-stepping horses are still the show, and, to many, their appearance is reminiscent of the Gay Nineties.

MORGAN

The Morgan has been known as the first family of American horses. The early development of the breed took place in the New England states, thus giving the eastern section of the country primary credit for founding three light-horse breeds.

Origin and Native Home

The origin of the Morgan breed was a mere happenstance, and not the result of planned effort on the part of breeders to produce a particular breed of horse which would be adapted to local conditions. Whatever may be said of the greatness of Justin Morgan, he was the result of a chance mating—one of nature's secrets for which there is no breeding formula. In fact, it may be said that had a British general downed his liquor in his own parlor and had a Springfield, Massachusetts, farmer been able to pay his debts, the first family

Fig. 10-7. Memorial to Justin Morgan, foundation sire of the Morgan breed, located on the former U. S. Morgan Horse Farm (now operated by the University of Vermont), Middlebury, Vermont. The inscription reads as follows: "1921. Given by the Morgan Horse Club to the U. S. Department of Agriculture in memory of Justin Morgan who died in 1821." (Photo by M. E. Ensminger)

of American horses might never have existed. Legend has it that, one evening during the Revolutionary War, Colonel De Lancey, commander of a Tory mounted regiment, rode up to an inn at King's Bridge and after hitching his famous stallion, True Briton, to the rail, went into the inn for some liquid refreshments, as was his custom. While the Colonel was celebrating with liquor and song, the Yankees stole his horse, later selling the animal to a farmer near Hartford, Connecticut. The whimsical story goes on to say that True Briton later sired the fuzzy-haired colt that was to be christened after his second owner, Justin Morgan.

According to the best authorities, Mr. Morgan, who first lived for many years near Springfield, Massachusetts, moved his family to Randolph, Vermont, in 1788. A few years later, he returned to Springfield to collect a debt. But instead of getting the money, he bartered for a three-year-old gelding and a two-year-old colt of Thoroughbred and Arabian extraction. The stud colt, later named after the new owner as was often the custom of the day, became the noted horse, Justin Morgan, the progenitor of the first famous breed of horses developed in America.

Justin Morgan was a dark bay with black legs, mane, and tail.

His high head was shapely; his dark eyes were prominent, lively, and pleasant; his wide-set ears were small, pointed, and erect; his round body was short-backed, close-ribbed, and deep; his thin legs were set wide and straight, and the pasterns and shoulders were sloping; his action was straight, bold, and vigorous; and his style was proud, nervous, and imposing. Justin Morgan was a beautifully symmetrical, stylish, vibrant animal—renowned for looks, manners, and substance. It was claimed of him that he could outrun for short distances any horse against which he was matched. He was a fast trotter, a great horse on parade under saddle, and he could outpull most horses weighing several hundred pounds more.

Justin Morgan lived his 32 years (1789-1821) in an era of horses rather than in an era of power machinery. The westward expansion had been limited; roads and trails were in the raw, as nature had left them, and were often impassible even with a horse and buggy. Virgin forest had to be cleared, and the tough sod of the prairie had to be broken. These conditions called for an extremely versatile type of horse—one that could pull a good load on the farm, could be driven as a roadster, could be raced under saddle, and could be ridden in a parade. Justin Morgan and his progeny filled this utility need in a most remarkable manner. In due time, in 1893 to be exact, many years following the death of the foundation sire and after a decade of exhaustive research, Colonel Joseph Battell published Volume I of the American Morgan Horse Register. Such was the beginning of preservation of the lineage of the breed—a registry assignment now handled under the same name by the Morgan Horse Club.

Morgan Characteristics

With shifts in use, it is but natural to find considerable variation in the size of present-day Morgans. Yet throughout the vicissitudes of time and shifts in emphasis that have occurred during the past hundred years, Morgan horses to an amazing degree have continued to have certain unique characteristics which distinguish them as a breed.

The height of representative animals ranges from 14-2 to 16 hands, with the larger animals now given preference by most horsemen. The average Morgan weighs from 800 to 1,200 pounds. Standard colors are bay, brown, black, and chestnut; and white markings are not uncommon.

In conformation, the breed has retained most of the characteristics

Fig. 10-8. Morgan stallion, Rex's Major Monte, bred and owned by Mr. and Mrs. F. W. Waer, Orange, California. (Courtesy, The Morgan Horse Club)

attributed to the foundation sire. With greater emphasis on use under saddle, however, modern Morgans are inclined to be more up-standing, to have longer necks, and to possess more slope to their shoulders and pasterns. Regardless of type changes, the breed continues to be noted for stamina, docility, beauty, courage, and longevity. The presence of only five lumbar vertebrae in many Morgans is attributed to the use of Arabian breeding.

Animals with wall-eye (lack of pigmentation of the iris), or with natural white markings above the knee or hock except on the face, are disqualified for registry.

Adaptation and Use

In the early formative period of the breed, the Morgan was thought of as a general purpose type of animal—for use in harness racing, as roadsters, on the farm, on the avenue, in the park, on the range, and on the trail. With the development of mechanization, many of these needs passed into oblivion. The more progressive breeders, fully cognizant of the change in needs, took stock of the breed's inherent possibilities and shifted their efforts in breeding and selection to the production of a superior riding horse. At the present time, therefore, it is not surprising to find that there is considerable variation in emphasis in different sections of the United States. In the West, the Morgan is primarily a stock horse; in the central states, it is still a general purpose breed; whereas in the East the emphasis is upon the Morgan as a saddle horse, particularly for general country use and for recreational purposes over the hundreds of miles of trails.

The comparatively small number of purebred Morgans today is no criterion of the true importance of the breed. Their influence has literally extended to the entire horse population of the continent. Morgan blood was used in laying the foundation for many breeds. The leading Standardbred families of today are a fusion of Hambletonian lines with the Morgan—Axworthy, Mako, and Peter the Great all carried Morgan blood in their veins. Likewise, the American Saddle Horse is indebted to the Morgan, for the Peavine and Chief families both contained Morgan ancestry. Allen, the foundation sire of the Tennessee Walking Horse, was a great grandson of a Morgan, Vermont Black Hawk.

Present Status of the Breed

During the period of transition and shift in emphasis from a utility and harness type of horse to use under the saddle, the registration of Morgan horses declined, and the identity of many registered animals was lost. This greatly reduced the number of available breeding animals to use as a base for the rapid expansion of breeding interest that has occurred during the past two decades.

In 1907, Colonel Battell—an admirer, breeder, and founder of the Register of Morgan Horses—presented to the U. S. Department of Agriculture what became known as the United States Morgan Horse Farm, near Middlebury, Vermont. Colonel Battell's primary objective in presenting the farm to the Federal Government was that of providing a place upon which the breed could be perpetuated and improved. Though it would appear ironical today, it was also rumored that the old gentleman was disturbed with the high taxes of the period and had decided that the only way to beat the Government was to give his holdings to the United States. Regardless of the possible latter objective, it must be agreed that the U. S. Morgan Horse Farm was a powerful influence in perpetuating and improving the Morgan breed. Effective July 1, 1951, by authorization of the U. S. Congress, the United States Morgan Horse Farm was transferred without cost to the Vermont Agricultural College.

PALOMINO

The word palomino correctly implies a horse of a golden color with white, silver, or ivory mane and tail. Originally, Palominos were not considered either a breed or a type, but simply a color. Today, animals of Palomino color and meeting certain other stipulations may be recorded in either of two registry associations.

Origin and Native Home

When, in the course of the Mexican War—which ended in 1848, over one hundred years ago—the United States acquired what is now the state of California, many attractive golden-colored horses of good type were found in the new territory.

According to the best records available, these animals were first introduced from Spain to the New World beginning with Cortez, in 1519, and their introduction was continued by other Spanish explorers. Evidently these horses had long been bred for color in Spain, being used exclusively as the distinctive mounts of the Royal Family, the nobility, and high military officials. In Spain these golden-colored animals were known as "The Horse of the Queen," and their use by commoners was forbidden. It is also known that the Spaniards obtained the golden horse from Arabia and Morocco, but further than this its origin is clouded in obscurity.

In the early days of California, Palominos were extremely popular. Spanish gentlemen took pride in ownership of these beautiful mounts, which were also used as the racehorses in early California. However, with the importation of the Thoroughbred and other horses of light-horse extraction from the eastern seaboard and Europe, the golden horse was threatened with extinction. Only in recent years has its popularity again come to the fore, finally resulting in the formation of two breed registry associations; the Palomino Horse Association, which was incorporated in 1936, and the Palomino Horse Breeders of America, which was organized in 1941.

Fig. 10-9. A three-year-old Palomino filly, sired by The Harvester—one of the founda-tion sires of the Palomino breed. (Courtesy, Edna Fagen, The Palomino Horse Association, Inc.)

Palomino Characteristics

The Palomino must be golden in color (the color of a newly minted gold coin or three shades lighter or darker), with a light-colored mane and tail (white, silver, or ivory, with not more than 15 percent dark or chestnut hair in either). White markings on the face or below the knees or hocks are acceptable. The skin and eyes shall be dark or hazel. The usual height range is from 14-2 to 16 hands and the weight from 1,000 to 1,200 pounds. As might be expected, in an attempt to form a new breed with a color requirement as first and foremost, considerable variation in type exists.

Some authorities feel that the Palomino color may be unfixable; that it cannot be made true breeding, no matter how long or how persistent the effort. (See discussion relative to Incomplete Dominance, in Chapter 12.) Further, there appears to be ample theory—substantiated by practical observation—to indicate that Palomino foals may be produced by any one of the following four types of matings:

1. Palomino x Palomino resulting in the production of foals in the ratio of 1 chestnut: 2 Palomino: 1 Albino.[4]

2. Palomino x chestnut producing foals in the ratio of 1 chestnut: 1 Palomino.

3. Palomino x Albino, producing foals in the ratio of 1 Palomino: 1 Albino.

4. Chestnut x Albino, producing only Palomino foals.

As indicated, when Palomino mares are bred to a Palomino stallion, the foals are, on the average, of the following colors: one-half of them Palominos, one-fourth of them chestnut, and one-fourth of them Albinos. Also, it is noteworthy that chestnut x Albino matings produce only Palomino foals.

Adaptation and Use

The American Horse Shows Association rule book states that competition for Palominos may exist in any one of the following classifications: (1) pleasure horses, (2) parade horses, (3) stock horses, and (4) all other types such as saddle, fine harness, walking horses, etc., provided that color shall count at least 25 percent in judging these events. Perhaps these classifications constitute the best summary of the diverse adaptations and uses now being made of Palominos.

Present Status of the Breed

It is to the credit of the Associations and the breed enthusiasts that they have done a wonderful job in selling the public on the beauty of the Palomino. They have accepted Palomino colors from among the light-horse breeds and have wisely admonished the breeders themselves to improve the type.

The following types of registries are maintained by the Palomino Horse Breeders of America (P.H.B.A.):

Palomino Breed Registry: Eligibility therein determined either by

---

[4] The term Albino as herein used is familiar to horsemen, but it does not refer to a true Albino as exists in white mice, rats, and rabbits.

(1) pedigree, or (2) progeny. To qualify by pedigree, both parents must be registered; either (1) in the P.H.B.A., or (2) one parent must be registered in the P.H.B.A. and the other must be registered in either the American Quarter Horse, Arabian, or Thoroughbred association. To qualify by progeny, a stallion must be registered with the P.H.B.A. and also must have five of his get registered therein; and a mare must be registered in the association and have three of her produce registered therein.

Regular Registry: A gelding may be registered therein provided he is of Palomino color and acceptable conformation, regardless of whether or not he has a registered sire or dam. Stallions and mares may be recorded in the Regular Registry provided either (1) their sire or dam is registered in the P.H.B.A., or (2) the animal itself, or its sire or dam, is registered in the Arabian Horse Club, American Remount Association, American Quarter Horse Association, American Saddle Horse Breeders Association, Jockey Club, Morgan Horse Club, Palomino Horse Association, Tennessee Walking Horse Breeders Association, or United States Trotting Association.

Junior Registry: For stallions under two years of age and fillies under one year of age, provided such animals qualify for registration on the basis of bloodlines, pedigree, and color.

In addition to the regular registry for progeny of parents registered in the Association, the Palomino Horse Association (the other of the two breed registries) maintains the following type of registry:

Associate Certificate: For animals not out of a registered sire or dam, provided the animal has no Albino or Pinto ancestry. When a stallion with an Associate Certificate has sired four qualified Palomino foals, or when a mare similarly registered has foaled two qualified Palomino foals, both it and its get may be issued a regular certificate.

The Thoroughbred and Arabian registries prohibit double entry; that is, registrations in their respective associations and also in a Palomino association; but the other associations contain many Palominos which are also registered in a Palomino registry association.

PINTO HORSE

The word pinto refers to a marked or spotted horse, a description first applied to the spotted descendants of the horses of the Spanish conquerors. Sometimes, though less correctly, animals of this color are referred to as piebald, skewbald, and calico.

Origin and Native Home

Spotted or Pinto horses first arrived in the New World with the
Spanish conquistadores. From that day forward, animals of this color
played a leading role in the development of the West. Many of
them were captured and used as the highly prized riding horses of the
American Indians. Later, they were found among the feral horses
of the West; and, most important, through the years many of them
have been used as stock horses.

Pinto Characteristics

The most distinctive characteristic of the Pinto horse is its color.[5]

Fig. 10-10. Rocket, Pinto stallion, a consistent winner, owned by J. Carrol Barnhill,
Bradenton, Florida. This horse is red and white, with black points. (Courtesy, Mr.
Barnhill)

[5] There are two distinct pattern markings of the Pinto: (1) Overo—a
colored horse with white areas extending upward from the belly and lower
regions, and possibly other white markings, and (2) Tobiana—in which
white areas of the dorsal region extend downward, and which may have
other white markings as well.

The perfectly marked representative is half color or colors and half white, with many spots well placed. The two distinct pattern markings are: Overo and Tobiana. The spots may range in size from two to twelve inches across, and they may or may not be uniform in placement, size, and regularity of shape. Thus, Pinto horses are renowned for their vari-colors and appeal.

The height ranges from 14-1 to 16-2 hands, and the weight from 750 to 1,300 pounds. In conformation, the best representatives of the breed are comparable to the type of any well-bred saddle horse of any breed. The glass eye is a part of the Pinto lineage and is not to be discounted. Animals under 14 hands or of pony or draft horse blood are disqualified from registry.

Adaptation and Use

Colonel F. W. Koester has well summarized the adaptation and use of the Pinto horse in the following statement:[6] "There is the Pinto pony—long the pride and joy of millions of American youth. We find Pintos, too, among the cow ponies and polo ponies, jumpers, hunters, and other sporting types. Again, among the pleasure types such as trail horses, hacks, and particularly parade horses, the Pinto enjoys wide and deserved popularity." In brief, the Pinto is adapted for use for any light-horse purpose, but it is especially superb as a show, parade, novice, and pleasure animal.

Present Status of the Breed

The Pinto is primarily of two types: (1) Western Saddle Horse, and (2) American Parade type. The breed enthusiasts have never attempted to dominate other breeds nor to make wild claims for their representatives. Rather, they are wisely attempting to preserve, improve, and extend the use of a type and color of horse whose development has gone hand in hand with the transformation of America itself.

The Pinto Horse Association of America, Inc., maintains the following types of registries:

Tentative Registry: This is for foals. They become eligible for permanent registry at two years of age if they meet the standards.

Permanent Registry: Horses recorded herein must be two years

----

[6] Koester, Colonel F. W., "The Pinto's Place Now and in the Future," *Official Stud Book and Registry, The Pinto Horse Society,* Vol. 4, December 31, 1945, pp. 13 and 14.

of age, 14-1 hands or over, and of acceptable conformation, quality, and refinement. They must have at least three noticeable spots on the body, not including the face and legs, and they must have dark or blue eyes.

Approved Breed Registry: This is open to Permanent Registered Pintos. To be eligible, stallions must have four foals in either the Permanent or Tentative Registry, and mares three.

PONY OF THE AMERICAS (POA)

The Pony of the Americas is an all-around pleasure pony that is small enough for a child but large enough for a teenager.

Origin and Native Home

The Pony of the Americas is, as the name indicates, a pony breed that originated in America. The registry, known as the Pony of the Americas Club, Inc. (POAC), was formed in 1954, with headquarters in Mason City, Iowa. From its inception, the POAC has had the good fortune to have the dedicated, enlightened, and progressive leadership of Mr. Leslie L. Boomhower, an able lawyer and horseman, as Executive Secretary.

Pony of the Americas Characteristics

The Pony of the Americas is a happy medium of Arabian and Quarter Horse in miniature, ranging in height from 46" to 54", with Appaloosa coloring. It's a western-type using pony.

Animals possessing the following characteristics are disqualified for registry: Not having the Appaloosa color; exceeding 54", or under 46" at maturity (6 years); with Pinto or albino color, or whose sires and dams were pinto or albino colored; loud-colored roans; or cryptorchids or monorchids.

Adaptation and Use

The primary use of the Pony of the Americas is for juniors who have outgrown Shetlands but who are not ready for horses.

Present Status of the Breed

The breed has made remarkable progress. In the formative years, it

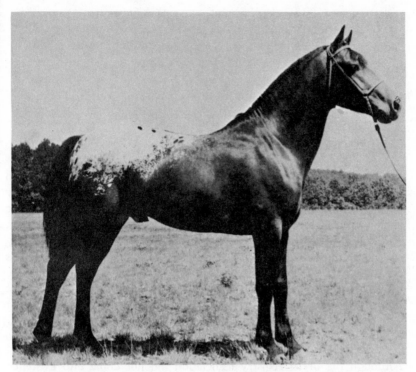

Fig. 10-11. Pony of the Americas stallion, Stewart's Danny Boy. This stallion and his get have won 15 international championships—more than any other lineage in the breed. Owned by John Ludwig, Mohnton, Pa. (Courtesy, Pony of the Americas, Inc.)

was not easy to obtain a pony of the size and color that would meet the type standard. However, much progress has been made, as evidenced by the announced intent of the registry to close the books beginning in 1970. Thereafter, one parent will have to be a registered POA before the foal is eligible for registration.

The two types of registrations are as follows:

1. *Tentative (T).*—Any foal with Appaloosa coloring is eligible for T registration. However, if the animal exceeds 54", or matures under 46" (at 6 years of age), its papers are cancelled and the registration fee is forfeited.

2. *Permanent.*—Any Appaloosa colored pony passing the inspection and within the following height range is eligible for permanent registration:

Age (yrs.)	Height (in.)
2	46-48
3	46-50
4	46-52
5	46-53
6	46-54

QUARTER HORSE

The earliest form of horse racing in America—particularly in Maryland, Virginia, and the Carolinas—was through necessity usually over a quarter-mile track. The topography and the wilderness were such as to make difficult the construction of formal racetracks. Rather, small race paths were literally hewn out of the wilderness. Many of these courses were down the main street of town, as this was the only straight and cleared stretch available. To race over these tracks, the pioneers selected sturdy stock possessed of a great burst of speed at short distances.

Origin and Native Home

Although the breed registry association did not come into existence until 1940, the Quarter Horse had its beginning some three hundred years earlier with the crude quarter-mile race paths of pioneer days. Those heavily muscled, sturdy animals, best adapted to rugged courses in matched races, were to serve as the foundation stock of a now popular western breed. With the advent of the Thoroughbred and the construction of formal racetracks of greater length in the East, Quarter Horse racing stock was pushed to the West and Southwest. In the range states these rugged animals continued to flourish for quarter racing, and they endeared themselves as the ideal cow pony.

There are two schools of thought relative to the ancestry of the Quarter Horse: (1) that the foundation stock consisted of the native mares of Spanish extraction in Virginia, Maryland, and the Carolinas which were mated to Thoroughbred stallions, and (2) that little or no Thoroughbred blood was infused, for—so it is argued—the foundation of the Quarter Horse was laid a hundred years before the first Thoroughbred horse was imported to America in 1730.

It is known that the early improvement of the Quarter Horse and that of the Thoroughbred were closely associated. Perhaps the truth of the matter is that certain animals contributed notably to each breed.

Most authorities recognize as the Quarter Horse patriarch, the imported Thoroughbred stallion Janus (1756-1780), a tested four-mile racer in England. It is reported that Janus' progeny were un-excelled for a great burst of speed over short distances, and, like their sire, they were sturdy in build and possessed powerful muscling in the hindquarters.

Since there was no Quarter Horse registry prior to 1940, it is incredible that the purity of the breed could have been maintained through more than three hundred years of an unplanned beginning. Suffice it to say that the distinctive breed that evolved at the end of this period is ample evidence of the potency of the foundation stock and of the superior quality of the blood infused through the years— regardless of its source.

Steel Dust, the most famous of all Quarter Horses, made his debut in Texas around the middle of the nineteenth century. Until his fame became known, it was said that he nearly bankrupted a certain Texas community in which he first appeared in a matched race with a notorious racer of the day. In commenting on the influence of Steel Dust in molding the breed, Robert Denhart[7] states that, "Every horse trader who has not recently joined a church will modestly admit that his horses are direct descendants of Steel Dust." There are some eleven prominent families listed in the Stud Book and Registry, most of which either originated in or were introduced in Texas.

Quarter Horse Characteristics

Quarter Horses are somewhat stout in build, seldom exceeding 15 hands in height, and they generally weigh from 1,000 to 1,200 pounds. The head, which is somewhat short, is distinct because of the small alert ear and heavily muscled cheeks and jaw. The neck is well developed, the back and loin short and heavily muscled, the forearms and rear quarters are powerfully muscled, and the legs relatively short. The entire ensemble is such as to make him an ideal stock horse—an animal that is agile and speedy, capable of outrunning any "critter." He possesses sufficient weight and power to hold a heavy steer when roped and has a calm disposition even in the round-up. Also, certain families are being selected for great race speed at short distances.

---

[7] The Quarter Horse—A History, *The American Quarter Horse Association, Stud Book and Registry*, Vol. I, 1941, p. 18.

Fig. 10-12. The Quarter Horse stallion, Forecast; one of only a relatively few horses known to be both "AAA" on the racetrack and an AQHA Champion. (Courtesy, American Quarter Horse Association. Photo by Bert Bollinger, P. O. Box 561, Austin, Texas)

At the present time, most Quarter Horse breeders and judges are selecting away from the extreme "bulldog type" that was so popular a few years ago. Although desiring to maintain a well-muscled and powerfully built horse, it is argued that a more moderately stocky type is more useful.

The most predominating colors of the breed are chestnut, sorrel, bay and dun. Palominos, blacks, browns, roans, and copper-colored animals, however, are not uncommon. Pintos, Appaloosas, and albinos are the only colors that are ineligible for registration.

Adaptation and Use

Quarter Horses are adapted and used chiefly for two purposes: (1) for quarter-mile racing, and (2) for cow ponies. Thus, it follows that there are two schools of thought as to the best method of testing the performance of Quarter Horses: (1) to race them up to distances of a quarter-mile; and (2) to work cattle with them.

Advocates of the first method are interested primarily in speed and racing, whereas advocates of the second method are interested chiefly in a superior cow pony. Perhaps some combination of the two criteria is most desirable.

Present Status of the Breed

Despite the decline in the horse and mule population during the past three decades, the stock horse will always remain on the western range. Even the versatile Jeep does not threaten to take over the job of roping a steer. Thus, the future of the Quarter Horse breed seems assured.

Since 1962, the American Quarter Horse Association has maintained (1) a *Numbered* (permanent and closed) registry, for which inspection is no longer required—following 22 years of such inspection, and (2) an *Appendix* registry for horses with one parent in the *Numbered* registry and the other parent registered in The Jockey Club (one cross and one breed only). The latter may advance to *Numbered* registry only after reaching two years of age, qualifying in performance (known as Register of Merit, of which there are two—one for working events, and the other for racing), and passing a conformation inspection.

SHETLAND PONY

The Shetland Pony is the smallest of all horses. In addition to its diminutive size, it is noted for its hardiness and good disposition.

Origin and Native Home

The Shetland Pony is native to the Shetland Isles, which lie one hundred miles north of Scotland, parallel with central Norway, and not more than four hundred miles from the Arctic Circle. Historic records give evidence that the breed was located in this rugged area as early as the sixth century A. D. This qualifies the breed as one of the oldest in existence. Centuries of survival in the rigors of the northland climate and on sparse vegetation have endowed the breed with that hardiness for which it is justly famed.

Early American Importations

The first importations of Shetlands to the United States took place about the middle of the nineteenth century. Large numbers of subsequent importations followed.

Shetland Pony Characteristics

There are two distinct types of Shetlands, one of which is a pocket-sized draft horse and the other a small edition of a road-type horse. The latter, which evolved in this country through selective breeding, is often referred to as the American type.

The true Shetland is less than 11-2 hands in height (ponies over 46″ in height are not eligible for registry), and most individuals are less than 10-2 hands. Colors run almost the whole gamut of horse colors, with both broken and solid colors existing. Spotted ponies are more likely to have "glass" eyes, which are not desired.

By heritage, the Shetland Pony is gentle and faithful, as it was

Fig. 10-13. Shetland Pony mare. (Courtesy, The American Shetland Pony Journal, West Lafayette, Ind.)

developed about the house and with children and dogs in its native Shetland Islands.

Adaptation and Use

Modern Shetland Ponies are used in many ways; as show ponies, for racing, as children's mounts, etc.

A harness-show type for use in the American show-ring has been developed by crossing Welsh or Hackneys on Shetlands. These crossbreds, which may be registered as such, are active, stylish, and showy —beautiful to behold on the tanbark.

Present Status of the Breed

Wherever there are children, Shetland Ponies will continue to be in demand. It is likely that more and more Shetlands will come to provide healthful outdoor recreation for the boys and girls of America.

In addition to registering purebred Shetlands, the American Shetland Pony Club also records the following:

Harness Show Ponies: Ponies which have one parent that is a Hackney or Welsh Pony and the other parent a Shetland, provided they meet the eligibility requirements laid down by the Club for Harness Show Ponies.

STANDARDBRED

Both the Standardbred and the American Saddle Horse are the result of a Thoroughbred top cross on native mares; both are truly American creations—the former developing as a road horse in the East and the latter as a saddle horse of the southern plantations. In each case, the descendants of one Thoroughbred individual dominated the breed. Messenger, imported in 1788, largely shaped the Standardbred through his great grandson, Hambletonian 10; whereas Denmark, foaled in 1839, largely determined the destiny of the American Saddle Horse through his illustrious son, Gaine's Denmark. Despite these similarities in background, two very different breeds evolved because of: (1) the differences in the native mares used, and (2) selection as influenced by the respective ends in view. In the case of the Standardbred, the native foundation mares were trotters or pacers adapted to fast driving in harness; wheareas the native mares used in molding the American Saddle Horse were amblers, easy to ride.

Origin and Native Home

The Standardbred, originally developed for road driving and racing, descended from five sources: (1) the Thoroughbred, (2) the Norfolk Trotter or Hackney, (3) the Arabian and Barb, (4) the Morgan, and (5) certain pacers of mixed breeding. Originally this breed was often referred to as the American Trotter, but this designation is now discarded because the breed embraces both trotters and pacers, all of which are registered in the same association. The name "Standardbred" is derived from the fact that, beginning in 1879, eligibility for registration was based on the ability of the animal to trot the mile at 2:30 or pace the same distance at 2:25. Today, a record of performance

Fig. 10-14. The immortal Hambletonian 10 (also known as Rysdyk's Hambletonian), the descendant of Messenger who solidified the Standardbred breed. William Rysdyk, a poor farm hand, purchased him as a suckling colt, along with his dam, for $125. Hambletonian 10 never raced. He began his stud career at two and lived to the age of twenty-seven, during which time he earned approximately $500,000 for his owner. Today, it is estimated that 99 percent of the trotters and pacers in America trace to this great sire. (Courtesy, The United States Trotting Association)

is no longer a prerequisite to registration—it is merely necessary that animals be the offspring of recorded sires and dams.[8]

The great pillar of the Standardbred was Rysdyk's Hambletonian, or Hambletonian 10 (the latter designating his Standard number in Vol. IV of the Register). This great stallion, foaled in 1849, carried the blood of Messenger, a gray Thoroughbred stallion imported from England to Philadelphia in 1788 at the age of eight, and Bellfounder, a Norfolk Trotter or Hackney, foaled in England in 1815 and imported to Boston in 1822. No breed can boast of a greater sire than Hambletonian 10. During his 21 years in the stud, he sired 1,321 foals, and so famous did he become by virtue of the speed of his get that his service fee was placed at $500.

Standardbred Characteristics

In general, animals of this breed are smaller, longer bodied, less leggy and possess less quality than the Thoroughbred, but they show more substance and ruggedness and they possess a more tractable disposition. The head, ears, and bone show less refinement, and the hind legs are not quite so straight as in the Thoroughbred. Standardbred animals attain speed through ability to extend themselves into long strides, repeated rapidly, because of the long forearm and long, narrow muscles.

In weight, the Standardbred ranges from 900 to 1,300 pounds, and in height from 15 to 16 hands, with the average being around 15-2 hands. Bay, brown, chestnut, and black are the most common colors; but grays, roans, and duns are found.

Though possessing a common ancestry, some families produce a much larger proportion of pacers than others. Many individuals show speed at both gaits. Shoeing and training are also important factors in determining whether an animal shall be a trotter or a pacer.

Adaptation and Use

As previously indicated, the Standardbred was primarily originated as a trotting horse and for the purpose of providing a superior road horse in the days of the horse and buggy. He was first put under saddle and eventually into harness hitched to a sulky. With the coming of improved highways and the automobile, the progressive breeders,

---

[8] On January 1, 1933, registration on performance alone was no longer granted, and registration of both sire and dam was required.

Fig. 10-15. Adios, leading Standardbred sire. Through 1966, his get had earned $16,860,238—the largest amount credited to any stallion, of any breed, in the world. (Courtesy, The United States Trotting Association)

ever alert to new developments, turned their attention almost exclusively to the production of a speedy harness racehorse—either at the trot or the pace. The gameness and stamina of the Standardbred is unexcelled, thus adapting him to race heats wherein it is necessary that he go mile after mile at top speed. Animals of this breed are also exhibited as light harness horses in the great horse shows of the land.

The early foundation animals of the Standardbred contributed to the development of the American Saddle Horse and the Tennessee Walking Horse. Many hunters are also of Standardbred extraction. It may be said that the Standardbred has proved to be a valuable utility horse—animals of such extraction having speed, endurance, and a tractable disposition.

Fig. 10-16. Bret Hanover, holder of the world's pacing record for a mile at 1:53 3/5, set at Lexington, Ky., October 7, 1966; owned by Richard Downing, Shaker Heights, Ohio, and trained and driven by Frank Ervin. Bret Hanover won $922,616 from 1964 to 1966. In 1966, he was sold for $2,000,000 to Castleton Farm, Lexington, Ky., as a stud. (Courtesy, The United States Trotting Association, Columbus, Ohio)

Present Status of the Breed

Greyhound, a gelding, established the world's trotting record for a mile at 1:55¼ in 1938; and Bret Hanover set a new world's pacing record for a mile at 1:53 3/5 in 1966.

It is quite likely that new harness racetracks will be developed; and with their development, a limited increase in numbers of Standardbreds may be expected. Further improvements in both conformation and speed may be expected, also.

The Standardbred breed has the unique distinction of being one of the few breeds of livestock that the United States has exported rather than imported. Many good specimens of the breed have been shipped to the U.S.S.R., Austria, Germany, and Italy.

In addition to registering animals both of whose parents are recorded in the United States Trotting Association, any horse sired by

Fig. 10-17. Greyhound, Standardbred harness racehorse, in action. He still holds the world's trotting record of 1:55¼ for the mile (the record was made in 1938). With a stride exceeding 27 feet, Greyhound was often referred to as the "Silver Groomed Flyer." Trotters and pacers are of similar breeding and type, the particular gaits being largely a matter of training. Today, harness racehorses are almost exclusively of the Standardbred breed. (Courtesy, United States Trotting Association)

a registered horse may be accepted for racing purposes as follows:

Non-Standard Bred: Any horse may be registered as Non-Standard if an application is filed showing satisfactory identification of the horse for racing purposes. This identification may be accomplished by furnishing the name, age, sex, sire, dam, color and markings; also required is a history of the previous owners, if any. A mating certificate must accompany this application, showing the sire to be some type of a registered horse.

An unregistered animal may progress to Standard registration provided it comes under one of the following classifications:

1. A stallion sired by a registered Standard horse, provided his dam and grandam were sired by registered Standard horses and he himself has a Standard record and is the sire of three performers with Standard records from different mares.

2. A mare whose sire is a registered Standard horse, and whose dam and grandam were sired by a registered Standard horse, provided she herself has a Standard record.

3. A mare sired by a registered Standard horse, provided she is the dam of two performers with Standard records.

4. A mare or horse sired by a registered Standard horse, provided its first, second, and third dams are each sired by a registered Standard horse.

TENNESSEE WALKING HORSE

Today, the Tennessee Walking Horse is synonymous with the Plantation Walking Horse, as the latter show-ring classification is constituted by this one breed. In the early formative period of the breed, animals of the walk, running walk, canter variety were referred to as the Plantation Walking Horse because the southern owners and overseers used this type of animal in riding over their estates daily. They liked these animals because of their stamina and comfortable gaits.

Origin and Native Home

Although the breed registry association is rather recent, the Tennessee Walking Horse has been at home in the Middle Basin of Tennessee for more than a hundred years. Like other American breed creations, the Tennessee Walking Horse is of composite origin. Yet, through constant breeding and selection, distinct characteristics evolved, molding the horse into an entity of its own. The sturdy native saddle stock of Tennessee accompanied the early settlers from Virginia. According to the best authorities, the breed represents an amalgamation of the Thoroughbred, Standardbred, Morgan, and American Saddle Horse breeds, together with whatever else may have constituted the native stock. Thus, throughout a century or more of meticulous breeding, the Tennessee Walking Horse has come to possess some of the endurance and upstanding qualities of the Thoroughbred, the substance and sturdiness of the Standardbred, the graceful lines and docility of the Morgan, and the style and beauty of the American Saddle Horse.

The real patriarch, or foundation sire, of the Tennessee Walking Horse was a stallion known as Allan, sometimes called Black Allan because of his color. This horse, of mixed Standardbred and Morgan ancestry, foaled in 1886, proved to be a progenitor of remarkable prepotency when crossed on native mares. Moreover, his offspring carried on. Thus, in many respects, the origin of the Tennessee Walking Horse is not unlike the development of the Morgan.

Tennessee Walking Horse Characteristics

In comparison with the American Saddle Horse, the average member of the Tennessee Walking Horse breed is larger, stouter, and more rugged. He is plainer about the head, shorter necked, carries the head lower, and possesses more massiveness about the body and quarters. Although he has less style and elegance, the Tennessee Walking Horse excels the American Saddle Horse when it comes to temperament and disposition. He has been referred to as the "gentleman of the equines."

Fig. 10-18. Tennessee Walking Horse stallion, Go Boy's Shadow; Twice Grand Championship Stake winner, Walking Horse National Celebration. (Courtesy, Wiser's Walking Horse Stables, Wartrace, Tenn.)

The Tennessee Walking Horse averages around 15-2 hands in height and weighs from 1,000 to 1,200 pounds. A great array of colors exists, including sorrel, chestnut, black, roan, white, bay, brown, gray, and golden. White markings on the feet and legs are common.

The three gaits characterizing the breed are all natural gaits. They are free and easy and are called the flat-foot walk, the running walk, and the canter. Particular emphasis is placed upon the running walk, an all-day gait which is executed at a speed of six to eight miles per hour. It is started like the flat-foot walk and is a diagonally-opposed foot movement. As the speed is increased, the hind foot usually oversteps the front track from a few to as many as 18 inches. This gives the rider a gliding sensation.

Adaptation and Use

Although the Tennessee Walking Horse arose as the business or plantation horse of Tennessee and the South, it is now largely a pleasure horse. Because of its gentle manners and easy gaits, it is an ideal horse for the amateur or the person who rides infrequently. The experienced horseman, likewise, enjoys these same traits.

Present Status of the Breed

In the early period of the breed, the Tennessee Walking Horse enjoyed a rapid rise in fame and numbers. In recent years, however, registration numbers and average prices have declined.

In addition to recording progeny out of registered Tennessee Walking Horse parents, the Association will register the following:

Geldings carrying fifty percent Walking Horse blood, two years of age or over, and broken, provided they perform the true Walking Horse gaits.

Mares that have as much as fifty percent Tennessee Walking Horse blood, and that have produced registered colts. (It is noteworthy that the latter rule has been effective since September 1, 1947, but since that date, no animal has been registered thereunder.)

THOROUGHBRED

The term "Thoroughbred" is applied properly only to the breed of running racehorses developed originally in England. It should not be confused with nor used synonymously with the designation purebred, an adjective used to denote the pure lineage of any breed of live-stock regardless of class or breed. Today, the Thoroughbred has become the equine synonym for speed and racing quality.

Origin and Native Home

The history of the Thoroughbred, as we think of it today, had its beginning in the seventeenth century, though the Oriental lineage of the breed is as old as civilization itself. The nature of man being what it is, there was racing wherever there were horses. However, the real molding of the fleet light horse in England became a necessity with the shift from medieval warfare—in which the fighting unit consisted of a mounted knight in full armor—to the use of arrows and finally gunpowder. Speed and stamina became imperative. Simultaneously, interest in horse racing in England was greatly accelerated. As early as the reign of Henry VIII, a royal stud was established.

The real impetus to the development of a superior English running horse, however, had its beginning under Charles II, who reigned from 1660 to 1685. King Charles imported a number of outstanding Barb mares for the royal stable. Upon the descendants of this improved foundation stock were subsequently crossed three immortal stallions known respectively as: the Byerly Turk, imported in 1689; the Darley Arabian, imported in 1706; and the Godolphin Arabian, brought from Paris in 1724. From these three illustrious sires sprang three male lines: Matchem, tracing to the Godolphin Arabian; Eclipse, tracing to the Darley Arabian; and Herod, tracing to the Byerly Turk. Such was the development of the Thoroughbred, a breed predominantly of Arabian, Barb,[9] and Turk[10] extraction; though it may have in its veins the blood of the Galloway, Scotch Pony, and Highland Dun—animals used for cart or draft purposes, and "heaven only knows what else."

Early American Importations

The first Thoroughbred imported to America was the 21-year-old stallion, Bulle Rock, by Darley Arabian and out of a dam by Byerly Turk, arriving in Virginia in 1730. Governors Ogle and Sharpe of

---

[9] The Barbs were native to the Barbary States of Northern Africa. They were more rugged than the Arabian but lacked the quality, refinement, and beauty of the latter.

[10] The Turk horse was found chiefly in Anatola and only to a limited extent in Turkey. These animals were noted for docility and beauty, but they lacked the vigor and endurance of the Arabian.

Maryland made subsequent importations between 1747 and 1755. The Revolution interrupted the growth of Thoroughbred breeding, but at its close the stream of importations was re-established. New race-tracks were built, and the breed became firmly entrenched in America.

Thoroughbred Characteristics

Thoroughbreds are bay, brown, chestnut, black, or, less frequently, gray in color. White markings on the face and legs are common. Animals of this breed range in height from 15 to 17 hands, with an average of around 16 hands. In racing trim, the Thoroughbred may weigh from 900 to 1,025 pounds, whereas stallions in breeding condition may approach 1,400 pounds.

The build of the Thoroughbred shows the speed type in the ex-

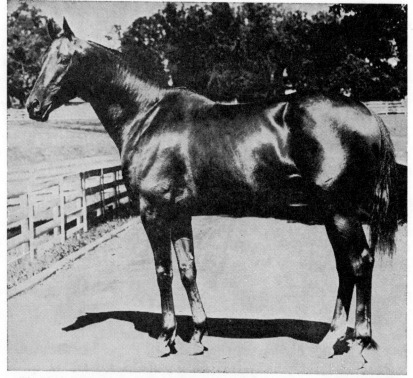

Fig. 10-19. Thoroughbred stallion, Swaps, Kentucky Derby winner; won $848,900 in racing purses; set six world's records. Note the long body, deep chest, rather long legs, and high degree of quality and refinement characteristic of the breed. (Courtesy, Mr. Olin Gentry, Darby Dan Farm, Lexington, Ky.)

treme. The body is long, deep chested, rather narrow, upstanding, and often a bit angular. This horse possesses a high degree of quality and refinement throughout. The head is small and well proportioned, with a straight face, small neat ear, and fine throttle. The shoulders and pastern are sloping, and the thigh and quarter are powerfully muscled. The temperament is active and energetic, being of the racy or highly nervous variety. The action of most Thoroughbreds is characterized by going low and pointed at the trot but executing the gallop or run to perfection.

Adaptation and Use

As a running racehorse, the Thoroughbred is without a peer. Yet, it is noteworthy that a considerable number of the Thoroughbreds foaled in the U.S. are never raced, and many that are raced never win.

Many excellent horses of straight- or part-Thoroughbred breeding have excelled as gaited saddle horses, stock horses, polo mounts, hunters, and cavalry mounts. No other breed of horses has found such diverse use and adaptation. Because of the almost incredible adaptation of the Thoroughbred and the use of his blood in producing new breeds, the breed has been referred to as the "essential oil of horse flesh."

It must be realized, however, that many of the new breeds that evolved from a Thoroughbred foundation have now reached such a high state of perfection that an out-cross to the Thoroughbred might now be a step backward. Such is the status of the American Saddle Horse, the Tennessee Walking Horse, and the Standardbred —when it comes to their respective performances as three- and five-gaited park hacks, plantation walking horses, and harness racers. But until other or new breeds become better adapted and more important, the blood of the Thoroughbred will continue to predominate in the production of polo mounts, hunters, and cavalry mounts.

Present Status of the Breed

Today, the race crowds are bigger than ever. New racetracks are being developed and pari-mutuels are being permitted in more and more states. These developments, together with the unquestioned value of the Thoroughbred for cross-breeding purposes, assure the breed a bright future.

About one-third of the nation's Thoroughbreds are bred in Kentucky.

The U.S. and world records for Thoroughbreds at some of the popular American distances are given in Table VI-1 of the Appendix.

All U.S. Thoroughbreds are registered in The Jocky Club; a registry association limited to fifty members, which is probably the most exclusive group of sportsmen in America.

WELSH PONY

The Welsh breed is especially recommended for use by older children who have outgrown the use of a Shetland—children up to 15 years of age.

Origin and Native Home

The Welsh Pony is native of the rough mountainous country of Wales. Here for unknown generations, probably since Saxon times in England, these horses have ranged in bands, living a vagabond existence on the sparse vegetation. Under these conditions only the more rugged, thrifty, and agile animals survived. In more recent years, improvement has been wrought by annually rounding up the semi-wild, nomadic bands and selecting the stallion leader for each.

Early American Importations

The first Welsh Ponies to be imported to America of which there is record were twenty head brought over by George Brown of Aurora, Illinois. Subsequent but infrequent importations followed.

Welsh Pony Characteristics

Present-day Welsh Mountain Ponies are usually gray, roan, black, bay, brown, or chestnut; though cream, dun, and white colors are found. In fact, any color except piebald and skewbald is eligible for registry. Gaudy white markings are not popular.

Representative animals range from 10 to 14 hands in height. In build, the modern Welsh Pony may be described as a miniature coach horse, being more upstanding than the Shetland. Individuals of this breed should possess good heads and necks, short coupling, plenty of muscling, and substance of bone; and with it all, there should be considerable speed and action at the trot and unusual endurance.

Fig. 10-20. Liseter Shooting Star, Welsh Pony stallion; a champion and fine breed representative; owned by Mrs. J. Austin duPont, Liseter Hall Farm, Newton Square, Pa. (Courtesy, Mrs. duPont)

Adaptation and Use

Welsh Ponies are unexcelled as advanced children's mounts, for riding by small adults, and for such other general purposes as are within their size limitations. Among their uses are: as roadsters, and for harness shows, racing, trail riding, parades, stock cutting, and hunting.

Present Status of the Breed

Although it is not likely that great numbers of Welsh Ponies will ever be found in America, they will always fill a need. With the greater emphasis on physical fitness, it is quite likely that present numbers in America will be increased.

The American Welsh Stud Book maintains two divisions, according to height stipulations: Those in the A Division cannot exceed

Table 10-2

NEW AND/OR LESS WIDELY DISTRIBUTED BREEDS OF LIGHT HORSES AND PONIES

Breed	Place of Origin	Color	Other Distinguishing Characteristics	Primary Uses	Disqualifications
American Albino Horse (or American White Horses and Ponies)	United States; on White Horse Ranch, Naper, Nebraska.	Snow-white hair; and pink skin; and light blue (near black), brown, or hazel eyes.	The breed ranges from 32" to 17 hands high; thus, it includes both ponies and horses.	Riding and utility. Their snow-white color makes them attractive as trained horses for exhibition purposes, parade horses, and flag bearer horses.	Pale cream or off white.
American Buckskin	United States	Buckskin, red dun, gruella.	Dorsal stripe and usually zebra-type stripes on the legs and transverse stripe over the withers and shoulders.	Stock horse, pleasure horse, and for show purposes.	White markings above knees and hocks; white spots on body.
American Gotland Horse	Baltic Island of Gotland, a part of Sweden.	Bay, brown, black, dun, chestnut, roan, palomino, and some leopard and blanket markings.	Average about 48" high, with a range of 11 to 13 hands.	Harness trot racing, pleasure horse and jumper; for children and moderately sized adults.	A pinto or an animal with large markings is disqualified.
American Paint Horse[1]	United States	White, plus any other color. Must be a recognizable paint.	No discrimination is made against glass, blue, or light-colored eyes.	Stock horse, pleasure horse, racing, and for show purposes.	Lack of natural white markings above the knees or hocks except on the face; horse with Appaloosa color or blood; adult horse under 14 hands; five-gaited horse.

(Continued on next page)

Footnote on last page of table.

Table 10-2 (Continued)

Breed	Place of Origin	Color	Other Distinguishing Characteristics	Primary Uses	Disqualifications
Cleveland Bay	England; in the Cleveland district of Yorkshire.	Always solid bay with black legs.	Larger than most light horse breeds; weighs from 1,150 to 1,400 pounds.	General utility horse; for riding, driving, and all kinds of farm work. Also used in crossbreeding to produce heavyweight hunters.	Any color other than bay, although a few white hairs on the forehead are permissible.
Connemara Pony	Ireland; along the west coast.	Gray, black, bay, brown, dun, cream, with occasional roans and chestnuts.	Average height of 14 hands. Heavy boned, hardy, and docile.	Jumper, showing under saddle and in harness; for both adults and children.	A piebald or a skewbald not accepted.
Galiceno	Galicia, a province in northwestern Spain. Horses of this lineage were first brought to America by the conquistadores, but it was not until 1958 that they were officially introduced to the U.S.	Solid colors prevail. Bay, black, chestnut (sorrel), dun (buckskin), gray, brown, and palomino are most common.	Intermediate in size; at maturity, it stands 12 to 13 hands and weighs 625 to 700 pounds.	Riding horse.	Albinos, pintos, and paints are ineligible for registry. Cryptorchids or monorchids.

(Continued on next page)

Table 10-2 (Continued)

Breed	Place of Origin	Color	Other Distinguishing Characteristics	Primary Uses	Disqualifications
Hungarian Horse	Hungary	All colors, either solid or broken.	A unique combination of style and beauty with ruggedness.	Stock horse, cutting horse, pleasure horse, trail riding, hunter and jumper.	Cryptorchid; glass-eyed.
Missouri Fox Trotting Horse	United States; in the Ozark Hills of Missouri and Arkansas.	Sorrels predominate, but any color is accepted.	The fox trot gait.	Pleasure horse, stock horse, and trail riding.	If animal cannot fox trot.
Paso Fino[2]	Peru, Puerto Rico, Cuba, and Colombia	Any color, although solid colors are preferred.	The paso fino gait, which may be described as a broken pace.	Pleasure, parade, and endurance horse.	Animals not possessing the paso fino gait.
Spanish Mustang	United States on the Robert E. Brislawn ranch, Oshoto, Wyo., beginning in 1925. Also, Robert's brother, Ferdenand L. Brislawn, Gusher, Utah, shared in the early development of the breed.	It runs the gamut of equine colors, including all the solid colors, and all the broken colors except tobiana.	Only five lumbar (loin region) vertebrae, whereas most breeds have six. Also, it is characterized by short ears, a low-set tail, and round leg bones.	Cow pony and trail riding.	

[1] Two different associations have evolved for the registration of these vari-colored horses. In the Pinto Horse Association of America, Inc., which is the oldest of the two registries, the breed is known as Pinto, whereas in the American Paint Horse Association, it is known as the American Paint Horse. Both groups of horses are more alike in background and color than the standards and policies of their respective breed registries would indicate.

[2] In the U.S. two different breed associations have evolved for the registration and promotion of horses of Paso Fino background. But each of the registries has slightly different standards. The American Paso Fino Pleasure Horse Assn., Inc., refers to its breed as American Paso Fino, whereas the American Assn. of Owners & Breeders of Peruvian Paso Horses calls its breed Peruvian Paso.

12-2 hands; the B Division includes those over 12-2, but under 14 hands.

NEW AND/OR LESS WIDELY DISTRIBUTED BREEDS

In addition to the more widely distributed breeds that have already been discussed, some new and/or less numerous breeds of light horses are listed in Table 10-2.

Fig. 10-21. Silver Slippers, American Albino Horse mare; owned by White Horse Ranch, Naper, Nebraska. (Courtesy, Miss Ruth White, Sec., American Albino Association, Inc.)

Fig. 10-22. The American Buckskin stallion, Davis Peco Don; owned by Cameron Thatcher, Montague, California; many times Grand Champion. (Courtesy, American Buckskin Registry Association)

Fig. 10-24. American Paint Horse stallion, Dual Image, owned by Larry Swain, San Antonio, Texas; Grand Champion of the 1967 Fort Worth, San Antonio, and Houston shows, and an AAA-rated racehorse. (Courtesy, The American Paint Horse Association)

Fig. 10-23. American Gotland mare, Gerta. This mare was imported and is owned by Krona Horse Farms, Columbia, Mo. (Courtesy, American Gotland Association)

Fig. 10-25. Cleveland Bay stallion, Cleveland Farnley; owned by A. Mackay-Smith, White Post, Va. (Courtesy, Mr. Mackay-Smith)

Fig. 10-26. The Connemara stallion, Bantry Bay; owned by Spring Ledge Farm, New London, New Hampshire. This stallion has compiled an impressive record, both in the show-ring and as a sire. (Courtesy, American Connemara Pony Society, Rochester, Ill.)

Fig. 10-27. The Hungarion mare, Hungarian Barna. (Courtesy, Mrs. Margit Sigray Bessenyey, Hamilton, Mont.)

Fig. 10-28. Spanish Mustang stallion, Syndicate, owned by Cayuse Ranch, Oshoto, Wyo. (Courtesy, R. E. Lougheed, Newtown, Conn.)

Selected References

Title of Publication	Author(s)	Publisher
Appaloosa	Francis Haines	Amon Carter Museum of Western Art, Fort Worth, Tex., 1963.
Appaloosa Horse, The	Francis Haines G. B. Hatley Robert Peckinpah	R. G. Bailey Printing Company, Lewiston, Ida., 1957.
Breeds of Livestock, The	C. W. Gay	The Macmillan Company, New York, N. Y., 1918.
Breeds of Livestock in America	H. W. Vaughan	R. G. Adams and Company, Columbus, Ohio, 1937.

Title of Publication	Author	Publisher
History of Thoroughbred Racing in America	Wm. H. P. Robertson	Prentice-Hall, Inc., Englewood Cliffs, N. J., 1965.
Horse, The	D. J. Kays	Rinehart & Company, New York, N. Y., 1953.
Horse America Made, The	Louis Taylor	American Saddle Horse Breeders Association, Urban Building, Louisville, Ky., 1944.
Horses: Their Selection, Care, and Handling	M. C. Self	A. S. Barnes and Company, New York, N. Y., 1943.
Horses of Today, Their History, Breeds, and Qualifications	H. H. Reese	Wood & Jones, Pasadena, Calif., 1956.
Kellogg Arabians, The	H. H. Reese G. B. Edwards	Borden Publishing Company, Los Angeles, Calif., 1958.
Light Horse Breeds, The	J. W. Patten	A. S. Barnes & Co., New York, N. Y., 1960.
Light Horses	M. E. Ensminger	Farmers' Bul. No. 2127, U. S. Department of Agriculture, Washington, D. C.
Modern Breeds of Livestock	H. M. Briggs	The Macmillan Company, New York, N. Y., 1958.
Pinto, The	1958-1959	Yearbook and Studbook of the Pinto Horse Association of America.
Shetland Pony, The	L. Frank Bedell	The Iowa State University Press, Ames, Iowa, 1959.
Shetland Pony, The	Maurice C. Cox	Adam & Charles Black, London, 1965.
Stockman's Handbook, The	M. E. Ensminger	The Interstate Printers & Publishers, Inc., Danville, Ill., 1970 .
Study of Breeds, The	Thomas Shaw	Orange Judd Company, New York, N. Y., 1912.
Types and Breeds of Farm Animals	C. S. Plumb	Ginn and Company, Boston, Mass., 1920.
Using the American Quarter Horse	L. N. Sikes	Saddlerock Corporation, Houston, Tex., 1958.
World Dictionary of Breeds, Types, and Varieties of Livestock, A	I. L. Mason	Commonwealth Agricultural Bureaux, Farnham House, Farnham Royal, Slough, Bucks., England, 1951.

Also, breed literature pertaining to each breed may be secured by writing to the respective breed registry associations (see Sec. VIII, Appendix, for the name and address of each association).

11

In this chapter . . .

11

Breeds of Draft Horses;
Jacks and Donkeys

TODAY, the pure breeds of draft horses are of negligible importance, and primarily of historical interest only. Table 11-1 presents conclusive proof of this fact, if any such evidence is needed.

The breeds of draft horses here considered are the American Cream Horse, Belgian, Clydesdale, Percheron, Shire, and Suffolk. Regardless of the distinct breed trademarks and the virtues ascribed to each breed, all are characterized by great massiveness—their adapted field of utility being the drawing of heavy loads at a comparatively slow gait, usually at the walk.

Power rather than speed is desired. In order to possess this power, the draft horse should be blocky or compact, low set or short legged, and sufficiently heavy to enable him to throw the necessary weight into the collar to move a heavy load and at the same time maintain a secure footing. This calls for a horse around 16 to 17 hands in height and weighing not less than 1,600 pounds.

All of the modern draft breeds of horses, regardless of color or breed or later infusions of other breeding, rest upon a Flemish foundation—the large, coarse, black, hairy, and sluggish horse which, from a very early time, existed in the low-lying sections of what is now Belgium, France, Holland, and Germany. Thus, the draft breeds were of European origin, whereas the light-horse breeds were of Oriental extraction.

Battle chariots, drawn by heavy horses and used to convey armored troops who fought on foot, were encountered by the Roman legions under Caesar when he invaded England in the year 55 B. C. Later, these ponderous beasts, imposing in height and bulk, were known as the Great Horses of the Middle Ages.

235

These animals were the cavalry mounts of the heavily armored knights when they rode forth to battle for king and country and at times to enforce their views of religion upon unbelievers in general and Mohammedans in particular. These animals had to be large and powerful in order to carry the immense weight of their riders, their arms, and their armor—including eventually the armor of both the horse and the rider. Often the combined weight of their load was up to 450 pounds.

Finally, in the nineteenth century, when the use of armor in warfare was abandoned after invention and adoption of gunpowder by the fighting nations and when the development of agriculture and commerce received new impetus, the Great Horse served as the foundation for the draft breeds as we know them today. Lighter horses came into use for riding and the Great Horse was relegated to pulling the cart and the plow and to hauling timber, coal, and other industrial materials.

RELATIVE POPULARITY OF BREEDS OF DRAFT HORSES

Table 11-1 shows the 1966 and total registration to date of the various breeds of draft horses. As may be noted, the draft registry associations are doing little business.

Table 11-1

1966 AND TOTAL REGISTRATIONS OF DRAFT HORSES, JACKS, AND DONKEYS IN UNITED STATES' BREED ASSOCIATIONS

Breed	1966 Registrations	Total Registrations
Belgian	617	69,641
Percheron	174	250,298
Miniature Donkeys	50	2,500
Clydesdale	17[1]	25,698
Shire	11[1]	22,030
Jacks and Jennets	9	37,369
Suffolk	6[1]	2,697
American Cream Horse	0	199

[1]1965 figures.

AMERICAN CREAM HORSE

This is a relatively new breed, which originated in the United States.

Origin and Native Home

The American Cream Horse is unique because it is the only draft breed to originate in the United States. The breed descended from a mare of unknown ancestry, in central Iowa during the early part of the twentieth century. Offspring of this cream-colored, foundation mare were mated to animals of the established draft breeds, thereby increasing numbers and improving the type and quality while retaining the cream color.

About 1935, a few men began linebreeding and inbreeding with the objective of establishing a distinct breed. In 1944, the American Cream Horse Association was organized and granted a charter by the State of Iowa. In 1950, the breed was recognized by the Iowa Department of Agriculture.

American Cream Horse Characteristics

The distinguishing characteristic of the breed is the color, which is cream, with white mane and tail, pink skin, and amber eyes (foals are born with nearly white eyes, which darken and turn to amber at maturity). Some white markings are considered desirable.

The American Cream Horse is classified as a medium draft breed. At maturity, mares weigh 1,600 to 1,800 pounds, and stallions from 1,800 to 2,000 pounds. Animals of the breed are noted for their good dispositions.

BELGIAN

The Belgian breed made marked progress in this country, considering that so few animals were imported prior to the beginning of the twentieth century. Belgian stallions have been especially valuable in improving the draftiness of the native stock on which they have been crossed.

Origin and Native Home

The Belgian breed originated in Belgium, from which country it derives its name. The agricultural needs of this low-lying country were such as to require a horse of size and bulk. So far as is known, no Oriental blood was fused with the native stock. Thus, it may be concluded that the Belgian breed is directly and exclusively descended from the old Flemish ancestry—indigenous to the country of its origin. Even today, the great massiveness of the Belgian breed more nearly resembles the Flemish horse than does any other breed.

In their native country, the breeding of Belgian draft horses is promoted by the government, which annually awards prizes and

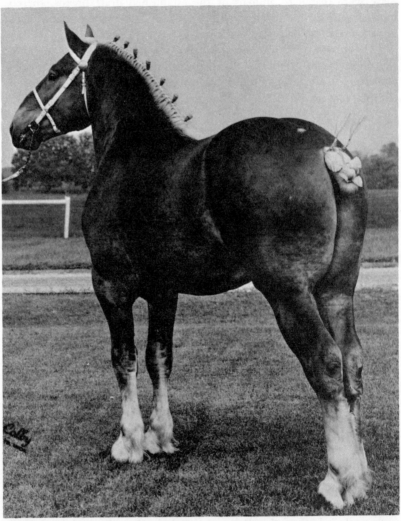

Fig. 11-1. The Belgian stallion, Conceur, as a 3-year-old. Conceur was the Grand Champion stallion in each of five major shows in both 1965 and 1966. Bred and owned by Mrs. Alfred G. Wilson, Rochester, Michigan. (Courtesy, Belgian Draft Horse Corporation of America)

subsidies to the best animals in the various provinces. Also, stallions that stand for public service must be approved by a commission appointed by the government.

Early American Importations

The first importation of the Belgian to the United States was made in 1886 by Dr. A. G. Van Hoorebeke of Monmouth, Illinois, but the breed attracted little attention until 1900. Thus, the introduction of the breed was more recent than that of the Percheron, Clydesdale, and Shire. Despite their late entry into this country, however, Belgians gave a good account of themselves. They lead in registration numbers at the present time.

Belgian Characteristics

Bay, chestnut, and roan are the most common colors, but browns, grays, and blacks are occasionally seen. Many Belgians have flaxen manes and tails and white-blazed faces. Mature stallions stand from 15-2 to 17 hands in height and weigh 1,900 to 2,200 pounds, or more.

The Belgian is noted for its draftiness—being the widest, deepest, most compact, most massive, and lowest set of any draft breed. Formerly, the breed was likely to be severely criticized for having small round hoofs, round bones, short thick necks, and lack of refinement. But it is to the everlasting credit of the American breeders that these defects have been very largely overcome.

The Belgian is extremely quiet, docile, and patient. The action is powerful, though less springy and high than found in the Clydesdale and Percheron. Because of their great width in front, many Belgians roll or paddle somewhat.

CLYDESDALE

Like all classes and breeds of livestock of Scotch origin—including Ayrshire, Aberdeen-Angus, Galloway, and Highland cattle, and Cheviot and Black-faced Highland sheep—the Clydesdale breed of horses is distinctive for style, beauty, and action.

Origin and Native Home

This Scotch breed of draft horses derives its name from the valley of the River Clyde, an area popularly known as Clydesdale, located in the County of Lanark, Scotland.

The breed is of mixed origin, and the early history is more or less obscure. It is probable that the blood of both Flemish and English horses entered quite largely into the breed during its early formative period. Rather frequent importations of horses of Flemish extraction from England and the low countries were made, thus giving the Scotch Clydesdale and the English Shire and Suffolk similar ancestry. However, the breeders in the respective countries had very different notions as to what constituted a desirable draft animal, and their selections were governed accordingly, the Scotch placing particular emphasis upon style and action.

Early American Importations

The first Clydesdales brought to North America were probably imported into Canada by the Scotch who settled there. Beginning in the early 1870's, Clydesdales were imported into the United States, both via Canada and direct from Scotland.

Clydesdale Characteristics

The Clydesdale is not so heavy as the Shire, Belgian, or Percheron. Average representatives of the breed are also more rangy and lack the width and compactness of the other draft breeds. Mature stallions in average condition weigh from 1,700 to 1,900 pounds and stand from 16 to 17 hands in height.

No other breed of draft horses equals the Clydesdale in style and action. The breed is noted for a prompt walk, with a good snappy stride and a short trot, and the hocks are well flexed and carried close together. Good, clean, flat bone; well-set, fairly long and sloping pasterns; and a moderate amount of fine feather or long hair at the rear of the legs below the knees and hocks are characteristic. Sometimes, in America, the breed has been criticized for lack of width and depth of body and for having too much feather and too much white. Usually, Americans do not fancy too much white on the face and legs in any breed of horses, and they object to the feather or long hair about the fetlocks because of the difficulty in keeping the legs and feet free from mud and snow. Bay and brown with white markings are the most characteristic colors, but blacks, grays, chestnuts, and roans are occasionally seen.

For show use in a six-horse hitch on the tanbark, a well-matched, carefully trained, and expertly handled hitch of Clydesdales is un-

Fig. 11-2. Linton Marcellus, a Chicago International Grand Champion Clydesdale stallion. No other breed of draft horses equals the Clydesdale in style and action. (Courtesy, Horse Association of America)

excelled. Their flowing white fetlocks and high action give them a picturesque appearance.

PERCHERON

Until recently, the Percheron was the most widely distributed of all draft breeds. Today, it ranks second in registration numbers (see Table 11-1).

Origin and Native Home

The Percheron horse originated in northwestern France, in the ancient district of La Perche, an area about one-fifteenth the size of the state of Iowa. The native stock was primarily of Flemish extraction upon which there was a subsequent and rather liberal infusion of Arab blood.

Although early records are lacking, it is known that with the defeat of the Saracens (the Moors from North Africa) at Tours and

Fig. 11-3. Lynwood Dixiana, champion Percheron mare owned by Lynwood Farm, Carmel, Ind. The Percheron is noted for its handsome, clean-cut head, good action, excellent temperament, and longevity. (Courtesy, Percheron Horse Association of America)

Poitiers, France, in 732 A. D. by Charles Martel, the Arab, Barb, and Turk horses upon which the Moors were mounted—mostly stallions as was the custom of the day—fell into the hands of the Franks and were eventually distributed throughout the country. The successful Crusaders of the twelfth, thirteenth, and fourteenth centuries also brought back stallions as spoils of war from Palestine, and this again furnished a direct, though unplanned, infusion of Oriental blood. Thus, on a cold blood base, the Flemish horse, repeated top crosses of Oriental blood were made. Finally, in about 1870, a systematic effort was made to transform the mixture into a true type. Eventually, the Percheron breed evolved, and the Percheron Society of France was organized in 1883.

Early American Importations

American importations of Percherons began about 1840, but it was not until the early 1850's that any great numbers came over. Brilliant 1271, a black stallion foaled in 1877 and imported in 1881, is recognized as the most famous and prepotent animal of the breed ever imported. Other importations followed, and the center of interest in the breed came to be located in the Corn Belt, an area which it still dominates.

Percheron Characteristics

Typical Percheron colors of today are black or gray (the latter being a probable Arab inheritance); but bays, browns, chestnuts, and roans are occasionally seen. Fully ninety per cent, however, are black or gray.

Mature stallions stand from 16-1 to 16-3 hands in height and weigh from 1,900 to 2,100 pounds. In size, the Percheron is intermediate between the larger Shire and Belgian and the smaller Clydesdale and Suffolk. In comparison with other draft breeds, the Percheron is noted for its handsome, clean-cut head; good action (being surpassed in style and action only by the Clydesdale); excellent temperament; and longevity.

SHIRE

England originated and developed two breeds of draft horses, the Shire and the Suffolk. Originally, the Shire was known by various names, such as the Great Horse, War Horse, Cart Horse, Old English Black Horse, Lincolnshire Cart Horse, etc.

Origin and Native Home

The Shire breed was originated on the low, marshy lands of east-central England, particularly in Lincolnshire and Cambridgeshire; hence comes the name "Shire."

The great size and bulk of this breed are derived directly from the Great Horse of the Middle Ages, of which Shires are held to be the nearest living reproductions. As previously indicated, the Great Horse was in turn descended from the ponderous black Flemish

Fig. 11-4. Robert Bakewell (1726-1795), English stockman. He contributed greatly to the improvement of the Shire. (Obtained for the author by Dr. John Hammond from the Royal Agricultural Society of England)

horse which existed in Great Britain long before the Christian era, more than two thousand years ago.

In the year 1066, England was conquered by an army of Normans led by William the Conqueror. This marked the beginning of improvement in the native draft stock of England. Importations of horses followed from France, Germany, and the low countries. Centuries later, Robert Bakewell (1726 to 1795), known as the first great improver of livestock, contributed to the further improvement of the Shire—as well as to that of Leicester sheep and Longhorn cattle. Bakewell imported from Holland several mares which were mated to native stallions, and selected and perpetuated the better offspring therefrom. During Bakewell's era, the Shire was being molded as a draft horse for agriculture and commerce, the use of armor in warfare having been abandoned.

Thus, the development and improvement of the Shire breed antedate that of any other breed of draft horses. This fact largely explains the present-day uniformity and prepotency of the breed when crossed on common stock.

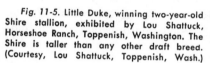

Fig. 11-5. Little Duke, winning two-year-old Shire stallion, exhibited by Lou Shattuck, Horseshoe Ranch, Toppenish, Washington. The Shire is taller than any other draft breed. (Courtesy, Lou Shattuck, Toppenish, Wash.)

Early American Importations

Shire horses were first imported to London, Ontario, Canada, in 1836. A gray stallion, known as Columbus, was imported to Massachusetts prior to 1844. Small scattered importations followed, but no great numbers came over until 1880. In 1887, more than four hundred Shires were imported. Very early, horsemen became aware of the fact that Shire stallions were unsurpassed in their ability to beget draft horses from mares lacking in size and bone.

Shire Characteristics

The Shire, as known today, is a much larger horse than was his ancestor used by the mounted warriors of old. He is equaled in weight only by the Belgian. Shire stallions in fair condition weighing 2,000 pounds or over are comparatively common. In height, representatives of this breed stand from 16 to 17-2 hands. They are less compact or more rangy than the Belgian and taller than any other draft breed.

In the past, the breed has been faulted for its heavy bone and feather, lack of quality and refinement, its shelly-textured hoof, its sluggish temperament, and its excessive white markings; but breeders have shown marked progress in overcoming these objections in recent years.

The common colors are bay, brown, and black with white markings; although grays, chestnuts, and roans are occasionally seen.

SUFFOLK

The Suffolk is unique among draft breeds in that (1) it was developed exclusively as a farm work horse and not for use on city streets, and (2) all animals of the breed are chestnut in color, this color being recessive. Often the breed is referred to as the Suffolk Punch, a name descriptive of the "punched-up" conformation of the old-fashioned animals of this breed.

Origin and Native Home

The native home of the Suffolk is in the county of Suffolk, on the eastern coast of England, bordering the North Sea. The origin of the breed is unknown, but horses of similar characteristics are known to have existed in Suffolk for many centuries. Although proof is lacking, it is claimed that Norman stallions were crossed on the native mares of Suffolk County five hundred years ago. Also, it has been conjectured that the chestnut color of the breed is due to a cross with Norwegian horses brought in by the early Norse invaders. It is known, however, that from a very early period these animals were produced in Suffolk by farmers and for farming purposes. It is said that every well-bred Suffolk of today is descended from a bright-colored chestnut stallion foaled in 1768 and owned by a Mr. Crisp of Ufford.

Early American Importations

Suffolks were first imported into the United States in the early eighties and have been imported since then in small numbers. In the first place, they are not available in large numbers, the area devoted to their production being rather limited and there being an active demand for them at home and in the British Dominions.

Suffolk Characteristics

The Suffolk is smaller than other drafters. Average animals weigh

Fig. 11-6. Riddlesworth Viscount, senior Suffolk stallion at Upwey Farm, Woodstock, Vermont. Suffolk horses are distinguished by their chestnut color and chunky build. (Photo by M. E. Ensminger)

from 1,600 to 1,800 pounds and range in height from 15-2 to 16-2 hands. Occasionally, a mature stallion may weigh 2,000 pounds or more, but such weight is not characteristic of the breed.

Suffolk horses are always chestnut in color, varying from light to dark, often with cream-colored mane and tail. When white markings occur, they are likely to be unobtrusive. Aside from color, the distinguishing characteristics of the breed include their close-to-the-ground and chunky build, smooth rotund form, and clean-boned leg devoid of the feather characteristic of the other two British draft breeds.

Although small in size, the Suffolk is celebrated for his courage and willingness to work and his excellent disposition. The story goes that in their native land the courage and strength of Suffolk horses was often tested by contests involving the hitching of individual animals or teams to an immovable object, such as a tree—with the winner being determined by the number of efforts the animal or animals made in throwing themselves into the collar and pulling with all their might at the command.

The Suffolk has never gained wide popularity in this country, primarily because of lack of size and lightness of bone.

JACKS AND JENNETS; DONKEYS

Biologists designate the ass as *Equus asinus;* the horse as *Equus*

Fig. 11-7. Newborn Miniature Donkey. (Courtesy, Daniel Langfeld, Miniature Donkey Registry, Omaha, Neb.)

Fig. 11-8. Red Oak Chief, Grand Champion Jack of the Kansas, Missouri, and Kentucky State Fairs. Note his heavy bone, well set legs, and good head and ears. This jack is owned by Hineman's Jack Farms, Dighton, Kans. (Courtesy, Horse Association of America)

caballus. The males of the ass family are known as jacks; the females as jennets. Compared with the horse, the ass is smaller; has shorter hairs on the mane and tail; does not possess the "chestnuts" on the inside of the hind legs; has much longer ears; has smaller, deeper hoofs; possesses a louder and more harsh voice, called a bray; is less subject to founder or injury; is more hardy and has a longer gestation period—jennets carry their young about 12 months. Small asses are commonly called donkeys or burros.

Selected References

Title of Publication	Author(s)	Publisher
Breeding and Rearing of Jacks, Jennets, and Mules, The	L. W. Knight	The Cumberland Press, Nashville, Tenn., 1902.
History of the Percheron Horse, A	A. H. Sanders Wayne Dinsmore	*Breeder's Gazette*, Sanders Publishing Co., Chicago, Ill., 1917.
Percheron Horse, The	M. C. Weld	O. Judd Co., New York, N. Y., 1886.

12

In this chapter . . .

12

Breeding Horses

HORSES WILL CONTINUE to be bred so long as they (1) serve the livestock industry of the West, and (2) provide recreation and sport. It is important, therefore, that both the student and the progressive horseman be familiar with the breeding of horses.

Part I.   Some Principles of Horse Genetics

Until very recent times, the general principle that "like begets like" was the only recognized concept of heredity. That the application of this principle over a long period of time has been effective in modifying animal types in the direction of selection is evident from a comparison of present-day types of animals within each class of livestock. Thus, the speed of the modern Thoroughbred—coupled with his general lithe, angular build and nervous temperament—is in sharp contrast to the slow, easy gaits and the docility of the Tennessee Walking Horse. Yet, there is good and substantial evidence to indicate that both breeds descended from a common ancestry. Because of the diversity of genes carried by the original parent stock, it has been possible, through selection, to evolve with two distinct breeds—one highly adapted to fast running at extended distances and the other to a slow, ambling gait. Also, through selection accompanied by planned matings, this same parent stock has been altered into horses especially adept as hunters, jumpers, stock horses, polo mounts, three- and five-gaited park hacks, harness racehorses, etc.

There can be little doubt that men like Bakewell, the English patriarch, and other eighteenth-century breeders had made a tremendous contribution in pointing the way toward livestock improvement before Mendel's laws became known to the world in the early part of the twentieth century. Robert Bakewell's use of progeny testing through his ram letting was truly epoch-making, and his improvement of Shire horses and Longhorn cattle was equally outstanding. He and other pioneers had certain ideals in mind, and, according to their standards, they were able to develop some nearly perfect specimens. These men were intensely practical, never overlooking the utility value or the market requirements. No animal met with their favor unless such favor was earned by meat upon the back, milk in the pail, weight and quality of wool, pounds gained for pounds of feed consumed, draft ability, or some other performance of practical value. Their ultimate goal was that of furnishing better animals for the market or lowering the cost of production. It must be just so with the master horse breeders of the present and future.

MENDEL'S CONTRIBUTION TO GENETICS

Modern genetics was really founded by Gregor Johann Mendel, a cigar-smoking Austrian monk, who conducted breeding experiments with garden peas from 1857 to 1865, during the time of the Civil War in the United States. In his monastery at Brunn (now Brno, in Czechoslovakia), Mendel applied a powerful curiosity and a clear mind to reveal some of the basic principles of hereditary transmission. In 1866, he published in the proceedings of a local scientific society a report covering eight years of his studies, but for 34 years his findings went unheralded and ignored. Finally, in 1900, 16 years after Mendel's death, three European biologists independently duplicated his findings, and this led to the dusting off of the original paper published by the monk 34 years earlier.

The essence of Mendelism is that inheritance is by particles or units (called genes), that these genes are present in pairs—one member of each pair having come from each parent—and that each gene maintains its identity generation after generation. Thus, Mendel's work with peas laid the basis for the two basic laws of inheritance: (1) the law of segregation, and (2) the independent assortment of genes. Later, other genetic principles were added; but all the phenomena of inheritance, based upon the reactions of genes, are generally known under the collective term, Mendelism.

Fig. 12-1. Gregor Johann Mendel (1822-1884), a cigar-smoking Austrian monk, whose breeding experiments with garden peas founded modern genetics. (Courtesy, The Bettmann Archive)

Thus, modern genetics is really unique in that it was founded by an amateur who was not trained as a geneticist and who did his work merely as a hobby. During the years since the rediscovery of Mendel's principles (in 1900), many additional genetic principles have been added, but the fundamentals as set forth by Mendel have been proved correct in every detail. It can be said, therefore, that inheritance in both plants and animals follows the biological laws formulated by Mendel.

SOME FUNDAMENTALS OF HEREDITY IN HORSES

The author has no intention of covering all of the diverse field of genetics and animal breeding. Rather, he will present a condensation of a few of the known facts in regard to the field and briefly summarize their application to horses.

Obviously, heredity in horses is identical in principle with that in other farm animals and man. Because of the difficulty in conducting breeding experiments with horses (due to their greater cost, slower reproductive rate, etc.), however, less applied knowledge of genetics is available in the equine field. Also, it is fully recognized that such systems of breeding as Inbreeding and Grading Up are seldom deliberately planned and followed in horse breeding; yet the enlightened horse breeder will wish to be fully informed relative to them.

The Gene as the Unit of Heredity

Genes determine all the hereditary characteristics of animals, from the body type to the color of the hair. They are truly the fundamental unit of genetics.

The bodies of all animals are made up of millions or even billions of tiny cells, microscopic in size. Each cell contains a nucleus in which there are a number of pairs of bundles, called chromosomes. In turn, the chromosomes carry pairs of minute particles, called genes, which are the basic hereditary material. The nucleus of each body cell of horses contains thirty pairs of chromosomes,[1] or a total of sixty, where-as there are perhaps thousands of pairs of genes. These genes determine all the hereditary characteristics of living animals. Thus, inheritance

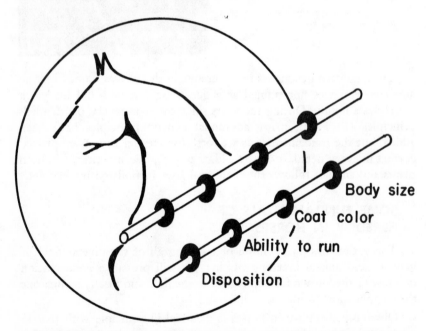

Body size

Coat color

Ability to run

Disposition

Fig. 12-2. A pair of bundles, called chromosomes, carrying minute particles, called genes. The genes determine all the hereditary characteristics of living animals, from length of leg to body size. (Drawing by R. F. Johnson)

---

[1]Cattle have sixty chromosomes; sheep have fifty-four and swine have forty.

goes by units rather than by blending of two fluids, as our grandfathers thought.

The modern breeder knows that the job of transmitting qualities from one generation to the next is performed by the germ cells—a sperm from the male and an ovum or egg from the female. All animals, therefore, are the result of the union of two such tiny cells, one from each of its parents. These two germ cells contain the basis of all the anatomical, physiological, and psychological characters that the offspring will inherit.

In the body cells of an animal, each of the chromosomes is duplicated; whereas in the formation of the sex cells, the egg and the sperm, a reduction division occurs and only one chromosome and one gene of each pair goes into a sex cell. This means that only half the number of chromosomes and genes present in the body cells of the animal go into each egg and sperm, but each sperm or egg cell has genes for every characteristic of its species. As will be explained later, the particular half that any one germ cell gets is determined by chance. When mating and fertilization occur, the single chromosomes from the germ cell of each parent unite to form new pairs, and the genes are again present in duplicate in the body cells of the embryo.

With all possible combinations in thirty pairs of chromosomes (the specie number in horses) and the genes that they bear, any stallion or mare can transmit over one billion different samples of its own inheritance; and the combination from both parents makes possible one billion times one billion genetically different offspring. It is not strange, therefore, that no two animals within a given breed (except identical twins from a single egg split after fertilization) are exactly alike. Rather, we can marvel that the members of a given breed bear as much resemblance to each other as they do.

Even between such closely related individuals as full sisters, it is possible that there will be quite wide differences in size, growth rate, temperament, conformation, speed, and in almost every conceivable character. Admitting that many of these differences may be due to undetected differences in environment, it is still true that in such animals much of the variation is due to hereditary differences. A stallion, for example, will sometimes transmit to one offspring much better inheritance than he does to most of his get, simply as the result of chance distribution of the genes that go to different sperm at the time of the reduction division. Such differences in inheritance in offspring have been called both the hope and the despair of the livestock breeder.

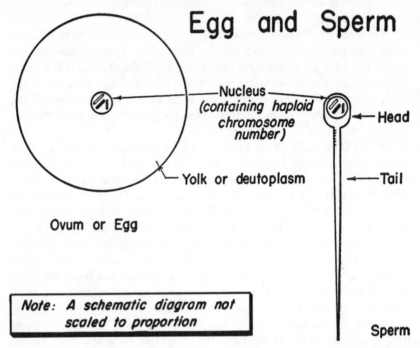

Fig. 12-3. Egg and sperm. The parent germ cells, the egg from the female and the sperm from the male, unite and transmit to the offspring all the characters that it will inherit. (Drawing by R. F. Johnson)

If an animal gets similar determiners or genes from each parent, it will in turn produce a uniform set of offspring,[2] because any half of its inheritance is just like any other half. For example, regardless of what combination of chromosomes go into a particular germ cell, it will be just like any other egg or sperm from the same individual. Such animals are referred to as being homozygous. Unfortunately, few, if any, of our animals are in this pure hereditary state at the present time; instead of being homozygous, they are quite heterozygous. This explains why there may be such wide variation within the offspring of any given sire or dam. The wise and progressive breeder recognizes this fact, and he insists upon the production records of all get rather than those of just a few meritorious individuals.

---

[2]Unless it is homozygous for a simple recessive and is mated to an animal that is heterozygous for that trait.

Variation between the offspring of animals that are not pure or homozygous is not to be marveled at, but is rather to be expected. No one would expect to draw exactly twenty sound apples and ten rotten ones every time he took a random sample of thirty from a barrel containing forty sound ones and twenty rotten ones, although on the average—if enough samples were drawn—he would expect to get about that proportion of each. Individual drawings would of course vary rather widely. Exactly the same situation applies to the relative numbers of "good" and "bad" genes that may be present in different germ cells from the same animal. Because of this situation, the mating of a mare with a fine track record to a stallion that on the average transmits relatively good performance will not always produce a foal of a merit equal to that of its parents, The foal could be markedly poorer than the parents or, happily, it could in some cases be better than either parent.

Selection and close breeding are the tools through which the horseman may obtain stallions and mares whose chromosomes and genes contain similar hereditary determiners—animals that are genetically more homozygous.

Genes Seldom Change

Gene changes are technically known as mutations. *A mutation may be defined as a sudden variation which is later passed on through inheritance and which results from changes in a gene or genes.* Not only are mutations rare, but they are prevailingly harmful. For all practical purposes, therefore, the genes can be thought of as unchanged from one generation to the next. The observed differences between animals are usually due to different combinations of genes being present rather than to mutations. Each gene probably changes only about once in each 100,000 to 1,000,000 animals produced.

Once in a great while a mutation occurs in a farm animal, and it produces a visible effect in the animal carrying it. These animals are commonly called "sports." Such sports are occasionally of practical value. The occurrence of the polled characteristic within the horned Hereford breed of cattle is an example of a mutation or sport of economic importance. Out of this has arisen the Polled Hereford breed.

Gene changes can be accelerated by exposure to X rays, radium, ultraviolet light, and several other mutagenic agents. Such changes may eventually be observed in the offspring of both the people and animals of Japan that were exposed to the atom bombs unleashed in World War II.

Simple Gene Inheritance (Qualitative Traits)

In the simplest type of inheritance, only one pair of genes is involved. Thus, a pair of genes may be responsible for the color of body hair in horses. This situation can be illustrated by the pedigree of Whirlaway.

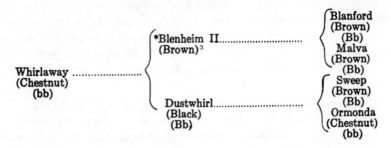

In reality, the fixation of coat color in horses may not be so simple as expected. The idea that certain basic colors may have a rather simple explanation of inheritance should not alter the fact that other genes or contributing factors may play an important role, through their influence on basic schemes. Other color patterns and shades, of more complex nature, may exhibit an almost unreal influence when crossed with the more simple genotypes. The action of certain dilution genes is, without doubt, responsible for various shades of basic colors; this is amply portrayed, for example, by the many and varied hues of chestnut (sorrel) color.

Also, it should be borne in mind that the various gene combinations and colors will appear in the offspring in the expected proportions only when relatively large numbers are concerned. The possible gene combinations, therefore, are governed by the laws of chance, operating in much the same manner as the results obtained from flipping coins. For example, if a penny is flipped often enough, the number of heads and tails will come out about even. However, with the laws of chance in operation, it is possible that out of any four tosses one might get all heads, all tails, or even three to one.

---

[3]This is not shown as (Bb) because some brown stallions mated to chestnut mares produce no chestnut offspring. Rather, it is suggested that the brown of Blenheim II was a modified black.

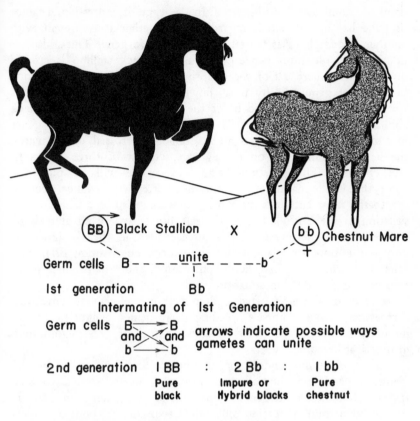

Fig. 12-4. An example of gene inheritance in horses. Note—
1. That each horse has at least a pair of genes for color, conveniently represented by symbols.
2. That each reproductive cell (egg or sperm) contains but one of each pair.
3. That the Bb genotypes, in the F_1 generation, can vary in the degree of blackness, thus tending to resemble the one black parent.
4. That the F_2 generation has the ratio of three blacks to one chestnut (phenotypically). The Bb's may be black or shading into brown.
5. That the pure blacks and certain hybrid blacks may not be distinguished on the basis of appearance, because the B gene obscures the b gene in varying degrees.
6. That the chestnut (bb) is quite likely the only pure color, in this example, that can be detected on sight.

Other possible examples of simple gene inheritance in horses (sometimes referred to as qualitative traits) might include eye color and the set of the ears on the head.

DOMINANT AND RECESSIVE FACTORS

In the example of horse colors shown in Figure 12-4, the phenomenon of "dominance" is illustrated. In this type of expression, a factor or gene has its full effect regardless of whether it is present with another like itself or is paired with a recessive gene. Thus, black is dominant to chestnut; hence when a pure black stallion is crossed on a chestnut mare, all of the offspring will be black. The resulting black is not genotypically pure, however; it is Bb, where B stands for the dominant black and b for the recessive chestnut. This black animal will produce germ cells carrying black and chestnut genes in equal proportion. Then if an F_1 stallion is crossed on F_1 mares, the F_2 population will, on the average, consist of three blacks to one chestnut. The chestnut—being a recessive—will be pure for color; that is, the mating of two chestnut horses will produce, according to the most authoritative work, chestnut offspring, which is the situation in the Suffolk breed of draft horses where all animals of the breed are chestnuts. Of the three blacks, in the F_2, however, only one is pure for black (with the genetic constitution BB). The other two will be Bb in genetic constitution, and will produce germ cells carrying b and B in equal proportion.

It is clear, therefore, that a dominant character may cover up a recessive. Hence a horse's breeding performance cannot be recognized by its phenotype (how it looks), a fact of great significance in practical breeding.

As can be readily understood, dominance often makes the task of identifying and discarding all animals carrying an undesirable recessive factor a difficult one. Recessive genes can be passed on from generation to generation, appearing only when two animals, both of which carry the recessive factor, happen to mate. Even then, only one out of four offspring produced will, on the average, be homozygous for the recessive factor and show it.

Assuming that a hereditary defect or abnormality has occurred in a herd and that it is recessive in nature, the breeding program to be followed to prevent or minimize the possibility of its future occurrence will depend somewhat on the type of herd involved—especially on whether it is a grade or purebred herd. In an ordinary commercial herd, the breeder can usually guard against further reappearance of the undesirable recessive by using an outcross (unrelated) sire within the same breed or by crossbreeding with a sire from another breed. With this system, the breeder is fully aware of the recessive being present, but he has taken action to keep it from showing up.

On the other hand, if such an undesirable recessive appears in a purebred herd, the action should be more drastic. A reputable purebred breeder has an obligation not only to himself but to his customers. Purebred animals must be purged of undesirable genes and lethals. This can be done by:

1. Eliminating those sires and dams that are known to have transmitted the undesirable recessive character.

2. Eliminating both the abnormal and phenotypically normal offspring produced by these sires and dams (approximately half of the normal animals will carry the undesirable character in the recessive condition).

3. In some instances, breeding a prospective herd sire to a number of females known to carry the gene for the undesirable recessive, thus making sure that the new sire is free from the recessive.

Such action in a purebred herd is expensive, and it calls for considerable courage. Yet it is the only way in which the purebred livestock of the country can be freed from such undesirable genes.

INCOMPLETE DOMINANCE

In some cases, dominance is neither complete nor absent, but incomplete or partial and expressed in a variety of ways. Perhaps the best known case of this type in horses is the Palomino color.

Genetic studies of the Palomino indicate that the color is probably unfixable;[4] that it cannot be made true breeding, no matter how long or how persistent the effort. Further, there appears to be ample theory—substantiated by practical observation—to indicate that Palomino foals may be produced by any one of several types of matings (see discussion relative to Palomino characteristics, in Chapter 10).

Certain investigations[5] have revealed that the Palomino color is due to the interaction of three pairs of genes; namely, bb = homozygous chestnut, Dd = heterozygous dilution, and AA or Aa = either homozygous or heterozygous bay coat pattern, resulting in the chestnut color bb being diluted to a cream or golden body color by Dd (DD animals being very pale or almost white). If it is assumed that the Palomino's color depends on the Dd gene pair being heterozygous, the Palomino color cannot breed true.

[4]Castle, W. E. and King, F. L., "New Evidence on Genetics of Palomino Horses," *The Journal of Heredity*, 42:60-64, 1951.
[5]*Ibid.*

Multiple Gene Inheritance (Quantitative Traits)

Relatively few characters of economic importance in farm animals
are inherited in as simple a manner as the ones just described. Rather,
important characters—such as speed—are due to many genes; thus they
are called multiple-gene characters. Because such characters show
all manner of gradation—from high to low performance, for example
—they are sometimes referred to as quantitative traits. Thus, quantitative inheritance refers to the degree to which a characteristic is inherited; for example, all Thoroughbred horses can run and all inherit
some ability to run, but it is the degree to which they inherit the
ability which is important.

In quantitative inheritance, the extremes (either good or bad)
tend to swing back to the average. Thus, the offspring of a world-
record stallion and a world-record mare is not apt to be so good as
either parent. Likewise, and happily so, the progeny of two very
mediocre parents will likely be superior to either parent.

Estimates of the number of pairs of genes affecting each economically important characteristic vary greatly, but the majority of
geneticists agree that for most such characters ten or more pairs
of genes are involved. Growth rate in a foal, therefore, is affected
by: (1) the animal's appetite or feed consumption; (2) the efficiency
of assimilation—that is, the proportion of the feed eaten that is absorbed
into the blood stream; and (3) the use to which the nutrients are put
after assimilation—for example, whether they are used for growth or
fattening. This example should indicate clearly enough that such a
characteristic as growth rate is controlled by many genes and that
it is difficult to determine the mode of inheritance of such characters.

Heredity and Environment

A beautiful horse, standing deep in straw and with a manger full
of feed before him, is undeniably the result of two forces—heredity
and environment (with the latter including training). If turned out
to pasture, an identical twin to the beautiful horse would present
an entirely different appearance. By the same token, optimum environment could never make a champion out of a horse with scrub
ancestry.

These are extreme examples, and they may be applied to any class
of farm animals; but they do emphasize the fact that any particular
animal is the product of heredity and environment. Stated differently,
heredity may be thought of as the foundation, and environment as

the structure. Heredity has already made its contribution at the time of fertilization, but environment works ceaselessly away until death. Generally horse trainers believe that heredity is most important, whereas horse owners believe that environment—particularly training —is most important, especially if they lose a race. Actually, qualitative traits (such as hair and eye color) are affected little by environment; whereas quantitative traits (such as ability to run) may be affected greatly by environment.

Experimental work has long shown conclusively enough that the vigor and size of animals at birth is dependent upon the environment of the embryo from the minute the ovum or egg is fertilized by the sperm, and now we have evidence to indicate that newborn animals are affected by the environment of the egg and sperm long before fertilization has been accomplished. In other words, perhaps due to storage of factors, the kind and quality of the ration fed to young, growing females may later affect the quality of their progeny. Generally speaking, then, environment may inhibit the full expression of potentialities from a time preceding fertilization until physiological maturity has been attained.

It is generally agreed, therefore, that maximum development of characters of economic importance—growth, body form, speed, etc.— cannot be achieved unless there are optimum conditions of nutrition and management.

Admittedly, after looking over an animal or studying its production record, a breeder cannot with certainty know whether it is genetically a high or a low producer. There can be no denying the fact that environment—including feeding, management, and disease— plays a tremendous part in determining the extent to which hereditary differences that are present will be expressed in animals. Yet, it would appear to be more difficult to estimate the possible effect of degree of suboptimal development than it would be to make selections on the basis of optimum environment.

Within the pure breeds of livestock—managed under average or better than average conditions—it has been found that, in general, only 15 to 30 percent of the observed variation in a characteristic is actually brought about by hereditary variations. To be sure, if we contrast animals that differ very greatly in heredity—for example, a champion horse and a scrub—90 percent or more of the apparent differences in type may be due to heredity. The point is, however, that extreme cases such as the one just mentioned are not involved in the advancement within improved breeds of livestock. Here the comparisons are between animals of average or better than average quality, and the observed differences are often very minor.

The problem of the progressive breeder is that of selecting the very best animals available genetically—these to be parents of the next generation. The fact that only 15 to 30 percent of the observed variation is due to heredity, and that environmental differences can produce misleading variations, makes mistakes in the selection of breeding animals inevitable. However, if the purebred breeder has clearly in mind a well-defined ideal and adheres rigidly to it in selecting his breeding stock, some progress can be made by selection, especially if mild inbreeding is judiciously used as a tool through which to fix the hereditary material.

How Sex Is Determined

On the average, and when considering a large population, approximately equal numbers of males and females are born in all common species of animals. To be sure, many notable exceptions can be found in individual herds or flocks.

The most widely accepted theory of sex determination at the present time is that sex is determined by the chromosomal makeup of the individual. One particular pair of the chromosomes is called the sex chromosomes. In farm animals, the female has a pair of similar chromosomes (usually called X chromosomes), whereas the male has a pair of unlike sex chromosomes (usually called X and Y chromosomes). In the bird, this condition is reversed, the female having the unlike pair and the male having the like pair.

The pairs of sex chromosomes separate out when the germ cells are formed. Thus, each of the ova or eggs produced by the mare contains the X chromosome; whereas the sperm of the stallion are of two types, one-half containing the X chromosome and the other one-half the Y chromosome. Since, on the average, the eggs and sperm unite at random, it can be understood that half of the progeny will contain the chromosomal makeup XX (females)[6] and the other one-half XY (males).[7]

---

[6]The scientists' symbols for the male and female, respectively, are:
♂ (the sacred shield and spear of Mars, the Roman god of war), and
♀ (the looking glass of Venus, the Roman goddess of love and beauty).
[7]See footnote 6.

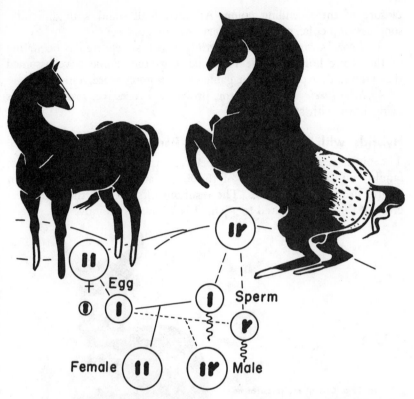

Fig. 12-5. Diagrammatic illustration of the mechanism of sex determination in horses, showing how sex is determined by the chromosomal makeup of the individual. The mare has a pair of like sex chromosomes, whereas the stallion has a pair of unlike sex chromosomes. Thus, if an egg and sperm of like sex chromosomal makeup unite, the offspring will be a filly; whereas if an egg and sperm of unlike sex chromosomal makeup unite, the offspring will be a colt. (Drawing by R. F. Johnson)

Lethals in Horses

The term lethal refers to a genetic factor that causes death of the animal, either during prenatal life, at birth, or later in life. Lethals which have been reported in horses include the following:

1. *Abnormal sex ratio.*—This is a recessive condition caused by a sex-linked gene, which was first reported in the Oldenburger breed of horses. Ratios of 55 males to 90 females were reported. About one-half of the males died before birth or during the early stages of prenatal development.

2. *Atresia coli.*—This is a recessive condition characterized by

closure of the ascending colon. Affected foals stand with difficulty, soon develop colic, and die. Surgery is unsuccessful.

3. *Lethal white.*—This low fertility was first reported as occurring in the white horses of the Frederiksborg stud. Some have assumed that factors destroying either gametes or zygotes were responsible.

4. *Stiff forelegs.*—This factor, probably a recessive, results in foals being born with stiff forelegs.

Hybrids with the Horse as One Parent

The mule, representing a cross between the jack (male of the ass family) on the mare (female of the horse family), is the best known hybrid in the United States. The resulting offspring of the reciprocal cross of the stallion mated to a jennet is known as a hinny.

Fig. 12-6. One of the rarest of nature's whims—a colt dropped by a mare mule. The colt, sired by a stallion, was born in St. Martinsville, La., Nov. 13, 1947. "Lou"—the 21-year-old mother mule—pulled a cane wagon all day on Nov. 12. She was owned by Acie Miller, a St. Martinsville mule trader. The case of this unusual birth was verified by Dr. Geo. P. Broussard, D.V.M., New Iberia, La. (Photo, courtesy Dr. Broussard)

Rarely have mules proved fertile; only five authentic cases of mare mules producing foals have been reported in the United States. This infertility of the mule is probably due to the fact that the chromosomes will not pair and divide equally in the reduction division.

The offspring of fertile mules are generally horse-like in appearance,[8] showing none of the characteristics of the mule's sire (or ass). For the most part, therefore, the eggs (ova) which produce them do not carry chromosomes from the ass; they are pure horse eggs without any inheritance from their maternal grandfathers. This indicates that in the production of eggs in mare mules the reduction division is such that all of the horse chromosomes go to the egg and none to the polar bodies.

The zebroid—a zebra x horse hybrid—is rather popular in certain areas of the tropics because of its docility and resistance to disease and heat.

The Relative Importance of the Stallion and the Mare

As a stallion can have so many more offspring during a given season or a lifetime than a mare, he is from a hereditary standpoint a more important individual than any one mare so far as the whole herd is concerned, although both the stallion and the mare are of equal importance so far as concerns any one offspring. Because of their wider use, therefore stallions are usually culled more rigidly than mares, and the breeder can well afford to pay more for an outstanding stallion than for an equally outstanding mare.

Experienced horsemen have long felt that stallions and their fillies usually resemble each other, and mares and their colts resemble each other. Some stallions and mares, therefore, enjoy a reputation based almost exclusively on the merit of their sons, whereas others owe their prestige to their daughters. Although this situation is likely to be exaggerated, any such phenomenon that may exist is due to sex-linked inheritance which may be explained as follows: The genes that determine sex are carried on one of the chromosomes. The other genes that are located on the same chromosome will be linked or associated with sex and will be transmitted to the next generation in combination with sex. Thus, because of sex linkage, there are more color-blind men than color-blind women. In poultry breeding, the

---

[8] Not all are horse-like, however. Thus, one of Old Beck's (fertile mule owned by Texas A & M College) three offspring was mule-like in appearance.

sex-linked factor is used in a practical way for the purpose of distinguishing the pullets from the cockerels early in life, through the process known as "sexing" the chicks. Thus, when a black cock is crossed with barred hens, all the cocks come barred and all the hens come black. It should be emphasized, however, that under most conditions it appears that the influence of the sire and dam on any one offspring is about equal. Most breeders, therefore, will do well to seek excellence in both sexes of breeding animals.

Prepotency

Prepotency refers to the ability of the animal, either male or female, to stamp its own characteristics on its offspring. The offspring of a prepotent stallion, for example, resemble both their sire and each other more closely than usual. The only conclusive and final test of prepotency consists of the inspection of the get.

From a genetic standpoint, there are two requisites that an animal must possess in order to be prepotent: (1) dominance and (2) homozygosity. All offspring that receive dominant genes will show the effects of those genes in the particular characters which result therefrom. Moreover, perfectly homozygous animals would transmit the same kind of genes to all of their offspring. Although entirely homozygous animals probably never exist, it is realized that a system of inbreeding is the only way to produce animals that are as nearly homozygous as possible.

It should also be emphasized that it is impossible to determine just how important prepotency may be in animal breeding, although many sires of the past have enjoyed a reputation for being extremely prepotent. Perhaps these animals were prepotent, but there is also the possibility that their reputation for producing outstanding animals may have rested upon the fact that they were mated to some of the best females of the breed.

In summary, it may be said that if a given stallion or mare possesses a great number of genes that are completely dominant for desirable type and performance and if the animal is relatively homozygous, the offspring will closely resemble the parent and resemble each other, or be uniform. Fortunate, indeed, is the breeder who possesses such an animal.

Nicking

If the offspring of certain matings are especially outstanding and in general better than their parents, breeders are prone to say that the animals "nicked" well. For example, a mare may produce outstanding foals to the service of a certain stallion, but when mated to another stallion of apparent equal merit as a sire, the offspring may be disappointing. Or sometimes the mating of a rather average stallion to an equally average mare will result in the production of a most outstanding individual both from the standpoint of type and performance.

So-called successful nicking is due, genetically speaking, to the fact that the right combinations of genes for good characters are contributed by each parent, although each of the parents within itself may be lacking in certain genes necessary for excellence. In other words, the animals nicked well because their respective combinations of good genes were such as to complement each other.

The history of animal breeding includes records of several supposedly favorable nicks. Because of the very nature of successful nicks, however, outstanding animals arising therefrom must be carefully scrutinized from a breeding standpoint; because, with their heterozygous origin, it is quite unlikely that they will breed true.

Family Names

In animals, depending upon the breed, family names are traced through either the males or females. Unfortunately, the value of family names is generally grossly exaggerated. Obviously, if the foundation stallion or mare, as the case may be, is very many generations removed, the genetic superiority of this head of a family is halved so many times by subsequent matings that there is little reason to think that one family is superior to another. The situation is often further distorted by breeders placing a premium on family names of which there are few members, little realizing that, in at least some cases, there may be unfortunate reasons for the scarcity in numbers.

Such family names have about as much significance as human family names. Who would be so foolish as to think that the Joneses as a group are alike and different from the Smiths? Perhaps, if the truth were known, there have been many individuals with each of these family names who have been of no particular credit to the clan, and the same applies to all other family names.

Family names lend themselves readily to speculation. Because of this, the history of livestock breeding has often been blighted by instances of unwise pedigree selection on the basis of not too meaningful family names.

On the other hand, certain linebred families—linebred to a foundation sire or dam so that the family is kept highly related to it—do have genetic significance. Moreover, if the programs involved have been accompanied by rigid culling, many good individuals may have evolved, and the family name may be in good repute.

SYSTEMS OF BREEDING

The many diverse types and breeds among each class of farm animals in existence today originated from only a few wild types within each species. These early domesticated animals possessed the pool of genes, which, through controlled matings and selection, proved flexible in the hands of man. In horses, for example, through various systems of breeding, there evolved animals especially adapted to riding, racing, and driving.

Perhaps at the outset it should be stated that there is no one best system of breeding or secret of success for any and all conditions. Each breeding program is an individual case, requiring careful study. The choice of the system of breeding should be determined primarily by the size and quality of the herd, by the finances and skill of the operator, and by the ultimate goal ahead.

Purebreeding

A purebred animal may be defined as a member of a breed, the animals of which possess a common ancestry and distinctive characteristics; and he is either registered or eligible for registry in that breed.

The breed association consists of a group of breeders banded together for the purposes of: (1) recording the lineage of their animals, (2) protecting the purity of the breed, and (3) promoting the interest of the breed.

The term purebred refers to animals whose entire lineage, regardless of the number of generations removed, traces back to the foundation animals accepted by the breed or to animals which have been subsequently approved for infusion. It should be emphasized that the word purebred does not necessarily guarantee superior type or high productivity. That is to say, the word purebred is not, within itself, magic, nor is it sacred. Many a person has found to his sorrow that there are such things as purebred scrubs. Yet, on the average, purebred animals are superior to non-purebreds.

For the man with experience and adequate capital, the breeding of purebreds may offer unlimited opportunities. It has been well said that honor, fame, and fortune are all within the realm of possible realization of the purebred breeder; but it should also be added that only a few achieve this high calling.

Purebred breeding is a highly specialized type of production. Generally speaking, only the experienced breeder should undertake the production of purebreds with the intention of furnishing foundation or replacement stock to other purebred breeders. Although we have had many constructive horse breeders and great progress has been made, it must be remembered that only a few achieve sufficient success to classify as master breeders. However, this need not discourage the small operator—the owner of one mare, or of a few mares —from mating to a good purebred stallion of the same breed, in order to produce some good horses.

Inbreeding

Most scientists divide inbreeding into various categories, according to the closeness of the relationship of the animals mated and the purpose of the matings. There is considerable disagreement, however, as to both the terms used and the meanings that it is intended they should convey. For purposes of this book and the ensuing discussion, the following definitions will be used.

Inbreeding is the mating of animals more closely related than the average of the population from which they came.

Closebreeding is the mating of closely related animals; such as sire to daughter, son to dam, and brother to sister.

Linebreeding is the mating of animals more distantly related than in closebreeding, and in which the matings are usually directed toward keeping the offspring closely related to some highly admired ancestor; such as half-brother and half-sister, female and grandsire, and cousins.

CLOSEBREEDING

Closebreeding is rarely practiced among present-day horsemen, though it was common in the foundation animals of most of the breeds. There is good reason why closebreeding is seldom followed with horses, especially racehorses; because (1) experiments (with other animals) clearly show that closebreeding results in less vigor, and (2) there is not available a desirable outlet for horses of poor type or performance, such as is afforded when discarded cattle, sheep, and swine are marketed for slaughter. Even so, the enlightened horseman will want to be familiar with the reasons for and the precautions against practicing closebreeding.

Closebreeding is that system of breeding in which closely related animals are mated. This includes the mating of: (1) sire to daughter, (2) son to dam, and (3) brother to sister; and the minimum number of different ancestors. In the repeated mating of a brother with his full sister, there are only two grandparents instead of four, only two great-grandparents instead of eight, and only two different ancestors in each generation farther back—instead of the theoretically possible 16, 32, 64, 128, etc. The most intensive form of inbreeding is self-fertilization. It occurs in some plants, such as wheat and garden peas, and in some of the lower animals.

The reasons for practicing closebreeding are:

1. It increases the degree of homozygosity within animals, making the resulting offspring pure or homozygous in a larger proportion of their gene pairs than in the case of linebred or outcross animals. In so doing, the less desirable recessive genes are brought to light so that they can be more readily culled. Thus, closebreeding, together with rigid culling, affords the surest and quickest method of fixing and perpetuating a desirable character or group of characters.

2. If carried on for a period of time, it tends to create lines or strains of animals that are uniform in type and other characteristics.

3. It keeps the relationship to a desirable ancestor highest.

4. Because of the greater homozygosity, it makes for greater prepotency. That is, selected inbred animals are more homozygous for desirable genes (genes which are often dominant), and they, therefore, transmit these genes with greater uniformity.

5. Through the production of inbred lines or families by closebreeding and the subsequent crossing of certain of these lines, it affords a modern approach to livestock improvement. Moreover, the best of the inbred animals are likely to give superior results in outcrosses.

6. Where a breeder is in the unique position of having his herd so far advanced that to go on the outside for seed stock would merely be a step backward, it offers the only sound alternative for maintaining existing quality or making further improvement.

The disadvantages of closebreeding may be summarized as follows:

1. As closebreeding greatly enhances the chances that recessives will appear during the early generations in obtaining homozygosity, it is almost certain to increase the proportion of worthless breeding stock produced. This may include such so-called degenerates as reduction in size, fertility, and general vigor. Lethals and other genetic abnormalities often appear with increased frequency in inbred animals.

2. Because of the rigid culling necessary in order to avoid the "fixing" of undesirable characters, especially in the first generations of a closebreeding program, it is almost imperative that this system of breeding be confined to a relatively large herd and to instances when the owner has sufficient finances to stand the rigid culling that must accompany such a program.

3. It requires skill in making planned matings and rigid selection, thus being most successful when applied by "master breeders."

4. It is not adapted for use by the man with average or below average stock because the very fact that his animals are average means that a goodly share of undesirable genes are present. Closebreeding would merely make the animals more homozygous for undesirable genes and, therefore, worse.

Judging from outward manifestations alone, it might appear that closebreeding is predominantly harmful in its effects—often leading to the production of defective animals lacking in the vitality necessary for successful and profitable production. But this is by no means the whole story. Although closebreeding often leads to the production of animals of low value, the resulting superior animals can confidently be expected to be homozygous for a greater than average number of good genes and thus more valuable for breeding purposes. Figuratively speaking, therefore, closebreeding may be referred to as "trial by fire," and the breeder who practices it can expect to obtain many animals that fail to measure up and have to be culled. On the other hand, if closebreeding is handled properly, he can also expect to secure animals of exceptional value.

Although closebreeding has been practiced less during the past century than in the formative period of the different pure breeds of livestock, it has real merit when its principles and limitations are fully understood. Perhaps closebreeding had best be confined to use

by the skilled master breeder who is in a sufficiently sound financial
position to endure rigid, intelligent culling and delayed returns and
whose herd is both large and above average in quality.

LINEBREEDING

From a biological standpoint, closebreeding and linebreeding are
the same thing; differing merely in intensity. In general, closebreeding
has been frowned upon by horsemen, but linebreeding (the less intensive form) has been looked upon with favor in some quarters.

*Linebreeding is that system of breeding in which the degree of
relationship is less than that in closebreeding, and in which the
matings are usually directed toward keeping the offspring closely
related to some highly admired ancestor.* In a linebreeding program,
therefore, the degree of relationship is not closer than half-brother
and half-sister or matings more distantly related; cousin matings,
grandparents and grand offspring, etc.

Linebreeding may be practiced in order to conserve and perpetuate
the good traits of a certain outstanding stallion or mare. Because such
descendants are of similar lineage, they have the same general type
of germ plasm and therefore exhibit a high degree of uniformity in
type and performance.

In a more limited way, a linebreeding program has the same advantages and disadvantages of a closebreeding program. Stated differently, linebreeding offers fewer possibilities both for good and harm
than closebreeding. It is a more conservative and safer type of program, offering less probability of either hitting the jackpot or sinking
the ship. It is a middle of the road program that the vast majority of
average and small breeders can safely follow to their advantage.
Through it, reasonable progress can be made without taking any
great risk. A greater degree of homozygosity of certain desirable genes
can be secured without running too great a risk of intensifying undesirable ones.

Usually a linebreeding program is best accomplished through
breeding to an outstanding sire rather than to an outstanding dam
because of the greater number of offspring of the former. If a horse
breeder found himself in possession of a great stallion—proved great
by the performance records of a large number of his get—a linebreeding program might be initiated in the following way: Select
two of the best sons of the noted stallion and mate them to their
half-sisters, balancing all possible defects in the subsequent matings.

The next generation mating might well consist of breeding the daughters of one of the stallions to the son of the other, etc. If, in such a program, it seems wise to secure some outside blood (genes) to correct a common defect or defects in the herd, this may be done through selecting a few outstanding proved mares from the outside— animals whose get are strong where the herd may be deficient—and then mating these mares to one of the linebred stallions with the hope of producing a son that may be used in the herd.

The small operator—the owner of one mare, or of a few mares— can often follow a linebreeding program by breeding his mares to a stallion owned by a large breeder who follows such a program— thus, in effect, following the linebreeding program of the larger breeder.

Naturally, a linebreeding program may be achieved in other ways. Regardless of the actual matings used, the main objective in such a system of breeding is that of rendering the animals homozygous—in desired type and performance—to some great and highly regarded ancestor, while at the same time weeding out homozygous undesirable characteristics. The success of the program, therefore, is dependent upon having desirable genes with which to start and an intelligent intensification of these good genes.

It should be emphasized that there are some types of herds that should almost never closebreed or linebreed. These include herds of only average quality.

With purebred herds of only average quality, more rapid progress can usually be made by introducing superior outcross sires. Moreover, were the animals of only average quality they would have a preponderance of "bad" genes that would only be intensified through a closebreeding or linebreeding program.

Outcrossing

Outcrossing is the mating of animals that are members of the same breed but which show no relationship close up in the pedigree (for at least the first four or six generations).

Most of our purebred animals of all classes of livestock are the result of outcrossing. It is a relatively safe system of breeding, for it is unlikely that two such unrelated animals will carry the same undesirable genes and pass them on to their offspring.

Perhaps it might well be added that the majority of purebred breeders with average or below average herds had best follow an outcrossing program, because, in such herds, the problem is that of retaining a heterozygous type of germ plasm with the hope that genes for undesirable characters will be counteracted by genes for desirable characters. With such average or below average herds, an inbreeding program would merely make the animals homozygous for the less desirable characters, the presence of which already makes for their mediocrity. In general, continued outcrossing offers neither the hope for improvement nor the hazard of retrogression of linebreeding or inbreeding programs.

Judicious and occasional outcrossing may well be an integral part of linebreeding or inbreeding programs. As closely inbred animals become increasingly homozygous with germ plasm for good characters, they may likewise become homozygous for certain undesirable characters even though their general overall type and performance remain well above the breed average. Such defects may best be remedied by introducing an outcross through an animal or animals known to be especially strong in the character or characters needing strengthening. This having been accomplished, the wise breeder will return to the original inbreeding or linebreeding program, realizing full well the limitations of an outcrossing program.

Grading Up

Grading up is that system of breeding in which a purebred sire of a given breed is mated to a native or grade female. Its purpose is to impart quality and to increase performance in the offspring. It is the common system of breeding followed on the western range, where mares of Mustang background are generally graded up by using a purebred stallion of a certain breed (usually either a Thoroughbred or a Quarter Horse), year after year, in producing cow ponies. Likewise, horse owners of the one- to two-mare variety frequently mate their grade mare(s) to a purebred stallion of the same breed, in order to produce hunters, jumpers, pleasure horses, etc.

Naturally, the greatest single step toward improved quality and performance occurs in the first cross. The first generation from such a mating results in offspring carrying 50 percent of the hereditary material of the purebred parent (or 50 percent of the "blood" of the purebred parent, as many horsemen speak of it). The next generation gives offspring carrying 75 percent of the "blood" of the purebred breed, and in subsequent generations the proportion of inheritance remaining from the original scrub parent is halved with each cross.

Later crosses will usually continue to increase quality and performance slightly more, though in less marked degree. After the third or fourth cross, the offspring compare very favorably with purebred stock in conformation, and only exceptionally good sires can bring about further improvement. This is especially so if the stallions used in grading up successive generations are derived from the same strain within a breed.

As evidence that horses of high merit may be produced through grading up, examples of champion performers among hunters, jumpers, polo ponies, cow ponies, etc., might be cited.

Crossbreeding

Crossbreeding is the mating of animals of different breeds. In a broad sense, crossbreeding also includes the mating of purebred sires of one breed with high grade females of another breed.

Perhaps in the final analysis, all would agree that any merits that crossbreeding may possess are and will continue to be based on improved "seed stock." Certainly, from a genetic standpoint, it should be noted that crossbred animals generally possess greater heterozygosity than outcross animals—with the added virtue of hybrid vigor. It may also be added that, as in outcrossing, the recessive and undesirable genes remain hidden in the crossbred animal.

On purely theoretical grounds, it would appear that crossbreeding should result in some increase in vigor because the desirable genes from both breeds would be combined and the undesirable genes from each would tend to be overshadowed as recessives.

In summary, it can be said that crossbreeding has a place, particularly from the standpoint of increased vigor, growth rate, efficiency of production, and in the creation of new breeds adapted to certain conditions; but purebreeding will continue to control the destiny of further improvement in horses and furnish the desired homozygosity and uniformity which many horsemen insist is a part of the art of breeding better horses.

RECORD FORMS

An important requisite in any horse breeding program is the keeping of relatively simple but meaningful records. Figures 12-7a, 12-7b, 12-8a, and 12-8b are record forms developed by the author. One is for the broodmare, and the other is for the stallion. These record forms may be modified somewhat to suit individual needs and desires.

INDIVIDUAL LIFETIME BROODMARE RECORD

Name of mare _____

Number or other identity _____

Birth date _____

Show or performance record _____
_____

Temperament _____ (gentle, nervous, cross)

Bred by _____ (name and address)

Purchased: from _____ (name and address)

Date _____ Price _____

Disposal: Sold to _____ (name and address)

Date _____ Price _____

Remarks _____

PHOTO

Production Record of Mares

Year	Sire of foal	Birth date of foal	Temperament of mare at foaling (gentle, nervous, cross)	Foaling (normal, requiring assistance, ret. placenta)	Vigor foal at birth (deformities)	Sex of foal	Identity of foal	Date foal was weaned	Score of foal				Disposal of foal				
									Under 1-year	Yearling	2-year-old	3-year-old	Sold to: (name and address)	Date	Price	Reasons	Remarks

Fig. 12-7a. Individual Lifetime Broodmare Record. (See Fig. 12-7b for reverse side of record form.)

Health Record

Date	Immunization				Type of parasite treatment	Other veterinary treatment	Remarks
	Encephal-omyelitis	Tetanus	Abortion				

Fig. 12-7b. Individual Lifetime Broodmare Record. (This is the reverse side of Fig. 12-7a.)

INDIVIDUAL YEARLY STALLION BREEDING RECORD

Name of stallion _____

Number or other identity _____

Birth date _____

Show or performance record _____

For breeding year of _____

For foaling year of _____

Total number of services _____

No. services/conception _____

PHOTO

Mares in Foal to Stallion

Name of mare	Date mare was bred	Date foaled	Vigor of foal at birth	Sex of foal	Disposal of foal					Remarks
					Sold to (name and address)	Date	Price	Reasons		

Fig. 12-8. Individual Yearly Stallion Breeding Record. (See Fig. 12-8b for reverse side of record form.)

Health Record

Date	Immunization			Type of parasite treatment	Semen Test	Veterinary Treatment	Remarks
	Encephal-omyelitis	Tetanus	Other				

Fig. 12-8b. Individual Yearly Stallion Breeding Record. (This is the reverse side of Fig. 12-8a.)

PERFORMANCE TESTING HORSES

The breeders of race horses have always followed a program of mating animals of proved performance on the track. For example, it is interesting to note that the first breed register which appeared in 1791—known as "An Introduction to The General Stud Book,"—recorded the pedigrees of all the Thoroughbred horses winning important races. In a similar way, the Standardbred horse—which is an American creation—takes its name from the fact that, in its early history, animals were required to trot a mile in two minutes and thirty seconds, or to pace a mile in two minutes and twenty-five seconds, before they could be considered as eligible for registry. The chief aim, therefore, of early-day breeders of race horses was to record the pedigree of outstanding performers rather than all members of the breed.

The simplest type of Progeny Testing in horses consists of the average record or merit of an individual stallion's or mare's offspring. Thus, the offspring of Thoroughbred or Standardbred animals bred for racing may be tested by timing on the track. Less satisfactory tests for saddle horses and harness horses have been devised. However, it is conceivable that actual exhibiting on the tanbark in the great horse shows of the country may be an acceptable criterion for saddle- and harness-bred animals.

Part II. Some Physiological Aspects of Reproduction in Horses

Horse producers have many reproductive problems, a reduction of which calls for a full understanding of reproductive physiology and the application of scientific practices therein.

THE REPRODUCTIVE ORGANS OF THE STALLION

The stallion's functions in reproduction are: (1) to produce the male reproductive cells, the sperm or spermatozoa, and (2) to introduce sperm into the female reproductive tract at the proper time. Figure 12-9 is a schematic drawing of the reproductive organs of the stallion.

The primary sex organ of the stallion is the testicle (there are two testicles). The testicles produce (1) sperm, and (2) a hormone called testosterone, which regulates and maintains the male reproductive tract in its functional state and is responsible for the masculine appearance and behavior of the stallion.

Sperm production takes place in the seminiferous tubules—a mass of minute, coiled tubules, the inner walls or surface of which produce the sperm. These tubules merge into a series of larger ducts which carry the sperm to a coiled tube called the epididymis. The epididymis is the place where the sperm are stored, and where they mature or ripen.

The testicles and epididymides are enclosed in the scrotum, the chief function of which is thermoregulatory—to maintain the testicles at temperatures several degrees cooler than the body proper.

From the epididymis, the sperm move through a tube, the vas deferens, into the urethra. The urethra has a dual role; it carries (1) urine from the bladder through the penis, and (2) sperm from the junction with the vas deferens to the end of the penis.

Among the urethra are the accessory glands—the prostate, the seminal vesicles, and Cowper's glands. Their fluids nourish and preserve the sperm, and provide a medium for its transport. The combined sperm and fluid is called semen.

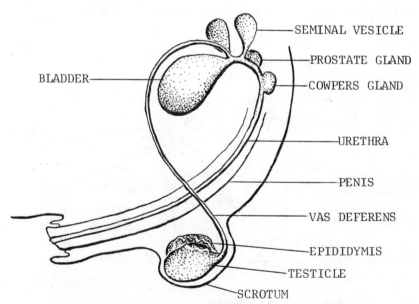

Fig. 12-9. The reproductive organs of the stallion. (Drawing by Ethel Gadberry)

THE REPRODUCTIVE ORGANS OF THE MARE

The mare's functions in reproduction are to (1) produce the female reproductive cells, the eggs or ova; (2) develop the new individual, the embryo, in the uterus; (3) expel the fully developed young at the time of birth or parturition; and (4) produce milk for the nourishment of the young. Actually, the part played by the mare in the generative process is much more complicated than that of the stallion. It is imperative, therefore, that the modern horseman have a full understanding of the anatomy of the reproductive organs of the mare and the functions of each part. Figure 12-10 shows the reproductive organs of the mare.

The primary sex organ of the mare is the ovary (there are two ovaries). These are somewhat bean-shaped organs two to three inches long. The ovaries produce eggs. Each egg is contained in a bubble-like sac on the ovary, called a follicle. There are hundreds of follicles on every ovary. Generally, the follicles remain in an unchanged state until the advent of puberty, at which time one of them begins to grow through an increase in the follicular liquid within, while the others remain small. The egg is suspended in the follicular fluid. When the follicle is about an inch in diameter (which coincides with the time of mating of mares that are bred), a hormone causes it to rupture and discharge the egg, which process is known as ovulation. The egg is

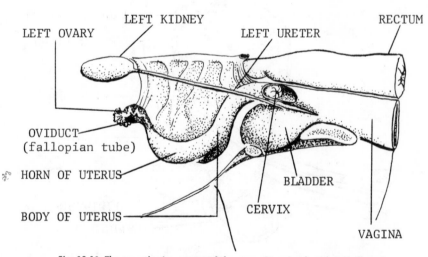

Fig. 12-10. The reproductive organs of the mare. (Drawing by Ethel Gadberry)

then trapped in a funnel-shaped membrane, called the infundibulum, that surrounds the ovary. The infundibulum narrows into a tube called the oviduct. The oviduct then carries the egg to the uterus, or womb, the largest of the female reproductive organs, where the unborn young (the fetus) will develop. The lining of the uterus is soft and spongy, containing a vast network of blood vessels, which provides a "bed" for the fertilized egg to settle into and develop. At birth, the heavy layers of muscles of the uterus wall contract with great pressure to force the new animal through the cervix and vagina (birth canal) and out into the new world.

NORMAL BREEDING HABITS OF MARES

Perhaps at the outset it should be emphasized that strictly normal breeding habits of the horse do not exist under domestication. In the wild state, each band of thirty to forty mares was headed by a stallion leader who sired all of the foals in that band. With plenty of outdoor exercise on natural footing, superior nutrition derived from plants grown on unleached soils, regular production beginning at an early age, little possibility of disease or infection, and frequent services during the heat period, ninety percent or higher foaling rates were commonplace. Under domestication, the average conception rate is less than fifty percent, and only the better establishment exceeds seventy percent. Thus, the low fertility usually encountered under domestication must be caused to a large extent by the relatively artificial conditions under which horses are mated.

Age of Puberty

Mares generally start coming in heat when 12 to 15 months of age.

Age to Breed Mares

Only exceptionally well-grown fillies should be bred as late two-year-olds, so as to foal at three years of age. Under a system of early breeding, the fillies must be fed exceptionally well in order to provide growth for their own immature bodies as well as for the developing fetus. Furthermore, they usually should not be bred the following year. Generally speaking, it is best to breed the mare as a three-year-old so that she will foal when four. Not only will the three-year-old be better grown, but there will not be the handicap of training her while she is heavy in foal.

If they are properly cared for, it is not uncommon for broodmares to produce regularly up to 14 to 16 years of age; and, of course, in the more exceptional cases they may produce up to 25 years of age.

In selecting a broodmare, it is usually advisable either to obtain a young three- or four-year-old or to make certain of the sure and regular breeding habits of any old mares.

Heat Periods

The heat periods recur approximately at 21-day intervals, with a spread of from 10 to 37 days. The duration of heat varies from one to thirty-seven days and averages four to six days, although some mares (especially maiden mares) will remain in heat up to fifty to sixty days in the early spring. Maiden mares that show "in heat" signs practically every day for many weeks should not be bred, as it is a waste of time and effort. In the vast majority of such cases, patience is rewarded by the mare subsequently settling into a normal cycle.

SIGNS OF ESTRUS

The experienced horseman who is familiar with a band of mares can usually detect those that are in season by observing (1) the relaxation of the external genitals, (2) more frequent urination, (3) the teasing of other mares, (4) the apparent desire for company, and (5) a slight mucus discharge from the vagina. In shy breeders or when there is any question about the mare being in season, she should be tried as subsequently discussed. When possible, it is usually good business regularly to present mares to the teaser every day or every other day as the breeding season approaches. A systematic plan of this sort will save much time and trouble.

Above all, precaution should be taken against false heats of mares in foal, the breeding of which may result in abortion. Such precaution is obtained by properly teasing the mare under the watchful eye of an experienced horseman who is familiar with the peculiarities of the individual animal.

Fertilization

Generally, the egg is liberated during the period of one day before to one day after the end of heat. Unfortunately, there is no reliable way of predicting the length of heat nor the time of ovulation; although an expert technician can predict the time of ovulation by feeling the ovary (follicle) with the hand through the rectum wall.

The sperm (or male germ cells) are deposited in the uterus at the time of service and from there ascend the reproductive tract. Under favorable conditions, they meet the egg, and one of them fertilizes it in the upper part of the oviduct near the ovary.

A series of delicate time relationships must be met, however, or the egg will never be fertilized. The sperm cells live only twenty-four to thirty hours in the reproductive tract of the female, and it probably requires four to six hours for them to ascend the female reproductive tract. Moreover, the egg is viable for an even shorter period of time than the sperm, probably for not more than four to six hours after ovulation. For conception, therefore, breeding must take place within twenty to twenty-four hours before ovulation.

As mares usually stay in heat from four to six days, perhaps the highest rate of conception may be obtained by serving the mare daily or every other day during the heat period, beginning with the third day. When many mares are being bred and heavy demands are being made upon a given stallion, this condition may be obtained by reinforcing a natural service with subsequent daily artificial inseminations as long as heat lasts. In no case should the mare be bred twice the same day.

Gestation Period

The average gestation period of mares is 336 days, or a little over eleven months. This will vary, however, with individual mares and may range from 310 to 370 days. A handy "rule-of-thumb" method that may be used to figure the approximate date of foaling is to subtract one month and add two days to the date the mare was bred. Hence, a mare bred May 20 should foal April 22 the following year.

Breeding After Foaling

Mares usually come in heat 9 to 11 days after foaling, with individual mares varying from 3 to 13 days after foaling. Provided that foaling has been entirely normal and there is no discharge or evidence of infection at this time, many good horsemen plan to rebreed the mare during this first recurrence of heat after foaling, or on about the ninth day. They believe that mares so handled are more likely to conceive than if bred at a later period. Mares suffering from an infection of the genital tract are seldom settled in service; and, even if they do conceive, there is danger of the foal being undersized and poorly developed. Also, the infection may be needlessly spread to the stallion and other mares by allowing such a practice. Mares not bred at this time or not conceiving will come in heat between the 25th and 30th day from foaling.

If any of the following conditions exist, the mare should not be bred at the first heat period following foaling:

1. If the placenta was retained over three hours.
2. If all lacerations have not entirely healed.
3. If there were severe bruises, particularly of the cervix.
4. If exudate or urine is present in the vagina.
5. If the mucous membrane is discolored or congested.
6. If there is lack of tone in either the uterus or vagina; if everything just seems to hang forward.

The usual reasons advanced in favor of rebreeding at the first heat period following foaling are:

1. It gives an added chance to rebreed the mare in an effort to get her in foal.
2. Occasionally a mare will not again show signs of heat during the breeding season.
3. If the mare conceives, she will foal about twenty days earlier the following year. This may be important where an early foal is desired.

Some arguments against rebreeding on the ninth day following foaling are:

1. If only one service is given on the ninth day following foaling, it is estimated that not more than 25 percent of the mares conceive.
2. During the period extending up to two weeks following foaling, the broodmare is more susceptible to genital infection than during any other period of her life.
3. Older mares that have been raising foals regularly each year may require a longer period of rest between pregnancies.
4. If the chances of conception are not too great, it may be unwise deliberately to overwork the stallion.

It is noteworthy that more and more of the good horsemen of Kentucky prefer not to breed mares on the ninth day following foaling.

PERCENT OF MARES BRED PRODUCING FOALS

Without question more difficulty is experienced in breeding mares than any other kind of livestock. The percentage of mares bred that actually conceive each year will vary from 40 to a high of 85, with an average probably running less than 50; and some of this number will fail to produce living foals. This means that, on the average, two mares are kept a whole year in order to produce one foal. By contrast, nationally, 86 percent of all beef cows that are bred, calve; 90 to 94 percent of all ewes, lamb; and 80 to 85 percent of all sows bred, farrow pigs.

The lower percentage conception in mares than in other classes of livestock is due primarily to the following: (1) research in the field has lagged, (2) an attempt is made to get mares bred in about 4 months instead of 12, and (3) the breeding season has been arbitrarily limited to a period (late winter and early spring) that at its best is only about 50 percent in agreement with nature.

In the bluegrass country of Kentucky, where there are both good horsemen and as desirable conditions for breeding as can be secured under domestication, 66 percent foaling is considered as average for the area.

Recognition of the following facts may help to increase the percentage of foals produced:

1. Mares bred in the late spring of the year are more likely to conceive. If mares are bred out of season, spring conditions should be duplicated as nearly as possible.

2. Mares bred as three- and four-year-olds and kept in regular production thereafter are more likely to conceive and produce living foals.

3. Infections or other unhealthy conditions of either the mare or stallion are not favorable for production.

4. More conceptions will occur if the mare is bred at the proper time within the heat period. Usually mares bred just before going out of heat are more likely to conceive.

5. Returning the mare to the stallion for retrial or rebreeding is important.

6. Mares in foal should be fed and cared for properly so as to develop the young. Balance of proteins, minerals, and vitamins is important.

7. It must also be remembered that old mares, overfat mares, or mares in a thin, run-down condition are less likely to be good breeders. Unfortunately, these conditions frequently apply to mares that are bred following retirement from the race track or the show-ring.

A shift of the date of birth (the January 1 birthday, for purposes of racing and showing) to somewhere between March 1 and May 1 would improve conception rate and foaling percentage, simply because mares would be bred under more natural and ideal spring conditions. Thus, it would have considerable virtue from the standpoint of the horse producer. On the other side of the ledger, however, it would create problems in racing and in registrations, both here and abroad. Also, such a deep-rooted tradition would be difficult to change; in fact, much consideration has been given to this matter from time to time. In the final analysis, therefore, stepping-up breeding research is the primary avenue through which the deplorably low percentage foal crop may be improved.

STERILITY OR BARRENNESS IN MARES

Sterility is a condition of infertility. Whatever the cause, there are no cure-alls for the condition. Rather, each individual case requires careful diagnosis and specific treatment for what is wrong. It should be recognized also that there are two types of sterility—temporary and permanent—although no sharp line can be drawn between them.

Regardless of the cause of sterility, it is well to give a word of caution against the so-called "opening up" of mares, which is the practice of inserting the hand and arm into the genital organs for the purpose of rearranging the organs in order to insure conception. Few laymen, no matter how expert they may classify themselves, have either sufficient knowledge of the anatomy of the mare or appreciation of the absolutely sterile methods necessary in such procedure to be probing about. Moreover, it is only rarely that the reproductive organs are out of place. Unless the "opening up" is recommended and conducted by a veterinarian, it should not be permitted. When performed by an amateur, or even most would-be experts, it is a dangerous practice that is to be condemned.

Temporary Sterility

Some common causes of temporary sterility are:

1. Lack of exercise, irregular work, and overfeeding accompanied by extremely high condition.

2. Overwork, underfeeding, and an extremely thin and run-down condition.

3. Nutritional deficiencies.

4. Infections of various kinds.

5. Some types of physiological imbalances characterized by such things as cystic ovaries or failure to ovulate at the proper time.

Temporary sterility can be reduced by removing the cause and correcting the difficulty, whatever it may be.

Permanent Sterility

Naturally, permanent sterility is much more serious to the horse breeder. Perhaps the most common causes of permanent sterility are:

1. Old age, which is usually accompanied by irregular breeding and eventual total sterility.

2. Infections in the reproductive tract, usually in the cervix, uterus, or fallopian tubes.

3. Some types of physiological imbalances characterized by such things as cystic ovaries or failure to ovulate at the proper time.

4. Closure of the female genital organs.

Sometimes a veterinarian is able to correct the latter two conditions; and, on an extremely valuable breeding mare, it may be worthwhile to obtain such professional service in an effort to bring about conception.

Retained afterbirth or other difficulties encountered in foaling may cause inflammation and infection that will prevent conception as long as the condition exists. There is real danger of spreading the infection if the mare is bred while in such a condition.

FERTILITY OF THE STALLION

Any stallion of breeding age that is purchased should be a guaranteed breeder; this is usually understood among reputable breeders.

The most reliable and obvious indication of potency is a large number of healthy, vigorous foals from a season's service. As an added protection, or in order to follow the horse during the midst of a heavy breeding program, a microscopic examination of the semen may be made by an experienced person. As the stallion dismounts from service, some of the semen is collected in a sterilized funnel by holding the penis over the plugged funnel. A sample of the semen is then strained through sterile gauze, and a small amount is placed on a slide for examination. A great number of active sperm cells is an indication, although not definite assurance, that the stallion is fertile. Some establishments make a regular practice of making such a microscopic examination twice each week during the breeding season. If it is desired to examine a stallion's semen after the breeding season or when a mare is not in season an artificial vagina may be used. When an entire ejaculate is available for study, the four main criteria of quality are: (1) semen volume, (2) spermatozoan count, (3) progressive movement, and (4) morphology.

If the stallion is a shy breeder or lacks fertility although one is certain that the feed and exercise have been up to standard, masturbation should be suspected. Some horses are very hard to catch in the act, but generally masturbation can be detected by (1) the shrinkage of the muscles over the loin, and (2) the presence of dried semen on the abdomen or on the back of the front legs. Once this practice is detected or even suspected, corrective measures should be taken. Stalling and turning the horse out where he can see other horses will help in some instances; also, giving the horse more sunshine, grass, and outdoor exercise. Another method consists in obtaining a plastic stallion ring of the proper size (they may be obtained from most breeder's supply houses in sizes to fit any horse) and fitting it snugly over the penis just back of the glans. It should be of such size that it will neither come off nor slide up the penis, yet loose enough that it does not interfere with normal circulation. The ring is removed when the horse is washed for breeding, and re-placed after service. Also, it should be removed and cleaned weekly when the horse is not used for breeding. Another very effective adaptation of the same idea is the "bird cage" type of stallion ring; in addition to having a ring, this type is made to encompass completely the end of the penis.

CONDITIONING THE MARE FOR BREEDING

Proper conditioning of the mare prior to breeding is just as important as in the stallion. Such conditioning depends primarily upon adequate and proper feed and the right amount of exercise.

For the highest rate of conception, mares should be neither too thin nor too fat; a happy medium in condition makes for best results. It is especially important that one avoid the natural tendency of barren or maiden mares to get too fat.

Time permitting, mares of the light-horse breeds may best be exercised and conditioned by riding under saddle or driving in harness. When these methods are not practical or feasible, permitting a band of mares to run in a large pasture will usually provide a satisfactory amount of exercise.

THE BREEDING OPERATIONS

No phase of horse production has become more unnatural or more complicated with domestication than the actual breeding operations.

Hand Breeding, Corral Breeding, and Pasture Breeding

Hand mating is undoubtedly the best way in which to breed mares; it is the accepted practice in the better breeding establishments throughout the world. It guards against injury to both the stallion and the mare.

Although leaving much to be desired, corral breeding is next best to hand breeding. In this system, after first ascertaining that the mare is in heat, she and the stallion are turned loose together in a small, well-fenced corral. The attendants should remain out of the corral, where they can see but not be seen by the animals, until service is completed, following which the stallion and the mare are returned to their respective quarters.

Pasture breeding simply consists of turning the stallion into a pasture with the band of mares which it is intended that he serve. Except on the ranges of the far West, this method of breeding is seldom practiced with domestic horses. With valuable animals, both corral and pasture breeding are too likely to cause injury, and the practices should be condemned. In pasture breeding, a stallion will handle fewer mares because of the repeated services of a mare, and he may even become sterile toward the end of the breeding season. Moreover, in pasture breeding, accurate breeding records are impossible.

Examination of the Mare

Before accepting a mare for service, the stallion owner should check every possible condition with care. The stallioner should examine the mare closely and question the owner concerning her health, last foaling date, breeding record, and similar matters. He should be well acquainted with the symptoms of dourine and other venereal diseases. Even though these diseases are not common in this country, there is always danger of finding them in imported stallions and mares and western horses. It is wise to require that barren mares be accompanied by a health certificate signed by a veterinarian.

The following types of mares should be rejected:

1. Mares showing the slightest symptoms of venereal disease.

2. Mares that have an abnormal discharge (such as blood or pus) from the vagina, commonly known as the "Whites."

3. Mares affected with skin diseases and parasites.

4. Mares suffering from high fevers, which accompany colds, strangles, influenza, shipping fever, and pneumonia.

5. Mares that have recently given birth to foals affected with navel-ill.

6. Mares that have recently suffered from retained afterbirth.

7. Mares that have suffered lacerations in foaling.

8. Mares that do not show definite signs of heat.

9. Mares under three years of age unless mature and well developed.

10. Mares that have a very narrow or deformed pelvis.

11. Mares that stay in heat incessantly (nymphomaniacs).

12. Mares that are extremely thin or emaciated.

13. Mares that have severe unsoundnesses which may be hereditary.

When mares have been barren over an extended period or when there is the slightest suspicion of infection, it is good protection to require a veterinarian's certificate to the effect that the mare is in a healthy breeding condition.

Mating Considerations and Serving the Mare

In addition to the above considerations concerning the examination of the mare, the following suggestions may be helpful:

1. Usually the mare should be taken to the stallion as breeding facilities are generally better where a stallion is stood for service.

2. If the mare has a foal and is to be away for a period of longer than five or six hours, the foal should be taken along—care being taken to avoid injury to the foal in transit. When the mare will not be away longer than five to six hours, the foal should be left home, and the mare should be hand-milked if necessary.

3. Newly arrived mares, especially those travelling by pub-

lic van or railway, may well be required to pass through a quarantine period prior to being bred.

Fig. 12-11. Teasing a mare, using a solid fence for separation. Breeding a mare that is not in season is a wasteful practice, and more important, it may result in damaging the future breeding efficiency. (Courtesy, Washington State University)

4. The mare should be allowed to become quiet and comfortable upon reaching the destination. Usually the most desirable practice is to tie the mare in a quiet stable. In cold weather or when the mare has been difficult to get in foal, some good horsemen recommend moderate exercise just prior to mating.

5. If excited or overheated, mares should be cooled out before being bred. Never should the mare be led behind a truck or car, or raced, in going to or returning from the stallion at the time of service.

6. Make certain that the mare is in season and ready for the stallion. Mares are most likely to conceive if bred 24 to 48 hours before the end of the heat period. The chute, gateway, open door, or solid fence are the usual methods employed for teasing. Some Thoroughbred establishments, and a few Standardbred stud farms, routinely employ the "jumping" procedure before using a valuable stallion on a young mare. The mare is restrained, as for breeding, and a gentle teaser is allowed to approach and mount her, but actual

breeding is prevented by directing the teaser to one side. This gives the young mare a chance to discover what is going to happen and serves as added protection to a valuable stallion.

Breeding a mare that is not absolutely ready is a wasteful practice, and, more important, it may result in damaging the future breeding efficiency.

7. After teasing the mare and making certain that she is in season, wash the reproductive organs of the stallion with castile soap and warm water, using cotton instead of a sponge. Then rinse with clean pure water. The reproductive organs should be washed in a similar manner following service.

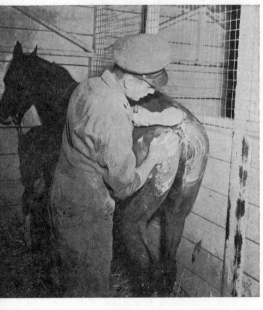

Fig. 12-12. Washing the mare in preparation for breeding. The external parts of the mare that are likely to come into contact with the reproductive organs of the stallion should be washed with castile soap and warm water and then rinsed with clean water. (Courtesy, Major C. B. Team, USDA)

8. Bandage the upper six to eight inches of the mare's tail using three-inch widths of cheese cloth or other inexpensive materials. This keeps the genital organs clean and avoids interference with tail hairs. The bandage is removed after service.

9. The external parts of the mare that are likely to come into contact with the reproductive organs of the stallion should be washed with castile soap and warm water and then rinsed with clean water. Use cotton instead of a sponge, and never put any cotton back in the bucket after it has touched the mare.

10. Use the twitch and hobbles[9] for the mare. This assures protection of both the stallion and mare. Hobbles are used only to protect the stallion as he approaches and dismounts and not in any way to force the mare into submission to service when not ready. The twitch is usually removed as soon as the stallion has entered the mare.

11. Keep the stallion under control at all times. Never allow him to mount until he is ready for service. Then allow him to remain on the mare until the sexual act is completed. The same man should always handle the stallion at the time of service.

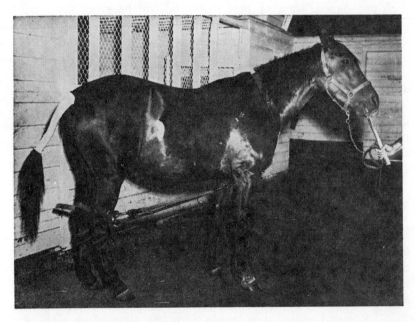

Fig. 12-13. A hobbled mare with twitch, and with tail properly bandaged, ready for service. Hobbles and twitches are used only to protect the stallion as he approaches and dismounts and not in any way to force the mare into submission to service when not ready. (Courtesy, Washington State University)

12. Allow the mare to remain quiet for a time following service. Avoid any undue excitement or exertion. If the mare has been in harness, she should not be worked for two or three days. Feed the mare as she was fed prior to breeding. Some good horsemen

---

[9]Or a leg strap may be used. If hobbles are used, they should be secured to stay put, but in such manner that they can be quickly released if desired.

have the mare led quietly for twenty minutes following service; for, in moving about, she has no opportunity to strain.

13. Return the mare for retrial approximately 21 days following the first service. Such a practice will increase the percentage of in-foal mares and guard against the arrival of foals much later in the season than desired.

SIGNS AND TESTS OF PREGNANCY

Some mares will continue to exhibit the characteristic heat symptoms even when in foal. Sometimes in-foal mares will show such pronounced signs of heat that they will be given the service of the stallion. This often results in abortion. Only the horseman knowing individual mares is capable of passing the best judgment on this question.

In order to produce as high a percentage of foals as possible and to have them arrive at the time desired, the good horseman will be familiar with the signs of and tests for pregnancy. This is doubly important when it is recognized that a great many mares may either be shy breeders or show signs of heat even when well advanced in gestation. The signs and tests of pregnancy may be listed as follows:

1. The cessation of the heat period—recognizing that this may be hard to determine and even misleading.

2. The movement of the living fetus. This movement can be seen or felt through the abdominal walls. It will not be possible, however, to use this test until about the seventh month of gestation. Movement of the fetus is most evident the first thing in the morning. This method is not so certain with young maiden mares, as the foal is carried nearer the backbone.

3. A rectal examination made forty to sixty days after the last service in which the uterus is felt through the rectum. This should be done only by an experienced horseman or veterinarian.

The following four tests for pregnancy have been developed:

1. *The blood serum test,* which may be used on mares any time after forty-five to fifty days following breeding and up to three months. Two ounces (one-half cup) of blood are drawn into a clean bottle, using a large bore needle in the usual manner. The blood is allowed to stand at room temperature for an hour to facilitate the separation of the serum and is then placed in a refrigerator. After the serum has separated, it is poured off and stored

in the refrigerator. The blood serum is injected into female rats (21 to 24 days of age), using 0.5 cc serum on each animal. During the period extending from 40 to 120 days after conception, the pregnant mare's serum contains a hormone, gonadotrophin, which, when injected into the test animals, causes activation of the ovary and consequent enlargement of the uterus. Observation of these changes may be made in the rat five days after treatment. In comparison with controls, rats treated with the blood serum of pregnant mares show enlarged ovaries and uteri.

2. *The urine test*,[10] which is used on mares from three months after breeding until termination. Four ounces of urine (and not blood) are collected in a clean bottle and are used as a sample. The urine test is used on spayed, mature female rats or mice, causing symptoms of heat in the vagina of treated animals.

3. *The male toad (Bufo) test*, developed by Dr. Raymond O. Berry, Texas A & M University. This ingenious test is based on the fact that the toad emits sperm only (a) when stimulated by amplexus with a female toad or (b) when stimulated by a gonadotropic hormone, such as is found in pregnant mare's blood at certain stages. Dr. Berry's test,[11] which may be used on mares that have been bred between 45 and 120 days, is conducted as follows:

a. Draw from the jugular vein of the mare 50 to 60 cc of blood and place it in a test tube.

b. Place a cork stopper in the tube and store it in a refrigerator in a slanting position until the blood clots.

c. Pipette off the straw colored serum for injection into the male toad.

d. Inject, at hourly intervals, into the dorsal lymph sac of the male toad (several species of toads, and the grass frog *Rana pipiens* may be used) 1 cc of the serum, until a total of 3 cc has been injected.

e. One hour after the last injection, check the toad for the presence of sperm by aspirating the cloaca with a pipette containing a few drops of water. Then mount the fluid on a slide and observe it under the microscope.

f. Consider the presence of sperm, either motile or nonmotile, as a positive test (meaning that the mare is pregnant).

---

[10]Among scientists, this test appears to be more controversial and less sure than the other tests given herein.

[11]From mimeographed class notes provided by Dr. Berry.

g. Recheck all negatives with another toad.

4. *The Mare Immunological Pregnancy Test* (*MIP-Test*), developed by Dr. Ronald Chak, DVM, Ocala (Florida) Stud Farm, and Mr. Max Bruss, Dorchester Laboratory, Ocala, Florida. This new test, which is accurate and simple to perform, was reported upon before the Equine Practitioners Association, in Philadelphia, Dec. 8, 1968.

The test utilizes the principle whereby pregnant mare serum (gonadotropin) inhibits the agglutination of gonadotropin-coated erythrocytes in the presence of gonadotropin antiserum. The result is the formation of a ring at the bottom of a test tube. The procedure is performed with two test tubes; a control test tube, and a sample test tube. Mare serum is placed in both, along with erythrocytes and reagents. However, antiserum is placed in the sample test tube, whereas a control solution is used in the other test tube. In the control tube, the pattern of a doughnut-like ring will show at the bottom, whether or not the mare is pregnant. But the sample tube with the antiserum will show the same pattern only if gonadotropin is present in the mare's serum—signifying that the mare is pregnant. The MIP-Test, which can be run in two hours time, can determine with virtually 100 percent accuracy equine pregnancy from a blood sample taken 41 to 63 days after the mare is serviced. The MIP-Test Kit contains all the supplies needed for running the test.[12]

CARE AND MANAGEMENT OF THE STALLION

Although certain general recommendations can be made, it should be remembered that each stallion should be studied as an individual, and his care, feeding, exercise, and handling should be varied accordingly.

Quarters for the Stallion

The most convenient arrangement for the stallion is a roomy box stall which opens directly into a two- or three-acre pasture paddock, preferably separated from the other horses by a double fence. A paddock fence made of heavy lumber is safest. The stall door opening into such a paddock may be left open except during extremely cold weather; this will give the stallion plenty of fresh air, sunshine, and additional exercise.

---

[12]The MIP-Test Kit may be secured from the Denver Chemical Manufacturing Co., Stamford, Conn. 06904.

Feeding the Stallion

The feed and water requirements of the stallion are adequately discussed in Chapter 13. In addition to this, it may be well to re-emphasize that, in season, clean lush pastures produced on fertile soils are excellent for the stallion. Grass is the horse's most natural feed, and it is a rich source of vitamins that are so necessary for vigor and reproduction. Perhaps the ideal arrangement in providing pasture for the stallion is to give him access to a well-sodded paddock.

Fig. 12-14. Stallion barn at the Washington State University, with each box stall opening directly into large pasture paddocks separated by a double fence. (Courtesy, Washington State University)

Exercise for the Stallion

Most horsemen feel that regular, daily exercise for the stallion is important. Certainly, it is one of the best ways in which to keep a horse in a thrifty, natural condition. It has also been assumed that forced exercise is of importance in improving semen quality. However, recent studies with dairy bulls cast considerable doubt on the relationship of exercise to fertility. For example, in one study involving dairy bulls used in artificial insemination, eight bulls which were forced exercised were compared with a like number which were kept in box or tie stalls, without forced exercise. The exercised group showed a non-return rate of 63.8%, whereas the bulls that were not exercised

Fig. 12-15. The Thoroughbred stallion, Nashua, winner of $1,288,565 and syndicated at $1,251,200, in breeding condition. (Courtesy, Mr. Leslie Combs II, Spendthrift Farm, Lexington, Ky.)

showed a non-return rate of 65%; hence, the bulls without exercise were actually a little more fertile than the exercised ones.[13] This points up the need for well-controlled experiments on the importance of exercise of the stallion on semen quality.

Stallions of the light-horse breeds are most generally exercised under saddle or hitched to a cart. Thus, Standardbred stallions are usually jogged three to five miles daily while drawing a cart. Thoroughbred stallions and saddle stock stallions of all other breeds are best exercised under saddle for from thirty minutes to one hour daily, especially during the breeding season. Exercise should not be hurried or hard; the walk and the trot are the best gaits to use for this purpose. After the stallion is exercised, he should be rubbed down and cooled off before he is put up, especially if he is hot. Better yet, the ride should be so regulated at the end that the horse will be brought in cool, in which case he can be brushed off and turned into his corral.

Frequently, in light horses, bad feet exclude exercise on roads, and faulty tendons exclude exercise under the saddle. Under such conditions, one may have to depend upon: (1) exercise taken voluntarily by the stallion in a large paddock, (2) longeing or exercising on a thirty- to forty-foot rope, or (3) leading.

Longeing should be limited to a walk and a trot; and, if possible, the stallion should be worked on both hands; that is, made to circle both to the right and to the left. It is also best that this type of exercise be administered within an enclosure. Two precautions in longeing are: (1) do not longe a horse when the footing is slippery, and (2) do not pull the animal in such manner as to make him pivot too sharply with the hazard of breaking a leg.

Leading is a satisfactory form of exercise for some stallions if it is not practical to ride them. In leading, a bridle should always be used—never a halter—and one should keep away from other horses and be careful that the horse being ridden is not a kicker.

Where several stallions are exercised, a properly installed mechanical exerciser driven by an electric motor may be used as a means of lessening labor. It is similar to the merry-go-round type of equipment used to exercise dairy bulls.

The objection to relying upon paddock exercises alone is that the exercise cannot be regulated, especially during inclement weather.

---

[13]*Physiology of Reproduction and Artificial Insemination of Cattle,* published by W. H. Freeman & Company, p. 625.

Some animals may take too much exercise and others too little. Moreover, merely running in the paddock will seldom, if ever, properly condition any stallion. Even so, a two- or three-acre grassy paddock should always be provided, even for horses that are regularly exercised. Stallions that are worked should be turned out at night and on idle days.

Grooming the Stallion

Proper grooming of the stallion is necessary, not only to make the horse more attractive in appearance, but to assist exercise in maintaining the best of health and condition. Grooming serves to keep the functions of the skin active. It should be thorough, with special care taken to keep all parts of the body clean and free from any foulness, but not so rough nor severe as to cause irritation either of the skin or temper.

AGE AND SERVICE OF THE STALLION

It should be remembered that the number and kind of foals that a stallion sires in a given season is more important than the total number of services. The number of services allowed during a season will vary with the age, development, temperament, health, and breeding condition of the animal and the distribution of services. Therefore, no definite best number of services can be recommended for any and all conditions, and yet the practices followed by good horsemen are not far different. All are agreed that excessive service of the stallion may reduce his fertility. Also, it must be realized that two or three services are required for each conception, and that there are breed differences, due primarily to differences in temperament.

Table 12-1 contains recommendations relative to the number of services for stallions of different ages, with consideration given to age and type of mating. Because of their more naturally nervous temperaments, stallions of the light-horse breeds are usually more restricted in services than stallions of the draft-horse breeds. Also, there is a difference between breeds.

The most satisfactory arrangement for the well-being of the stallion is to allow not more than one service each day. With proper handling, however, the mature, vigorous stallion may with certainty and apparently without harm serve two mares in a single day. During the heavy spring breeding season, this may often be necessary.

Table 12-1

HANDY STALLION MATING GUIDE[1]

Age	No. of Matings/Yr.		Comments
	Hand-mating	Pasture-mating	
2-yr.-old-------------	10-15	Preferably no pasture-mating unless the stallion is prepared for same and certain precautions are taken.	1. Limit the 2-yr.-old to 2-3 services/week; the 3-yr.-old to 1 service/day; and the 4-yr.-old or over to 2 services/day.
3-yr.-old-------------	20-40		
4-yr.-old-------------	30-60		
Mature horse------	80-100		2. A stallion should remain a vigorous and reliable breeder up to 20 to 25 yrs. of age.
Over 18 yrs. old----------------	20-40		

[1]There are breed differences. Thus, when first entering stud duty, the average 3-year-old Thoroughbred should be limited to 20 to 25 mares per season, whereas a Standardbred of the same age may breed 25 to 30 mares; and the 4- or 5-year-old Thoroughbred should be limited to 30 to 40 mares, whereas a Standardbred of the same age may breed 40 to 50 mares. Mature stallions of the draft breeds may and do breed up to 100 mares in a season.

It is a good plan to allow a stallion to rest at least one day a week.

In order to secure higher conception of the mares and yet avoid overwork of the stallion with an excessive number of natural services, most Thoroughbred breeders now reinforce each natural service with one artificial insemination. According to Jockey Club regulations, this must be done at once after natural service, "with semen from the stallion performing the natural service on the mare that has just been covered."

Stallions often remain virile and valuable breeders until 20 to 25 years of age, especially if they have been properly handled. However, it is usually best to limit the number of services on a valuable old sire in order to preserve his usefulness and extend his longevity as long as possible.

Occasionally, Thoroughbred and Standardbred stallions are used to a limited extent before retirement to the stud, although many good horsemen seem to feel that it is not best to use them until it is time for them to be retired. Saddle horses may be bred to a few mares and still be used in the show-ring. However, sometimes it makes them more difficult to handle.

It frequently happens that a wonderful horse is injured in the midst of his racing career, and while awaiting the next racing season, he is bred to a few mares.

If two services a day are planned with the mature stallion, one should be rather early in the morning and the other late in the afternoon. It is also best not to permit teasing or services immediately before or soon after feeding the stallion; for this may result in a digestive disturbance, particularly in nervous, fretful individuals.

STALLION STATIONS

Recently, there has been a trend toward grouping ten to twenty stallions on a breeding farm, commonly referred to as a Stallion Station. This development has been especially strong in the Thoroughbred, Standardbred, and Quarter Horse breeds.

These highly specialized breeding establishments have the following *advantages:*

1. It makes it convenient for an owner wishing to breed several mares to avail himself of the selection of a number of stallions.

2. It is more practical to employ expert personnel to handle the breeding operations.

3. It usually makes for superior facilities for this specialized purpose.

4. It generally results in a higher percentage of in-foal mares, earlier conception, and more efficient use of the stallion—primarily due to more expert management; examination, and medication if necessary; and improved facilities.

As with all good things, there may be, and sometimes are, *disadvantages*, such as the following:

1. The hazard of spreading contagious diseases is increased where there is a great concentration of horses, thus requiring extreme cleanliness and precautions.

2. There is considerable expense in operating a highly specialized service of this kind.

3. There is difficulty in obtaining a battery of really outstanding sires.

CARE OF THE PREGNANT MARE

Barren and foaling mares are usually kept separately because pregnant mares are sedate; whereas barren mares are more likely to run, tease, and kick. Precautions in handling the pregnant mare will be covered in the discussion that follows.

Quarters for the Mare

If mares are worked under saddle or in harness, they may be given quarters like those accorded to the rest of the horses used similarly, at least until near parturition time. Idle mares may best be turned to pasture. Even in the wintertime, a simple shelter is adequate. In some sections of the country, an open shed is satisfactory.

Feeding the Pregnant Mare

The feed and water requirements for the pregnant mare are adequately discussed in Chapter 13, so repetition is unnecessary.

Exercise for the Pregnant Mare

The pregnant mare should have plenty of exercise. This may be obtained by allowing a band of broodmares to roam over large pastures in which shade, water, and minerals are available.

Mares of the light-horse breeds may be exercised for an hour daily under saddle or hitched to a cart. When handled carefully, the broodmare may be so exercised to within a day or two of foaling. Above all, when not receiving forced exercise or on idle days, she should not be confined to a stable or a small drylot.

CARE AT FOALING TIME

A breeding record should be kept on each mare so that it will be known when she is due to foal. As has been previously indicated, the period of gestation of a mare is about 336 days, but it may vary as much as a month in either direction. Therefore, the careful and observant horseman will be ever alert and make certain definite preparations in ample time.

The period of parturition is one of the most critical stages in the life of the mare. Through carelessness or ignorance, all of the advantages gained in selecting genetically desirable and healthy parent stock and in providing the very best of environmental and nutritional conditions through gestation can be quickly dissipated at this time. Generally speaking, less difficulty at parturition was encountered in the wild state, when the females of all species brought forth their young in the fields and glens.

Work and Exercise

Saddle or light-harness mares should be exercised moderately in the accustomed manner. If they are not used, other gentle exercise, such as leading, should be provided. This is especially important if they have not been accustomed to being on pasture and if it is desired to avoid any abrupt changes in feeding at this time.

Signs of Approaching Parturition

Perhaps the first sign of approaching parturition is a distended udder, which may be observed two to six weeks before foaling time. About seven to ten days before the arrival, there will generally be a marked shrinkage or falling away of the muscular parts of the top of the buttocks near the tailhead and a falling of the abdomen. Although the udder may have filled out previously, the teats seldom fill out to the ends more than four to six days before foaling; and the wax on the ends of the nipples generally is not present until within two to four days before parturition. About this time the vulva becomes full and loose. As foaling time draws nearer, milk will drop from the teats; and the mare will show restlessness, break into a sweat, urinate frequently, lie down and get up, etc. It should be remembered, however, that there are times when all signs fail and a foal may be dropped when least expected. Therefore, it is well to be prepared as much as thirty days in advance of the expected foaling time.

Preparation for Foaling

When signs of approaching parturition seem to indicate that the foal may be expected within a week or ten days, arrangements for the place of foaling should be completed. Thus, the mare will become accustomed to the new surroundings before the time arrives.

During the spring, summer, and fall months when the weather is warm, the most natural and ideal place for foaling is a clean, open pasture away from other livestock. Under these conditions, there is decidedly less danger of either infection or mechanical injury to the mare and foal. Of course, in following this practice, it is important that the ground be dry and warm. Small paddocks or lots that are unclean and foul with droppings are unsatisfactory and may cause such infectious troubles as navel-ill.

During inclement weather, the mare should be placed in a roomy, well-lighted, well-ventilated, comfortable, quiet box stall which should first be carefully cleaned, disinfected, and bedded for the occasion. It is best that the mare be stabled therein at nights a week or ten days before foaling so that she may become accustomed to the new surroundings. The foaling stall should be at least 12 feet square

Fig. 12-16. A mare and her newborn foal on pasture. When the weather is warm, the most natural and ideal place for foaling is a clean open pasture away from other livestock. Under these conditions, there is less danger of either infection or mechanical injury to the mare and foal. (Courtesy, National Cottonseed Products Association, Inc.)

and free from any low mangers, hay racks, or other obstructions that might cause injury to either the mare or the foal. After the foaling stall has been thoroughly cleaned, it should be disinfected to reduce possible infection. This may be done by scrubbing with boiling hot lye water, made by using 8 oz. of lye to 20 gallons of water (one-half this strength of solution should be used in scrubbing mangers and grain boxes). The floors should then be sprinkled with air-slaked lime. Plenty of clean, fresh bedding should be provided at all times.

A foaling stall somewhat away from other horses and with a smooth, well-packed clay floor is to be preferred. The clay floor may be slightly more difficult to keep smooth and sanitary than concrete or other such surface materials, but there is less danger to the mare and the newborn foal from slipping and falling; and it is decidedly better for the hoofs.

Feed at Foaling Time

Shortly before foaling, it is usually best to decrease the grain allowance slightly and to make more liberal use of light and laxative feeds, especially wheat bran. If there are any signs of constipation, a wet bran mash should be provided.

The Attendant

A good rule for the attendant is to *be near but not in sight*. Some mares seem to resent the presence of an attendant at this time, and they will delay foaling as long as possible under such circumstances. Mares that have foaled previously and which have been properly fed and exercised will usually not experience any difficulty. However, young mares foaling for the first time, old mares, or mares that are either overfat or in a thin, run-down condition may experience considerable difficulty. The presence of the attendant may prevent possible injury to the mare and foal; and, when necessary, he may aid the mare or call a veterinarian.

Parturition

The immediate indications that the mare is about to foal are extreme nervousness and uneasiness, lying down and getting up, biting of the sides and flanks, switching of the tail, sweating in the flanks, and frequent urination.

The first actual indication of foaling is the rupture of the outer fetal membrane, followed by the escape of a large amount of fluid. This is commonly referred to as the rupture of the "water bag." The inner membrane surrounding the foal appears next, and labor then becomes more marked.

With normal presentation, a mare foals rapidly, usually not taking more than 15 to 30 minutes. Usually, when the labor pains are at

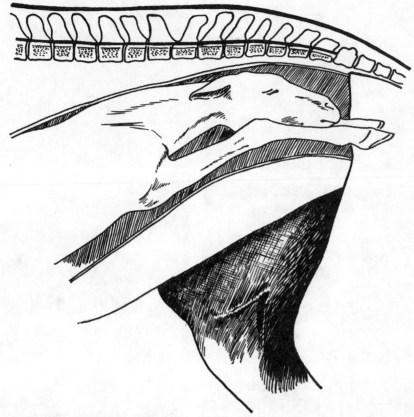

Fig. 12-17. Normal presentation. The back of the fetus is directly toward that of the mother, the forelegs are extended toward the vulva with the heels down, and the nose rests between the forelegs. (Drawing by Steve Allured)

their height, the mare will be down; and it is in this position that the foal is generally born, while the mare is lying on her side with all legs stretched out.

In normal presentation, the front feet, with heels down, come first, followed by the nose which is resting on them, then the shoulders, the middle (with the back up), the hips, and then the hind legs and feet. If the presentation is other than normal, a veterinarian should be summoned at once, for there is great danger that the foal will smother if its birth is delayed. If the feet are presented with the bottoms up, it is a good indication that they are the hind ones, and there is likely to be difficulty.

If after reasonable time and effort have been expended a mare

Fig. 12-18. Birth of a foal. From start to finish, it took only about 15 minutes. Pictures 1 through 11 were taken at approximately one-minute intervals. The last picture (no. 12), taken 15 minutes after birth, shows Pocohontas, the newborn Pony of the Americas foal, with a newly-found friend, Debbie. (Courtesy, Dean Kenney, Blue Ribbon Ranch, Culver City, California)

Fig. 12-18 (Continued)

appears to be making no progress in parturition, it is advisable that an examination be made and assistance be rendered before the animal has completely exhausted her strength in futile efforts at expulsion. In rendering any such assistance, the following cardinal features should exist:

1. Cleanliness.
2. Quietness.
3. Gentleness.
4. Perseverance.
5. Knowledge, skill, and experience.

When parturition is unduly delayed or retarded, the fetus often dies from twists or knots in the umbilical cord, or from remaining too long in the passage. In either case, there may be stoppage of fetal circulation or lack of oxygen for the fetus, or both.

If foaling has been normal, the attendant should enter the stable to make certain that the foal is breathing and that the membrane has been removed from its mouth and nostrils. If the foal fails to breathe immediately, artificial respiration should be applied. This may be done by blowing into the mouth of the foal, working the ribs, rubbing the body vigorously and permitting the foal to fall around. Then after the navel has been treated, the mare and foal should be left to lie and rest quietly as long as possible so that they may gain strength.

The Afterbirth

If the afterbirth is not expelled as soon as the mare gets up, it should either be tied up in a knot or tied to the tail of the mare. This should be done so that the foal or mare will not step on the afterbirth and thereby increase the danger of inflammation of the uterus and foal founder in the mare. Usually the afterbirth will be expelled within 1 to 6 hours after foaling.

If it is retained for a longer period or if lameness is evident, the mare should be blanketed, and an experienced veterinarian should be called. Retained afterbirth often causes laminitis, which is recognized by lameness in the mare. This is usually treated by feeding easily digested feed for a period of 36 hours and by applying cold applications to the mare's feet until the condition is relieved.

To prevent development of bacteria and foul odors, the afterbirth should be removed from the stall and burned or buried in lime as soon as possible.

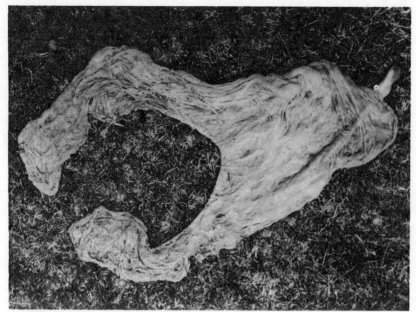

Fig. 12-19. The placenta (afterbirth), showing both horns. (Courtesy, F. W. Koester, Editor, and B. K. Beckwith, Associate Editor, The Thoroughbred of California)

Cleaning the Stall

Once the foal and mare are up, the stall should be cleaned. Wet, stained, or soiled bedding should be removed. The floor should be sprinkled with lime; and clean, fresh bedding should be provided. Such sanitary measures will be of great help in preventing the most common type of joint-ill.

If the weather is extremely cold and the mare hot and sweaty, she should be rubbed down, dried, and blanketed soon after getting on her feet.

Feed and Water After Foaling

Following foaling, the mare usually is somewhat hot and feverish. She should be given small quantities of lukewarm water at intervals but should never be allowed to gorge. It is also well to feed lightly and with laxative feeds for the first few days. The very first feed might well be a wet bran mash with a few oats or a little oat meal soaked in warm water. About one-half the usual amount should be fed. Usually, for the first week, no better grain ration can be provided than bran and oats. The quantity of feed given should be governed by the milk flow, the demands of the foal, and the appetite and condition of the mare. Usually the mare can be back on full feed within a week or ten days after foaling.

Observation

The good horseman will be ever alert to discover difficulties before it is too late. If the mare has much temperature (normal for the horse is about 101° F.), something is wrong and the veterinarian should be called. As a precautionary measure, many good horsemen take the mare's temperature a day or two after foaling. Any discharge from the vulva should be regarded with suspicion.

Handling the Newborn Foal

Immediately after the foal has arrived and breathing has started, it should be throughly rubbed and dried with warm towels. Then it should be placed in one corner of the stall on clean, fresh straw. Usually the mare will be less restless if this corner is in the direction of her head. The eyes of a newborn foal should be protected from a bright light.

THE NAVEL CORD

At the time the umbilical cord is ruptured, there is a direct communication from without to some of the vital organs and the blood of the foal. Usually this opening is soon closed by the ensuing swelling and final drying and sloughing-off process. Under natural conditions, the wild state, there was little danger of navel infection, but domestication and foaling under confined conditions have changed all this.

To reduce the danger of navel infection (which causes a disease known as joint-ill or navel-ill) the navel cord of the newborn foal should be treated at once with a solution of tincture of iodine (or metaphen or merthiolate may be used). This may be done by placing the end of the cord in a wide-mouthed bottle nearly full of tincture of iodine while pressing the bottle firmly against the abdomen. This, of course, is best done with the foal lying down. The cord should then be dusted with a good antiseptic powder. Dusting with the powder should be continued daily until the stump dries up and drops off and the scar heals, usually in three or four days. If an antiseptic powder is not available, air-slaked lime may be used. Any foreign matter that

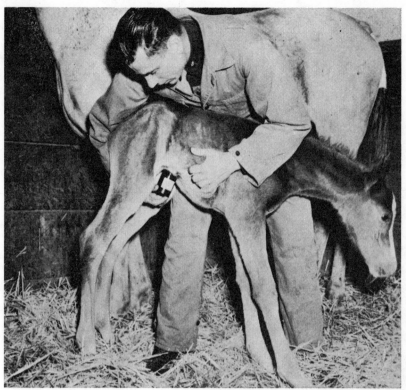

Fig. 12-20. Treating the navel cord of the newborn foal with iodine. This is done by placing the end of the cord in a wide-mouthed bottle nearly full of tincture of iodine while pressing the bottle firmly against the abdomen. (Courtesy, Col. F. W. Koester, General Manager, Calif. Thoroughbred Breeders Association, Arcadia, Calif.)

accumulates on the navel should be pressed out, and a disinfectant should be applied.

If left alone, the navel cord of the newborn foal usually breaks within two to four inches from the belly. Under such conditions, no cutting is necessary. However, if it does not break it should be severed about two inches from the belly with clean, dull shears or it may be scraped in two with a knife. Never cut diagonally across. A torn or broken blood vessel will bleed very little; whereas one that is cut directly across may bleed excessively. If severing of the cord is resorted to, it should be immediately treated with iodine.

NAVEL INFECTION (JOINT-ILL OR NAVEL-ILL)

Although most newborn foal infections are referred to as navel infection—implying that the infection is postnatal, with entrance to the body gained through the umbilical cord after birth—many such troubles are of prenatal origin. In the latter type, infection of the foal takes place in the uterus (womb) of the dam before the foal is born. The infection may either be present in the dam before she is bred, or it may be introduced by the stallion, if he is infected or

Fig. 12-21. Foal with navel infection (joint-ill or navel-ill). The disease is fatal in about fifty percent of the cases. Also, a large proportion of the animals that survive are left with deformed joints like the foal pictured. (Courtesy, Dept. of Veterinary Pathology and Hygiene, College of Veterinary Medicine, University of Illinois)

if he has previously bred other infected mares. If prenatal infection does not result in abortion and the mare carries the fetus the normal term, the foal is often born weak or develops navel-ill within a few days and dies; or if it does not die, it becomes a hopeless cripple that must be destroyed.

Under unsanitary conditions, there is also great danger from germs that may enter the blood stream through the opening of the navel cord prior to the time that it has dried up and the scar has healed over. When weather conditions permit foaling on a clean pasture in the fresh air and sunshine, danger of such infection is held to a minimum. On the other hand, foaling in a filthy paddock or stall and with no precautions taken is very likely to result in infection and navel-ill. For this reason, when it is necessary to have mares foal in the stall, every precaution should be taken. The stall should be thoroughly cleaned, disinfected, and bedded; and the navel should be

treated with iodine immediately after the foal arrives and then dusted
with a good antiseptic powder several times daily.

Navel infection (joint-ill or navel-ill) may be recognized by a
loss of appetite, soreness and stiffness in the joints, and a general
listlessness of the foal. If this is recognized in the early stages and
a veterinarian is called at once, the infected foal may be treated and
may recover. If, however, the disease has reached the pus-forming
stage, very likely it will be fatal. Blood transfusions from the dam to
foal have been given in all types of foal infections, usually with good
results. With certain specific types of infections, antibiotics, sulfanila-
mides, serums, or bacterins may be used successfully; but always these
should be administered by a veterinarian. Prevention is decidedly the
best protection.

In summary, it may be stated that the practice of sanitation and
hygiene, starting with the stallion and broodmare at the time of
mating and continuing with the broodmare and young foal at foaling
time, usually prevents the most common type of joint-ill. In certain

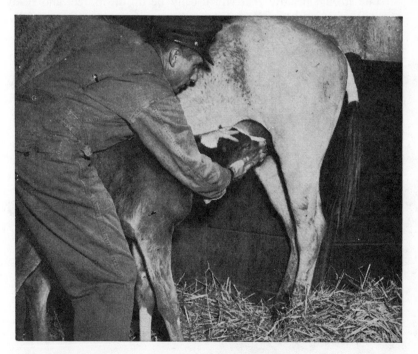

Fig. 12-22. Assisting newborn foal to nurse. (Courtesy, Col. F. W. Koester, General
Manager, Calif. Thoroughbred Breeders Association, Arcadia, Calif.)

areas, particularly those known to be goiterous or semi-goiterous, such as the Pacific Northwest, the feeding of stabilized iodized salt to in-foal mares has seemed to reduce losses from joint-ill.

THE COLOSTRUM

The colostrum is the milk that is secreted by the dam for the first few days following parturition. It differs from ordinary milk in the following aspects:

1. It is more concentrated.
2. It is higher in protein content, especially globulins.
3. It is richer in vitamin A.
4. It contains more antibodies.
5. It has a more stimulating effect on the alimentary tract.

Because of these many beneficial qualities of colostrum, the horseman should make very certain that the newborn foal secures this first milk.

The strong, healthy foal will usually be up on its feet and ready to nurse within thirty minutes to two hours after birth. Occasionally,

Fig. 12-23. Giving an enema to a foal, using a tube and can. (Courtesy, Major C. B. Team, USDA)

however, a big awkward foal will need a little assistance and guidance during its first time to nurse. The stubborn foal should be coaxed to the mare's teats (forcing is useless). This may be done by backing the mare up on additional bedding in one corner of the stall and coaxing the foal with a bottle and nipple. The attendant may hold the bottle while standing on the opposite side of the mare from the foal. The very weak foal should be given the mare's first milk even if it must be drawn in a bottle and fed by nipple for a time or two. Sometimes these weak individuals will nurse the mare if steadied by the attendant.

Aside from the difference in chemical composition, the colostrum (the milk yielded by the mother for a short period following the birth of the young) seems to have the following functions:

1. It contains antibodies that temporarily protect the foal against certain infections, especially those of the digestive tract.

2. It serves as a natural purgative, removing fecal matter that has accumulated in the digestive tract.

This, therefore, explains why mares should not be milked out prior to foaling and why colostrum is important to the newborn foal.

Before allowing the foal to nurse for the first time, it is usually good practice to wash the mare's udder with a mild disinfectant and to rinse it with clean, warm water.

BOWEL MOVEMENT OF THE FOAL

The regulation of the bowel movement in the foal is very important. Two common abnormalities are constipation and diarrhea or scours.

Impaction in the bowels of the excrement accumulated during the development prior to birth—material called meconium—may prove fatal if not handled promptly. Usually a good feed of colostrum will cause elimination, but not always—especially when foals are from stall-fed mares.

Bowel movement of the foal should be observed within four to twelve hours after birth. If by this time there has been no discharge and the foal seems rather sluggish and fails to nurse, it should be given an enema. This may be made by using one to two quarts of water at blood heat, to which a little glycerin has been added; or warm, soapy water is quite satisfactory. The solution may be injected with a baby syringe (one having about a three-inch nipple) or a tube and can. This treatment may be repeated as often as necessary until the normal yellow feces appear.

Diarrhea or scours in foals may be associated with infectious diseases or may be caused by unclean surroundings. Any of the following conditions may bring on diarrhea: contaminated udder or teats; non-removal of fecal matter from the digestive tract; fretfulness or temperature above normal in the mare; an excess of feed affecting the quality of the mare's milk; cold, damp bed; or continued exposure to cold rains. As treatment is not always successful, the best practice is to avoid the undesirable conditions.

Some foals scour during the foal heat of the mare, which occurs between the seventh and ninth day following foaling.

Diarrhea is caused by an irritant in the digestive tract that should be removed if recovery is to be expected. Only in exceptional cases should an astringent be given with the idea of checking the diarrhea; and such treatment should be prescribed by the veterinarian.

If the foal is scouring, the ration of the mare should be reduced, and a part of her milk should be taken away by milking her out at intervals.

RAISING THE ORPHAN FOAL

Occasionally a mare dies during or immediately after parturition, leaving an orphan foal to be raised. Also, there are times when mares fail to give a sufficient quantity of milk for the newborn foal. Sometimes there are twins. In such cases, it is necessary to resort to other milk supplies. The problem will be simplified if the foal has at least received the colostrum from the dam, for it does play a very important part in the well-being of the newborn young.

If at all possible, the foal should be shifted to another mare. Some breeding establishments regularly follow the plan of breeding a mare that is a good milk producer but whose foal is expected to be of little value. Her own foal is either destroyed or raised on a bottle, and the mare is used as a foster mother or nurse mare.

Some nurseries keep a supply of colostrum on hand. They remove colostrum from mares that (1) have had dead foals or (2) produce excess milk, then store it in a freezer for future use for foals that do not receive colostrum from their dams. When needed, it can be removed from the freezer, heated, and fed. This is an excellent practice.

If no colostrum is available, the foal should be placed on either (1) cow's milk made as nearly as possible of the same composition as mare's milk or (2) a synthetic milk replacer.

A comparison of cow's and mare's milk is given in Table 12-2.

Table 12-2
COMPOSITION OF MILK FROM COWS AND MARES[1]

Source	Water	Protein	Fat	Sugar	Ash
	(%)	(%)	(%)	(%)	(%)
Cow -----------------	87.17	3.55	3.69	4.88	0.75
Mare ----------------	90.78	1.99	1.21	5.67	0.35

[1]USDA Farmers' Bulletin No. 803.

As can be observed, mare's milk is higher in percentage of water and sugar than cow's milk and is lower in other components.

For best results in raising the orphan foal, milk from a fresh cow, low in butterfat, should be used. To about a pint of milk, add a tablespoonful of sugar and from three to five tablespoonfuls of lime water. Warm to body temperature and for the first few days feed about one-fourth of a pint every hour. After three or four weeks the sugar can be stopped, and at five or six weeks skimmed milk can be used entirely.

Orphan foals may also be raised on synthetic milk replacer, fed according to the directions of the manufacturer. Here again the situation is simplified if the foal has first received colostrum.

For the first few days, the milk (either cow's milk or milk replacer) may be fed by using a bottle and a rubber nipple. The foal then should be taught to drink from a pail. It is important that all receptacles be kept absolutely clean and sanitary (cleaned and scalded each time) and that feeding be at regular intervals. Grain feeding should be started at the earliest possible time with the orphan foal.

NORMAL BREEDING SEASON AND THE TIME OF FOALING

The most natural breeding season for the mare is in the spring of the year. Usually mares are gaining in flesh at this time; the heat period is more evident; and they are more likely to conceive. Furthermore, the springborn foal may be dropped on pasture—with less danger of infection and with an abundance of exercise, fresh air, and sunshine to aid in its development. Also, there will be good, green, succulent pasture for the mare. Such conditions are ideal.

However, when the demands for using the mares are such that spring foaling interferes and fall or perhaps late-winter foals are desired, plans may be changed accordingly. Under such circumstances, spring conditions should be duplicated at the breeding season. That is, the mare should be fed to gain in flesh, and, if necessary, should be blanketed for comfort.

Also, it must be remembered that the showman will want to give consideration to having the foals dropped at such a time that they may be exhibited to the best advantage. The same applies to the person who desires to sell well-developed yearlings or to race two-year-olds. It is noteworthy, however, that the percentage of barren mares that conceive at an early breeding is markedly lower than is obtained later in the season. Nevertheless, some mares do conceive early in the year, and even a small percentage is advantageous to some breeders.

HOW TO LOWER THE COST OF RAISING HORSES

Some principles that should receive consideration in lowering the cost of raising horses are:

1. Attain higher fertility in both mares and stallions; secure a higher percent foal crop. With a fifty percent foal crop, two mares are kept a whole year to raise one foal.

2. Eliminate unnecessary concoctions, including drugs, vitamins, and minerals if they are not needed.

3. Begin using the horses moderately at two years of age, at which time their use should more than compensate for the feed cost.

4. Keep all horses of usable age earning their way. Animals that are not necessary or that do not increase in value at a profitable rate are a needless expense.

5. Utilize pastures to the maximum. Such a practice will supply nutritious feeds at a low cost, save time in feeding, reduce man labor in caring for the horses, and do away with bedding the stalls and cleaning the barn.

6. Utilize the less salable roughage as much as possible, particularly during the second and third years.

7. Do not construct or maintain costly quarters for the young, growing horse.

8. Keep animals free from parasites, both internal and external. Feeding parasites is always too costly.

9. Provide least-cost balanced rations, including a balance of pro-

Fig. 12-24. Mares and foals on pasture. The cost of raising horses can be materially lessened by utilizing pastures to the maximum. (Courtesy, *The Morgan Horse Magazine*)

teins, necessary minerals, and vitamins. Also, plenty of good, clean water should be available at all times.

BUYING HORSES OR RAISING FOALS

Where horses are needed, either they must be purchased or foals must be raised. The primary factors to consider in determining whether horses will be bought or foals raised are: (1) the experience of the individual, (2) comparative cost, and (3) risks surrounding the introduction of horses.

Experience of the Horseman

Certainly it must be recognized that the man who would attempt to raise replacements must have more knowledge of horse production than the person buying mature horses. In addition to knowing the regular care and management aspects of horse production, the man who raises his replacements must be somewhat familiar with the breeding of horses and the rearing of foals.

Comparative Cost

In determining whether horses will be bought or foals raised, the comparative cost of the two methods should be computed. In arriving at such comparative cost figures, the following factors should be remembered:

Fig. 12-25. Yearling Thoroughbred colt being sold at public auction at Keeneland Race Course, under the auspices of the Breeders' Sales Company, Lexington, Ky.

Shown is a bay colt by Bimelech out of Durazna, consigned by Mr. Leslie Combs II, Spendthrift Farm, Lexington, Ky., and sold for $40,000. (Courtesy, Breeders' Sales Company, Lexington, Ky.)

1. Such figures should be on the basis of animals of equal merit and usefulness for the purpose desired. Consideration should also be given to age and future depreciation.

2. Computing the purchase price on horses should be on the basis of price delivered to the farm. Commission, freight or trucking, and insurance charged should not be overlooked.

3. In computing the cost of raising a foal to usable age, feed price should be figured on the basis of farm values rather than on actual grain market values. Also, consideration should be given to the fact that cheap and somewhat unsalable roughages may often be used. Further, such items as service fees, manure produced, and handling charges should be considered.

Risks Surrounding the Introduction of Horses

After giving full consideration to the experience of the horseman and the comparative cost of the two methods, there are still some rather perplexing problems encountered in introducing horses. These difficulties may be summarized as follows:

1. *Misrepresentations.*—The inexperienced man, especially, is likely to encounter misrepresentations as to age, soundness, vices, and the training and usefulness of the horse.

2. *Diseases.*—In moving a horse, there is always a possible exposure

to the many ills. Sometimes these are of sufficiently serious nature as to make the use of the animal impossible at a time when most needed; occasionally they even prove fatal. Also, it must be remembered that such diseases as are contracted very likely may spread to the other horses on the farm and even to those in the community, thus exposing them to the same risk.

3. *Acclimating.*—Horses coming from a distance usually need time to become acclimated before being most useful.

4. *Condition.*—In all too many instances, horses brought in for sale and speculative purposes have been made fat for the occasion. Usually such liberal feeding has been made even more harmful through accompanying lack of work and confinement to a stall. Such horses are soft and require a period of gradual fitting for work. Also, it must be remembered that fat will cover up a multitude of defects.

ARTIFICIAL INSEMINATION

Artificial insemination is, by definition, *the deposition of spermatozoa in the female genitalia by artificial rather than by natural means.*

Legend has it that artificial insemination had its origin in 1322, at which time an Arab chieftain used artificial methods to impregnate a prized mare with semen stealthily collected by night from the sheath of a stallion belonging to an enemy tribe. There is no substantial evidence, however, to indicate that the Arabs practiced artificial insemination to any appreciable degree.

The first scientific research in artificial insemination of domestic animals was conducted with dogs by the Italian physiologist, Lazarro Spallanzani, in 1780. A century later, American veterinarians employed artificial means to get mares in foal that persistently had failed to settle to natural service. They noticed that because of obstructions the semen was often found in the vagina and not in the uterus following natural service. By collecting the semen into a syringe from the floor of the vagina and injecting it into the uterus, they were able to impregnate mares with these anatomical difficulties.

The Russian physiologist, Ivanoff, began a study of artificial insemination of farm animals, particularly horses, in 1899; and, in 1922, he was called upon by the Russian government to apply his findings in an effort to reestablish the livestock industry following its depletion during World War I. Crude as his methods were, his work with horses must be considered the foundation upon which the success of the more recent work is based.

The shifting of the large-scale use of artificial insemination to cattle and sheep, two decades after it was first introduced for horses, was not caused by the fading importance of the horse and the increased demand for cattle and sheep. Rather, it was found that progress was quicker and more easily achieved with these animals, because the physiological mechanism of reproduction in cattle and sheep is more favorable than in horses.

Today, there is renewed interest in artificial insemination of horses, as a result of a successful method of freezing stallion semen in 1964. Stallion semen is now being collected, processed, and frozen somewhat similarly to bull semen. However, the extender and freezing process are patented and not available as public information.

Mares are inseminated by (1) using a syringe and catheter arrangement with a speculum, (2) placing a gelatin capsule, holding 10 to 25 milliliters of extended semen, in the cervix by hand, or (3) introducing a rubber catheter by hand into the cervix and injecting the semen by means of a syringe attached to the opposite end of the tube.

Advantages of Artificial Insemination

Some of the advantages of artificial insemination are:

1. *It increases the use of outstanding sires.*—Through artifical insemination, many breeders can avail themselves of the use of an outstanding sire, whereas the services of such an animal formerly were limited to one owner, or, at the most, a small group of owners.

2. *It alleviates the danger and bother of keeping a sire.*—Some hazard and bother is usually involved in keeping a sire, especially a stallion.

3. *It makes it possible to overcome certain physical handicaps to mating.*—Artificial insemination is of value (a) to mating animals of greatly different sizes, and (b) in using stifled or otherwise crippled sires that are unable to perform natural service.

4. *It lessens sire costs.*—In smaller herds, artificial insemination is usually less expensive than the ownership of a sire together with the accompanying building, feed, and labor costs.

5. *It reduces the likelihood of costly delays through using infertile sires.*—Because the breeding efficiency of sires used artificially is checked constantly, it reduces the likelihood of breeding females to a sire that is of low fertility or even sterile for an extended period of time.

6. *It makes it feasible to prove more sires.*—Because of the small

size of the herds in which they are used in natural service, many sires are never proved. Still others are destroyed before their true breeding worth is known. Through artificial insemination, it is possible to determine the genetic worth of a sire at an earlier age and with more certainty than in natural service.

7. *It creates large families of animals.*—The use of artificial insemination makes possible the development of large numbers of animals within a superior family, thus providing uniformity and giving a better basis for a constructive breeding program. Some horsemen fear that too much closebreeding would follow. But the latter need not be so, for the breeder would still select the bloodlines of his choice; in fact, he could ship semen from great distances so as to avoid the closebreeding which may become localized in his area.

8. *It increases pride of ownership.*—The ownership of progeny of outstanding sires inevitably makes for pride of ownership, with accompanying improved feeding and management.

9. *It may lessen and control certain diseases.*—Artificial insemination may prove to be equally valuable as a means of preventing and controlling the spread of certain types of diseases, especially those associated with the organs of reproduction—such as dourine (equine syphilis) in horses. However, when improperly practiced, it may be an added means of spreading disease. Therefore, it is most essential (a) that all males be carefully examined for symptoms of transmissible diseases, (b) that bacterial contamination be avoided during the collection and storage of semen, and (c) that clean, sterile equipment be used in the insemination.

10. *It increases profits.*—The offspring of outstanding sires used artificially are usually higher and more efficient producers, and thus more profitable. Also, artificial insemination provides a means of using such sires more widely.

Limitations of Artificial Insemination

Like many other wonderful techniques, artificial insemination is not without its limitations. A full understanding of such limitations, however, will merely accentuate and extend its usefulness. Some of the limitations of artificial insemination are:

1. *It must conform to physiological principles.*—One would naturally expect that the practice of artificial insemination must conform to certain physiological principles. Unfortunately, much false information concerning the usefulness of artificial insemination has been

encountered—for example, the belief that females will conceive if artificially inseminated at any time during the estrual cycle. Others have even accepted exaggerated claims that the quality of semen may be improved through such handling, only to be disappointed.

2. *It requires skilled technicians.*—In order to be successful, artificial insemination must be carried out by skilled technicians who have had considerable training and experience.

3. *It necessitates considerable capital to initiate and operate a cooperative breeding program.*—Considerable money is necessary to initiate a cooperative artificial insemination program, and still more is needed to expand and develop it properly.

4. *It is not always possible to obtain the services of a given sire.*—In cooperative insemination programs, a member cannot always obtain the service of the sire of his choice. Also, sires are generally collected from according to a definite schedule.

5. *It may accentuate the damage of a poor sire.*—It must be realized that when a male sires the wrong type of offspring his damage is merely accentuated because of the increased number of progeny possible. But this seldom happens, for the reason that untried or untested males are not used extensively in a stud. For example, in dairy cattle artificial insemination, 60 percent of the dairy sires are proved and these sires account for about 80 percent of the matings made.

6. *It may restrict the sire market.*—The fact that the market demand for poor or average sires will decrease if artificial insemination is widely adopted should probably be considered an attribute rather than a limitation.

7. *It may increase the spread of disease.*—As previously indicated, the careful and intelligent use of artificial insemination will lessen the spread of disease. On the other hand, carelessness or ignorance may result in the rapid spread of disease. However, artificial insemination organizations follow a rigid "Sire Health Code" adopted by the National Association of Animal Breeders and approved by the American Veterinary Medical Association.

8. *It may be subject to certain abuses.*—Of course, the greatest opposition to more liberalized use of artificial insemination is always voiced on the grounds of inaccurate pedigrees—through accident, carelessness, or intention; especially, the possibility of fraud in a "colt by mail order program." Certainly, if semen is transported from farm to farm, the character of the technician must be above reproach.

Trained workers can detect differences in the spermatozoa of the bull, ram, boar, stallion, or cock; but even the most skilled scientist is unable to differentiate between the semen of a Thoroughbred and a Morgan, to say nothing of the difference between two stallions of the same breed. However, it appears that such abuse is more suspicioned than real. In a blood type study[14] with cattle, Rendel found 4.2 percent family records in error out of 615 animals by natural service, compared to 4.0 percent family records in error out of 199 sired by artificial insemination.

Of course, with skilled workers performing the techniques required in artificial insemination, there usually is more check on the operations and perhaps less likelihood of dishonesty than when only the owner is involved, such as is usually the situation with natural service.

SOME PROBLEMS NEED TO BE SOLVED

Until recently, stallion semen could not be stored sufficiently long—it is viable for only one to two days in the liquid state. However, stallion semen has now been frozen successfully, and its use will grow. This development may write a new chapter in horse breeding, especially in breeding grade mares.

But, before wide-scale use can be made of artificial insemination of horses, solutions to additional problems must be found. These include the following needs:

1. *The ability to breed more mares per stallion.*[15]—At the present time, too few mares can be bred per stallion in any one breeding period or season. For example, it is possible to breed 600 cows from one collection of a bull, compared to perhaps 8 to 15 for the stallion.

2. *The ability to detect when mares are ready for breeding.*—It is sometimes difficult to determine exactly when a mare should be serviced. If a mare is not bred at the proper time (within 20 to 24 hours before ovulation), conception rate will be very low.

3. *The ability to bring mares in heat at will.*—Many advantages would accrue from bringing mares in heat and ovulation when desired: (a) Breeding artificially would be simplified; and (b) it would be

---

[14] *Acta Agric. Scand.* VIII 2, page 140.

[15] Dr. Pei-Liu Cheng, Research Institute of Animal Production, Academy of Agricultural Sciences of China, at Peking, reported the following results in using one stallion artificially: 2,798 mares bred in one year; 15 mares per collection; 73.9 percent conception. (Reported in *The Blood Horse*, Nov. 18, 1961, pp. 1302 and 1304.)

possible to have the young born exactly when desired—horsemen could even swap help with each other at foaling time. By using hormones, planned parenthood in horses may be imminent; perhaps we shall soon be able to breed a mare on the day desired instead of waiting for the natural occurence of the estrual cycle.

Without doubt, in due time these barriers will be overcome, and artificial insemination of horses will expand just as it has in the American dairy industry.

Registration of Foals Produced Through Artificial Insemination

Ironically enough, although artificial insemination was first practiced with horses, many American registry associations now frown upon or forbid the practice. Moreover, there is little unanimity of opinion among them so far as their rules and regulations apply to the practice. By breeds, the situation relative to registration of foals produced through artificial insemination is summarized in Table 12-3.

Summary of Artificial Insemination

Today, artificial insemination is taking on a new look. Stallion semen is being frozen and stored, with the result that these "King Tuts" may be in production long after death.

In 1967, 7,184,939 head, or 49 percent, of the dairy cows and heifers were bred by artificial insemination. Additionally, that same year, 662,688 head of beef cows were bred by artificial insemination. Without doubt, from a technical standpoint, the wide-scale use of artificial insemination in all classes of farm animals only awaits the time when a few of the remaining problems are overcome. To be sure, there is and will continue to be resistance on the part of some horse registry associations and some breeders, with the result that research in the area of artificial insemination of horses will continue to lag. But progress cannot be stopped! Artificial insemination will expand in horses, especially with grade mares, just as it has in the dairy industry as soon as the remaining barriers are removed.

Who would not like to use a valuable stallion (1) as widely as possible, and (2) long after death? Imagine being able substantially to increase the number of offspring per year from a syndicated stallion whose stud fee is $5,000 or $20,000! Also, through the wide-scale

Table 12-3

RULES OF HORSE REGISTRY ASSOCIATIONS RELATIVE TO
REGISTERING FOALS PRODUCED ARTIFICIALLY

Class of Horse	Breed	Registry Association	Pertinent Rules or Attitudes of Each Registry Association Relative to Artificial Insemination
Light Horses:	American Albino Horse	American Albino Horse Club, Inc., Naper, Neb.	Will accept for registration if they quality otherwise. Certification required of collector of semen and inseminator of mare, who must be a veterinarian or a qualified A.I. technician.
	American Gotland Horse	American Gotland Horse Association, Columbia, Mo.	No provisions for artificial insemination.
	American Saddle Horse	American Saddle Horse Breeders' Association, Louisville, Ky.	Foals produced artificially eligible for registry, provided (1) the insemination takes place on the premises where the stallion is standing, and (2) the insemination takes place in the presence of the owner or party authorized to sign certificates of breeding for the stallion used.
	Appaloosa	Appaloosa Horse Club, Inc., Moscow, Ida.	When artificial insemination is used, it must be accompanied by natural insemination in order for the resulting foal to be registered.
	Arabian	Arabian Horse Club of America, Chicago, Ill.	Not eligible for registration.
	Half-Arabian Anglo-Arabian	International Arabian Horse Assn., Burbank, Calif.	Not eligible for registration.
	Cleveland Bay	Cleveland Bay Assn. of America, Middleburg, Va.	Foals produced artificially accepted, provided that adequate evidence is furnished.
	Hackney	American Hackney Horse Society, Fair Lawn, N.J.	Not eligible for registration.
	Missouri Fox Trotting Horse	Missouri Fox Trotting Horse Breed Association, Ava, Mo.	No rules at present, but Association is favorable toward A.I.
	Morgan	Morgan Horse Club, Inc., Hartford, Conn.	Not eligible for registration.
	Palomino	Palomino Horse Breeders of America, Box 249, Mineral Wells, Tex.	Accepted, provided the breeder's certificate accompanies the application for registration.
	Pinto	The Pinto Horse Association of America, Inc., San Diego, Calif.	Foals produced artificially accepted provided that adequate evidence is furnished and the horse is approved by the Executive Committee of the Association.
	Quarter Horse	American Quarter Horse Assn., Amarillo, Tex.	Limited to use (1) at the place or premises of collection, and (2) immediately following its collection.
	Spanish Mustang	Spanish Mustang Registry, Finley, Okla.	Accepted.

(Continued)

Table 12-3 (Continued)

Class of Horse	Breed	Registry Association	Pertinent Rules or Attitudes of Each Registry Association Relative to Artificial Insemination
	Standardbred	U.S. Trotting Assn. (Standardbred), Columbus, O.	A colt conceived by semen transported off the premises where it is produced is not eligible for registration.
	Tennessee Walking Horse	Tennessee Walking Horse Breeders' & Exhibitors' Assn. of America, Lewisburg, Tenn.	Not eligible for registration.
	Thoroughbred	The Jockey Club, New York, N.Y.	Not eligible for registry unless begotten by natural service, although it is permissible to reinforce at once the natural service by artificial insemination with semen from the stallion performing the natural service on the mare that has just been covered.
Ponies:	Pony of the Americas	Pony of the Americas Club, Inc., Mason City, Ia.	Artificial insemination may be done on the farm, but semen cannot be mailed.
	Shetland Pony	American Shetland Pony Club, Lafayette, Ind.	The breeder must (1) own both the mare and stallion at the time the mare is artificially inseminated, and (2) retain both parents until the foal has been registered.
	Welsh Pony	Welsh Pony Society of America, Inc., Edwardsville, Va.	Artificial insemination is not permitted.
Draft Horses:	American Cream Horse	American Cream Horse Assn., Hubbard, Ia.	No rules on the registry of foals produced artificially.
	Belgian	Belgian Draft Horse Corp. of America, Unionville, Pa.	Foals eligible for registry only if the stallion and the mare were on the same farm at the time semen was taken and the mare impregnated.
	Clydesdale	Clydesdale Breeders' Assn. of United States, Batavia, Ia.	No rules on the registry of foals produced artificially.
	Percheron	Percheron Horse Assn. of America, Fair Oaks, Ind.	Foals eligible for registry only if the stallion and mare were on the same farm at the time semen was taken and the mare impregnated.
	Shire	American Shire Horse Assn., Lynden, Wash.	Foals accepted provided satisfactory proof accompanies application.
	Suffolk	American Suffolk Horse Assn., Inc., Lynden, Wash.	Foals produced artificially accepted provided that adequate evidence is furnished.
Jacks and Jennets:		Standard Jack and Jennet Registry of America, Lexington, Ky.	Eligible for registration. No stipulations.

use of artificial insemination in horses, many stallions could be eliminated (one stallion is now kept for each 7.3 foals produced), thereby effecting a considerable saving in keep.

The knowledge of the reproductive processes gained from artificial insemination can contribute materially to the increased efficiency of animal production. Perhaps, among its virtues, therefore, artificial insemination does offer some promise of assuring a higher conception rate in horses.

STALLION ENROLLMENT LAWS

At one time, twenty-two states had stallion enrollment laws, enacted to bring about the improvement of horses and mules through the control of the public service stallions and jacks. With the decline in horse and mule numbers, some states repealed these laws; others have been lax in enforcing them. Also, the National Stallion Board was legally liquidated several years ago.

The first stallion law was passed by the legislature of Wisconsin in 1906. In 1907, Minnesota and Iowa enacted similar laws. Other states soon followed suit. Although the laws varied considerably between states, all had similar objectives. They were designed to accomplish one or more of the following things:

1. To prevent false representation as to breeding.
2. To bar heritably unsound and diseased horses.
3. To label unsound horses and jacks.
4. To eliminate the inferior sire, whether he be scrub, grade, or purebred.

At the time these stallion laws were enacted, there was much controversy among horse breeders concerning the heritability of certain unsoundnesses and diseases; consequently, many were listed that now are not considered transmissible from parent to offspring. Even now, there is no unanimity of opinion relative to the inheritance of certain unsoundnesses, and new information is constantly revising past thinking.

The majority of stallion enrollment laws barred from public service stallions that were affected with any of the following unsoundnesses or diseases: bone spavin, ring-bone, side-bone, heaves, stringhalt, roaring, blindness, glanders (farcy), dourine, and urethral gleet.

Most horsemen agree that much improvement in the horse population came about through stallion legislation, but that the time has come when existing laws should be either modified or repealed. If the laws are amended, consideration should be given to incorporating the following provisions:

1. Include privately used stallions as well as those stood for public service.

2. License only purebred registered stallions of approved types.

3. Revise the list of hereditary unsoundnesses and transmissible diseases, and license only stallions that are free from these afflictions.

4. Scrutinize the qualifications of the veterinarians who inspect the stallions.

5. Classify stallions relative to: (a) conformation, (b) performance (track record, show record, etc.), (c) breeding, and (d) progeny performance (the record of the get).

6. "Put teeth into the law" by providing for enforceable penalties for violations.

7. Provide simple lien laws for protection of the stallion owner.

Selected References

Title of Publication	Author(s)	Publisher
Animal Breeding	A. L. Hagedoorn	Crosby Lockwood & Son, Ltd., London, England, 1950.
Animal Breeding	L. M. Winters	John Wiley & Sons, Inc., New York, N. Y., 1948.
Animal Breeding Plans	J. L. Lush	Collegiate Press, Inc., Ames, Ia., 1963.
Arabian Horse Breeding	H. H. Reese	Borden Publishing Company, Los Angeles, Calif., 1953.
Artificial Insemination in Livestock Breeding	A. H. Frank	U. S. Department of Agriculture, Circ. No. 567, Washington, D. C., 1952.
Breeding and Improvement of Farm Animals	V. A. Rice F. N. Andrews E. J. Warwick J. E. Legates	McGraw-Hill Book Co., Inc., New York, N. Y., 1967.
Breeding Better Livestock	V. A. Rice F. N. Andrews E. J. Warwick	McGraw-Hill Book Co., Inc., New York, N. Y., 1953.
Breeding Thoroughbreds	Col. J. F. Wall	Charles Scribner's Sons, New York, N. Y., 1946.
Care of Light Horses, The	J. M. Kays	Circular 353, Agri. Expt. Sta., University of Missouri, Columbia, Mo., 1950.

Title of Publication	Author(s)	Publisher
Farm Animals	John Hammond	Edward Arnold & Co., London, England, 1952.
Genetics of Livestock Improvement	John F. Lasley	Prentice-Hall, Englewood Cliffs, N. J., 1963.
Horse, The	D. J. Kays	Rinehart & Company, New York, N. Y., 1953.
Horseman's Handbook on Practical Breeding, A	Col. J. F. Wall	Washington Planograph Company, Inc., Washington, D. C., 1950.
Improvement of Livestock	Ralph Bogart	The Macmillan Co., New York, N. Y., 1959.
Light Horses	M. E. Ensminger	Farmers' Bul. No. 2127, U.S. Department of Agriculture, Washington, D. C.
Practical Horse Breeding and Training	Jack Widmer	Charles Scribner's Sons, New York, N. Y., 1942.
Practical Light Horse Breeding	J. F. Wall	Monumental Printing Company, Baltimore, Md., 1936 (out of print).
Reproductive Physiology	A. V. Nalbandov	W. H. Freeman & Co., San Francisco, Calif., 1958.
Robert Bakewell, Pioneer Livestock Breeder	H. Cecil Pawson	Crosby Lockwood & Son, Ltd., London, England.
Some Horse Breeding Problems	J. M. Kays	Bulletin 590, Agri. Expt. Sta., University of Missouri, Columbia, Mo., 1953.
Stud Manager's Handbook	December, 1961	Washington State University, Pullman, Wash.
Study on the Breeding and Racing of Thoroughbred Horses Given Large Doses of Alpha Tocopherol, A	F. G. Darlington J. B. Chassels, D.V.M.	Reprint from *The Summary*, Vol. 8, No. 1, Feb., 1956 (London, Canada).
Veterinary Notebook	W. R. McGee, D.V.M.	The Blood Horse, Lexington, Ky., 1958.
Veterinary Notes for the Standardbred Breeder	W. R. McGee D.V.M.	The United States Trotting Association, 750 Michigan Ave., Columbus, Ohio
Your Shetland Pony	J. M. Kays	The American Shetland Pony Club, Lafayette, Ind.

13

In this chapter . . .

13

Feeding Horses[1]

FEED is the most important influence in the environment of the horse. Unless the horse is fed properly, its maximum potential in reproduction, growth, body form, speed, endurance, style, and attractiveness cannot be achieved. Also, feed constitutes the greatest single cost item in the horse business. For all feeds (purchased and home grown; and including grain, hay, and pasture), the total yearly feed bill is about $360 per horse. Hence, it cost about 2.5 billion dollars to feed the nation's 6.8 million horses in 1969. Additionally, 20 million dollars are spent annually for horse minerals.

EVOLUTION OF HORSE PARALLELED HIS FEED

Through fossil remains, it is evident that the horse's evolution has always paralleled soil and vegetation. In the beginning, little eohippus, which was about the size of a fox terrier dog, had four toes on the front foot and three on the hind, had soft teeth, and was adapted to feeding on the herbage of the swamp. Gradually, it grew taller, its teeth grew stronger and harder, its legs grew longer, and all but one toe disappeared; thereby enabling it to feed farther from water and adapting it to the prairies.

[1]The author is very grateful to the following scientists who reviewed the material in this chapter: Dr. Donald J. Balch, The University of Vermont, Burlington, Vermont; Dr. Wilton W. Heinemann, Washington State University, Prosser, Washington; Dr. Robert B. Jordan, University of Minnesota, St. Paul, Minnesota; Dr. William J. Tyznik, Ohio State University, Columbus, Ohio; and Professor George W. Vander Noot, Rutgers University, New Brunswick, New Jersey.

It is only natural, in a world so big, that some equines should fare better than others. Thus, the ponderous horse of Flanders, progenitor of the modern draft horse, was the product of fertile soils, a mild climate, and abundant vegetation; whereas the diminutive, hardy Shetland Pony evolved on the scanty vegetation native to the long, cold winters of the Shetland Isles.

The effect of feed and nutrition as a creative force on the horse did not end with his domestication, about 5,000 years ago, At that time, man replaced nature as the horse's keeper, for, from that day forward, he assumed primary responsibility for the breeding, feeding, care, and management of his charges. When one considers that among wild bands 95 percent foal crops were common and unsoundnesses were relatively unknown, it's apparent that the horse hasn't fared so well with man serving as his provider.

FEEDS, FABLES, AND TRADE SECRETS

Hand in hand with the horse boom, the fabulous days of the "hoss doctor"—along with fads, fables, and trade secrets—returned. At least this has been true in altogether too many cases.

Like Topsy, the light horse industry just grew. There was precious little organized planning. With the passing of the draft horse, the Horse and Mule Association of America was inactivated, the Army Remount Service was stilled, and those great horse specialists of the United States Department of Agriculture and our land grant colleges retired and were not replaced.

Conditions were ripe for "fast operators" to make a "quick buck." Many folks with more money than animal knowledge owned horses, and the breeding and using of horses shifted from farms and ranches to suburban areas. As a result, "horse practitioners" whose products and sales pitch were reminiscent of the "medicine men" of old developed a flourishing business, pawning off on unsuspecting horsemen a myriad of potions, cure-alls, tonics, reconditioners, worm expellers, mineral mixes, vitamin mixes, and feeds of a kind.

Generally speaking, claims are made for increased growth, improved breeding, better development, more speed, and increased stamina; and the feeding directions call for a cup or for 3 or 4 tablespoonful per horse daily.

But such "horse practitioners" are not entirely to blame. Many owners insist on some kind of treatment. Like the ulcer patient who had to go to six different doctors before he could find one who would tell him that he could have a drink, they'll keep going until they get it. Especially when a horse "starts down," they'll grasp for straws. In such frantic moments, they'll buy and try almost any formula for which claims are made, completely oblivious to the facts (1) that distilled water might do just as much good—and far less harm, and (2) that they are buying losing tickets with their eyes wide open.

Horsemen are also great imitators. They'll single out some great horse, and, in one way or another, find out what it's getting. Then, they'll get some of the "same stuff" and use it from then 'til doomsday. The author has known them to pay $50 for a gallon of a mysterious concoction, in a green jug, made in some little hamlet in Kentucky. Of course, the fallacy of such imitation—of feeding what the "great horse" got—is that the "name" horse might have been even greater had it been fed properly, and that there must be a reason why there are so few truly great horses. Also, the following searching question might well be asked: Why do many horses start training in great physical shape, only to slow down and lose appetite, and be taken out of training for some rest?

It's Time for a Change in Horse Nutrition

There is no panacea in the horse business. Success cannot be achieved through witchcraft or old wives' tales; some merely achieve despite such handicaps. Instead, it calls for the combined best wit, wisdom, and judgment of science, technology, and practical experience.

The horse of today cannot be fed as it was yesterday and be expected to perform as the horse of tomorrow!

SOME PERTINENT HORSE AND FEED FACTS

The following facts are pertinent to horse feeding, either directly or indirectly, and of importance to horsemen and those who counsel with them:

1. Horse owners are[2]—

   a. Spending millions for concoctions, unbalanced and deficient rations.

   b. Producing a 50 percent foal crop. How many cattlemen

---

[2]Appendix of this book, under "Practices and Problems of Horsemen."

could afford to keep two cows a whole year to produce one calf?

c. Keeping a stallion for each 7.3 foals produced.

d. Getting a 1.2 percent return on breeding establishments. How many persons would buy stock on the New York Stock Exchange if they thought that they would get a return of only 1.2 percent on the investment? Yet, in a nationwide survey, the author found that that was the amount of horsemen's return on investments. The survey included horse breeding establishments, and not just those people who keep horses merely as a hobby; the latter don't expect to make money, any more than hunters or fishermen expect to reap a profit.

e. Retiring an appalling number of horses from tracks, shows, and other uses, due to unsoundness.

f. Losing millions of dollars through inefficiency and from deaths due to diseases and parasites.

2. Artificial conditions have been created which have caused unsoundnesses. In the wild state, horses roamed the plains in bands, with plenty of outdoor exercise on natural footing and fed on feeds derived from unleached soils; also, they were in unforced production. Today, many horses spend 95 percent of their time in a stall or corral, are exercised before daylight, forced for early growth and use (being ridden and raced as 2-year-olds), and put under terrific stress when shown, ridden, or raced (when running, horses expend up to 100 times the energy utilized at rest).

3. During the past 25 years, remarkable progress has been made in feeding meat animals, as a result of which: (a) feed required per pound of gain has been reduced 14 percent, and (b) rate of gain has been increased by 21 percent. But no such progress has been made in horses; altogether too many of them are being fed the same old oats and the same old timothy hay. In fact, many horses of today are being fed about the same as they were a century ago. How many meat animal producers could survive were they to turn back the pages of time and feed as their great, great grandfathers did 100 years ago?

4. The following conditions make it imperative that the nutrition of horses be the best that science and technology can devise:

a. *Leached and depleted soils.* This condition has come with the passing of time. Since soil nutrients affect plant nutrients, many horses are being shortchanged nutritionally.

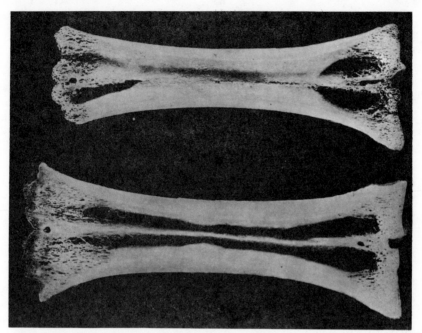

Fig. 13-1. Soil nutrients made the difference! Split bones from two animals of similar breeding and age. Small, fragile, pitted bone (top) obtained from animal pastured on belly-deep grass grown on weathered soil low in mineral content. Big, rugged, strong bone (bottom) from animal grown on moderately weathered, but highly mineralized soil. (From *Animal Science*, by Dr. M. E. Ensminger.)

b. *Confinement.*—Many horses are kept in stables or corrals.

c. *Fitting Yearlings.*—When forcing young equines, it is important to their development and soundness that the ration be nutritionally balanced.

d. *Racing 2-year-olds.*—In the U. S., we race more 2-year-olds than any other nation in the world; our richest races are for them. If the nutrient content of the ration is not adequate, there is bound to be more breakdown on the track. This is costly.

e. *Stress.*—This may be caused by excitement, temperament, fatigue, number of horses together, previous nutrition, breed, age and management. Race and show horses are always under stress; and the more tired they are and the greater the speed, the greater the stress. Thus, the ration for race and show horses should be scientifically formulated, rather than based on fads, foibles, and trade secrets. The greater the stress, the more exacting the nutritive requirements.

5. Much can, and will, continue to be done through improved horse breeding, but this takes time. By contrast, improved nutrition makes for immediate results.

6. Horses differ from other farm animals and should not be fed the same feeds. They have greater value; are kept for recreation, sport, and work; are fed for a longer life of usefulness; have a smaller digestive tract; should not carry surplus weight; and are fed for nerve, mettle, animation, and character of muscle.

7. At one time, nearly all lamenesses in horses were attributed to faulty shoeing. Later, this thought gave way to the traumatism (injury) theory—bone ailments were blamed upon bruising, pounding, and violent exertion. Still others maintain that skeletal troubles are primarily genetic in origin, that they're inherited from the parents.

8. Today, we know that a big head, bulging forehead, weak and crooked legs, enlarged joints, certain faulty conformation, and "ouch-iness" are, in a vast majority of cases, deficiency symptoms resulting from improper nutrition. Many of the bone ailments that plague breeders and trainers—the sprains, spavins, splints, and ringbones—are the tragic result of improper skeletal development during the fetal and early growth stages.

9. Grass hays and farm grains are inadequate in quantity and quality of proteins, in certain minerals and vitamins, and in unidentified factors.

10. Horses are the most poorly nourished of all domestic animals from a scientific point of view.

11. Feeding horses for show or racing is more complicated and difficult than feeding any other farm animal. This is primarily because of the stress and strain under which they are put and the absolute necessity for soundness.

12. Equine feed formulations are becoming more complex.

13. The average horse eats 11,000 pounds, or 5½ tons, of feed (hay and grain, or equivalent in pasture), each year.

14. Feed storage and labor costs have spiraled.

15. Horses reach maturity at four to five years of age. This means that many are expected to work hard, especially the racing breeds, as mere juveniles. No other animal is subjected to such stress and expected to perform so well at such an early age. This calls for the best in nutrition, so as to assure maximum growth and soundness of muscle and bone.

16. A major problem of breeders of racehorses today is to produce enough sound horses to supply the demands of racetracks.

17. If we are to improve nutrition, it must start with the fertility of the soil; it must be "from the ground up."

18. The grass on the other side of the fence *is* usually greener. What's more, if it's on a highway shoulder or right-of-way, it's usually more nutritious because of growing on more fertile soil.

19. Much more research has been done on diseases and parasites of horses *per se* than on their nutrition. Yet, it is recognized that nutrition plays a major role in disease and parasite resistance. This is true of bacterial infections, azoturia, "tying up," some cases of periodic ophthalmia, and digestive disturbances.

20. The following parallel to the altogether too common breakdown of young horses in training or on the track is noteworthy: When young lambs or young pigs are pushed for daily gains that are twice as rapid as they were 50 years ago without simultaneously meeting their increased and more critical nutrient needs, they usually become crooked legged and crippled, much as happens to young equines that are forced. But, through proper nutrition, we generally alleviate this condition in young lambs and pigs.

21. Horsemen, and others, sometimes ask, "If so little nutrition research has been done on horses, how can one formulation or ration be superior to others?" In the judgment of the author, the answer is simple: We have made rapid strides in the fields of animal and human nutrition during the past two decades. These can be used as guides. It's a matter of fitting all these parts together, and, scientifically and practically, adapting them to the horse. It's not unlike the making of the atom bomb, which necessitated the scientific and practical fitting together of research for a specific purpose.

DIGESTIVE SYSTEM

The alimentary canal proper includes the entire tube extending from the mouth to the rectum.

An understanding of the principal parts and functions of the digestive system of the horse is requisite to intelligent feeding.

Fig. 13-2 shows the anatomical position of the digestive system of the horse, whereas Table 13-1 and Fig. 13-3 show the comparative structures and sizes of the digestive tracts of farm animals. As noted, the digestive tract of the horse is anatomically and physiologically quite different from that of the ruminant.

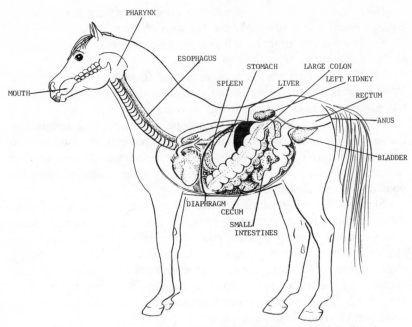

Fig. 13-2. The digestive system of the horse. (Drawing by Ethel Gadberry)

Table 13-1

Parts and Capacities of Digestive Tracts
of Horse, Cow, and Pig

	Horse	Cow	Pig
	(Qts. capacity)		
Stomach	8-16	(200)	6-8
Rumen (paunch)		160	
Reticulum (honeycomb)...........................		10	
Omasum (manyplies)		15	
Abomasum (true stomach)		15	
Small intestine	48	62	9
Cecum..	28-32		
Large intestine	80	40	10

Mouth

The mouth is the first part of the alimentary canal. In the horse, it is long and cylindrical. It includes the teeth (both uppers and lowers—24

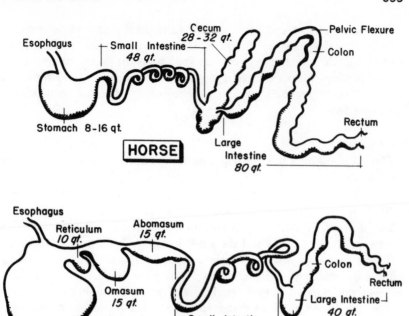

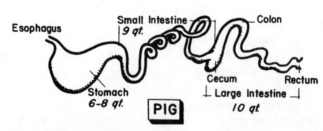

Fig. 13-3. Schematic diagram of digestive tracts of horse, cow, and pig.

molars and 12 incisors in the mature horse), the tongue, and three pairs of large salivary glands.

Digestion starts in the mouth. The feed is masticated by the teeth and moistened with saliva. In the mature horse, approximately 85 pounds (10 gallons) of saliva are secreted daily. It wets feedstuffs, thereby making for easier passage down the esophagus. In addition, the saliva contains the enzyme ptyalin, which transforms starch into maltose.

The mouth of the horse differs anatomically and physiologically from the ruminant as follows: Horses have upper incisor teeth, ruminants do not; horses masticate feed with the teeth, ruminants are cud-chewing; horses secrete a larger volume of saliva, and the saliva of the horse contains ptyalin, whereas the saliva of ruminants is enzyme-free.

Esophagus

This 50-to 60-inch tube provides passage of feed from the pharynx to the stomach.

Stomach

The stomach is the enlarged part of the alimentary canal which lies between the esophagus and the small intestine. It holds 8 to 16 quarts (but it functions best at two-thirds capacity); and it secretes gastric juices by which proteins and fats are broken down.

At the time of eating, feed passes through the horse's stomach very rapidly—so much so that feed eaten at the beginning of the meal passes to the intestine before the last part of the meal is completed.

Some basic differences between the stomach of the horse and the stomach of the ruminant are:

1. The ruminant has four compartments (rumen, reticulum, omasum, and the abomasum or true stomach), whereas the horse has one.

2. The stomach capacity of the horse is much smaller—8 to 16 quarts for the mature horse as opposed to about 200 quarts for the mature cow. Because of its small stomach, if a horse is fed too much roughage, labored breathing and quick tiring may result. Actually the horse's stomach is designed for almost constant intake of small quantities of feed, rather than large amounts at one time.

3. Without feed, the horse's stomach will empty completely in 24 hours, whereas it takes about 72 hours (three times as long) for the ruminant's stomach to empty.

4. There is comparatively little microbial action in the stomach of the horse, but much such action in the stomach (rumen) of the ruminant.

Small Intestine

The small intestine is the tube that connects the stomach with the large intestine. The average is about 7 feet long, and 3 to 4 inches thick when distended, with a capacity of about 12 gallons.

The small intestines of the horse and the cow have about the same total capacity, although the organ of the cow is nearly twice as long and half as thick.

In the horse, as in the ruminant, the enzymes of the pancreas and liver assist in further breaking down the protein, fats, and sugars which escape breakdown by the gastric juices of the stomach.

Large Intestine

The large intestine of the horse is divided into the cecum[3] (4 feet long and 1 foot in diameter; contents fluid), great colon (12 feet long and 10 inches in diameter; contents fluid to semi-fluid), small colon (10 feet long and 4 inches in diameter; contents solid), and rectum.

In the cecum, sometimes called the water gut, digestion (fermentation) continues, limited vitamin synthesis occurs, and nutrients are absorbed.

The great colon is usually distended with food. In it, there is a continuation of the digestion of feed by digestive juices, bacterial action, and absorption of nutrients.

In the small colon, the contents of the digestive tract become solid and balls of dung are formed.

Anatomical and Physiological Differences

Anatomically and physiologically, the digestive tract of the horse more nearly resembles that of the pig, and other simple-stomach animals, than the ruminant.

The cecum (the horse's fermentation vat) is located on the wrong end of the gut, a fact that is of far greater significance than its size. It follows the small intestine, with the result that the ingesta pass from the cecum directly to the large intestine. By contrast, the anatomical arrangement of the cow is such that the ingesta pass from the rumen (the cow's fermentation vat) to the small intestine, thence to the large intestine.

These anatomical and physiological differences are of great importance nutritionally, for the following reasons:

1. There is less microbial activity in the horse than in the ruminant. As a result—

    a. The horse does not break down more than about 30 percent of the cellulose of feed, whereas the ruminant breaks down 60 to

---

[3]Also spelled caecum.

70 percent. Hence, horses cannot handle so much roughage as can ruminants. Also, higher quality (lower cellulose content) forages must be fed to horses.

b. The horse synthesizes only limited proteins, B vitamins, and vitamin K, whereas the ruminant synthesizes sizeable quantities of these. Thus, the addition of B vitamins to the ration (along with vitamins A and D, which are dietary essentials and not synthesized in the digestive tract of any class of farm animals) is good insurance.

2. The efficacy of absorption of nutrients synthesized by the microorganisms in the cecum is questioned. This is so because the small intestine of the horse never gets a chance at the ingesta from the cecum, for the latter empties directly into the large intestine.

It may be concluded, therefore, that, in comparison with the cow, the horse should be fed less roughage, higher quality proteins (and not such nonprotein nitrogenous products as urea), and added B vitamins and vitamin K. These facts, along with the stress and strain to which most modern light horses are subjected, lead the author to the judgment that the nutritive requirements of the horse more nearly parallel those of the pig than of the cow.

THE FUNCTIONS OF FEEDS

The feed consumed by horses is used for a number of different purposes, the exact usage varying somewhat with the class, age, and productivity of the animal. A certain part of the feed is used for the maintenance of bodily functions aside from any useful production. This is known as the maintenance requirement. In addition, feed is used to take care of the functions for which horses are kept. Thus, young growing equines need nutrients suitable for building muscle tissue and bone; horses being readied for show or sale need a surplus of energy feeds for formation of fat; broodmares require feed for the development of their fetuses, and, following parturition, for the production of milk; whereas work (or racing) animals use feed to supply energy for work.

Maintenance

A horse differs from an engine in that the latter has no fuel requirement when idle; whereas the horse requires fuel every second of the day, whether it is idle or active.

The maintenance requirement may be defined as a ration which is adequate to prevent any loss or gain of tissue in the body when there is no production. Although these requirements are relatively simple, they are essential for life itself. A mature horse must have heat to maintain body temperature, sufficient energy to cover the internal work of the body and the minimum movement of the animal, and a small amount of proteins, vitamins, and minerals for the repair of body tissues.

No matter how quietly a horse may be standing in the stall, it still requires a certain amount of fuel, and the least amount on which it can exist is called its basal maintenance requirement. Even under the best of conditions, about one-half of all the feed consumed by horses is used in meeting the maintenance requirements.

Growth

Growth may be defined as the increase in size of the muscles, bones, internal organs, and other parts of the body. Naturally, the growth requirements become increasingly acute when horses are forced for early use, such as the training and racing of a two- or three-year-old.

Growth has been referred to as the foundation of horse production. Breeding animals may have their productive ability seriously impaired if they have been raised improperly. Nor can the most satisfactory performance be expected unless they have been well developed. For example, running horses do not possess the desired speed and endurance if their growth has been stunted or if their skeletons have been injured by inadequate rations during the growth period.

Fitting (Fattening)

This is the laying on of fat, especially in the tissues of the abdominal cavity and in the connective tissues just under the skin and between the muscles.

Usually, fitting rations contain more energy than do maintenance rations. However, the same formulation may be used for both fitting and maintenance purposes, but with larger quantities being supplied to horses that are being fitted.

In practical fitting rations, higher condition in mature animals is usually obtained through increasing the allowance of feeds high in carbohydrates and fats—a more liberal allowance of grains. Any surplus of protein may also serve for the production of fat, but usually such feeds are more expensive and are not used for economy reasons. In fitting mature horses, very little more proteins, minerals, and vitamins are required than for maintenance. In fitting young, growing animals, however, it is essential that, in addition to supplying more carbohydrates and fats, ample proteins, minerals, and vitamins be provided to meet their accelerated growth.

Reproduction and Lactation

Regular and normal reproduction is the basis for profit on any horse breeding establishment. Despite this undeniable fact, it has been estimated that only 40 to 60 percent of all mares bred actually produce foals. Certainly, there are many causes of reproductive failure, but most scientists are agreed that inadequate nutrition is a major one.

With all species, most of the growth of the fetus occurs during the last third of pregnancy, thus making the reproductive requirements most critical during this period. The ration of the pregnant mare should supply sufficient amounts of protein, minerals, and vitamins.

The nutritive requirements for moderate to heavy milk production are much more rigorous than the pregnancy requirements. There is special need for a rather liberal protein, mineral, and vitamin allowance.

In the case of young, growing, pregnant females, additional protein, minerals, and vitamins, above the ordinary requirements, must be provided; otherwise, the fetus will not develop properly or milk will be produced at the expense of the tissues of the dam.

It is also known that the ration exerts a powerful effect on sperm production and semen quality. Too fat a condition can even lead to temporary or permanent sterility. Moreover, there is abundant evidence that greater fertility of stallions exists under conditions where a well-balanced ration and plenty of exercise are provided.

Work (Horses in Use)

In many respects, work requirements are similar to the needs for fitting, both functions requiring high-energy feeds.

For mature horses, not in reproduction, work is performed primarily at the expense of the carbohydrates and fats of the ration—energy that can be supplied in the form of additional grain. Theoretically, the protein is not drawn upon so long as the other nutrients are present in adequate amounts. From a practical standpoint, however, it is usually desirable to feed more proteins than the maintenance requirement, merely to insure that the animal can make efficient use of the remainder of the nutrients in the ration. In other words, when a ration too low in protein is fed, more feed is required because the animal is unable to utilize the ration efficiently. For work animals, the mineral and vitamin requirements are practically the same as for comparable idle animals—except for the greater need for salt because of increased perspiration.

NUTRITIVE NEEDS

To supply all the needs of horses—maintenance, growth, fitting, reproduction, lactation, and work—the different classes of horses must receive sufficient feed to furnish the necessary quantity of proteins, energy (carbohydrates and fats), minerals, vitamins, and water. A ration that meets all these needs is said to be balanced. More specifically, by definition, *a balanced ration is one which provides an animal the proper proportions and amounts of all the required nutrients for a period of twenty-four hours.*

Protein Needs

For more than a century, proteins and their structural units, the amino acids, have been studied and recognized as important dietary constituents. Proteins are complex organic compounds made up chiefly of amino acids, which are present in characteristic proportions for each specific protein. This nutrient always contains carbon, hydrogen, oxygen, and nitrogen, and, in addition, it usually contains sulfur and frequently phosphorus. Proteins are essential in all plant and animal life as components of the active protoplasm of each living cell.

In plants, the protein is largely concentrated in the actively growing portions, especially the leaves and seeds. Legumes also have the ability to synthesize their own proteins from such relatively simple soil and air compounds as carbon dioxide, water, nitrates, and sulfates. Thus, plants, together with some bacteria which are able to synthesize these products, are the original sources of all proteins.

In animals, proteins are much more widely distributed than in plants. Thus, the proteins of the animal body are primary constituents of many structural and protective tissues—such as bones, ligaments, hair, hoofs, skin and the soft tissues which include the organs and muscles. The total protein content of a horse's body ranges from about 10 percent in very fat mature horses to 20 percent in thin young foals. By way of further contrast, it is also interesting to note that, except for the bacterial action in the cecum, horses lack the ability of the plant to synthesize proteins from simple materials. They must depend upon plants as a source of dietary protein. In brief, except for the proteins built by the bacterial action in the cecum, they must have amino acids or more complete protein compounds in the ration.

Horses of all ages and kinds require adequate amounts of protein of suitable quality—for maintenance, growth, fattening, reproduction, and work. Of course, the protein requirements for growth and reproduction are the greatest and most critical.

A deficiency of proteins in the horse may result in the following deficiency symptoms: depressed appetite, poor growth, loss of weight, reduced milk production, irregular estrus, lowered foal crops, loss of condition, and lack of stamina.

Since the vast majority of protein requirements given in feeding ' standards meet minimum needs only, the allowances for race, show, breeding, and young animals should be higher.

QUALITY OF PROTEINS

In addition to an adequate quantity of proteins being supplied, it is essential that the character of proteins be thoroughly understood. Proteins are very complex compounds with each molecule made up of hundreds of thousands of amino acids combined with each other. The amino acids, of which some twenty-three are known, are sometimes referred to as the building stones of proteins. Certain of these amino acids can be made by the animal's body to satisfy its needs. Others cannot be formed fast enough to supply the body's needs, and, therefore are known as essential (or indispensable) amino acids. These must be supplied in the feed. Thus, rations that furnish an insufficient amount of any of the essential amino acids are said to have proteins of poor quality, whereas those which provide the proper proportions of the various necessary amino acids are said to supply proteins of good quality. In general, proteins of plant origin (linseed meal, cottonseed meal, soybean meal, and peanut meal) are not of so good a quality as proteins of animal origin and their by-products.

The necessity of each amino acid in the diet of the experimental rat has been thoroughly tested, but less is known about the requirements of large animals or even the human. According to our present knowledge, based largely on work with the rat, the following division of amino acids as indispensable and dispensable seems proper:

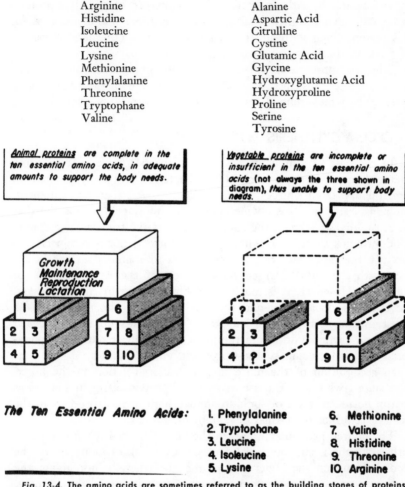

Indispensable

Arginine
Histidine
Isoleucine
Leucine
Lysine
Methionine
Phenylalanine
Threonine
Tryptophane
Valine

Dispensable

Alanine
Aspartic Acid
Citrulline
Cystine
Glutamic Acid
Glycine
Hydroxyglutamic Acid
Hydroxyproline
Proline
Serine
Tyrosine

Animal proteins are complete in the ten essential amino acids, in adequate amounts to support the body needs.

Vegetable proteins are incomplete or insufficient in the ten essential amino acids (not always the three shown in diagram), *thus unable to support body needs.*

Growth
Maintenance
Reproduction
Lactation

The Ten Essential Amino Acids:

1. Phenylalanine
2. Tryptophane
3. Leucine
4. Isoleucine
5. Lysine
6. Methionine
7. Valine
8. Histidine
9. Threonine
10. Arginine

Fig. 13-4. The amino acids are sometimes referred to as the building stones of proteins. Rations that furnish an insufficient amount of the essential building stones (amino acids) are said to have proteins of poor quality.

Because of more limited amino acid synthesis in the horse than in ruminants, plus the fact that the cecum is located beyond the small intestine—the main area for digestion and absorption of nutrients—, it is recommended that high-quality protein rations, adequate in amino acids, be fed to horses. This is especially important for young equines, because cecal synthesis is very limited early in life.

Fortunately, the amino acid content of proteins from various sources varies. Thus, the deficiencies of one protein may be improved by combining it with another, and the mixture of the two proteins often will have a higher feeding value than either one alone. It is for this reason, along with added palatability, that a considerable variety of feeds in the horse ration is desirable.

The feed proteins are broken down into amino acids by digestion. They are then absorbed and distributed by the bloodstream to the body cells, which rebuild these amino acids into body proteins.

CECUM SYNTHESIS

In the case of ruminants (cattle and sheep), there is tremendous bacterial action in the paunch. These bacteria build body proteins of high quality from sources of inorganic nitrogen that non-ruminants (humans, rats, chickens, swine, poultry, and dogs) cannot. Farther on in the digestive tract, the ruminant digests the bacteria and obtains good proteins therefrom. Although the horse is not a ruminant, apparently the same bacterial process occurs to a limited extent in the cecum—that greatly enlarged blind pouch of the large intestine of the horse. However, it is much more limited than in ruminants, and the cecum is located beyond the small intestine, the main area for digestion and absorption of nutrients. This points up the fallacy of relying on cecum synthesis in the horse; above all, it must be remembered that little cecum synthesis exists in young equines.

In recognition of the more limited bacterial action in the horse, most state laws forbid the use of such nonprotein nitrogen sources as urea in horse rations. For such an animal, high quality proteins in the diet are requisite to normal development.

The limited protein synthesis in the horse (limited when compared with ruminants), and the lack of efficiency of absorption due to the cecum's being on the lower end of the gut (thereby not giving the small intestine a chance at the ingesta after it leaves the cecum), clearly indicate that horse rations should contain high-quality proteins, adequate in amino acids.

PRACTICAL PROTEIN SOURCES

Grass hays and farm grains are low in quality and quantity proteins. Hence, they must be supplemented with other sources of protein.

In practical horse feeding, foals should be provided with some protein feeds of animal origin in order to supplement the proteins found in grains and forages. In feeding mature horses, a safe plan to follow is to provide plant protein from several sources.

In general, feeds of high protein content are more expensive than those high in carbohydrates or fats. Accordingly, there is a temptation to feed too little protein. On the other hand, when protein feeds are the cheapest—as is often true of cull peas in certain sections of the West—excess quantities of them may be fed as energy feeds without harm, provided the ration is balanced in all other respects. Any amino acids that are left over, after the protein requirements have been met, are deaminated or broken down in the body. In this process, a part of each amino acid is turned into energy, and the remainder is excreted via the kidneys. Some opinions to the contrary, there is no such thing as "protein poisoning" from feeding rations high in protein content—provided the ration is balanced in all other respects.

Urea for Horses

It is recognized that horses frequently consume urea-containing cubes and blocks intended for cattle and sheep, particularly on the western range. Moreover, it appears that mature horses are able to do so without untoward effects. The latter observation was confirmed in one limited experiment in which four horses consumed an average of 4.57 pounds per day of a urea-containing supplement, or 0.55 lb./head/day of feed urea (262 percent), for 5 months.[4] Also, the Louisiana Station did not find urea detrimental or toxic to horses when it constituted up to 5 percent of the grain ration, with up to 0.5 lb. per day of urea consumed.[5] There are reports, however, of urea toxicity in foals, in which bacterial action is more limited than in older horses.

Energy Needs

The energy needs of horses vary with the individuality and size of animals, and the kind, amount, and severity of work performed. In racing, horses may use up to 100 times the energy utilized at rest.

It is common knowledge that a ration must contain proteins, fats, and carbohydrates. Although each of these has specific functions in maintaining a normal body, they can all be used to provide energy for maintenance, for work, or for fattening. From the standpoint of

---

[4]*Veterinary Medicine*, Vol. 58, No. 12, Dec. 1963, pp. 945-46

[5]"Non-Toxicity of Urea Feeding to Horses," *Veterinary Medicine/Small Animal Clinician*, Nov. 1965.

supplying the normal energy needs of horses, however, the carbohydrates are by far the most important, more of them being consumed than any other compound, whereas the fats are next in importance for energy purposes. Carbohydrates are usually more abundant and cheaper, and they are very easily digested, absorbed, and transformed into body fat. Also, carbohydrate feeds may be more easily stored in warm weather and for longer periods of time. Feeds high in fat content are likely to become rancid, and rancid feed is unpalatable, if not actually injurious in some instances. Also, fats are utilized very poorly by horses.

Generally, increased energy for horses is met by increasing the grain and decreasing the roughage.

A lack of energy may cause slow and stunted growth in foals, and loss of weight, poor condition, and excessive fatigue in mature horses.

CARBOHYDRATES

The carbohydrates are organic compounds composed of carbon, hydrogen, and oxygen. This group includes the sugars, starch, cellulose, gums, and related substances. They are formed in the plant by photosynthesis as follows:

$$6CO_2 + 6H_2O + \text{energy from sun} = C_6H_{12}O_6 \text{ (glucose)} + 6O_2$$

On the average, the carbohydrates comprise about three-fourths of all dry matter in plants, the chief source of horse feed. They form the woody framework of plants as well as the chief reserve food stored in seeds, roots, and tubers. When consumed by horses, carbohydrates are used as a source of heat and energy, and any excess of them is stored in the body as fat, or, in part, secreted.

No appreciable amount of carbohydrate is found in the horse's body at any one time, the blood supply of animals being held rather constant at about 0.05 to 0.1 percent for most animals, but with the pig ranging from 0.05 to 0.25 percent. However, this small quantity of glucose in the blood, which is constantly replenished by changing the glycogen of the liver back to glucose, serves as the chief source of fuel with which to maintain the body temperature and to furnish the energy needed for all body processes. The storage of glycogen (so-called animal starch) in the liver amounts to 3 to 7 percent of the weight of that organ.

From a feeding standpoint, the carbohydrates consist of nitrogen-free extract (N.F.E.) and fiber. The nitrogen-free extract includes the more soluble, and, therefore, the more digestible, carbohydrates—such as the starches, sugars, hemicelluloses, and the more soluble part of the celluloses and pentosans. Also, N.F.E. contains some lignin. The fiber is that woody portion of plants (or feeds) which is not dissolved out by weak acids and alkalies. Fiber, therefore, is less easily digested. It includes cellulose, hemicellulose, and lignin.

The ability of horses to utilize roughages—to digest the fiber therein—depends chiefly on bacterial action. It is a true symbiotic type of relationship, carried out chiefly by anaerobic bacteria, mostly in the cecum and colon of the horse. This bacterial digestion breaks down the cellulose and pentosans of feeds into usable organic acids (chiefly acetic, propionic and butyric acids).

The fiber of growing pasture grass, fresh or dried, is more digestible than the fiber of most hay. Likewise, the fiber of early cut hay is more digestible than that of hay cut in the late-bloom or seed stages. The difference is due to both chemical and physical structure, especially to the presence of certain encrusting substances (notably lignin) which are deposited in the cell wall with age. This is understandable when it is recognized that lignin is the principal constituent of wood, for no one would think of feeding wood to horses.

Young equines and working (or running) horses must have rations in which a large part of the carbohydrate content of the ration is low in fiber, and in the form of nitrogen-free extract.

To promote normal physiological activity of the gastrointestinal tract, one must feed a minimum amount of coarse roughage to horses. Finely ground roughages will not suffice.

FAT

Lipids (fat and fat-like substances), like carbohydrates, contain three elements: carbon, hydrogen, and oxygen. As horse feeds, fats function much like carbohydrates in that they serve as a source of heat and energy and for the formation of fat. Because of the larger portion of carbon and hydrogen, however, fats liberate more heat than carbohydrates when digested, furnishing approximately 2.25 times as much heat or energy per pound on oxidation as do carbohydrates. A smaller quantity of fat is required, therefore, to serve the same function.

The physical and chemical properties of fats are quite variable. From a chemical standpoint, a molecule of fat consists of a combination of three molecules of certain fatty acids with one molecule of glycerol. Fats differ in their melting points and other properties, depending on the particular fatty acids which they contain. Thus, because of the high content of unsaturated acids (such as oleic and linoleic) and acids of low molecular weight, corn fat is a liquid at ordinary temperatures; whereas, because of the high content of stearic and palmitic acids, beef fat is solid at ordinary temperatures.

Because of their unsaturation, fats often become rancid through oxidation or hydrolysis, resulting in disagreeable flavors and odors which lessen their desirability as feeds. The development of rancidity may be retarded through proper storage or by adding anti-oxidants. The hydrogenation of fats (adding hydrogen to the double bonds) also lessens rancidity. The latter process has long been effectively used in improving the keeping qualities of vegetable shortenings, and is now used in lard.

Some fatty acids are unsaturated, which means that they have the ability to take up oxygen or certain other chemical elements. Chemically, these unsaturated acids contain one or more pairs of double-bond carbon atoms.

A small amount of fat in the ration is desirable, as fat is the carrier of the fat-soluble vitamins (vitamins A, D, E, and K). There is evidence that some species (humans, swine, rats, and dogs) require certain of the fatty acids. Although the fatty-acid requirements of horses have not been settled, it is thought that ordinary farm rations contain ample quantities for these nutrients.

METHODS OF MEASURING ENERGY[6]

Scientists generally agree that the units used to measure the nutritive requirements of animals and to evaluate feeds should be one and the same. But, there is considerable disagreement as to what units, or system, to use. Generally speaking, there are two schools of thought, and each is inclined to be militant and uncompromising. On the one hand, there are those who will fight for a continuation of the total digestible nutrient system (TDN), rather than switch to the calorie system. Most of them recognize the weaknesses of the TDN system, but they favor a "let well enough alone" policy because, so they argue, folks are generally using it, whereas a change would confuse them. On the other hand, those who champion the adoption of the calorie system are usually impatient; they want to dump the TDN system and move on.

The author favors a gradual transition from the TDN system to the

[6]The author gratefully acknowledges the authoritative help of Dr. Lorin E. Harris, Utah State University, in the preparation of this section.

calorie system. For this reason, both systems are presented in this book, and both TDN and digestible energy values are given.

The Total Digestible Nutrient (TDN) System

Total digestible nutrients (TDN) is the sum of the digestible protein, fiber, nitrogen-free extract, and fat × 2.25.

Back of TDN values are the following steps:

1. *Digestibility*—The digestibility of a particular feed for a specific class of stock is determined by a digestion trial. It is made by determining the percentage of each nutrient in the feed through chemical analysis; giving the feed to the test animal for a preliminary period, so that all residues of former feeds will pass out of the digestive tract; giving weighed amounts of the feed during the test period; collecting, weighing and analyzing the feces; determining the difference between the amount of the nutrient fed and the amount found in the feces; and computing the percentage of each nutrient digested. The latter figure is known as the *digestion coefficient* for that nutrient in the feed.

2. *Computation of percent digestible nutrients*—Digestible nutrients are computed by multiplying the percentage of each nutrient in the feed [protein, fiber, N-free extract (NFE) and fat] by its digestion coefficient. The result is expressed as digestible protein, digestible fiber, digestible NFE, and digestible fat. Thus, for corn the digestible nutrients could be estimated as shown in Table 13-2.

Table 13-2
COMPUTATION OF DIGESTIBLE NUTRIENTS OF CORN

Total % of Nutrient in Feed		Digestion Coefficient / 100	=	% Digestible Nutrient	
				Digestible Nutrient	
				(%)	*(lb.)*
9.3% protein	X	67/100	=	6.2 (protein)	6.2
1.9% fiber	X	39/100	=	0.7 (fiber)	0.7
70.1% nitrogen-free extract (NFE)	X	85/100	=	59.6 (NFE)	59.6
3.9% ether extract (fat)	X	85/100	=	3.3 (fat)	3.3

3. *Computation of total digestible nutrients*—To approximate the greater energy value of fat, the percentage of digestible fat is multiplied by 2.25. Hence, for the preceding sample of corn, the TDN may be calculated as follows:

	%		%
Digestible protein	6.2 × 1	=	6.2
Digestible crude fiber........	0.7 × 1	=	0.7
Digestible NFE	59.6 × 1	=	59.6
Digestible ether extract (fat)	3.3 × 2.25	=	7.4

73.9% TDN, or
73.9 lb. TDN/100
lb. corn

4. *Animal requirements or feeding standards*—In the TDN system, the feed requirements (energy) of farm animals are given as pounds of total digestible nutrients.

The main *advantage* of the TDN system is that it has been used a long time and many people are acquainted with it.

The main *disadvantages* of the TDN system are:

1. It is based on physiological fuel values for humans and dogs. These do not apply to ruminants. The factors of 1 for protein, crude fiber and nitrogen free extract, and 2.25 for fat are not always constant.

2. It overevaluates high fiber feeds (roughages) in relation to low fiber feeds (concentrates) when fed for high rates of production, due to the higher heat loss per pound of TDN in the case of the high fiber feeds.

3. It does not measure energy in energy units.

4. It does not measure all losses of energy from the body.

The Calorie System

Energy is used in many forms—as light, electricity, atomic force, work, or heat; and it is measured by several units such as candle power, kilowatts, feet, pounds, joules, and calories. In animals, energy is expended as work and/or heat or stored as products. It would appear, therefore, that it should be measured in units suitable for these purposes. Thus, heat unit is an excellent way in which to measure the potential energy of feeds, the energy of animal products, and the heat that results from body processes. The heat unit used by animal nutritionists is the calorie.

A calorie (cal), always written with a small (c), is the amount of heat required to raise the temperature of one gram of water one degree centigrade. To measure this heat, an instrument known as the bomb calorimeter is used, in which the feed (or other substance) tested is placed and burned with the aid of oxygen (see Fig. 13-5).

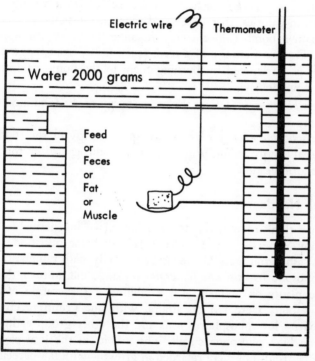

Fig. 13-5. Diagrammatic sketch of a bomb calorimeter used for the determination of the gross energy value (caloric content) of various materials. (Courtesy, Dr. Lorin E. Harris, Utah State University)

It is noteworthy that the determination of the heat of combustion with a bomb calorimeter is not as difficult or time consuming as the chemical analyses used in arriving at TDN values. Briefly stated, the procedure is as follows: An electric wire is attached to the material being tested, so that it can be ignited by remote control; 2,000 grams of water are poured around the bomb; 25 to 30 atmospheres of oxygen are added to the bomb; the material is ignited; the heat given off from the burned material warms the water; and a thermometer registers the change in temperature of the water. For example, if one gram of material is burned and the temperature of the water is raised one degree centigrade, 2,000 cal are given off. Hence, the material contains 2,000 cal per gm, or 907,200 cal per pound. This value is known as the gross energy (GE) content of the material.

Definitions of terms pertinent to the use of the energy system follow (also, see Section I of the Appendix):

Gross energy (GE) (or heat of combustion) is the amount of heat, measured in calories, that is released when a substance is completely oxidized in a bomb calorimeter containing 25 to 30 atmospheres of oxygen. The gross energy of a feed, feces, urine, tissue, eggs, or other materials is determined by burning them in the bomb calorimeter as described previously.

Digestible energy (DE) is the gross energy of the food intake minus fecal energy.

Metabolizable energy (ME) is the gross energy of the food intake minus fecal energy, minus urinary energy, minus energy in the gaseous products of digestion.

Mineral Needs

When we think of minerals for the horse, we instinctively think of bones. But minerals play a multiple role in horse nutrition.

At Washington State University, in a study with rabbits, the effect of soil phosphorus—*just one mineral*—on plants, and, in turn, the effects of these plants on animals, was established.[7] Generation after generation, rabbits were fed on alfalfa, with one group receiving hay produced on low phosphorus soils and the other group eating alfalfa grown on high phosphorus soils. The rabbits in the low phosphorus soil-alfalfa group (1) were retarded in growth—with 9.8 percent lower weaning weights, (2) required 12 percent more matings per conception, and (3) had a 47 percent lower breaking strength of bones than the rabbits on the high phosphorus soil-alfalfa group. There is reason to believe that soil nutrients can affect horses similarly—in growth, conception, and soundness of bone; but more experimental work on this subject is needed.

---

[7]Heinemann, W. W., *et al.*, Wash. Agri. Exp. Sta., Tech. Bul. 24, June, 1957.

Fig. 13-6. Rabbit with bowed legs and enlarged joints resulting from eating alfalfa produced on low phosphorus soils. There is reason to believe that the same thing happens to horses. (Courtesy, Washington State University)

A horse's skeleton is large and heavy, weighing 100 pounds or more in a full-grown horse, of which more than half consists of inorganic matter or minerals.

It has long been known that minerals play an important role in horse nutrition. Aside from furnishing structural material for the

growth of bone, teeth, and tissue, the minerals regulate many of the
vital life processes.

Also, it is recognized that mineral allowances given with the ration
or in a mineral mix should vary according to the mineral content of
the soil on which feeds are grown.

Although acute mineral-deficiency diseases and actual death losses
are relatively rare, inadequate supplies of any one of the 15 essential
mineral elements may result in lack of thrift, poor gains, inefficient
feed utilization, lowered reproduction, and decreased production of
work. Thus, like a thief in the night, sub-acute mineral deficiencies
in horses each year steal away millions of dollars from the horsemen
of America, and, for the most part, go unnoticed. Only when the
mineral deficiency reaches such proportions that it results in excess
emaciation, reproductive failure, or death is it likely to be detected.

Approximately 70 percent of the mineral content of the horse's body
consists of calcium and phosphorus. About 99 percent of the calcium
and over 80 percent of the phosphorus are found in the bones and teeth.
Since the greatest development of the skeleton takes place in the young,
growing animal, it is evident that adequate minerals must be provided at
an early age if the bone is to be sound.

The 15 mineral elements which, up to the present time, have been
shown to be essential are: calcium, phosphorus, sodium, chlorine,
iodine, iron, copper, manganese, magnesium, sulfur, zinc, potassium,
cobalt, selenium, and molybdenum. This list of essential mineral elements is based upon experiments with one or more species, for all
elements have not been tested with all species. It is highly probable,
however, that all 15 are required by horses. This does not mean
that all of these minerals must always be included in the mineral supplement. Rather, only the specific minerals that are deficient—and in the
quantities necessary—should be supplied. Excesses and mineral imbalances are to be avoided.

The proper development of the bone is particularly important in
the horse, as evidenced by the stress and strain on the skeletal structure
of the racehorse, especially when racing the two-year-old.

The classical horse ration of grass hay and farm grains is usually
deficient in calcium, but adequate in phosphorus. Also, salt is almost
always deficient, and usually iodine.

Salt, in either granulated or block form (preferably the former),
should always be available in the stall, paddock, or pasture. When
salt is fed free-choice, only enough to meet the body requirements

will be consumed. But with irregular use, an abnormal appetite develops for salt, and this is often followed by an excessive consumption and digestive troubles if unlimited access is allowed.

On the average, a horse will consume about 2 to 3 ounces of salt daily, or up to 1⅓ pounds per week, although the salt requirements vary with work and temperature. When at hard work during warm weather—conditions accompanied by profuse perspiration and consequent loss of salt in the sweat—even greater quantities may be required. The white, encrusted sides of a horse after work are evidence of the large amount of salt drawn from the body through sweat (2 gms of salt/lb. of sweat). Horses at moderate work may lose 50 to 60 grams of salt in the sweat and 35 grams in the urine daily. Unless this salt is replaced, the animal will soon exhibit signs of excessive fatigue. Overheating of horses seldom occurs if the animals are allowed free access to salt at all times and are given water at frequent intervals.

In some sections of the country, such as the northwestern part of the United States, and in the Great Lakes region, iodine deficiencies are prevalent. In these areas, unless iodine is provided to the pregnant mare, foals often are born either dead or very weak. Iodine-deficient

Fig. 13-7. Newborn weak colt affected with simple goiter due to deficiency of iodine during prenatal period. (Courtesy, Western Washington Agricultural Experiment Station)

foals also appear to be more subject to navel-ill. There may even be beneficial results in such deficient areas from supplying horses other than pregnant mares with iodine. It is sound protection always to feed *stabilized iodized salt*, containing 0.01 percent potassium iodide, in areas known or suspected to be deficient in iodine.

Table

HORSE

Minerals Which May Be Deficient Under Normal Conditions	Conditions Usually Prevailing Where Deficiencies Are Reported	Function of Mineral	Some Deficiency Symptoms
Salt (sodium and chlorine)	Negligence, for salt is cheap. Horses sweating excessively, as with vigorous exercise and during warm weather.	Sodium and chlorine help maintain osmotic pressure in body cells, upon which depends the transfer of nutrients to the cells and the removal of waste materials. Also, sodium is important in making bile, which aids in the digestion of fats and carbohydrates, and chlorine is required for the formation of hydrochloric acid in the gastric juice so vital to protein digestion.	In warm or hot weather, work horses show heat stress. Long-term deficiency symptoms in cool climates are: depraved appetite, rough hair coat, reduced growth of young animals, and decreased milk production.
Calcium	The classical horse ration of grass hay and farm grains—usually deficient in calcium.	Builds strong bones and sound teeth. Very important during lactation. Affects availability of phosphorus.	Rickets in young horses; osteomalacia in mature horses.
Phosphorus	The classical horse ration of grass hay and farm grains—possibly adequate in phosphorus.	Important in the development of bones and teeth. Essential to metabolism of carbohydrates and fats, and enzyme activation.	Rickets in young horses; osteomalacia in mature horses.
Magnesium			
Iron	Suckling foals kept away from soil and feed other than milk.	Necessary for formation of hemoglobin, an iron-containing compound which enables the blood to carry oxygen. Also, important to certain enzyme systems.	Loss of appetite, progressive emaciation, and death.
Zinc		Required for cartilage formation, an important component of hoofs. Also required in bone formation.	

13-3

MINERAL CHART[1]

Recommended Allowances[2]		Practical Sources of the Mineral	Comments
Daily Nutrients (per 1,000 lb. horse)	Per Ton or Percent of Total Rations[3]		
2.0 oz. (56 grams)	10 lbs./ton	Salt provided free choice, preferably in loose form, or 0.5% salt added to the ration.	Sodium and chlorine are low in feeds of plant origin. Horses at work (or running) have a high salt requirement because of loss of salt through sweat. The white, encrusted sides of a horse after work are evidence of the large amount of salt drawn from the body through sweat (2 gm salt/lb. of sweat). Thus, the salt requirements of horses vary with work and temperature. There is little danger of overfeeding salt unless a salt-starved animal is suddenly exposed to too much salt, or if liberal amounts of water are not available.
0.1 lb. (45 grams)	0.5%	Ground limestone or oyster shell flour. Where both Ca and P are needed, use bone meal, dicalcium phosphate, or defluorinated phosphate. (See Table 13-4)	The Ca: P ratio should be maintained close to 1:1, although 2:1 is acceptable when the higher calcium content is due to the presence of legume. Narrower ratios may cause osteomalacia in mature horses. Where there is a shortage of calcium in the ration, it is withdrawn from the bones.
0.1 lb. (45 grams)	0.5%	Monosodium phosphate. Where both Ca and P are needed, use bone meal, dicalcium phosphate or defluorinated phosphate. (See Table 13-4)	(Same as stated for Ca under "Comments" above.) If plenty of vitamin D is present, the ratio of Ca to P becomes less important. Apparently phosphorus cannot be withdrawn from the bone.
3,200 mg	256 g/ton		
640 mg	51.2 g/ton		The horse's body contains about 0.004% iron. Milk is deficient in iron, and the iron content of the mother cannot be increased through feeding iron. Thus, foals should be creep fed as soon as they are old enough. A variable store of both iron and copper is located in liver and spleen, and some iron is found in the kidneys. Too much iron may be harmful.
400 mg	32 g/ton		In the pig, with high calcium rations, levels of zinc of 100 to 150 ppm (45 to 67 mg/lb.) of ration are used.

Minerals Which May Be Deficient Under Normal Conditions	Conditions Usually Prevailing Where Deficiencies Are Reported	Function of Mineral	Some Deficiency Symptoms
Manganese		Considered essential in utilization of calcium and phosphorus, for proper functioning of mammary glands and normal reproduction.	
Copper	Suckling foals.	Copper, along with iron, is necessary for hemoglobin formation, although it forms no part of the hemoglobin molecule of red blood cells.	Same as iron deficiency.
Iodine	Iodine-deficient areas or soils (in Northwestern U. S. and in the Great Lakes Region) when iodized salt is not fed. Use of feeds that come from iodine-deficient areas.	Iodine is needed by the thyroid gland in making thyroxin (an iodine-containing compound which controls the rate of body metabolism or activity).	Foals born dead, or very weak and unable to stand or nurse. Appear to be more subject to navel-ill.
Cobalt		As a constituent of vitamin B_{12}.	Anemia.

[1]Mineral recommendations for all classes and ages of horses: Provide free access to a two-compartment mineral box with (1) salt (iodized salt in iodine-deficient areas) in one side, and (2) a mixture of 1/3 salt (salt added for purposes of palatability) and 2/3 steamed bone meal (or other calcium-phosphorus supplement) in the other side. Or a good commercial mineral may be used.

If desired, the mineral supplement may be incorporated in the ration in keeping with the recommended allowances given in this table.

Young equines, breeding animals, and animals being forced for race or show are most likely to be affected by deficiencies of calcium and/or phosphorus because of their greater needs for these minerals.

The Ca:P ratio of horse rations should be maintained close to 1:1. Osteomalacia may develop in mature horses when rations with a calcium-phosphorus ration of 0.8 to 1 are fed for 6 to 12 months and will progress rapidly when the ratio is 0.6 to 1. The disease may be arrested by adding calcium to increase the ratio to 1.4 to 1. If the concentration of calcium in a ration is below 0.15 percent or if feedstuffs unusually rich in phosphorus are fed, some calcium supplement will be needed. It is recommended that the total ration contain at

13-3   (Continued)

Recommended Allowances[2]		Practical Sources of the Mineral	Comments
Daily Nutrients (per 1,000 lb. horse)	Per Ton or Percent of Total Rations[3]		
160 mg	12.8 g/ton		Manganese is needed for growth and reproduction of most animals.
64 mg	5.1 g/ton		Milk is deficient in copper. A copper deficiency in horses has been reported in Australia. High molybdenum in forages does not appear to affect horses so much as ruminants. However, in high molybdenum areas, more copper may be added to horse rations; but excesses and toxicity should be avoided.
4.0 mg	0.3 g/ton	Stabilized iodized salt containing 0.01% potassium iodide; or calcium iodate may be used.	
1.0 mg	0.08 g/ton		Cobalt may be provided in the salt; add 1 oz. of cobalt sulfate, or its equivalent, per 100 lbs. salt.

[2]These are recommended allowances, and not requirements. The author's position on recommended allowances vs. requirements for horses is clearly stated in the narrative of this book under the heading entitled "Nutritive Allowances."

[3]Where hay is fed separately, double these amounts should be added to the concentrate.

least 0.5 percent calcium and 0.45 percent phosphorus. Because phosphorus is more expensive than calcium, there is a tendency to be long on calcium and short on phosphorus.

Other minerals (in addition to salt, calcium, phosphorus, and iodine) required by horses include iron, copper, and cobalt; but little information is available as to the amounts needed.

The needed minerals for horses may be incorporated in the ration in keeping with the recommended allowances given in Table 13.3. Additionally, horses should have free access to calcium and phosphorus in a supplement.

CALCIUM AND PHOSPHORUS

Horses are more apt to suffer from a lack of phosphorus and of calcium than from any of the other minerals except salt. These two minerals comprise about three-fourths the ash of the skeleton and from one-third to one-half of the minerals of milk.

The following general characteristics of feeds in regard to calcium and phosphorus are important in rationing horses:

1. The cereal grains and their by-products and straws, dried mature grasses, and protein supplements of plant origin are low in calcium.

2. The protein supplements of animal origin and legume forage are rich in calcium.

3. The cereal grains and their by-products are fairly high or even rich in phosphorus, but a large portion of the phosphorus is not readily available.

4. Almost all protein-rich supplements are high in phosphorus. But, here again, plant sources of phosphorus contain much of this element in a bound form.

5. Beet by-products and dried, mature nonleguminous forages (such as grass hays and fodders) are likely to be low in phosphorus.

6. The calcium and phosphorus content of plants can be increased through fertilizing the soil upon which they are grown.

In considering the calcium and phosphorus requirements of horses, it is important to realize that the proper utilization of these minerals by the body is dependent upon three factors: (1) an adequate supply of calcium and phosphorus in an available form, (2) a suitable ratio between them (somewhere between one to two parts of calcium to one to two parts of phosphorus), and (3) sufficient vitamin D to make possible the assimilation and utilization of the calcium and phosphorus. Many "cure-alls" and commercial mineral mixtures fail to take such factors into consideration.

If plenty of vitamin D is present (as provided either by sunlight or through the ration), the ratio of calcium to phosphorus becomes less important. Also, less vitamin D is needed when there is a desirable calcium-phosphorus ratio.

Table 13-4 gives several sources of calcium and phosphorus and the approximate percentages of the two elements in various mineral supplements.

The author favors the use of *high-quality* steamed bone meal for

Table 13-4

COMPOSITION OF CALCIUM AND PHOSPHORUS SUPPLEMENTS[1]

Mineral Supplement	Calcium		Phosphorus	
	(percent)	(grams per pound)	(percent)	(grams per pound)
Oyster shells, ground	38.05	172	... ...	....
Limestone, ground.............	33.84	154	... ...	....
Bone black, spent..............	22.00	100	13.10	60
Bone meal, raw feeding......	22.70	103	10.10	46
Bone meal, steamed...........	30.00	136	13.90	63
Dicalcium phosphate.........	26.50	120	20.50	93
Tricalcium phosphate	32.00	145	18.00	82
Defluorinated phosphate....	33.00	150	18.00	82
Monosodium phosphate	... ...	....	22.40	102
Defluorinated phosphate....	... ...	....	23.00	104

[1]From Table 4, *Nutrient Requirements of Domestic Animals,* Number 3, pub. 1349, 3rd. Ed., NRC, National Academy of Sciences, 1966.

horses.[8] But it is recognized that it is increasingly difficult to get good bone meal. Some of the imported products are high in fat, rancid and/or odorous and unpalatable. Where good bone meal is not available, dicalcium phosphate is generally recommended.

When calcium alone is needed, ground limestone or oyster shell flour are commonly used, either free-choice or added to the ration in keeping with nutrient requirements.

Where phosphorus alone is needed, monosodium phosphate or de-fluorinated phosphate are minerals of choice.

Earlier experiments cast considerable doubt on the availability of phosphorus when the phosphorus was largely in the form of phytin. Although wheat bran is very high in phosphorus, containing 1.32 per-cent, there was some question as to its availability due to the high phytin content of this product. More recent studies, however, indicate that cattle, and perhaps mature swine, can partially utilize phytin phosphorus. Cattle can utilize about 60 percent of the total phosphorus from most plant sources, whereas swine can utilize only about 50 per-

[8]Bone meal contains many ingredients in addition to calcium and phosphorus; it is really very complex. In addition to being a good source of iron, manganese, and zinc, it contains such trace minerals as copper and cobalt; but it is felt that the content of the latter is too low to be of much value as a supplement for them.

cent. The situation relative to horses is unknown. It must be emphasized, however, that phosphorus availability depends to a large extent on phosphorus sources, dietary supplies of calcium, and adequate vitamin D.

Likewise, for humans, the availability of the calcium of certain leafy materials is impaired by the presence of oxalic acid—the acid precipitating the calcium and preventing its absorption. On the other hand, the deleterious effects of oxalic acid are reduced in the ruminant because of the ruminant's apparent ability to metabolize oxalic acid in the body. The situation relative to horses is unknown.

During World War II, the shortage of phosphorus feed supplements led to the development of defluorinated phosphates for feeding purposes. Raw, unprocessed rock phosphate usually contains from 3.25 to 4.0 percent fluorine, whereas feeding steamed bone meal normally contains only 0.05 to 0.10 percent. Fortunately, through heating at high temperatures under conditions suitable for elimination of fluorine, the excess fluorine of raw rock phosphate can be removed. Such a product is known as defluorinated phosphate.

Under the definition of the Association of American Feed Control Officials, to qualify as a defluorinated phosphate, rock phosphate cannot contain more than one part of fluorine to 100 parts of phosphate.

Excess fluorine results in abnormal development of bones; softening, mottling, and irregular wear of the teeth; roughened hair coat; delayed maturity; and less efficient utilization of feed.

SODIUM CHLORIDE, OR SALT

Salt, which serves as both a condiment and a nutrient, is needed by all classes of animals, but more especially by herbivora (grass-eating animals). It may be provided in the form of granulated, rock, or block salt. In general, the form selected is determined by price and availability. It is to be pointed out, however, that it is difficult for horses to eat very hard block and rock salt. This often results in sore tongues and inadequate consumption. Also, if there is much competition for the salt block, the more timid animals may not get their requirements.

Both sodium and chlorine are essential for animal life. They are necessary in maintaining the osmotic pressure of body cells (thereby assisting in the transfer of nutrients to the cells and the removal of waste materials). Also, sodium is important as one of the main body buffers and in making bile, which aids in the digestion of fats and carbohydrates. Chlorine is required for the formation of the hydrochloric acid in the gastric juice so vital to protein digestion. The blood contains 0.25 percent chlorine, 0.22 percent sodium, and 0.02 to 0.22 percent potassium; thus, the chlorine content is higher than that of any other mineral in the blood. The salt requirement is greatly increased under conditions which cause heavy sweating, thereby resulting in large losses of this mineral from the body. Unless it is replaced, fatigue will result. For this reason, when engaged in hard work and perspiring profusely, horses should receive liberal allowances of salt.

Salt can be fed free-choice to horses, provided they have not been salt-starved. That is, if the animals have not previously been fed salt for a considerable length of time, they may overeat, resulting in digestive disturbances and even death. Salt-starved animals should first be hand-fed salt, and the daily allowance should be increased gradually until they start leaving a little in the mineral box. When this point is reached, self-feeding may be followed. The Indians and the pioneers of this country handed down many legendary stories about the large numbers of buffalo and deer that killed themselves simply by gorging at a newly found "salt-lick" after having been salt-starved for long periods of time.

When added to the concentrate ration, salt should be added at a level of 0.5 to 1.0 percent.

TRACE MINERALS

There is renewed interest in trace elements and a general recognition of the importance of many of them in all livestock rations, horses included. But there is a paucity of experimental work upon which to make recommendations.

Tables 13-3 and 13-8 represent the author's best judgment relative to trace mineral allowances in light of the information presently available. Until such time as more experimental evidence is available, it is recommended that the trace elements listed in these tables be added to the rations of horses at approximately the levels shown.

OTHER PERTINENT MINERAL FACTS

Other facts pertinent to minerals for horses follow.

1. *Expenditure for horse minerals.*—It is estimated that 20 million

dollars are spent annually for minerals for horses.

2. *Iron and copper deficiencies.*—If horses are fed diets that are too low in iron, or in iron and copper, nutritional anemia will result.

3. *Body store of iron and copper at birth.*—Nature has planned wisely. Young equines are born with a store of iron and copper in their bodies, which usually suffices until they normally begin to eat feeds which supply these constituents. This is most fortunate, as milk is very low in iron and copper. When young animals are continued on a milk diet for a long period of time, particularly under confined conditions and with little or no supplemental feeds, nutritional anemia will likely develop.

4. *Natural sources of iron.*—In obtaining sources of iron, it is well to remember that simple inorganic iron salts, such as ferric chloride, are readily utilized, whereas the iron in the complex organic compounds in the hemoglobin of the blood is much less readily available, if at all. Also, though certain small amounts of iron are very essential, too much of this element in the diet may actually be deleterious—interfering with phosphorus absorption by forming an insoluble phosphate—and rickets may thus result from a diet otherwise adequate.

5. *Copper.*—A copper deficiency in horses has been reported in Australia.

In any mineral mixtures containing copper, thorough mixing must be obtained in order to prevent copper toxicity or poisoning. Only limited quantities of copper can be put into the mineral mixture for this reason.

In high molybdenum areas, it is recommended that the copper level for horses be about five times higher than the normal level.

6. *Iodine.*—It is estimated that the mature animal body contains less than 0.00004 percent iodine, but if this minute amount is not maintained in the diet, disaster results. More than half of the total iodine content of the body is located in the thyroid gland of the neck. Iodine, which is secreted by the thyroid gland in the form of thyroxine (an iodine-containing hormone), controls the rate of metabolism of the body.

7. *Iodine deficiencies.*—If the soil—and the water and food crops coming therefrom—is low in iodine, the body is likely to show deficiency symptoms in the form of simple goiter, unless an adequate source of iodine is provided artificially. A goiter is simply an enlargement of the thyroid gland, which is nature's way of trying to make enough thyroxine when there is insufficient iodine in the feed. How-

ever, iodine-deficiency symptoms are not always evidenced by the appearance of goiter, although this is the most common characteristic of such deficiency in humans, calves, lambs, and kids. Cows and ewes give birth to goiterous (big-neck) calves and lambs, respectively. In pigs, the outstanding symptom of the deficiency is hairlessness, whereas in foals the only symptom may be extreme weakness at birth, resulting in an inability to stand and suck. There is also some evidence to indicate that navel-ill in foals may be lessened by feeding iodine to broodmares.

In general, it may be said that goiter is an advanced symptom of iodine deficiency but that the chief loss is from interference with reproductive processes and the birth of weak, deformed offspring that fail to survive.

Iodine deficiencies are worldwide. In the United States, the Northwestern States, the Pacific Coast, and the Great Lakes region are classed as goiter areas.

8. *Recommended iodine supplements.*—The simplest method of supplying iodine in deficient areas is through use of salt containing (a) 0.01 percent potassium iodide (0.0076 percent iodine), or (b) calcium iodate. Most of the salt companies now manufacture stabilized iodized salt.

9. *Precautions in feeding iodized salt.*—Although iodized salt is an effective preventive measure, no satisfactory treatment has been developed for animals which have developed pronounced deficiency symptoms. In fact, studies with goiter in humans have clearly established that, although iodine is an effective preventative, it may be harmful rather than beneficial as a treatment after the goiter has developed.

Iodized salt should always be kept in a dry place and it should be kept fresh. It should also be provided in such form and quantities as to insure an adequate intake of iodine.

In no instance should iodine be fed in excess. Such excesses have proved toxic to lambs, and very probably the same hazard applies to other classes of livestock. For this reason, thorough mixing of iodized salt is important, whether it be a commercial or a home-prepared product.

10. *Cobalt.*—Cobalt is essential for cattle and sheep. However, horses have apparently fared well when grazed on pastures so low in cobalt that ruminants died when kept on them. This means that the cobalt requirement, if any, of the horse is lower than that of ruminants. However, it is noteworthy that an anemia in horses has re-

sponded to vitamin B_{12} treatment; and, of course, B_{12} contains cobalt in the molecular structure. Thus, inclusion of cobalt in the ration of horses is in the nature of good insurance.

In different sections of the world, a cobalt deficiency is known as Denmark disease, coast disease, enzootic marasmus, bush sickness, salt sickness, nakuritis, and pining disease.

11. *Chelated trace minerals.*—The word chelate is derived from the Greek chelae, meaning a claw or pincer-like organ. Those selling chelated minerals generally recommend a smaller quantity of them (but at a higher price per pound) and extoll their "fenced-in" properties.

When it comes to synthetic chelating agents, much needs to be learned about their selectivity toward minerals, the kind and quantity most effective, their mode of action, and their behavior with different species of animals and with varying rations. It is possible that their use may actually create a mineral imbalance. These answers, and more, must be forthcoming through carefully controlled experiments before they can be recommended for valuable horses.

Vitamin Needs

Until early in the twentieth century, if a ration contained proteins, fats, carbohydrates, and minerals, together with a certain amount of fiber, it was considered to be a complete diet. True enough, the disease known as beriberi made its appearance in the rice-eating districts of the Orient when milling machinery was introduced from the West, having been known to the Chinese as early as 2600 B.C.; and scurvy was long known to occur among sailors fed on salt meat and biscuits. However, for centuries these diseases were thought to be due to toxic substances in the digestive tract caused by pathogenic organisms rather than food deficiencies, and more time elapsed before the discovery of vitamins. Of course, there was no medical profession until 1835, the earlier treatments having been based on superstition rather than science.

Funk, a Polish scientist working in London, first referred to these nutrients as "vitamines," in 1912. Presumably, the name vitamines alluded to the fact that they were essential to life, and they were assumed to be chemically of the nature of amines (the chemical assumption was later proved incorrect, with the result that the "e" was dropped—hence, the word vitamin).

The actual existence of vitamins, therefore, has been known only since 1912, and only within the last few years has it been possible

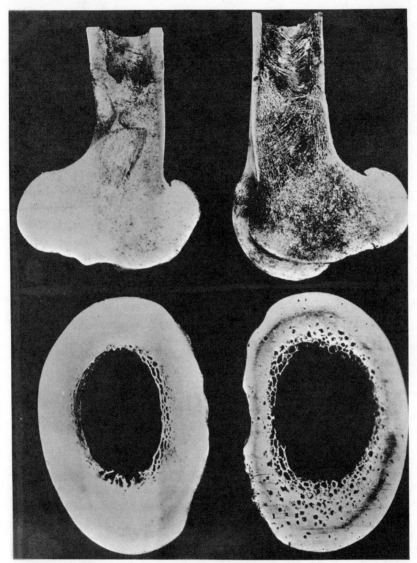

Fig. 13-8. **Vitamin A made the difference!** Upper: On the right is shown the sagittal section of the distal end of the femur of a vitamin A-deficient horse compared to normal bone (left). Lower: On the right is shown the cross section of the cannon bone from a vitamin A-deficient horse compared to normal bone (left). (Courtesy, G. E. Howell, Calif. Agricultural Experiment Station)

to see or touch any of them in a pure form. Previously, they were merely mysterious invisible "little things," known only by their effects.

In fact, most of the present fundamental knowledge relative to the vitamin content of both human foods and animal feeds was obtained through measuring their potency in promoting growth or in curing certain disease conditions in animals—a most difficult and tedious method. For the most part, small laboratory animals were used, especially the rat, guinea pig, pigeon, and chick.

The lack of vitamins in a horse ration may, under certain conditions, be more serious than a short supply of feed. Deficiencies may lead to failure in growth or reproduction, poor health, and even characteristic disorders known as deficiency diseases.

Unfortunately, there are no warning signals to tell a caretaker when a horse is not getting enough of certain vitamins. But a continuing inadequate supply of any one of several vitamins can produce illness which is very hard to diagnose until it becomes severe, at which time it is difficult and expensive—if not too late—to treat. The important thing, therefore, is to insure against such deficiencies occurring. But horsemen should not shower a horse with mistaken kindness through using shotgun-type vitamin preparations. Instead, the quantity of each vitamin should be based on available scientific knowledge.

Deficiencies may occur during periods (1) of extended drought or in other conditions of restriction in diet, (2) when production is being forced, or during stress, (3) when large quantities of highly refined feeds are being fed, or (4) when low-quality forages are utilized.

Although the occasional deficiency symptoms are the most striking result of vitamin deficiencies, it must be emphasized that in practice mild deficiencies probably cause higher total economic losses than do severe deficiencies. It is relatively uncommon for a ration, or diet, to contain so little of a vitamin that obvious symptoms of a deficiency occur. When one such case does appear, it is reasonable to suppose that there must be several cases that are too mild to produce characteristic symptoms but that are sufficiently severe to lower the state of health and the efficiency of production.

It has long been known that the vitamin content of feeds varies considerably according to soil, climatic conditions, and curing and storing.

Certain vitamins are necessary in horse rations in order to permit proper growth, development, health, and reproduction. Although the particular role played by vitamins in the nutrition of the horse has not been explored extensively, there is reason to suppose that the vitamin requirements of the horse are similar to those of the pig. Also, they may be accentuated during stress and strain, to which modern horses are subjected. Certainly, deficiencies of vitamins A and D are encountered. Although very little information is available, indications

Fig. 13-9. Foal with severe rickets. Note the enlarged joints and crooked legs. Rickets may be caused by a lack of vitamin D or of calcium or phosphorus. (Courtesy, Dept. of Veterinary Pathology and Hygiene, College of Veterinary Medicine, University of Illinois)

are that vitamin E and some of the B group of vitamins, especially riboflavin and perhaps thiamine, pantothenic acid, and B_{12}, are required by the horse. Further, it is recognized that single, uncomplicated vitamin deficiencies are the exception rather than the rule.

A severe deficiency of vitamin A may cause night blindness, reproduction difficulties, uneven and poor hoof development, respiratory symptoms, incoordination, and fanciful appetite. (See Table 13-5) There is also evidence which indicates that a lack of vitamin A may cause or contribute to certain leg bone weaknesses. At the first sign of a vitamin A deficiency symptom, the horseman should add a therapeutic amount of a stabilized vitamin A product to the ration.

Vitamins Which May Be Deficient Under Normal Conditions	Conditions Usually Prevailing Where Deficiencies Are Reported	Functions of Vitamins	Some Deficiency Symptoms
Vitamin A	Extended drought. Bleached hays. Stall-feeding where there is little or no green forage or yellow corn. Following great stress, as when race or show horses are put in training.	Promotes growth and stimulates appetite. Assists in reproduction and lactation. Keeps the mucous membranes of respiratory and other tracts in healthy condition. Makes for normal vision. Prevents night blindness.	Reproductive failure, nerve degeneration, night blindness, uneven and poor hoof development, a predisposition to respiratory infection, lachrymation (tears), incoordination, keratenization of the cornea, progressive weakness, certain bone disorders, and fanciful appetite.
Vitamin D$_2$	Limited sunlight, and/or limited sun-cured hay, especially when horse is kept inside most of the time.	Assimilation and utilization of calcium and phosphorus, necessary in normal bone development—including the bones of the fetus.	Rickets in foals, osteomalacia in mature horses. Both conditions result in large joints and weak bones.
Vitamin E (Tocopherols)	It is possible that more vitamin E is destroyed or used up by horses during times of stress or strain than can be obtained through normal feeds.	Serves as insurance against destruction of vitamin A; makes for improved reproduction and performance.	Lowered breeding performance in both mares and stallions. Lack of stamina.
Choline		Essential in building and maintaining cell structure and in the transmission of nerve impulses.	
Pantothenic Acid		Part of Co-enzyme A, a necessary factor for life processes.	Poor growth, skin rashes, poor appetite, nervous disorders.
Niacin (Nicotinic Acid)		Component of two enzymes. Essential for carbohydrate, lipid, and protein metabolism.	Skin rashes, diarrhea, nerve disorders.

Footnotes on last page of table.

VITAMIN CHART

Recommended Allowances [1]		Practical Sources of the Vitamin	Comments
Daily/ 1,000 lb. Horse	Per Ton of Total Feed[2]		
20,000 to 30,000 U.S.P.	1,600,000 to 2,400,000 U.S.P.	Stabilized Vitamin A. Green Grass. Grass or legume silage. Green hay not over 1 yr. old.	A considerable margin of safety in vitamin A and carotene is provided in the recommended allowances due to the oxidative destruction of these materials in feeds during storage. Hay over 1 year old, regardless of green color, is usually not an adequate source of carotene or vitamin A activity. The younger the animal, the quicker vitamin A deficiencies will show up. Mature animals may store sufficient vitamin A to last 6 months. When deficiency symptoms appear, add to the ration either (1) dehydrated alfalfa or grass, or (2) a stabilized vitamin A product. Fish liver oil (cod-liver oil) is a rich source of vitamin A, but some horses will refuse to eat feeds to which it has been added.
3,000 U.S.P.	240,000 U.S.P.	Exposure to sunlight. Sun-cured hay. Irradiated yeast.	The vitamin D requirement is less when a proper balance of calcium and phosphorus exists in the ration. When animals are exposed to direct sunlight, the ultraviolet light produces vitamin D from traces of cholesterol in the skin. Stabled horses, exercised in the early morning, will not get sufficient vitamin D in this manner.
200 I.U.	16,000 I.U.	Alpha tocopherol, a stable form of vitamin E. Most rations contain ample vitamin E. Before adding it, the horseman should seek the advice of a competent authority.	
400 mg	32,000 mg		
60 mg	4,800 mg		
50 mg	4,000 mg		The horse can convert the essential amino acid tryptophan into niacin. Hence, it is important to make certain that the ration is adequate in niacin; otherwise, the horse will use tryptophan to supply niacin needs.

(Continued)

Table 13-5

Vitamins Which May Be Deficient Under Normal Conditions	Conditions Usually Prevailing Where Deficiencies Are Reported	Functions of Vitamins	Some Deficiency Symptoms
Thiamine (Vitamin B₁)	Poor-quality hay and grain. When sulfa drugs or antibiotics are given to the horse, the synthesis of B vitamins is impaired.	Promotes appetite and growth, required for normal carbohydrate metabolism, and aids reproduction. Essential for sound nervous system.	Decreased feed consumption, (loss of weight, incoordination (especially in the hindquarters), lowered blood thiamine, elevated blood pyruvic acid, enlarged heart, and nervous symptoms.
Riboflavin	When green feeds (pasture, hay, or silage) are not available.	Probably for synthesis of ocular vitamin C or its protecting substance. Important in protein metabolism.	Periodic ophthalmia (or moon blindness). Decreased rate of growth and feed efficiency. Porous and weak bones; ligaments and joints impaired.
Vitamin K	Following intestinal disorders.	Concerned with blood coagulation.	Increased clotting time of the blood.
Folic Acid		An anti-anemia factor.	Anemia.
B₁₂		Stimulates appetite, increases rate of growth and efficiency of feed utilization, and necessary for normal reproduction. Anti-anemic principles.	Loss of appetite, poor growth, lowered reproduction, and anemia.
Unidentified Factors	Since the U. S. foal crop is only around 50%, it is obvious that there is room for improvement somewhere along the line; and perhaps unidentified factors are involved. Also, optimal results with horses during the critical periods (growth, gestation-lactation and when under stress as in racing or showing) appear to be dependent upon providing unidentified factors through such ingredients as distillers dried solubles, alfalfa meal, condensed fish solubles, brewers dried yeast, antibiotic fermentation residues, dried whey, and corn fermentation solubles.		

¹These are recommended allowances, and not requirements. The author's position on recommended allowances vs. requirements for horses is clearly stated in the narrative of this book under the heading entitled "Nutritive Allowances."

A foal sometimes develops rickets, which is caused by lack of vitamin D, or of calcium or phosphorus. This condition may be prevented by exposing the animal to direct sunlight as much as possible, allowing access to a suitable mineral mixture, and/or providing good-quality sun-cured hay or luxuriant pasture grown on well-fertilized

(Continued)

Recommended Allowances[1]		Practical Sources of the Vitamin	Comments
Daily/ 1,000 lb. Horse	Per Ton of Total Feed[2]		
25 mg	2,000 mg	Good-quality feeds, especially pastures and hays, usually contain adequate thiamine.	Thiamine is synthesized in the lower gut of the horse by bacterial action, but there is some doubt as to its sufficiency. When neither green pasture nor high-quality roughage is available, B vitamins may be provided by adding to the ration distillers dried solubles, dried brewers yeast, animal-liver meal, dried fish solubles. Since carbohydrate metabolism is increased during physical exertion, it is important that B_1 be available in quantity at such times.
20 mg	1,600 mg	Green pasture. Green hay. Silages.	Sometimes moon blindness follows leptospirosis in horses.
8 mg	640 mg		High levels of vitamin K will overcome bleeding due to dicumarol.
2.5 mg	200 mg		
125 mcg	10,000 mcg	It is associated with animal protein sources; hence, it is sometimes referred to as Animal Protein Factor. Grass.	

[2]Where hay is fed separately—that is, where an all-in-one pellet is not fed, for example—double these amounts should be added to the concentrate.

soils. In areas lacking in sunshine, horsemen should provide the foal with a vitamin D supplement.

Horses seem to require vitamin E, but most practical rations contain liberal quantities of it—perhaps enough except under conditions of stress or reproduction, or where there is interference with its utilization.

A deficiency of riboflavin may cause periodic ophthalmia (moon blindness), but it is known that lack of this vitamin is not the only factor in producing the condition. Periodic ophthalmia due to a nutritional deficiency may be lessened by feeding green hays and green pastures—feeds high in riboflavin—or by adding crystalline riboflavin to the ration.

A thiamine deficiency has been observed in horses fed on poor-quality hay and grain.

Although some of the B vitamins and unidentified factors are synthesized in the cecum of the horse, it is doubtful that this microbial activity is sufficient to meet the needs during the critical periods—growth, reproduction, and when animals are subjected to great stress as in showing or racing. Also, there is reason to question the efficacy of absorption this far down the digestive tract; for in comparison with that of man and other animals, the cecum is on the wrong end of the digestive tract. Moreover, it is known that horses fed thiamine-deficient rations lose weight, become nervous, and show incoordination in the hindquarters; then, when thiamine is added to the ration, this condition is cured. For these reasons, in valuable horses it is not wise to rely solely on bacterial synthesis. The B vitamins, along with un-identified factors, may be provided by adding to the ration such ingredients as distillers dried solubles, dried brewers yeast, dried fish solubles, or animal liver meal; usually though a reputable commercial feed.

Table 13-5 contains a list of vitamins of practical importance in horse nutrition, together with the pertinent information relative to each.

The author subscribes to the view that most light horses are under stress, and that the more exacting the performance, the greater the stress; hence, that the vitamin requirements of most light horses are higher than those for draft horses. This fact is taken into consideration in the "recommended allowances" given in Table 13-5.

OTHER PERTINENT VITAMIN FACTS

Other facts pertinent to vitamins for horses follow.

1. *The known vitamins.*—A number of the known vitamins have been isolated chemically, and even synthesized. Also, many of them can be distinguished by chemical and physical properties as well as

by biological and bacteriological assay. Each of the vitamins is as much a distinct chemical compound as is cane sugar, for example. Although they are present in feeds in exceedingly minute amounts, they are extraordinarily potent.

2. *Vitamin deficiencies.*—It must be remembered that single, uncomplicated vitamin deficiencies are the exception rather than the rule. Multiple deficiencies are altogether too common, making diagnosis difficult even to the trained observer. A summary of each of the vitamin deficiency diseases is contained in Table 13-13.

3. *Vitamin A.*—Vitamin A is strictly a product of animal metabolism, no vitamin A being found in plants. The counterpart in plants is known as carotene, which is the precursor of vitamin A. Because the animal body can transform carotene into vitamin A, this compound is often spoken of as Provitamin A.

4. *Carotene.*—Carotene is the yellow-colored, fat-soluble substance that gives the characteristic color to carrots and to butterfat (vitamin A is nearly a colorless substance). Carotene derives its name from the carrot, from which it was first isolated over 100 years ago. Although its empirical formula was established in 1906, it was not until 1919 that Steenbock discovered its vitamin A activity. Though the yellow color is masked by the green chlorophyll, the green parts of plants are rich in carotene and thus have a high vitamin A value. Also, the degree of greenness in a roughage is a good index of its carotene content, provided it has not been stored too long. Early cut, leafy green hays are very high in carotene.

Aside from yellow corn, practically all of the cereal grain used in horse feeding have little carotene or vitamin A value. Even yellow corn has only about one-tenth as much carotene as well-cured hay. Dried peas of the green and yellow varieties and carrots are also valuable sources of carotene.

Studies by the New Jersey station (1965 mimeographed report by Fonnesbeck and Vander Noot) indicate that the carotene content of alfalfa hay may be more available to the horse and more efficiently converted into vitamin A than the carotene of timothy hay.

5. *Circumstances conducive to vitamin A deficiencies.*—The circumstances most conducive to vitamin A deficiencies are (a) extended periods of drought, resulting in the pastures becoming dry and bleached; (b) a long winter feeding period on bleached hays or straws, especially overripe cereal hays and straws; and (c) using feeds which

have lost their vitamin A potency through extended storage (for example, it has been found that alfalfa may lose nine-tenths of its vitamin A value in a year's storage). There is reason to believe that mild deficiencies of vitamin A, especially in the winter and early spring, are fairly common.

Fortunately, horses are able to store vitamin A, primarily in the liver, during periods of abundance to tide them through periods of scarcity. Thus, horses on green pasture store reserves to help meet their needs during the winter feeding period when their rations may be deficient. Mature horses may be able to store up a six-month supply; young equines store much less.

It is generally believed that stressed horses have a higher vitamin A requirement than those not under stress. Among such stress factors are: racing, showing, fatigue, hot weather, confinement, excitement, and number of animals run together.

The vitamin A requirements for gestating mares may be five times the minimum maintenance requirements. Therefore, unless properly fed, broodmares may become almost depleted of their vitamin A reserves by the end of winter—at a time when a vitamin A deficiency could be critical to the rapid development of the fetus.

When the first deficiency symptom appears, it is recommended that there be added to the ration a stabilized vitamin A product.

6. *Vitamin D, and cholesterol and ergosterol.*—Most of the commonly used feeds contain little or no vitamin D, yet there is no widespread need for special supplements containing this factor. Fortunately, the skin of horses and many feeds contain provitamins in certain forms of cholesterol and ergosterol, respectively, which, through the action of ultra-violet light (light of such short wave length that it is invisible) from the sun, are converted into vitamin D. These certain forms of cholesterol and ergosterol themselves have no anti-rachitic effect.

7. *Vitamin D limited in feeds.*—Of all the known vitamins, vitamin D has the most limited distribution in common feeds. Very little of this factor is contained in the cereal grains and their by-products, in roots and tubers, in feeds of animal origin, or in growing pasture grasses. The only important natural sources of vitamin D are sun-cured hay and other roughages. The chief vitamin-D-rich concentrates include sun-cured hay, cod-liver and other fish oils, irradiated cholesterol and ergosterol, and irradiated yeast.

As might be suspected from the preceding discussion, artificially dehydrated hay contains little vitamin D.

8. *Effectiveness of sunlight in producing vitamin D.*—The effectiveness of sunlight is determined by the lengths and intensity of the ultraviolet rays which reach the body. It is more potent in the Tropics than elsewhere, more potent at noon than earlier or later in the day, more potent in the summer than in the winter, and more potent at high altitudes. The ultraviolet rays are largely screened out by clothing, window glass, clouds, smoke, or dust. Also, some biochemists theorize that the color of the skin of humans is nature's way of regulating the manufacture of vitamin D—that the dark skin of races near the equator filters out excess ultraviolet light. Perhaps color of hair and skin in horses exercises a similar control, although this is not known.

9. *Vitamin C.*—The importance of vitamin C is inconclusive. If it is needed, it is likely synthesized in ample quantities in the body. Moreover, all green forages (pastures, hay, and silages) are high in vitamin C. An adult human needs about 75 mg of vitamin C per day.

10. *Vitamin E.*—Although the need for vitamin E supplementation is not clear, it is possible that under stress and strain vitamin E is destroyed or used up so rapidly that supplementation is needed. Many horsemen also feel that vitamin E supplementation improves fertility of mares and stallions.

11. *The B vitamins.*—It is known that the horse needs some of the B vitamins. However, it is less clear as to which ones are needed, in what quantities they are needed, and their status from the standpoints of synthesis and absorption in the horse. Thiamine, riboflavin, niacin, panthothenic acid, choline, and B_{12} must be considered.

The addition of other B vitamins may be in the nature of good insurance, especially for horses that are under stress, as in racing and showing.

12. *Oral administration.*—The oral administration of supplemental vitamins is much preferred to the injecting of them, for a number of reasons—not the least of which is lower cost.

UNIDENTIFIED FACTORS

This includes those vitamins which the chemist has not yet isolated and identified. For this reason, they are sometimes referred to as the vitamins of the future. There is mounting evidence of the importance of unidentified factors for both man and swine. Among other things, they lower the incidence of ulcers in each species. Also, for horses, they appear to increase growth, improve feed efficiency and breeding performance when added to rations thought to be complete with regard to known nutrients. The anatomical and physiological mechanism of the digestive system of the horse, plus the stresses and strains to which modern horses are subjected, would indicate the wisdom of adding unidentified factor sources to the ration of the horse; namely, dehydrated alfalfa meal, dried whey, dried brewers grain, dried fish solubles, antibiotic fermentation residue, etc.

Unidentified factors appear to be of special importance during breeding, gestation, lactation and growth.

Water Needs

Water is one of the most vital of all nutrients. In fact, horses can survive for a longer period without feed than they can without water. Yet, comparatively little discussion will be given to this nutrient simply because, under ordinary conditions, it can be readily provided in abundance and at little cost.

Water is one of the largest single constituents of the animal body, varying in amount with condition and age. The younger the animal, the more water it contains. Also, the fatter the animal, the lower the water content. Thus, as an animal matures, it requires proportionately less water on a weight basis, because it consumes less feed per unit of weight and the water content of the body is being replaced by fat.

Water performs the following important functions in horses:

1. It is necessary to the life and shape of every cell and is a constituent of every body fluid.

2. It acts as a carrier for various substances, serving as a medium in which nourishment is carried to the cells and waste products are removed therefrom.

3. It assists with temperature regulation in the body, cooling the animal by evaporation from the skin as perspiration.

4. It is necessary for many important chemical reactions of digestion and metabolism.

5. As a constituent of the synovial fluid, it lubricates the joints; in the cerebrospinal fluid, it acts as a water cushion for the nervous system; in the perilymph in the ear, it transports sound; and in the eye, it is concerned with sight and provides a lubricant for the eye.

Surplus water is excreted from the body, principally in the urine, and to a slight extent in the perspiration, feces, and water vapor from the lungs.

The average mature horse will consume about 12 gallons of water daily—the amount varying according to the type and severity of work (sweating), weather conditions, and the kind of feed consumed. It is recommended that the horse be watered (1) regularly and frequently, and (2) lightly when very warm or thirsty. Water may be given before, during, or after feeding.

Automatic waterers are the modern way to provide clean, fresh water at all times—as nature intended. Also, frequent but small waterings avoid gorging. All waterers should have drains for easy cleaning, and should be heatetd to 40° to 45° F. in cold regions.

Waterers should be available in both stalls and corrals.

NUTRITIVE ALLOWANCES

As used herein, a distinction is made between "nutrient requirements" and "recommended allowances." In nutrient requirements, no margins of safety are provided; whereas in recommended allowances, reasonable margins of safety are provided to allow for variations in feed composition (due to soils on which grown, stage of maturity, weathering, and processing and storage), environment and stress, individuality, etc.

Because of lack of experimental work with light horses, most nutritionists have arrived at estimated nutritive requirements of horses either (1) by proportioning down data on draft horses to a size and weight of light horses, and/or (2) by extrapolating data from cattle. The fallacy of each method is obvious. Draft horse research was conducted on ponderous, quiet beasts, that performed most of their work at the walk—animals that were subjected to few stresses in comparison with today's light horses. Extrapolating from other species (especially cattle) leaves much to be desired, simply because horses are quite different from them, anatomically and physiologically. In brief, employing such methods may be sound arithmetic, but they do not necessarily lead to sound horse feeding.

In presenting the recommended nutritive allowances given in Table 13-8, the author makes no claim to either their perfection, horse experimental derivation, or finality. Rather, they represent his best judgment based on the scientific and practical information presently available, much of it obtained from swine; without regard to fads, foibles, and trade secrets. Also, those using these recommended allowances as guides in horse ration formulations must give consideration to nutrients provided by the ingredients of the ration, for it's the total composition of the finished feed that counts.

A Nutrient Deficiency May Limit Performance

Nutrient deficiencies in horse rations can be, and often are, limiting factors in reproduction, growth, endurance, speed, etc. It's not unlike the "egg story" presented in Table 13-6.

In the horse, the same principle applies to speed, endurance, and every conceivable type of performance.

Table 13-6

HOW MANY EGGS WILL BE PRODUCED?

If the following nutrients are required for egg production, with each nutrient identified by No. only (for example, No. 1 might be an essential amino acid, No. 2 might be vitamin A., etc., etc.):	If to produce 12 (one doz.) eggs, the total units of each nutrient required are:	If the units of each nutrient present in the ration are:	Comments
No. 1 12		.... 9	The ration lacks 3 units of having enough of this nutrient for 12 eggs.
No. 2 20		.... 30	A surplus; 1/3 more of the nutrient than needed.
No. 3 12		.... 13	Barely over.
No. 4 11		.... 11	Even with the board.
etc.			
etc.			

Conclusion: Nutrient No. 1 will be the limiting factor; only nine eggs can be produced.

Protein Levels of Swine and Horses Compared

The author contends that the protein requirements of horses and hogs are similar because:

1. Both species are single stomached.
2. Neither is equipped to handle much roughage.
3. Both make half their mature weight the first year.
4. Both require high-quality proteins (the essential amino acids).

Table 13-7 shows the comparative recommended protein levels for swine and horses.

Swine rations of approximately the protein content shown in Table 13-7 are the accepted practice. But most horse rations run considerably lower. Even if horse rations meet the National Research Council re-

Table 13-7

RECOMMENDED CRUDE PROTEIN CONTENT

FOR SWINE AND HORSES

	Breeding Animals (% crude protein)	Sucklings (% crude protein)	From Weaning on (% crude protein)
Swine[1]	Sows and boars 14-15	Baby pigs 17-22	Weaning to market 13-18
Horses[2]	Mares and stallions 13-14	Sucklings to past weaning 21	1. Weanlings 14
			2. Half maturity (yearlings and 2-year-olds) 13

[1]From *Swine Science*, by Dr. M. E. Ensminger, 4th ed., 1969.
[2]Recommended for horses, by Dr. M. E. Ensminger.

quirements, it must be remembered that they provide for *minimum* needs only, without margins of safety or provision for stress. With valuable horses it is good business that adequate proteins be provided. Also, it becomes doubly important that sufficient quantity and quality of protein be provided during the critical periods of growth, reproduction, and lactation, and for race and show horses.

Some Recommended Nutrient Allowances

The writer recommends the nutrient allowances given in Table 13-8.

VITAMIN A

Vitamin A is not synthesized in the cecum; thus, it must be provided in the feed, either (1) as vitamin A *per se*, or (2) as carotene, the precursor of vitamin A. In the past, it has been assumed that 1 mg of carotene equals 400 I.U. of vitamin A for beef cattle and horses.[9]

It is now known that cattle are only about 25 percent as efficient as rats in converting carotene to vitamin A. As a result, many beef cattle nutritionists are adding sufficient vitamin A *per se* to meet all the needs for this particular vitamin and completely disregarding the carotene present in the ration. It seems prudent that the same thinking apply in formulating horse rations.

[9]*The Stockman's Handbook*, 3rd ed., footnote on pp. 101 and 108.

There should be adequate vitamin A, but excesses are to be avoided. Exorbitant amounts are costly and wasteful, and they may even be harmful. The latter caution is based on some indications that too high levels of vitamin A over an extended period of time appear to be harmful to man and some animals. The reported vitamin A deficient symptoms are: skin lesions, coarse and falling hair, thin and brittle bones, liver and kidney damage, and degeneration of muscles.

Vitamin A is destroyed by heat, and lost in storage. Storage losses can be materially lessened by adding an anti-oxidant.

Measurement of Vitamin A Potency

The vitamin A potency (whether due to the vitamin itself, to carotene, or to both) of feeds is usually reported in terms of I.U. or U.S.P. units. These two units of measurement are the same. They are based on the growth response of rats, in which several different levels of the test product are fed to different groups of rats, as a supplement to a vitamin A-free diet which has caused growth to cease. A U.S.P. or I.U. is the vitamin A value for rats of 0.30 microgram of pure vitamin A alcohol, or of 0.60 microgram of pure beta-carotene. The carotene or vitamin A content of feeds is commonly determined by colorimetric or spectroscopic methods.

VITAMIN D

With vitamin D, too, there is need for adequacy without harmful excesses. In 1964, Dr. Robert E. Cooke, Director of Pediatrics at Johns Hopkins Hospital, reported[10] evidence that the consumption of high levels of vitamin D by pregnant mothers may cause mental retardation, changes in the bony structure of the face, and effects upon the aortic value of the hearts of babies. Admittedly, more research on the subject is needed.

The author recommends a vitamin D level for horses within the range of about one-seventh the vitamin A level.

CALCIUM AND PHOSPHORUS

The calcium:phosphorus ratio should approach 1:1 as closely as possible. When a legume is used in the ration, this is not easily achieved, due to the high, naturally occurring calcium content of the legume.

---

[10]*New England Journal of Medicine*, 271:117-120 (July 16), 1964.

Table 13-8

RECOMMENDED NUTRIENT ALLOWANCES

	Crude Protein	Crude Fiber	Energy	
	(min. %)	(max. %)	(TDN min. %)	(1,000 Kcal)
Most mature horses (used for race, show, or pleasure)	12	25	53-70[1]	106-140[1]
Broodmares	13	25	50-60	100-120
Stallions	14	25	50-68[2]	100-136[2]
Young equines:				
Foals, 2 weeks to 10 months	21	8	68-74	136-148
Weanlings to 18 months ...	14	20	60	120
18 months to 3 years	13	25	50-60	100-120

Minerals	Daily/1000 Lb. (or 454 Kg) Horse[3]	Per Ton of Finished Feed (basis hay and grain combined)[4]
Salt	2.0 oz. (56 grams) (plus free choice)	10 lbs.
Calcium ....(g)	30	5.25 lbs. (0.5% Ca)
Phosphorus................(g)	30	5.25 lbs. (0.45% p)
	(mg)	(g)
Magnesium	3200	256
Iron	640	51.2
Zinc	400	32.0
Manganese	160	12.8
Copper	64	5.1
Iodine	4	0.3
Cobalt	1	0.08

Vitamins	Daily/1000 Lb. (or 454 Kg) Horse[3]	Per Ton of Finished Feed (basis hay and grain combined)[4]
Vitamin A ....(USP)	20,000 to 30,000	1,600,000 to 2,400,000
Vitamin D-2 ....(USP)	3,000	240,000
Vitamin E ....(I. U.)	200	16,000
Choline ....(mg)	400	32,000
Pantothenic acid ....(mg)	60	4,800
Niacin.....................(mg)	50	4,000
Thiamine (B$_1$) ....(mg)	25	2,000
Riboflavin..................(mg)	20	1,600
Vitamin K ....(mg)	8	640
Folic acid ....(mg)	2.5	200
Vitamin B$_{12}$ ....(mcg)	125	10,000

[1] The heavier the work, the higher the energy.
[2] Increase the energy immediately before and during the breeding season.
[3] Basis of an allowance of 25 pounds of feed/1000 lb. horse/day, or 2½ lbs./cwt. live weight.
[4] Where hay is fed separately, double this concentration should be added to the concentrate.

Also, it is recommended that the level of both calcium and phosphorus in the total ration of horses be above 0.4 percent.

Nutrient Needs Vary

The feed requirements of horses do not necessarily remain the same from day to day or from period to period. The age and size of the animal; the stage of gestation or lactation of a mare; the kind and degree of activity; climatic conditions; the kind, quality, and amount of feed; the system of management; and the health, condition, and temperament of the animal are all continually exerting a powerful influence in determining its nutritive needs. How well the horseman understands, anticipates, interprets, and meets these requirements usually determines the success or failure of the ration.

No set of instructions, calculator, or book of knowledge can substitute for experience and born horse intuition. Skill and good judgement are essential.

APPLIED HORSE FEEDING

Skill and good judgment enter into the success or failure of feeding horses more than into that of any other class of stock. Under similar conditions, two caretakers may obtain widely different results. In one stable, the horses may have animation, nerve, speed, and endurance—ample evidence that they are in the best of condition. In the other, the lack of speed, dull eye, and rough coat show, better than words can express, the lack of judgment in feeding and management.

Results More Important Than Cost per Bag

It's net returns that count! And, it may well be added, horsemen generally get about what they pay for. This is true whether it be a suit of clothes, a dinner, or a horse feed. Thus, horse feed should be bought on the basis of quality, rather than what is cheapest—results are more important than cost per bag.

How to Balance a Horse Ration

A good horseman should know how to balance a ration. Then, if the occasion demands, he can do so. Perhaps of even greater importance, he will then be able more intelligently to select and buy rations with informed appraisal, to check on how well his manufacturer (or dealer) is meeting his guarantees, and to evaluate the results.

The author has already made clear his position relative to most recommended "nutritive requirements" and "recommended allowances" for horses (see earlier section under "Nutritive Allowances." Hence, the stated allowances given in the two examples that follow are his "recommended allowances," and not "minimum requirements."

Two problems are stated here, followed by their solutions—an exercise on how to balance a ration.

Problem No. 1: Prepare a balanced ration for a 1,000 pound lactating mare.

Step by step, here is how it's done:

1. *Set down the desired allowances.*—In order to balance a ration, it is first necessary to know what allowances we wish to meet. Here they are for a 1,000 pound lactating mare (see Table 13-8).

Daily feed[11]	Crude protein[12]	Digestible protein[13]	TDN[12]	Calcium[12]	Phosphorus[12]	Vitamin A[12]	Vitamin D[12]
(lbs.)	(%)	(%)	(%)	(%)	(%)	(I.U.)	(I.U.)
25	13	9.1	50-60	0.5	0.45	20,000-30,000	3,000

2. *Apply the "trial-and-error method"*—Next, let us see if we can meet these desired allowances by using a ration of equal parts of oats and timothy hay.

	Daily feed	Crude protein	Digestible protein	TDN	Calcium	Phosphorus	Vitamin A	Vitamin D
	(lbs.)	(%)	(%)	(%)	(%)	(%)	(I.U.)	(I.U.)
Timothy Hay (late cut)........	12.5	6.8	3.1	45	.37	.19	7,333	922
Oats.................	12.5	11.8	9.4	60	.11	.39	0	0
	25.0	9.3	6.3	52.5	.24	.29	7,333	922

Upon checking the above with step 1 (the allowances that we wish to meet), it is quite obvious that a ration of equal parts of timothy hay and oats is very unsatisfactory for the 1,000 pound broodmare; it is low in protein, calcium, phosphorus, vitamin A, and vitamin D. The only requisites that it meets are to provide 25 pounds of feed daily and barely enough TDN.

3. *Let's add some other ingredients.*—Oats and timothy hay can be

---

[11]From section on "Amount to Feed" of this chapter.
[12]From Table 13-8 of this chapter.
[13]Assuming a 70% digestibility of protein.

used, provided they are balanced with certain other ingredients. Here's how:

Ingredients	Daily feed	Crude protein	Digestible protein	TDN	Calcium	Phosphorus	Vitamin A	Vitami
	(lbs.)	(%)	(%)	(%)	(%)	(%)	(I.U.)	(I.U
Timothy (late cut)..................	12.5	6.8	3.1	45.0	.37	.19		
Oats...................................	.5	11.8	9.4	60.0	.11	.39		
Alfalfa meal sun cured	2.6	15.4	11.1	53.2	1.46	.31		
Corn (Grade No. 2)	.8	9.3	7.2	80.0	.02	.33		
Wheat bran...........................	1.8	16.0	13.0	78.0	.08	.74		
Molasses (cane)	2.5	3.2	—0—	72.0	.89	.08		
Linseed meal (exp.)................	1.7	35.3	30.6	75.5	.37	.86		
Soybean meal (exp.)..............	2.2	43.8	36.8	73.0	.27	.63		
Salt......................................	.1							
Dicalcium phosphate.............	.2				27.00	19.07		
Premix min.-vit.	.1							
	25.0	13.2	9.3	55.8	.75	.51	57,500[14]	11,25

This is an excellent ration. It contains adequate amounts of protein, TDN, calcium, phosphorus, vitamin A, and vitamin D; and the calcium:phosphorus ratio is a very excellent 1.5:1.

Problem No. 2: A horseman grows his own oats and alfalfa-bromegrass hay. He wants to balance these feeds out for a 600 pound weanling, 10 months of age, that is expected to weigh 1,200 pounds when mature—using a commercial protein supplement carrying the following guarantees:

Brand X, 25% Supplement	Guarantee	
	(min.) %	(max.) %
Crude protein.....................................	25	
Fiber..		8.0
Fat...	2.75	
Calcium...	1.5	
Phosphorus	1.0	
Salt..		0.75
Ash		12.0
TDN	65.0	
Vitamin A, I. U./lb............................	17,250	
Vitamin D, I. U./lb............................	3,375	

[14]Obtained in the premix. Vitamin A and D from other sources not computed.

Step by step, here is the answer to Problem No. 2:

1. *Set down the desired allowances*—Here they are for a 600 pound weanling (see Table 13-8):

Daily[15] feed	Crude[16] protein	Digestible[17] protein	TDN[16]
(lbs.)	*(%)*	*(%)*	*(%)*
13.1	14	9.8	60.0

Calcium[16]	Phosphorus[16]	Vitamin A[16]	Vitamin D[16]
(%)	*(%)*	*(I. U.)*	*(I. U.)*
0.50	0.45	15,000	1,800

2. *Apply the trial and error method*—To start with, let's estimate that about 1½ pounds of the 25% supplement would balance this ration:

Ingredients	Daily feed	Crude protein	Digestible protein	TDN	Calcium	Phosphorus	Vitamin A	Vitamin D
	(lbs.)	*(%)*	*(%)*	*(%)*	*(%)*	*(%)*	*(I.U.)*	*(I.U.)*
lfa-brome hay	6	11.8	7.6	47.9	.77	.20		
s	6	11.8	9.4	60.0	.11	.39		
supplement	1.5	25.0	17.5	65.0	1.50	1.00	25,875	5,062
	13.5	13.2	9.5	55.1	.55	.37	25,875[18]	5,062[18]

This is a good ration. However, it could be improved by using alfalfa hay in place of alfalfa-brome hay and by using equal parts of oats and corn instead of oats alone, thereby obtaining more protein and TDN (energy).

A Feed for Every Need

The nutritive requirements of all farm animals vary according to age, weight, use or demands, growth, stage of gestation or lactation, and environment. Horses are no exception.

For swine, the following distinct and different rations are usually formulated:[19]

1. For early weaned (2 to 3 weeks of age) pigs.
2. For creep feeding suckling pigs.

---

[15]From section on "Amount to Feed," of this chapter.
[16]From table 13-8 of this chapter.
[17]Assuming a 70% digestibility of protein.
[18]Obtained in the premix. Vitamins A and D from other sources not computed.
[19]Ensminger, M. E., *Swine Science*, 4th ed., chapter VI.

3. Confinement growing-finishing rations for—
   a. 45-75 pounds weight
   b. 75-130 pounds weight
   c. 130-220 pounds weight
4. Pasture growing-finishing rations for—
   a. 45-75 pounds weight
   b. 75-130 pounds weight
   c. 130-220 pounds weight
5. For gestating gilts and sows, and for boars.
6. For lactating gilts and sows.

Thus, several different rations are commonly used for hogs.

It would appear, therefore, that the horse feeds shown in Table 13-9 are necessary if one is (1) to meet every need, and (2) to feed horses as well as most pigs are fed.

Table 13-9

HORSE FEEDS AND NEEDS

Needed Horse Feeds	Prevailing Conditions	Crude Protein (%)	Used for
Complete (hay and grain combined in a pellet)	For the horseman who must buy all feeds.	13	All horses 10 mo. or older.
Concentrate	For the horseman who has satisfactory hay and/or pasture.	14	All horses 10 mo. or older.
Protein supplement	For supplementing available hay and grain.	25	All horses 10 mo. or older.
Foal ration	For creep feeding.	21	2 wk. to 10 mo. of age.
Protein-salt block	For free-choice feeding in corral or on pasture.	20	All horses 10 mo. of age or older.
Enriched vitamin-trace mineral-unidentified factor supplement	For the horseman who has hay and grain that meet all needs except vitamin-trace mineral-unidentified factors.		All horses not receiving any of above feeds.

FEEDING THE BROODMARE

Broodmares need a ration that will meet their own body needs plus (1) meeting the body needs of the fetus, or (2) furnishing the nutrients required for milk production. If work is also being performed, additional energy feeds must be provided. Moreover, for the young, growing mare additional proteins, minerals, and vitamins, above the ordinary requirements, must be provided; otherwise, the fetus will not develop normally, or milk will be produced at the expense of the tissues of the dam. Also, protein deficiency may affect undesirably the fertility of the mare.

Most of the growth of the fetus occurs during the last third of pregnancy, thus the reproductive requirements are greatest during this period. In this connection, it is noteworthy that the cannon bones (the lower leg bones extending from the knees and hocks to the fetlocks) are as long at the time of birth as they will ever be, and that in an amazingly short time after birth a foal can run almost as fast as its mother. This points up the importance of bone-building minerals and vitamins for the broodmare.

As with the females of all species, the nutritive requirements for milk production in the mare are much more rigorous than the pregnancy requirements. It is estimated that, two months following foaling, mares of mature weights of 600, 800, 1,000, and 1,200 pounds may produce 36, 42, 44, and 49 pounds of milk daily. Thus, it can be appreciated that a mare's feed requirements during the suckling period are not far different from those of a high-producing dairy cow. In general, it is important that the ration of the gestating-lactating mare supply sufficient energy, protein, calcium and phosphorus; and vitamins A and D (the D being provided through the feed if the animal is not exposed to sunlight), and riboflavin.

Broodmares should be kept in thrifty condition, but they should not be allowed to become too fat nor too thin.

The correct feeding of a broodmare that is worked is often simpler than the feeding of an idle one, for the condition of the animal can be regulated more carefully under working conditions. In addition to a ration that will meet the maintenance and work requirements largely through high-energy feeds, the working broodmare needs ample protein, calcium, and phosphorus with which to take care of the growth of the fetus and/or milk production.

The broodmare should be fed and watered with care immediately before and after foaling. For the first 24 hours after parturition, she may have a little hay and a limited amount of water from which the chill has been taken. A light feed of bran or a wet bran mash is suitable for the first feed and the following meal may consist of oats or a mixture of oats and bran. A reasonably generous allowance of good-quality hay is permissible after the first day. If confined to the stable, as may be necessary in inclement weather, the mare should be kept on a limited and light grain and hay ration for about 10 days after foaling. Feeding too much grain at this time is likely to produce digestive disturbances in the mare; and even more hazardous, it may produce too much milk, which may cause indigestion in the foal. If weather conditions are favorable and it is possible to allow the mare to foal on a clean, lush pasture, she will regulate her own feed needs most admirably.

In comparison with geldings or unbred mares, the following differences in feeding gestating-lactating broodmares should be observed:

1. A greater quantity of feed is necessary—usually about 20 to 50 percent more—the highest requirement being during lactation.

2. Dusty or moldy feed and frozen silage should be avoided in feeding all horses, but especially in feeding the broodmare, for such feed may produce complications and possible abortion.

3. More proteins are necessary for the broodmare.

4. More attention must be given to supplying the necessary minerals and vitamins.

5. The bowels should be carefully regulated through the providing of regular exercise and the feeding of such laxative feeds as bran, linseed meal, and alfalfa hay.

6. A few days before and after foaling, the ration should be decreased and lightened by using wheat bran.

7. Regular and ample exercise is a necessary adjunct to proper feeding of the broodmare.

FEEDING THE STALLION

"Reduce the ration and increase the exercise when the stallion is not a sure breeder" has been the advice given to many worried stallion owners. In all too many instances, little thought is given to the feeding and care of the stallion, other than during the breeding season. The program throughout the entire year should be such as to keep the stallion in a vigorous, thrifty condition at all times. Immediately before the breeding season, the feed might very well be increased in quantity so that the stallion will gain in weight. The quantity of grain fed will vary with the individual temperament and feeding ability of the stallion, the work and exercise provided, services allowed, available pastures, and quality of roughage. Usually this will be between ¾ and 1½ pounds daily of the grain mixture per 100 pounds weight, together with a quantity of hay within the same range.

During the breeding season, the stallion's ration should contain more protein and additional minerals and vitamins than are given in rations fed work horses or stallions not in service. During the balance of the year (when not in service), the stallion may be provided a ration like that of other horses similarly handled.

In addition to the grain and roughage, there should be free access to a mineral supplement and salt. These should be placed in separate compartments of a suitable box. During the winter months or when little work or exercise is provided, the stallion should receive a succulent feed such as carrots or silage (carrots or silage should be neither moldy nor frozen). Also, laxative feeds, such as wheat bran or linseed meal, should be supplied at these times. Plenty of fresh, clean water should be provided at all times. Drugs or stock tonics should not be fed in an attempt to increase virility.

Overfitted, heavy stallions should be regarded with suspicion, for they may be uncertain breeders. On the other hand, a poor, thin, run-down condition is also to be avoided.

FEEDING THE YOUNG HORSE

As with all young mammals, milk from the dam gives the foal a good start in life. Within 30 minutes to 2 hours after birth, the foal should be up on its feet and getting the colostrum.

But milk is not the perfect food, as once claimed. It is deficient in iron and copper, with the result that suckling young may suffer from anemia. This may be prevented, and increased growth, durability, and soundness may be obtained by creep feeding foals.

FEEDING FOALS BEFORE WEANING

The need for a creep feeding program, starting early in life, is due to the decline in mare's milk in both quantity and nutrients following foaling. The Michigan Station[20] reported that the crude protein content of the milk dropped from 19.1 percent within 30 minutes after birth of the foal, to 3.8 percent 12 hours later, and 2.2

[20]Ullrey, D. E., et al., Journal of Animal Science, Vol. 25, No. 1, February 1966, pp. 217-222.

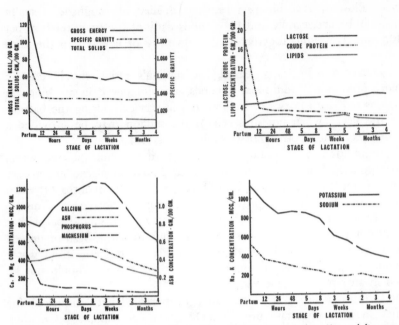

Fig. 13-10. Changes in mare's milk at different stages of lactation: *Upper left.*—gross energy, specific gravity, and total solids; *Upper right.*—lactose, crude protein, and lipids; *Lower left.*—calcium, ash, phosphorus, and magnesium; and *Lower right.*—potassium and sodium. (Courtesy, D. E. Ullrey, Department of Animal Husbandry, Michigan State University)

percent 2 months later. Also, the gross energy, total solids, ash, magnesium, and sodium in mare's milk were relatively high at birth, but dropped rather abruptly 12 hours later, then declined more slowly (see Figure 13-10).

When the foal is between 10 days and 3 weeks of age, it will begin to nibble on grain and hay. In order to promote thrift and early development and to avoid setback at weaning time, it is important to encourage the foal to eat supplementary feed as early as possible. For this purpose, a low-built grain box should be provided especially for the foal; or, if on pasture, the foal may be creep fed.

The choice between creep and individual feeding can be left to the horseman; the important thing is that the foals receive supplemental feed.

A creep is an enclosure for feeding purposes, made accessible to the foal(s), but through which the dam cannot pass. For best results, the creep should be built at a spot where the mares are inclined to loiter. The ideal location is on high ground, well drained, in the shade, and near the place of watering. Keeping the salt supply nearby will be helpful in holding mares near the creep.

It is important that foals be started on feed carefully, and at an early age. At first only a small amount of feed should be placed in the trough each day, any surplus being removed and given to other horses. In this manner, the feed will be kept clean and fresh, and the foals will not be consuming any moldy or sour feed.

When foals are on luxuriant pasture and their mothers are milking well, difficulty may be experienced in getting them to eat. Thus, patience on the part of the caretaker is extremely important. However, foals are curious. Usually, they'll examine a creep. But it may be necessary to start them on the creep ration by first letting them nibble a little feed from the hand.

At four to five weeks of age, the normal healthy foal should be consuming ½ pound of grain daily per 100 pounds of live weight. By weaning time, this should be increased to about ¾ pound or more

Fig. 13-11. Creep at Murrieta Stud, Murrieta, California. Note the protective rubber ends on the feeder. (Courtesy, F. W. Koester, Editor, and B. K. Beckwith, Associate Editor, The Thoroughbred of California)

per 100 pounds live weight (or 6 to 8 pounds of feed/head/day), the exact amount varying with the individual and the development desired.

Because of the difficulty in formulating and home-mixing a foal ration, the purchase of a good commercial feed usually represents a wise investment.

In addition to its grain ration, the foal should be given good-quality hay (preferably a legume) or pasture.

Free access to salt and a suitable mineral mixture should be provided. The mineral will be consumed to best advantage if placed in a convenient place and under shelter; or it may be incorporated in the ration. Plenty of fresh water must be available at all times.

Under such a system of care and management, the foal will become less dependent upon its dam, and the weaning process will be facilitated. If properly cared for, foals will normally attain one-half of their mature weight during the first year. Most Thorough-bred and Standardbred breeders plan to have the animals attain full height by the time they are two years of age. However, such results require liberal feeding from the beginning.

It is well recognized that the forced development of race, show, and sale horses must be done expertly if the animals are to remain durable and sound. Also, and equally important, a foal stunted in the first year by insufficient feeding cannot be developed properly later in life.

THE WEANLING

Perhaps the most critical period in the entire life of a horse is that interval from weaning time (about six months of age) until one year of age. Foals suckling their dams and receiving no grain may develop very satisfactorily up to weaning time. However, lack of preparation prior to weaning and neglect following the separation from the dam may prevent the animal from gaining proper size and shape. The primary objective in the breeding of horses is the economical production of a well-developed, sound individual at maturity. To achieve this result requires good care and management of weanlings.

As previously indicated, no great setback or disturbances will be encountered at weaning time provided that the foals have developed a certain independence from proper grain feedings during the suckling period. Generally, weanlings should receive 1 to 1½ pounds of grain and 1½ to 2 pounds of hay daily per each 100 pounds of live weight. The amount of feed will vary somewhat with the individuality of the animal, the quality of roughage, available pastures, the price of feeds, and whether the weanling is being developed for show, race, or sale. Naturally, animals being developed for early use or sale should be fed more liberally, although it is equally important to retain clean, sound joints, legs, and feet—a condition which cannot be obtained so easily in heavily fitted animals.

Because of the rapid development of bone and muscle in weanlings, it is important that, in addition to ample quantity of feed, the ration also provide quality of proteins, and adequate minerals and vitamins.

THE YEARLING

If foals have been fed and cared for so that they are well grown and thrifty as yearlings, usually little difficulty will be experienced at any later date.

Yearlings that are being grown for show or sale should be fed while on pasture. They should be kept up in the daytime during the hot days and turned out at night (because of not being exposed to sunshine, adequate vitamin D must be provided). This point needs to be emphasized when forced development is desired; for, good as pastures may be, they are roughages rather than concentrates.

The winter feeding program for the rising two-year-olds should be such as to produce plenty of bone and muscle rather than fat. From ½ to 1 pound of grain and 1 to 1½ pounds of hay should be fed for each 100 pounds of live weight. The quantity will vary with the quality of the roughage, the individuality of the animal, and the use for which the animal is produced. In producing for sale, more liberal feeding may be economical. Access to salt and to a mineral mixture should be provided at all times; or the minerals should be incorporated in the ration. An abundance of fresh, pure water must be available.

THE TWO- AND THREE-YEAR-OLDS

Except for the fact that the two- and three-year-olds will be larger, and, therefore, will require more feed, a description of their proper care and management would be merely a repetition of the principles that have already been discussed for the yearling.

With the two-year-old that is to be raced, however, the care and feeding at this time become matters of extreme importance. Once the young horse is placed in training, the ration should be adequate enough to allow for continued development and to provide necessary maintenance and additional energy for work. This means that special attention must be given to providing adequate proteins, minerals, and vitamins in the ration. Overexertion must be avoided, the animal must be properly groomed, and the feet must be cared for properly. In brief, every precaution must be taken if the animal is to remain sound —a most difficult task when animals are raced at an early age, even though the right genetic make-up and the proper environment are present.

Fitting for Show or Sale

Each year, many horses are fitted for shows or sales. In both cases, a fattening process is involved, but exercise is doubly essential.

For horses that are being fitted for shows, the conditioning process is also a matter of hardening, and the horses are used daily in harness or under saddle. Regardless of whether a sale or a show is the major objective, fleshing should be obtained without sacrificing action or soundness or without causing filling of the legs and hocks.

In fattening horses, the animals should be brought to full feed rather gradually, until the ration reaches a maximum of about 2 pounds of grain daily for each 100 pounds of live weight. When on full feed, horses make surprising gains. Daily weight gains of 4 to 5 pounds are not uncommon. Such animals soon become fat, sleek, and attractive. This is probably the basis for the statement that "fat will cover up a multitude of sins in a horse."

Although exercise is desirable from the standpoint of keeping the animals sound, it is estimated that such activity decreases the daily rate of gains by as much as 20 percent. Because of the greater cost of gains and the expense involved in bringing about forced exercise, most feeders of sale horses limit the exercise to that obtained naturally from running in a paddock.

In comparison with finishing cattle or sheep, there is more risk in fattening horses. Heavily fed horses kept in idleness are likely to become blemished and injured through playfulness, and there are more sicknesses among liberally fed horses than in other classes of stock handled in a similar manner.

In fitting show horses, the finish must remain firm and hard, the action superb, and the soundness unquestioned. Thus, they must be carefully fed, groomed, and exercised to bring them to proper bloom.

Training is also extremely important in preparing for the show-ring. Horsemen who fit and sell yearlings or younger animals may feed a palatable milk replacer or commercial feed to advantage.

Feeding Racehorses

In a study made by the author,[21] it was found that, on the average, it costs $5,099 to produce and raise a Thoroughbred to two years of age, plus an added cost of $3,410 to keep him in training the first year. Thus, when a Thoroughbred breaks down permanently at the end of the third year, following one year in training and on the track, an investment of $8,509 is involved. Obviously, the stakes are high to keep him sound and running.

It is recognized that some unsoundnesses may be inherited, others may be due to accident and injury, and still others may be due to subjecting horses to stress and strain far beyond the capability of even the best structure and tissue. However, nutritional deficiencies appear to be the major cause of unsoundnesses.

Racehorses are equine athletes whose nutritive requirements are the most exacting, but the most poorly met, of all animals. This statement may be shocking to some, but it's true for the reasons that follow:

Racehorses are commonly:

1. Started in training very shortly past 12 months of age, which is comparable to an adolescent boy or girl doing sweatshop labor.

2. Moved from track to track under all sorts of conditions.

3. Trained the year around, raced innumerable times each year, and forced to run when fatigued.

4. Outdoors only a short time each day—usually before sun-up, with the result that the sun's rays have little chance to produce vitamin D from the cholesterol in the skin.

5. Without opportunity for even a few mouthfuls of grass—a rich, natural source of the B vitamins and unidentified factors.

6. Fed oats, grass hay, and possibly bran—produced in unknown areas, and on soils of unknown composition. Such an oats-grass hay-bran ration is almost always deficient in vitamins A and D and the B vitamins, and lopsided and low in calcium and phosphorus.

7. Given a potion of some concoction of questionable value—if not downright harmful.

By contrast, human athletes—college football teams and partici-

---

[21]See Appendix of this book, section on "Practices and Problems of Horsemen."

pants in the Olympics, for example—are usually required to eat at a special training table, supervised by nutrition experts. They are fed the best diet that science can formulate and technology can prepare. It's high in protein, rich in readily available energy, and fortified and balanced in vitamins and minerals.

It's small wonder, therefore, that so many equine athletes go unsound, whereas most human athletes compete year after year until overtaken by age.

Indeed, high strung and highly stressed, racehorses need special rations just as human athletes do—and for the same reasons; and, the younger the age, the more acute the need. This calls for rations high in protein, rich in readily available energy, fortified with vitamins, minerals, and unidentified factors—and with all nutrients in proper balance.

A racehorse is asked to develop a large amount of horsepower in a period of one to three minutes. The oxidations that occur in a racehorse's body are at a higher pitch than in a draft horse, and, therefore, more vitamins are required. In this connection, it is noteworthy that the late Clyde Beatty, great animal trainer of the circus, sweated off a pound every 18-minute performance,[22] under stress.

Also, racehorses are the *prima donnas* of the equine world; most of them are temperamental, and no two of them can be fed alike. They vary in rapidity of eating, in the quantity of feed that they will consume, in the proportion of concentrate to roughage that they will take, and in response to different caretakers. Thus, for best results, they must be fed as individuals.

Most racehorse rations are deplorably deficient in protein, simply because they are based on the minimum requirements of little-stressed, slow, plodding draft horses.

During the racing season, the hay of a racehorse should be limited to 7 or 8 pounds, whereas the concentrate allowance may range up to 16 pounds. Heavy roughage eaters may have to be muzzled, to keep them from eating their bedding. A bran mash is commonly fed once a week.

FEEDS AND THEIR PREPARATION

Individual feeds vary widely in feeding value. Oats and barley, for example, differ in feeding value according to the hull content

---

[22]*Time*, July 30, 1965, p. 55.

and weight per bushel, and forages vary according to the stage of maturity at which they are cut and how well they are cured and stored. Also, the feeding value of certain feeds is materially affected by preparation.

Regardless of the feeds selected, they should be of sound quality, and not moldy, spoiled, or dusty. This applies to both hay and grain. This careful selection of feeds is more important for horses than for any other class of livestock.

The sad truth is that many horses manage to exist in spite of the feed, and not because of it. This becomes evident when one compares the nutrients in a ration consisting of oats and stemmy timothy hay with the recommended nutrient allowances.

Not too many years ago, alfalfa hay was not considered fit feed for a horse. Today, some horsemen are feeding it exclusively, with good results.

Selection of Feeds

In general, successful horsemen use well balanced rations, with special consideration given to supplying quality protein, the proper minerals, and the necessary vitamins. Attention is also given to the laxative or constipating qualities of feeds and the palatability of the ration.

DISTANCE LENDS ENCHANTMENT

Many horsemen believe not only that there is something magical about certain horse feeds, but that they must be grown in a specific area(s). For example, timothy hay and oats are frequently extolled on the basis that they are grown in certain "name" areas; they are even referred to as "racehorse oats" or "racehorse timothy hay." Such specialty areas may produce superior products, but their feeding value is generally exaggerated far beyond their price with much of their added cost going for hundreds of miles of transportation and for middlemen.

Concentrates

Unlike ruminants, horses cannot handle very large quantities of roughages. Moreover, horses used for heavy work, for pleasure, or for racing must be even more restricted in their roughage allowance and should receive a higher proportion of concentrates.

Because of less bulk and lower shipping and handling costs, the concentrates used for horse feeding are less likely to be locally grown than the roughages. Even so, the vast majority of grains fed to horses are home grown, thus varying from area to area, according to the grain crops best adapted.

Of all the concentrates, heavy oats most nearly meet the needs of horses; and, because of the uniformly good results obtained from their use, they have always been recognized as the leading grain for horses. Corn is also widely used as a horse feed, particularly in the Central States. Despite occasional prejudice to the contrary, barley is a good horse feed. As proof of the latter fact, if such evidence is necessary, it might be pointed out that the Arab—who was a good horseman— fed barley almost exclusively. Also, wheat, wheat bran, and commercial mixed feeds are extensively used. It is to be emphasized, therefore, that careful attention should be given to the prevailing price of feeds available locally, for many feeds are well suited to horses. Often substitutions can be made that will result in a marked saving without affecting the nutritive value of the ration. When corn or other heavy grains are fed, it is important that a little linseed meal or wheat bran be used, in order to regulate the bowels.

Hay

Through mistaken kindness or carelessness, horses are often fed too much hay or other roughage, and labored breathing and quick tiring are the result. With cattle and sheep, on the other hand, it is usually well to feed all the roughage they will eat. This difference between horses and ruminants is due primarily to the relatively small size of the simple stomach of the horse in comparison with the four-fold stomach of the ruminant.

When limiting the allowance of roughage, it is sometimes necessary to muzzle greedy horses (gluttons) to prevent them from eating the bedding.

Usually, young horses and idle horses can be provided with an unlimited allowance of hay. But one should gradually increase the grain and decrease the hay as work or training begins.

Much good will result from feeding young and idle horses more roughage and less grain.

The hay should be early cut, leafy, green, well cured, and free from dust and mold. Hay native to the locality is usually fed. However, horsemen everywhere prefer good-quality timothy. With young stock and breeding animals especially, it is desirable that a sweet grass-legume mixture of alfalfa hay be fed. The legume provides a source of high-quality proteins and certain minerals and vitamins.

Horses like variety. Therefore, if at all possible, it is wise to have more than one kind of hay in the stable. For example, timothy may be provided at one feeding and a grass-legume mixed hay at the other feeding. Good horsemen often vary the amount of alfalfa fed, for increased amounts of alfalfa in the ration will increase urination and give a softer consistency to the bowel movements. This means that elimination from kidneys and bowels can be carefully regulated by the amount and frequency of alfalfa feedings. Naturally, such regulation becomes more necessary with irregular use and idleness. On the other hand, in some areas alfalfa is fed as the sole roughage with good results.

Silage

Well-preserved silage of good quality, free from mold and not frozen, affords a highly nutritious succulent forage for horses during the winter months. *As horses are more susceptible than cattle or even sheep to botulism or other digestive disturbances resulting from the feeding of poor silage, none but choice, fresh silage should ever be fed.*

Various types of silages may be fed successfully to horses, but corn silage and grass-legume silage are most common. If the silage contains much grain, the concentrate allowance should be reduced accordingly.

Good as the silage may be, it should not be used as the only roughage for horses. Usually it should be fed in such quantity as to replace not more than one-third to one-half of the roughage ration, considering that ordinarily 1 pound of hay is equivalent to approximately 3 pounds of wet silage. This means that the silage allowance usually does not exceed 10 to 15 pounds daily per head for mature animals, although much larger amounts have been used satisfactorily in some instances. Silage is especially suited for the winter feeding of idle horses, broodmares, and growing foals.

Antibiotics

The newer knowledge of antibiotics—products of molds, bacteria, and green plants—dates from the discovery of penicillin by Dr. Alexander Fleming, a British scientist, in 1928.[23] Quite by accident, a stray

---

[23]Actually, the presence of antibiotics was known much earlier than the discovery of penicillin, but no commercial use was made of them.

mold spore floated in on the breeze, and landed on a culture plate of bacteria with which Dr. Fleming was working. It inhibited the growth of the bacteria. Dr. Fleming correctly interpreted his observation—the possible value of the mold in the treatment of disease, thus ushering in the antibiotic era. However, penicillin did not come into prominence until 10 years later, and it was not until 1944 that streptomycin, the second most widely known of the antibiotics, was discovered by Waksman, a soil microbiologist, and his colleagues at the New Jersey station.

The author was a member of the research team that conducted the first U. S. study on feeding antibiotics to foals, which study was subsequently used in obtaining Food and Drug Administration approval for feeding aureomycin to foals. This experiment revealed that an 85 milligram level of aureomycin, fed to foals from 5 days of age to 5 months, produced 22 pounds more weight.[24]

Certain antibiotics, at stipulated levels, are approved by the Food and Drug Administration for growth promotion and for the improvement of feed efficiency of young equines up to one year of age. Also, antibiotics are used for therapeutic purposes by veterinarians.

It appears that antibiotics may be especially helpful for young foals which suffer setbacks from infections, digestive disturbances, inclement weather, and other stress factors. Also, horses may benefit from antibiotics (1) when being transported from one location to another—for example, when being moved to a new show or track; (2) when there is a low disease level in the herd; or (3) when mares are foaling.

The poorer the feed, the greater the response from antibiotics; and the poorer the management, the greater the response from antibiotics. It follows, therefore, that there is a temptation to use antibiotics as a "crutch," rather than improve the regimen.

When used in feed, the level of antibiotics should be in keeping with the directions of the manufacturer and with the Food and Drug Administration standards.

Processing Grains

If properly done, steam rolling of grains is preferred to grinding for horses, because the ration is lighter and fluffier, and fewer digestive disturbances are encountered. However, there is great variation

---

[24]Washington Agricultural Experiment Station Circular 263, April 1955.

in steam rolling. Altogether too much steam rolling consists in exposing the grain to steam for 3 to 5 minutes, using a temperature of about 180°F., and adding an unknown amount of moisture. Such processing is little better than dry rolling.

Recent experimental studies at the University of Arizona, with cattle, showed that proper steam rolling of barley and milo is achieved as follows: The grain should be subjected to 20 pounds of steam pressure for 20 minutes, at approximately 205°F.; then at this temperature, and with 18 to 20 percent moisture content, it should be run through large rollers operated at one-third to one-half capacity, and rolled to thin flakes. Of course, excess moisture must be removed prior to storage.

Dry rolling, crimping, and grinding can be, and are, used in preparing horse feeds. The important thing is to keep the grain as coarse as possible and to avoid fines.

A very attractive and palatable mixed feed concentrate can be

Fig. 13-12. Milo properly steam rolled into dustless flakes. (Courtesy, Dr. Al Lane, Extension Livestock Specialist, The University of Arizona. From *Horse Feeding*, Circular 288, The University of Arizona)

prepared by flaking the grains and pelleting the fines. However, feeds prepared in this manner are very subject to mustiness; hence, it is important that they not contain excess moisture, and that they be stored properly.

Pelleting

The preparation of feeds by pelleting may be, and is, applied to (1) concentrates alone, (2) forage alone, and (3) concentrates and roughage combined in a complete ration.

COMPLETE ALL-PELLETED RATIONS

Currently, horsemen are much interested in complete, all-pelleted rations, in which the hay and grain are combined—a development which has increased with mechanization and automation. It is note-worthy, however, that all-pelleted horse feeds are not new. They were used extensively by both the German and Russian armies during World War II.

The use of all-pelleted rations for horses will increase in the years ahead because:

1. Pelleted feeds are less bulky (pelleted roughage requires one-fifth to one-third as much space as is required by the same roughage in loose or chopped form) and easier to store and handle—thus lessening transportation, building, and labor costs. For these reasons, it is particularly advantageous to use pelleted feeds where storage space is limited and feed must be transported considerable distances, conditions which frequently characterize small enterprises and the suburban horse owner.

2. Pelleting prevents horses from selectively refusing ingredients likely to be high in certain dietary essentials; each bite is a balanced feed.

3. Pelleting practically eliminates wastage. Since horses may waste up to 20 percent of long hay, less pelleted feed is required. Wastage of conventional feed is highest where low-quality hay is fed and/or feed containers are poorly designed.

4. Pelleting eliminates dustiness and lessens heaves.

5. Pellet-fed horses are trimmer in the middle and more attractive, due to their consuming less bulk—there are no "hay bellies."

Those who have tried all-pelleted (grain and hay combined) rations are very enthusiastic about them. Based on experiments and observations, the following comments are pertinent to the proper understanding and use of all-pelleted rations:

1. One-half inch pellets are preferred for mature horses, and one-fourth inch pellets for weanlings and short yearlings. Also, very hard pellets should be avoided; if horses cannot chew them, they will spit them out.

2. It is recommended that the ratio of roughage to concentrate be higher in all-pelleted rations than when long hay is fed. For most horses, 60.5 to 69 percent roughage and 31 to 39.5 percent concentrate is about right.

3. It is important that any horse feed form a loose mass in the stomach, thereby assuring (a) ease of digestion, (b) fewer digestive disturbances, and (c) less impaction. To this end, in a complete (all-pelleted) ration, such feeds as oats or barley should be crimped or steam rolled (not finely ground), and the roughage should be ¼ inch chop or coarser. Otherwise, a couple of pounds of long hay may be fed daily to each horse.

The finer the grind (or processing) of feed (hay and grain), the higher the roughage content necessary to minimize digestive disturbances. This is so because coarsely chopped hay and steam rolled grains form a loose mass in the digestive tract, whereas finely processed feeds do not.

4. The heavier the work or the younger the animal, the higher the energy requirement; and the lower the roughage and the higher the concentrate.

5. The lower the roughage and the higher the concentrate, the more horsemen are apt to overfeed and get idle horses, or to get horses at light to medium work too fat. Also, if the total feed consumption is limited too severely in order to hold the weight down, the problem of wood chewing is increased, simply because of a lack of physical filling of the digestive tract.

6. When the roughage consists of high-quality legume hay, a higher percentage of roughage may be used than where grass or other nonlegumes are used—all or in part.

7. If more energy is needed for race or young stock on all-pelleted rations, it can be provided either by (a) increasing the daily allowance of the all-pelleted ration, or (b) replacing a portion of the all-pelleted ration with a suitable concentrate or supplement.

8. Because of eliminating waste, less of all-pelleted feed is required than of conventional rations. For a horse at light work, 14 to 18

pounds daily of a 53 to 56 percent TDN pellet per 1,000 pounds of live weight should be fed. The feed allowance should be increased with the severity of the work.

9. As with any change in feed, the switch to an all-pelleted ration should be made gradually, otherwise such vices as wood chewing and bolting (eating too rapidly) may be induced. Continue to offer all the long hay the horse wants, and slowly replace the grain portion of the conventional ration with the complete pelleted feed. Increase the pelleted feed by 1 to 2 pounds daily while gradually lessening the hay. After a few days, the horse will usually stop eating the hay on its own accord, following which the hay can be completely eliminated.

10. The feces of pellet-fed horses are softer than the feces of those not fed pellets; they are more comparable to those of horses on pasture—as nature intended.

More and more knowledgeable horsemen will feed all-pelleted rations. Also, they will feed them with benefit throughout the life of the horse—beginning with special creep rations for foals, and continuing for horses of all ages, classes, and uses.

The biggest deterrent to increased pelleting at the present time is difficulty of processing chopped forage which is coarse enough so that it will not cause digestive disturbances. A minimum of ¼-inch chop is recommended. One highly successful horseman, who has fed pelleted feed for several years, puts his roughage through a ⅜-inch screen and steam rolls the grain.

All-Pelleted Rations and Wood Chewing

Among many horsemen, the feeling persists that horses on all-pelleted rations are more prone to wood chewing than those fed long hay. Perhaps this is true—at least to some degree. But wherever there's wood, some horses will chew it, regardless of what they're fed. This stems from the fact that pellet-fed horses have more time to indulge in vices, simply because they can eat an all-pelleted ration more quickly than where long hay is involved. As a result, they get bored; and, to pass the time, they chew wood. This leads to the conclusion that there's only one sure way to prevent wood chewing—simply use metal, masonry, or other non-wood materials for all buildings, fences, and other equipment. Of course, this isn't always practical.

But, regardless of the cause of the wood chewing vice, it can be lessened, although not prevented entirely, through one or more of the following management practices:

1. Stepping up the exercise.

2. Feeding three times a day, rather than twice a day, even though the total daily feed allowance remains the same.

3. Spreading out the pellets in a larger feed container, and/or placing a few large stones about the size of a baseball in the feed container, thereby making the horse work harder and longer to obtain his pellets.

4. Providing 2 to 4 pounds of straw or coarse grass hay per animal per day, thereby giving the horse something to nibble on during his spare time.

AMOUNT TO FEED

The main qualities desired in horses are trimness, action, spirit, and endurance. These qualities cannot be obtained with large, paunchy stomachs or lack of energy, which may result from excessive use of roughage. Moreover, a healthy condition is desired, but excess fat is to be avoided. The latter is especially true with horses used for racing, where the carrying of any surplus body weight must be avoided.

The quantity of grain and hay required by horses depends primarily upon the following:

1. The individuality; horses vary in keeping qualities, just as people do. Some horses simply utilize their feed more efficiently than others. A hard keeper will require considerably more feed than an easy keeper when doing the same amount of work.

2. The age, size, and condition of the animal.

3. The kind, regularity, amount, and speed of work performed. With greater speed, the horse requires proportionately greater energy; hence, considerably more concentrate is required when performing work at a trot than a walk.

4. The weather; for example, under ideal October weather conditions in Missouri, a horse may require 14 pounds of 60 percent TDN feed daily, whereas in the same area, the same horse may require 16 pounds daily of the same feed in July and August, and 20 pounds in the winter.

5. Kind, quality, and amount of feed.

6. System of management.

7. Health, condition, and temperament of the animal.

Because the horse has a rather limited digestive capacity, the amount of concentrates must be increased and the roughages decreased when the energy needs rise with the greater amount, severity, or speed of work. The following are general guides for the daily ration of horses under usual conditions:

1. *For horses at light work* (1 to 3 hours per day of riding or driving), allow 2/5 to 1/2 pound of grain and 1¼ to 1½ pounds of hay per day per 100 pounds of live weight.

2. *For horses at medium work* (3 to 5 hours per day of riding or driving), allow ¾ to 1 pound of grain to 1 to 1¼ pounds of hay per 100 pounds of live weight.

3. *For horses at hard work* (5 to 8 hours per day of riding or driving), allow about 1¼ to 1⅓ pounds of grain and 1 to 1¼ pounds of hay per 100 pounds of live weight.

As will be noted from these recommendations, the total allowance of concentrates and hay should be within the range of 2.0 to 2.5 pounds daily per 100 pounds of live weight. No grain should be left from one feeding to the next, and all edible forage should be cleaned up at the end of each day.

About 6 to 12 pounds of grain daily is an average grain ration for a light horse at medium or light work. Racehorses in training usually consume 10 to 16 pounds of grain per day—the exact amount varying with the individual requirements and the amount of work. The hay allowance averages about 1 to 1¼ pounds daily per hundred pounds live weight, but it is restricted as the grain allowance is increased. Light feeders should not be overworked.

It is to be emphasized that the quantities of feeds recommended above are intended as guides only. The feeder will increase the allowance, especially the concentrates, when the horse is too thin, and decrease the feed when the horse is too fat.

The regular practice of turning horses on pasture at night and on idle days is good for the health and well-being of the animals and decreases the quantity of grain and hay required. If the horse must be confined to the stall on idle days, the grain ration should be reduced by 50 percent in order to avoid azoturia or other digestive disturbances. When idle, it is also advisable to add some wheat bran to the ration. A mixture of two-thirds grain and one-third bran is quite satisfactory. Many good horsemen regularly give a feeding of bran, either dry or as a wet mash, on Saturday night.

During off-work seasons, pastures may be used to advantage for idle horses—with or without grain, depending upon the individuality and condition of the horse.

SOME SUGGESTED RATIONS FOR HORSES

Oats, corn, and barley—all farm-grown concentrates—are the grains most commonly used for horses; whereas wheat bran, linseed meal, soybean meal, and cottonseed meal are the favored supplements to the grains. Alfalfa, clover, soybean, timothy, prairie grass, Johnson grass, lespedeza, cereal hays, and dried corn and sorghum fodder constitute the chief forages fed to horses. To be sure, the concentrate and roughage combination used varies in different sections of the United States—home-grown feeds and economy being the primary determining factors. Horses of the West, for example, are fed largely on barley and alfalfa or cereal hay; in the northern Mississippi Valley, the ration consists of oats and corn with timothy or mixed hay for roughage; whereas in the deep South, corn is the leading grain and Johnson grass, lespedeza, and corn fodder the chief roughages.

The addition of a few sliced carrots to the ration and an occasional bran mash, or a small amount of linseed meal, are desirable, particularly during the wintering period. Also, such feeds may be used in regulating the bowels, on idle days, and at other times as required. Such cooling feeds should be given also to horses whose legs must undergo blistering or firing; for they reduce the tendency toward feverish, inflammatory symptoms. Care must be taken to prevent the animal from getting flabby or washy from too much soft feed while undergoing treatment. Whether the animal is working or idle, the trainer must never relax his vigilant observation nor let his judgment sleep.

Table 13-10 contains some suggested rations for different classes of horses. This is merely intended as a general guide. The feeder should give consideration to (1) the quality, availability, and cost of feeds; (2) the character and severity of the work; and (3) the age and individuality of the animal. Under many conditions, it may be more satisfactory to buy ready-mixed feeds.

FEED SUBSTITUTION TABLE

The successful horseman is a keen student of values. He recognizes that feeds of similar nutritive properties can and should be interchanged in the ration as price relationships warrant, thus making it possible at all times to obtain a balanced ration at the lowest cost.

Table 13-10

HANDY LIGHT HORSE FEEDING GUIDE

Age, Sex, and Use	Daily Allowance	Kind of Hay	Suggested Grain Rations (In lbs. of each ingredient/cwt. of mixture)		
			Rations No. 1	Rations No. 2	Rations No. 3
			lbs.	lbs.	lbs
Stallions in breeding season (weighing 900 to 1,400 lbs.)	¾ to 1½ lbs. grain per 100 lbs. live weight, together with a quantity of hay within same range.	Grass-legume mixed; or ⅓ to ½ legume hay, with remainder grass hay.	Oats——— 55 Wheat——— 20 Wheat bran——— 20 Linseed meal——— 5	Corn——— 35 Oats——— 35 Wheat ——— 15 Wheat bran——— 15	Oats (alone).
Pregnant mares (weighing 900 to 1,400 lbs.)	¾ to 1½ lbs. grain per 100 lbs. live weight, together with a quantity of hay within same range.	Grass-legume mixed; or ⅓ to ½ legume hay, with remainder grass hay (straight grass hay may be used first half of pregnancy).	Oats——— 80 Wheat bran——— 20	Barley ——— 45 Oats——— 45 Wheat bran——— 10	Oats——— 95 Linseed meal——— 5
Foals before weaning (weighing 100 to 350 lbs. with projected mature weights of 900 to 1,400 lbs.)	½ to ¾ lb. grain per 100 lbs. live weight, together with a quantity of hay within same range.	Legume hay.	Oats——— 50 Wheat bran——— 40 Linseed meal——— 10	Oats——— 30 Barley——— 30 Wheat bran——— 30 Linseed meal——— 10	Oats——— 30 Wheat bran——— 20
			Rations balanced on basis of following assumption: Mares of mature weights of 600, 800, 1,000, and 1,200 lbs. may produce 36, 42, 44, and 49 lbs. of milk daily.		
Weanlings (weighing 350 to 450 lbs.)	1 to 1½ lbs. grain and 1½ to 2 lbs. hay per 100 lbs. live weight.	Grass-legume mixed; or ½ legume hay, with remainder grass hay.	Oats——— 30 Barley——— 30 Wheat bran——— 30 Linseed meal——— 10	Oats——— 70 Wheat bran——— 15 Linseed meal——— 15	Oats——— 80 Linseed meal——— 20

Table 13-10 (Continued)

Age, Sex, and Use	Daily Allowance	Kind of Hay	Suggested Grain Rations (In lbs. of each ingredient/cwt. of mixture)		
			Rations No. 1	Rations No. 2	Rations No. 3
			lbs.	*lbs.*	*lbs.*
Yearlings, second summer (weighing 450 to 700 lbs.)	Good luxuriant pastures. (If horses are in training or for other reasons without access to pastures, the ration should be intermediate between the adjacent upper and lower groups.)				
Yearlings, or rising 2-year-olds, second winter (weighing 700 to 1,000 lbs.)	½ to 1 lb. grain and 1 to 1½ lbs. hay per 100 lbs. live weight.	Grass-legume mixed; or ⅓ to ½ legume hay, with remainder grass hay.	Oats————— 80 Wheat bran——— 20	Barley————— 35 Oats————— 35 Bran————— 15 Linseed meal——— 15	Oats (alone).
Light horses at work; riding, driving, and racing (weighing 900 to 1,400 lbs.)	*Hard use.*—1¼ to 1⅓ lbs. grain and 1 to 1¼ lbs. hay per 100 lbs. live weight. *Medium use.*—¾ to 1 lb. grain and 1 to 1¼ lbs. hay per 100 lbs. live weight. *Light use.*—⅖ to ½ lb. grain and 1¼ to 1½ lbs. hay per 100 lbs. live weight.	Grass hay.	Oats (alone).	Oats———— 70 Corn———— 30	Oats———— 70 Barley——— 30
Mature idle horses; stallions, mares, and geldings (weighing 900 to 1,400 lbs.)	1½ to 1¾ lbs. hay per 100 lbs. live weight.	Pasture in season; or grass-legume mixed hay.	(With grass hay, add ¾ lb. of a high protein supplement daily.)		

Note: With all rations and for all classes and ages of horses, provide free access to separate containers of (1) salt (iodized salt in iodine-deficient areas) and (2) a mixture of 1 part salt and 2 parts steamed bone meal or other suitable calcium-phosphorus supplement.

Table 13-11, Handy Feed Substitution Table for Light Horses, is a summary of the comparative values of the most common U. S. feeds. In arriving at these values, chemical composition, feeding value, and palatability have been considered.

In using this feed substitution table, the following facts should be recognized:

1. That, for best results, different ages of animals should be fed differently.

2. That individual feeds differ widely in feeding value. Barley and oats, for example, vary widely in feeding value according to the hull content and the test weight per bushel, and forages vary widely according to the stage of maturity at which they are cut and how well they are cured and stored.

3. That nonlegume forages may have a higher relative value to legumes than herein indicated provided the chief need of the animal is for additional energy rather than for supplemented protein. Thus, the nonlegume forages of low value can be used to better advantage for wintering mature horses than for young foals.

On the other hand, legumes may have a higher actual value relative to nonlegumes than herein indicated provided the chief need is for additional protein rather than for added energy. Thus, no protein supplement is necessary for broodmares provided a good quality legume forage is fed.

4. That, based primarily on available supply and price, certain feeds—especially those of medium protein content, such as brewers dried grains, distillers dried solubles, and peas (dried)—are used interchangeably as (a) grains and by-products feeds, and/or (b) protein supplements.

5. That the feeding value of certain feeds is materially affected by preparation. The values herein reported are based on proper feed preparation in each case.

For these reasons, the comparative values of feeds shown in the feed substitution table (Table 13-11) are not absolute. Rather, they are reasonably accurate approximations based on average-quality feeds.

COMMERCIAL HORSE FEEDS

Commercial feeds are just what the name implies—feeds mixed by manufacturers who specialize in the feed business, rather than farm

Table 13-11

HANDY FEED SUBSTITUTION TABLE FOR LIGHT HORSES

Feedstuff	Relative Feeding Value (lb. for lb.) in Comparison with the Designated (underlined) Base Feed Which = 100	Maximum Percentage of Base Feed (or comparable feed or feeds) Which It Can Replace for Best Results	Remarks	Feed Preparation
GRAINS, BY-PRODUCT FEEDS, ROOTS, AND TUBERS:[1] (Low and Medium Protein Feeds)				
Oats................	<u>100</u>	<u>100</u>	The leading horse feed. The feeding value of oats varies according to the hull content and test weight per bushel. Because of their bulky nature, they form a desirable loose mass in the stomach which prevents impaction. Musty oats should never be used because they may cause colic.	Steam rolled, crimped, or fed whole.
Barley	110	100	The Arab, who was a good horseman, fed barley exclusively. It is also the leading horse feed in western U. S. Most horsemen feel that it is preferable to feed barley along with more bulky feeds; for example, 25% oats or 15% wheat bran.	Steam rolled, or ground coarsely.

Footnotes on last page of table.

(Continued)

Table 13-11 (Continued)

Feedstuff	Relative Feeding Value (lb. for lb.) in Comparison with the Designated (underlined) Base Feed Which = 100	Maximum Percentage of Base Feed (or comparable feed or feeds) Which It Can Replace for Best Results	Remarks	Feed Preparation
Beet pulp, dried	100	33⅓	Not palatable to horses.	
Beet pulp, molasses, dried...	100	33⅓	Not palatable to horses.	
Brewers dried grains	100	50		
Carrots....................	15-25	10	Horses are very fond of carrots.	Fresh or dried.
Corn, No. 2	115	100	Ranks second to oats as a light horse feed. It has a lower value than indicated when forage is of low protein content.	On the cob, shelled, cracked, corn-and-cob meal, or flaked.
Corn, gluten feed (gluten feed)	100	50		
Distillers dried grains	90-100	25		
Distillers dried solubles.......	90-100	25		
Hominy feed	115	100		
Milo (sorghum, grain)	110-115	85	All varieties have about the same feeding value.	Steam rolled, or ground coarsely.
Molasses, beet.............	80-95	20	In hot, humid areas, molasses should be limited to 5%; otherwise, mold may develop. Cane molasses is slightly preferred to beet molasses.	Where mustiness is a hazard, add calcium propionate to the feed according to manufacturer's directions.
Molasses, cane	80-95	25	(Same remarks as for beet molasses.)	

Footnotes on last page of table.

(Continued)

Table 13-11 (Continued)

Feedstuff	Relative Feeding Value (lb. for lb.) in Comparison with the Designated (underlined) Base Feed Which = 100	Maximum Percentage of Base Feed (or comparable feed or feeds) Which It Can Replace for Best Results	Remarks	Feed Preparation
Peas, dried................	100	40		Ground for horses.
Rice (rough rice)..........	115	50		
Rye......................	115	33⅓	Higher levels, or abrupt changes to rye, may cause digestive disturbances. Not palatable.	
Wheat	115	20	Wheat should be mixed with a more bulky feed in order to prevent colic.	Steam rolled, or crushed.
Wheat bran................	100	20	Valuable for horses because of its bulky nature and laxative properties.	May be fed as a wet mash.
Wheat-mixed feed (mill run)......	105	20	Excessive quantities will cause colic or other digestive upsets.	
PROTEIN SUPPLEMENTS:				
Linseed meal (33%)........	100	100	Linseed meal is the preferred vegetable protein supplement for horses. It is valued because of its laxative properties, and because of the sleek hair coat which it imparts.	
Brewers dried grains	65-70	50		

Footnotes on last page of table.

(Continued)

Table 13-11 (Continued)

Feedstuff	Relative Feeding Value (lb. for lb.) in Comparison with the Designated (underlined) Base Feed Which =100	Maximum Percentage of Base Feed (or comparable feed or feeds) Which It Can Replace for Best Results	Remarks	Feed Preparation
Buttermilk, dried............	100	100	May be used in place of dried skimmed milk for foals.	
Copra meal (coconut meal).........	90-100	50	Somewhat unpalatable to horses.	
Corn gluten feed (gluten feed)......	70	100		
Corn gluten meal (gluten meal)......	100	50		
Cottonseed meal (41%)............	100	100	Satisfactory if limited to amounts necessary to balance ordinary rations. Some prejudices to the contrary, good grade cottonseed meal is satisfactory for horses.	
Peanut meal (41%)............	100	100		
Peas, dried................	75	50	Especially valuable for young equines; for creep feeding until past weaning.	
Skimmed milk, dried...........	100	100		
Soybean meal (41%)............	100	100	Soybeans should be limited to ⅓ of the concentrate ration.	
Soybeans.................	100	100		
Whey, dried................	50	50	Whey may be laxative.	
Many horsemen prefer commercial protein supplements which are well fortified with vitamins and minerals.				

(Continued)

Table 13-11 (Continued)

Feedstuff	Relative Feeding Value (lb. for lb.) in Comparison with the Designated (underlined) Base Feed Which =100	Maximum Percentage of Base Feed (or comparable feed or feeds) Which It Can Replace for Best Results	Remarks	Feed Preparation
DRY FORAGES AND SILAGES:[2]				
Timothy hay.............	<u>100</u>	<u>100</u>	The preferred hay of horsemen.	
Alfalfa hay, all analyses	133⅓	100	Good-quality alfalfa is excellent for horses. Alfalfa may be ground and pelleted. It provides high-quality proteins, and certain minerals and vitamins.	
			It is somewhat laxative. Contrary to some "old wives' tales," it will not damage the kidneys.	
Barley hay.............	100	100	Lower value if not cut at the early dough stage.	
Bromegrass hay............	100	100		
Clover hay, crimson............	125	100	Crimson clover hay has considerably lower value if not cut at an early stage.	
Clover hay, red............	125	100	Clover hay should be well cured and free from dust and mold.	

Footnotes on last page of table.

(Continued)

Table 13-11 (Continued)

Feedstuff	Relative Feeding Value (lb. for lb.) in Comparison with the Designated (underlined) Base Feed Which = 100	Maximum Percentage of Base Feed (or comparable feed or feeds) Which It Can Replace for Best Results	Remarks	Feed Preparation
Clover-timothy hay..............	110-115	100	Value of clover-timothy mixed hay depends on the proportion of clover present and the stage of maturity at which it is cut.	
Corn fodder..............	100	50	Preferably fed along with a good legume hay.	Shredded.
Corn silage..............	45-55	33⅓-50	Preferably fed along with a good legume hay.	Shredded.
Corn stover..............	60	50		
Cowpea hay..............	110	100		
Grass-legume mixed hay..............	110-115	100		
Grass-legume silage..............	45-50	33⅓-50		
Grass silage..............	40-45	33⅓-50		
Johnson grass hay..............	90-95	100	Johnson grass thrives in the South.	
Lespedeza hay..............	115	100	Lower value if not cut at the early dough stage.	
Oat hay..............	100	100	Should be cut before maturity. It is a safe feed for horses.	
Orchard grass..............	100	100	Considerable prairie hay is fed in the West.	
Prairie hay..............	100	100		
Reed canary grass..............	90-95	100	Preferably fed along with a good legume hay.	Shredded.
Sorghum fodder..............	100	50		

Footnotes on last page of table.

(Continued)

Table 13-11 (Continued)

Feedstuff	Relative Feeding Value (lb. for lb.) in Comparison with the Designated (underlined) Base Feed Which =100	Maximum Percentage of Base Feed (or comparable feed or feeds) Which It Can Replace for Best Results	Remarks	Feed Preparation
Sorghum silage...............	40-45	33⅓-50	Preferably fed along with a good legume hay.	
Sorghum stover...............	60	50		Shredded.
Soybean hay...............	110	100		
Sudangrass hay...............	90-95	100		
Vetch-oat hay...............	110-115	100	The higher the proportion of vetch, the higher the value.	
Wheat hay...............	100	100		

[1]Roots and tubers are of lower value than the grain and by-product feeds due to their higher moisture content.
[2]Well-preserved silage of good quality, free from mold and not frozen, affords a highly nutritious succulent forage for horses during the winter months—especially for idle horses, broodmares, and growing foals. Silages are of lower value than dry forages due to their higher moisture content.

mixed. Today, over 50 million tons of commercial feeds are marketed each year. It's big and important business, and it will get bigger.

The commercial feed manufacturer has the distinct advantages of (1) the purchasing of feed in quantity lots, making possible price advantages, (2) economical and controlled mixing, (3) the hiring of scientifically trained personnel for use in determining the rations, and (4) quality control. Most horsemen have neither the know-how nor the quantity of business to provide these services on their own. In fact, due to (1) the small quantities of feed usually involved and (2) the complexities of horse rations, horsemen have more reason to rely on good commercial feeds than do owners of other classes of farm animals and poultry. Because of these advantages, commercial feeds are finding a place of increasing importance in horse feeding.

Also, it is to the everlasting credit of reputable feed dealers that they have been good teachers, often getting horsemen started in the feeding of balanced rations.

How to Select Commercial Feeds

There is a difference in commercial feeds! That is, there is a difference from the standpoint of what a horseman can purchase with his feed dollars. The smart horseman will know how to determine what constitutes the best in commercial feeds for his specific needs. He will not rely solely on how the feed looks and smells. The most important factors to consider or look for in buying a commercial feed are:

1. *The reputation of the manufacturer.*—This may be determined by conferring with other horsemen who have used the particular product and checking on whether or not the commercial feed under consideration has consistently met its guarantees. The latter can be determined by reading the bulletins or reports published by the respective state departments in charge of enforcing feed laws.

2. *The specific needs.*—Feed needs vary according to (a) the class, age, and productivity of horses, and (b) whether animals are fed primarily for maintenance, growth, fattening (or show-ring fitting), reproduction, lactation, or work (running). The wise operator will buy different formula feeds for different needs.

3. *Flexible formulas.*—Feeds with flexible formulas are usually the best buy. This is because the price of feed ingredients in different source feeds varies considerably from time to time. Thus, a good feed manufacturer will shift his formulas as prices change, in order to give the horseman the most for his money. This is as it should be, for (a)

there is no one best ingredient, and (b) if substitutions are made wisely, the price of the feed can be kept down, and the horseman will continue to get equally good results.

4. *What's on the tag?*—Horsemen should be able to study and interpret what's on the feed tag. Figures 13-13 and 13-14 show a tag taken from a foal ration:

(BRAND X)

(Net Weight 50 pounds)

GUARANTEED ANALYSIS

Crude Protein, not less than 21.00%
Crude Fat, not less than 2.00%
Crude Fiber, not more than 9.00%
Ash, not more than 9.00%
Added Mineral, not more than 3.00%
Calcium, not less than 1.00%
Phosphorus, not less than .... .75%
Salt, not more than .... .50%
Iodine, not less than .... .00035%
TDN, not less than 68.00%

Ingredients: Rolled Oats, Dried Whey, Soybean Meal, Cottonseed Meal, Linseed Meal, Dehydrated Alfalfa Meal, Wheat Bran, Wheat Shorts, Wheat Flour, Cane Molasses, Bone Meal, Iodized Salt, Distillers Dried Grains with Solubles, Alfalfa Leaf Meal, Condensed Fish Solubles (Dried), Brewers Dried Yeast, Streptomycin Mycelia Meal, Vitamin A Palmitate with Increased Stability, Fleischman's Irradiated Dry Yeast (Source of Vitamin D-2), d-Alpha-Tocopherol Acetate (Source of Vitamin E), Choline Chloride, Ferrous Carbonate, Niacin, Calcium Pantothenate (Source of d-Pantothenic Acid), Riboflavin Supplement, Copper Oxide, Manganous Oxide, Thiamine, Sulphur, Menadione Sodium Bisulfate (Source of Vitamin K), Calcium Iodate, Folic Acid, Cobalt Carbonate, Vitamin B-12 Supplement, Preserved with Ethoxyquin (1, 2-dihydro-6-ethoxy-2, 2, 4-trimethylquinoline), Anise.

FEEDING DIRECTIONS—SEE OTHER SIDE

Manufactured by
ADAIR MILLING COMPANY
(Address and Phone Number)

Fig. 13-13. Feed tag (front)

(BRAND X)

FEEDING DIRECTIONS

	Lbs. daily/100 lbs. weight/foal
Before weaning	½ - 1
After weaning	1¼ - 1½

Plus pasture or hay

Fig. 13-14. Feed tag (reverse side).

An analysis of the tag reveals the following:

a. The "brand" or name of the feed.

b. The net weight.

c. The guaranteed analysis, each stated in percent, in minimum crude protein and crude fat; maximum crude fiber, ash, and mineral; minimum calcium and phosphorus; maximum salt;

and minimum iodine and TDN. But guaranteed analysis, within itself, will not suffice. For example, on the basis of chemical composition, soft coal (9.06% crude protein) and coffee grounds (11.23% crude protein) are comparable in protein content to many commonly used grains. Yet, no one would be so foolish as to feed these products to horses.

d. The ingredients, (the constituent material making up the feed) listed in descending order of amounts, by weight.

e. The name, address, and phone number of the manufacturer.

f. The feeding directions, on the reverse side.

Many states differ slightly from the tag just analyzed. Some require both the minimum and maximum percentage of calcium and salt.

By studying this tag, a knowledgeable user can, readily and easily, see what's in the feed and determine if it will meet the requirements of the horse to which it is to be fed.

COMMERCIAL MINERALS

Commercial mineral mixtures are minerals mixed by manufacturers who specialize in the commercial mineral business, either handling minerals alone or a combination of feeds and minerals. Most commercial minerals are very good.

The commercial mineral manufacturer has the same advantages over farm- or ranch-mixing as does the commercial feed manufacturer (see second paragraph under "Commercial Horse Feeds").

Good minerals supply only the specific elements that are deficient, and in the quantities necessary. Excesses and mineral imbalances are avoided. Thus, the value of any mineral mixture can easily be determined by how well it meets the needs.

How to Select Commercial Mineral Mixes

The informed horseman will know what constitutes the best commercial mineral mix for his needs, and how to determine the best buy. Here are the factors to consider when buying a commercial mineral:

1. *The reputation of the manufacturer.*—This can be determined (a) by checking on the manufacturer's integrity, (b) conferring with other horsemen who have used the particular product, and (c) checking on whether the product under consideration has consistently met its guarantees. The latter point can be determined by reading the

Fig. 13-15. Good pastures are excellent for mares and foals. But foals on grass should also be fed individually or in a creep.

bulletins or reports published by the respective state departments in charge of enforcing feed laws.

2. *Determination of your needs.*—The mineral requirements of horses are much the same everywhere, although it is recognized that age, pregnancy, and lactation make for differences. Additionally, there are some area differences. For example, the Northern Great Plains and the Southwest are generally recognized as phosphorus-deficient areas—their grasses and hays are usually low in phosphorus. Accordingly, a high-phosphorus mineral is needed for horses in such areas—one containing 10 to 15 percent phosphorus.

3. *What's on the tag?*—Horsemen should study, and be able to interpret, what's on the tag. Does it contain what he needs?

4. *Determination of the best buy.*—When buying a mineral, the horseman should check price against value received. For example, let's assume that the main need is for phosphorus, and that we wish to compare two minerals, which we shall call brands X and Y. Brand X contains 12 percent phosphorus and sells at $8.50 per hundredweight,

whereas brand Y contains 10 percent phosphorus and sells at $8.00 per hundredweight. Which is the better buy?

COMPARATIVE VALUE OF BRANDS X AND Y
(Based on Phosphorus Content Alone)

Brand	Phosphorus	Price/cwt.	Cost/lb. phosphorus
	(%)	($)	(¢)
X	12	8.50	71
Y	10	8.00	80

Hence, brand X is the better buy, even though it costs 50 cents more per hundred.

One other thing is important. As a usual thing, the more scientifically formulated mineral mixes will have plus values in terms of (a) trace mineral (needs and balance), and (b) palatability (horses will eat just the right amount of a good mineral, but they won't overdo it—due to appetizers, rather than needs).

Commercial mineral mixtures costing 60 to 80 cents per pound of phosphorus are not excessively priced. If the average consumption per horse per month of a mineral mix costing $8.50 per hundredweight is 3 pounds, the monthly per head cost will be about 26 cents, or less than 1 cent per horse per day.

STATE COMMERCIAL FEED LAWS

Nearly all the states have laws regulating the sale of commercial feeds. These benefit both the horseman and reputable feed manufacturers. In most states, the laws require that every brand of commercial feed sold in the state be licensed, and that the chemical composition be guaranteed.

Samples of each commercial feed are taken each year, and analyzed chemically in the state's laboratory to determine if the manufacturer lived up to his guarantee. Additionally, skilled microscopists examine the sample to ascertain that the ingredients present are the same as those guaranteed. Flagrant violations on the latter point may be prosecuted.

Results of these examinations are generally published, annually, by the state department in charge of such regulatory work. Usually, the publication of the guarantee alongside any "short-changing" is sufficient to cause the manufacturer promptly to rectify the situation, for such public information soon becomes known to both users and competitors.

Medicated Feed Tags and Labels

Medicated feeds (those which contain drug ingredients intended or represented for the cure, mitigation, treatment, or prevention of diseases of animals) must also carry the following information in their labeling: (1) the purpose of the medication; (2) directions for the use of the feed; (3) the names and amounts of all active drug ingredients; (4) a warning or caution statement for a withdrawal period when required for the particular drug contained in the feed; and (5) warnings against misuse.

Vitamin Product Labels

When a product is marketed as a vitamin supplement *per se*, the quantitative guarantees (unit/lb.) of vitamins A and D are expressed in U. S. P. units; of E in I. U.; and of other vitamins in milligrams per pound.

Mineral Product Labels

Some states require that all minerals except salt (NaCl) be quantitatively guaranteed in terms of percentage of the element(s); others require milligrams per pound.

Other Rules and Regulations

Generally, the following rules and regulations also apply in the different states:

1. The brand or product name must not be misleading.

2. The sliding scale or range (for example, 15% to 18% crude protein) method of expressing guarantees is prohibited.

3. Ingredient names are those adopted by the Association of American Feed Control Officials.

4. The term "dehydrated" may precede the name of any product that has been artificially dried.

5. Urea and ammonium salts of carbonic and phosphoric acids cannot be used in horse feeds.

TERMS USED IN ANALYSES
AND GUARANTEES

Knowledge of the following terms is requisite to understanding analyses and guarantees:

Dry matter is found by determining the percentage of water and subtracting the water content from 100 percent.

Crude protein is used to designate the nitrogenous constituents of a feed. The percentage is obtained by multiplying the percentage of total nitrogen by the factor 6.25. The nitrogen is derived chiefly from complex chemical compounds called amino acids.

Crude fat is the material that is extracted from moisture-free feeds by ether. It consists largely of fats and oils with small amounts of waxes, resins, and coloring matter. In calculating the heat and energy value of the feed, the fat is considered 2.25 times that of either nitrogen-free extract or protein.

Crude fiber is the relatively insoluble carbohydrate portion of a feed consisting chiefly of cellulose. It is determined by its insolubility in dilute acids and alkalies.

Ash is the mineral matter of a feed. It is the residue remaining after complete burning of the organic matter.

Nitrogen-free extract consists principally of sugars, starches, pentoses and non-nitrogenous organic acids. The percentage is determined by subtracting the sum of the percentages of moisture, crude protein, crude fat, crude fiber, and ash from 100.

Carbohydrates represent the sum of the crude fiber and nitrogen-free extract.

Calcium and phosphorus are essential mineral elements that are present in feeds in varying quantities. Mineral feeds are usually high in source materials of these elements.

TDN—The digestible nutrients of any ingredient are obtained by multiplying the percentage of each nutrient by the digestion coefficient. For example, dent corn contains 8.9 percent protein of which 77 percent is digestible. Therefore, the percent of digestible protein is 6.9.

The TDN is the sum of all the digestible organic nutrients—protein, fiber, nitrogen-free extract, and fat (the latter multiplied by 2.25).

CALCULATING CHEMICAL ANALYSIS

Most of the larger feed manufacturers maintain strict product control. Among other things, they sample and analyze their feeds from time to time, as a means of satisfying themselves that they are meeting their guarantees.

Smaller manufacturers who do not have their own chemical laboratories usually use a commercial laboratory; or, in some states, the college of agriculture provides a feed testing laboratory service on a nominal charge basis. Horsemen can also check any feed in this same manner.

An actual chemical analysis is always best when it comes to checking on a guarantee. However, where the pounds of each ingredient in a mixed feed are known, the chemical analysis can be calculated. Of course, with closed formula feeds this is not possible.

Table 13-12 and the discussion that follows show how to calculate the chemical analysis of a protein supplement for horses:

Table 13-12

A HORSE PROTEIN SUPPLEMENT

Ingredients	Lbs./1,000-Lb. Batch	Lbs. of Crude Protein	Lbs. of Fat	Lbs. of Fiber
Linseed meal..................	80	28	4.8	6.4
Soybean meal................	320	146	4.2	18.9
Dried skimmed milk	50	16.5	.5	....
Alfalfa meal, 17% dehy. .	105	18.4	2.7	26.3
Wheat bran...................	100	16.4	4.5	10.0
Hominy feed	157.50	16.9	10.2	7.9
Molasses (cane)	100	3.0	....	....
Salt.............................	7.50	....	....	....
Dical...........................	42.50	....	....	....
Vit.-trace min. premix	37.50	....	....	....
	1,000.00	245.2	26.9	69.5

Step by step, here's how the calculation in Table 13-12 was done:

1. The ingredients were listed in the first column, followed in the second column with the pounds of each ingredient in a batch (the size batch need not total 1,000 pounds; it could be 100 pounds, 1 ton, or any other quantity).

2. By using a feed ingredient table, a calculation was made of the number of pounds each of protein, fat, and fiber furnished by each ingredient; this was recorded in the proper column. For example, 80 pounds of linseed meal × 35.0 percent protein = 28 pounds of protein in 80 pounds of linseed meal.

3. The sum of each column gives the total number of pounds of protein, fat, and fiber in the particular batch.

4. To obtain the percentages of protein, fat, and fiber, each total was divided by the total pounds in the batch as follows:

$$\text{a. Protein} \ldots \frac{245.2 \times 100}{1,000} = 24.52\% \text{ protein}$$

$$\text{b. Fat} \ldots \frac{26.9 \times 100}{1,000} = 2.69\% \text{ fat}$$

$$\text{c. Fiber} \ldots \frac{69.5 \times 100}{1,000} = 6.95\% \text{ fiber}$$

For these percentages, the suggested guarantees would be:

	Guarantee	
	(Min.)	(Max.)
Crude protein, %	24	
Fiber %		7.5
Fat %	2.5	

HOW TO DETERMINE THE BEST BUY IN FEEDS

When buying feed, the horseman should check price against value received. One criterion is the cost per unit of protein. Let us apply this to two horse feeds, which we shall call brands X and Y:

Brand X contains 10 percent crude protein and sells at $3.20 per hundredweight. How much can you afford to pay for Brand Y which has 14 percent protein (and other likely plus values that we shall discuss later)?

COMPARATIVE VALUES OF BRAND X AND Y
(Based on Protein Content Alone)

Brand	Crude protein (%)	Price/ Cwt. ($)	Cost/lb. protein (cents)
X	14	4.50	32
Y	10	3.20	32

This shows that if 10 percent crude protein horse feed sells at $3.20 per hundredweight, one could afford to pay $4.50 per hundredweight for a 14 percent crude protein feed, based on the added value of the protein alone. And that's not all! As a usual thing, if a horse ration is scientifically formulated from the standpoint of quantity of protein, it will also have other plus values, among them:

1. Quality of proteins (the essential amino acids).
2. Energy.
3. Minerals, vitamins, and unidentified factors—which are adequate, without imbalances.
4. Palatability and digestibility. Although horses must like feeds well enough to eat them, it is recognized that—

   (a) Palatability is, in part, a matter of habit—of being used to a certain feed. For this reason, changes in horse feeds should be made gradually.

   (b) It does not necessarily follow that everything is good for a horse just because he likes it. In this respect an analogy may be made to boys and girls. If given a choice between a well balanced diet and candy, most boys and girls will take the latter; yet, few parents or M.D.s would be so foolish as to say that sweets are good for them. The same can be said relative to many of the "sweet feeds" and concoctions fed to horses.

5. The end results—superior performance.

In other words, when a ration is deficient in one category—in protein, for example—you're apt to be short changed all along the line.

PASTURES

The great horse breeding centers of the world are characterized by good pastures. Thus, the bluegrass area of Kentucky is known for its lush pastures produced on residual limestone soils. In short, good horsemen, good horses, and good pastures go hand in hand—the latter being the cornerstone of successful horse production. Yet, it is becoming increasingly difficult to provide good pastures for many horses, especially for those in suburban areas. Also, it is recognized that many folks are prone to overrate the quality of their grass.

In season, there is no finer forage for horses than superior pastures—pastures that are much more than gymnasiums. This is especially true for idle horses, broodmares, and young stock. In fact, pastures have a very definite place for all horses, with the possible exception of animals at heavy work or in training. Even with the latter groups, pastures may be used with discretion. Work horses may be turned to pasture at night or over the weekend. Certainly, the total benefits derived from pasture are to the good, although pasturing may have some laxative effects and produce a greater tendency to sweat.

In addition to the nutritive value of the grass, pasture provides invaluable exercise on natural footing—with plenty of sunshine, fresh air, and lowered feeding costs as added benefits. Feeding on pasture is the ideal existence for young stock and breeding animals.

But grass—the nation's largest crop, grown on 49.4 percent of the land area—should not be taken for granted. Again and again, scientists and practical farmers have demonstrated that the following desired goals in pasture production are well within the realm of possibility:

1. To produce higher yields of palatable and nutritious forage.

2. To extend the grazing season from as early in the spring to as late in the fall as possible.

3. To provide a fairly uniform supply of feed throughout the entire season.

The use of a temporary pasture (grown in a regular crop rotation), instead of a parasite-infected permanent pasture, is recommended. Legume pastures are excellent for horses, as equines are less subject to bloat than cattle or sheep. The specific grass or grass-legume mixture will vary from area to area, according to differences in soil, temperature, and rainfall. The County Agricultural Agent or state agricultural college can furnish recommendations for the area that they serve.

Sudan and Sudan hybrids should not be pastured by horses. When in the growing stage these plants sometimes cause cystitis, or inflammation of the bladder. This disease is characterized by incoordination of the rear quarters, uncontrolled urination, and false estrus and abortion in mares. Once urine dribbling is evident, the animal usually dies.

Horse pastures should be well drained and not too rough or stony. All dangerous places—such as pits, stumps, poles, and tanks—should be guarded. Shade, water, and suitable minerals should be available in all pastures.

Most horse pastures can be improved by seeding new and better varieties of grasses and legumes, and by fertilizing and management. Also, horsemen need to give attention to balancing pastures. Early-in-the-season pastures are of high-water content and lack energy. Mature weathered grass is almost always deficient in protein (being as low as 3 percent or less) and low in carotene. But these deficiencies can be corrected by proper supplemental feeding.

Supplementing Early Spring Grass

Turning horses on pasture when the first sprigs of green grass appear will usually make for a temporary deficiency of energy, due to (1) washy (high water content) grasses and (2) inadequate forage for animals to consume. As a result, owners are often disappointed in the poor condition of horses.

If there is good reason why grazing cannot be delayed until there is adequate spring growth, it is recommended that early pastures be supplemented with grass hay or straw (a legume hay will accentuate looseness, which usually exists under such circumstances), preferably placed in a rack; perhaps with a high energy concentrate provided, also.

Supplementing Dry Pasture

Dry, mature, weathered, bleached grass characterizes (1) drought periods and (2) fall-winter pastures. Such cured-on-the-stalk grasses are low in energy, in protein, in carotene, and in phosphorus and perhaps certain other minerals. These deficiencies become more acute following frost and increase in severity as winter advances. This explains the often severe loss in condition of horses following the first fall freeze.

In addition to the deficiencies which normally characterize whatever plants are available, dry pasture may be plagued by a short supply of feed.

Generally speaking, a concentrate or supplement is best used during droughts or on fall-winter pastures. However, when there is an acute shortage of forage, hay or other roughage also should be added.

Pasture Supplements

Horsemen face the question of what supplement to use, when to feed, and how much to feed.

In supplying a supplement to horses on pasture, the following guides should be observed:

1. It should balance the diet of the horses to which it is fed, which means that it should supply all the nutrients missing in the forage.

2. It should be fed in such a way that each horse gets its proper proportion, which generally means (a) the use of salt blocks, (b) tying up horses during concentrate feeding when more than one animal is fed in a given pasture, or (c) taking them to their stalls at feeding time.

3. The daily allowance of the supplement should be determined by (a) the available pasture (quantity and quality), and (b) the condition of the horse.

The results from the use of the supplement, rather than cost per bag, should determine the choice of supplement.

Supplementing Show and Sale Horses on Pasture

The horseman who is producing animals for show or sale must give attention to (1) eye appeal—sleek, bloomy, well conditioned animals that attract judges and buyers; and (2) growth and development of young stock. Further, the acid test is that these objectives shall be achieved without jeopardizing soundness and without lowering the reproductive ability of breeding animals—and this isn't easy.

In draft horses, where rapid growth and early use were not too important, good pastures produced on well-fertilized soils met the nutritive requirements of most horses. However, the nutritive requirements of most light horses are more critical. Among other things, light horses are usually forced for more rapid development and are subjected to more stress. Consequently, their nutritive requirements are greater —especially from the standpoints of energy, protein, minerals, and vitamins.

Eye Appeal Important in Pastured Purebreds

Successful purebred breeders recognize the importance of maintaining animals in good condition and attractive surroundings where they can be seen and admired by potential buyers. Certainly, a lush pasture is ideal from the standpoint of presenting horses. Obtaining proper condition without overfatness and unsoundness is not easy. However, a combination of outdoor exercise, good grass, and proper supplement is the answer.

It must be recognized that, no matter how good pasturees may be, they are roughages and not concentrates. Therefore, for the purebred herd judicious supplemental feeding on grass is usually warranted and profitable.

THE ART OF FEEDING

Feeding horses is both an art and a science. The art consists of knowing each horse's individual nutritive requirements. The science has to do with knowing the proper combination of ingredients with which to meet these requirements.

Starting Horses on Feed

It is important that horses be accustomed to feed gradually. In general, they may be given as much nonlegume roughage as they will consume. On the other hand, it is necessary that they be accustomed gradually to high-quality legumes, which may be very laxative. The latter can be accomplished by slowly replacing the nonlegume roughage with greater quantities of legumes. Of course, as the grain ration is increased the consumption of roughages will be decreased.

Starting horses on grain requires care and good judgment. Usually it is advisable first to accustom them to a bulky type of ration, a starting ration with considerable rolled oats being excellent for this purpose.

The keenness of the appetites and the consistency of the droppings of the animals are an excellent index of their capacity to take more feed. In all instances, scouring—the bane of the caretaker—should be avoided.

Frequency, Regularity, and Order of Feeding

The frequency and distribution of the feeds have a great deal to do with their utilization and the condition of the horse. The grain ration is usually divided into three equal feeds—given morning, noon, and night. Because a digestive tract distended with hay is a hindrance in hard work, it is best to feed most of the hay at night. The common practice is to feed one-fourth of the daily hay allowance at each of the morning and noon feedings and the remaining one-half at night, when the animals have plenty of time in which to eat leisurely.

Horses learn to anticipate their feed. Accordingly, they should be fed with great regularity, as determined by a timepiece. During warm weather, they will eat better if the feeding hours are early and late, in the cool of the day.

Usually the grain ration is fed first, with the roughage following. In this manner, the animals eat the bulky roughages more leisurely.

Feeds Should Not Be Changed Abruptly

Sudden changes in diet are to be avoided, especially when changing from a less concentrated ration to a more concentrated one. When this rule of feeding is ignored, digestive disturbances result, and horses "go off feed." In either adding or omitting one or more ingredients, the change should be made gradually. Likewise, caution should be exercised in turning horses to pasture or in transferring them to more lush grazing.

Sometimes horsemen experience difficulty in switching horses from an overly sweet or highly flavored feed to a more nutritious ration. But the end results usually justify the effort.

Attention to Details Pays

The successful horseman pays great attention to details. In addition to maintaining the health and comfort of animals, he should also give consideration to their individual likes and temperaments.

It is important to avoid excessive exercise to the point of fatigue and undue stress. Also, rough treatment, excitement, and noise usually result in nervousness and inefficient use of feed.

Methods of Feeding Mineral Supplements

Horses may be allowed free access to mineral supplements, with salt and a mineral mix placed in a separate compartment of a suitable box or self-feeder. Then their particular needs will guide them in consuming sufficient of those elements necessary to correct any deficiencies of the ration. If the minerals are incorporated in the ration, such additions should be in keeping with known requirements plus a reasonable overage, otherwise horses may either consume too much or not enough, with the result that mineral imbalances may be forced upon them. Where the free-choice method is followed, it is necessary to guard against mineral-starved animals. Such animals should be gradually accustomed to minerals in order to prevent gorging and digestive disturbances.

Other General Rules

In addition to the guides already mentioned, observance of the following general rules will help avoid some of the common difficulties:
  1. Know the approximate weight and age of each animal.
  2. Never feed moldy, musty, dusty, or frozen feed.

3. Inspect the feed box at frequent intervals; by so doing it is easy to detect when a horse goes off his feed.

4. Keep the feed and water containers clean.

5. Make certain that the horse's teeth are sound.

6. Don't feed concentrates to a hot horse; and allow time for digestion following feeding before working him.

7. Feed the horse as an individual—learn the peculiarities and desires of each animal; each one is different, just as people are different.

8. See that the horse gets adequate exercise. It improves its appetite, digestion, and overall well-being.

9. Do not feed from your hand. This can lead to "nibbling."

10. A horse fitted for show or sale should be let down in condition gradually. Experienced horsemen accomplish this difficult task and yet retain strong vigorous animals by (a) cutting down gradually on the feed allowance, and (b) increasing the exercise.

SIGNS OF A WELL-FED, HEALTHY HORSE

Good horsemen know the signs of a well-fed, healthy horse, any departure from which constitutes a warning signal. They are:

1. *Contentment.*—It looks completely unworried when resting.

2. *Alertness.*—In horse vernacular, it is "bright eyed and bushy tailed," and it will pick up its ears at the slightest provocation.

3. *Eating with relish.*—The appetite is good, as indicated by the horse's neighing and pawing prior to feeding, and by its attacking the feed with relish.

4. *Sleek coat and pliable and elastic skin.*—A sleek, oily coat and a pliable and elastic skin characterize a healthy horse. When the hair coat loses its luster and the skin becomes dry, scurfy and hidebound, there is usually trouble.

5. *Pink eye membranes.*—The membranes, which can be seen when the lower lid is pulled down, are pink and moist.

6. *Normal feces and urine.*—The consistency of the feces varies with the diet; for example, lush pasture usually makes for looseness, and pellets generally make for moist feces. Neither extreme dryness nor scouring should exist. Both the feces and urine should be passed without effort, and should be free from blood, mucus or pus.

7. *Normal temperature, pulse rate, and breathing rate.*—Normals for the horse are:

Rectal Temp., degrees F.		Normal Pulse Rate	Normal Breathing Rate
Average	Range		
100.5	99-100.8	32-44	8-16

In general, any marked and persistent deviations from these normals may be looked upon as signs of ill health.

NUTRITIONAL DISEASES AND AILMENTS

The feeding of forages and grains produced on leached and depleted soils has created many problems in horse nutrition. This condition has been further aggravated through increased stall-feeding, the fitting of yearlings for sale, and the racing of two-year-olds. Under these unnatural conditions, nutritional diseases and ailments have become increasingly common.

Little controlled research has been done in this field. Many of the unsoundnesses and poor growth and breeding problems are attributed to nutritional deficiencies. In particular, the lack of various minerals and vitamins has been cited as the cause of equine deficiency diseases, yet the exact role of many of these minerals and vitamins is unknown. Much more research is needed in this area.

Table 13-13 contains a summary of the important nutritional diseases and ailments affecting horses.

Fig. 13-21. Horse with colic. This digestive disturbance may be caused by feed to which the animal is unaccustomed, sudden changes in the ration, rapid eating, imperfectly cured or damaged feeds, the horse's being worked too soon or too hard after feeding, or gorging on water—especially when warm. (Courtesy, Pitman-Moore, Indianapolis, Ind.)

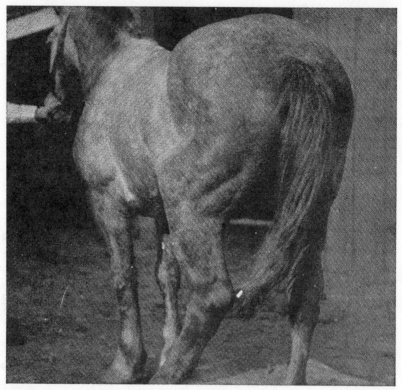

Fig. 13-22. Horse with azorturia, which is generally attributed to faulty metabolism. Prevention lies in restricting the ration and providing daily exercise when the animal is not at work. (Courtesy, Pitman-Moore, Indianapolis, Ind.)

SOME COMMON QUESTIONS

Here are some of the most commonly asked questions, along with the answers of the author.

Q. *Why do horses chew wood and eat materials that are not natural foods? What can be done to alleviate this problem?*

A. Horses, particularly those confined to stalls or lots, frequently chew wood (they eat up their stalls or fences, and bark trees), or they consume such materials as dirt, hair, bones, or feces. Such depraved appetites are known as "pica." This condition is usually caused by one or more of the following conditions:

1. *Boredom,* because they have nothing to do. The more limited

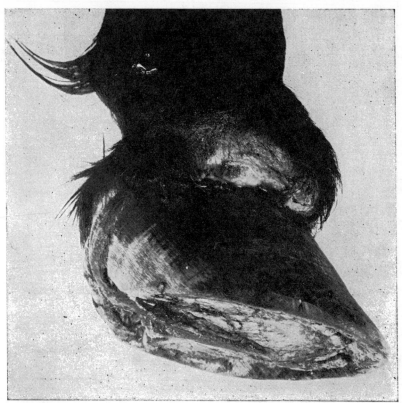

Fig. 13-23. Horse's foot affected by founder, which is most often caused by overeating. (Courtesy, USDA)

the exercise, and the more quickly they consume their feed, the greater the unoccupied time available and the consequent boredom.

By contrast, little eohippus (the dawn horse of 58 million years ago) was a denizen of the swamp. Later, through evolution, he became a creature of the prairies. Although his natural habitat shifted during this long pre-domestication period, until man confined him, he gleaned the feeds provided by nature. Inevitably, this occupied his time and provided exercise.

2. *Nutritional inadequacies*, which may be due to (a) a deficiency of one or more nutrients, (b) an imbalance between certain nutrients, or (c) objection to the physical form of the ration—for example, it may be ground too finely.

Table 13-13

Disease	Species Affected	Cause	Symptoms (and age or group most affected)	Distribution and Losses Caused by
Anemia, nutritional	All warm-blooded animals and man.	Commonly an iron deficiency, but may be caused by a deficiency of copper, cobalt, and/or certain vitamins (riboflavin, pyridoxine, pantothenic acid, and/or folic acid).	Loss of appetite, poor performance, progressive emaciation and death.	Worldwide. Losses consist of retarded growth and deaths.
Azoturia (Hemoglobinuria, Monday morning disease, Blackwater) Fig. 13-16	Horses	Associated with faulty carbohydrate metabolism, and with work following a period of idleness in the stall on full rations.	Profuse sweating, abdominal distress, wine-colored urine, stiff gait, reluctance to move, and lameness. Finally, animal assumes a sitting position, and eventually falls prostrate on the side.	Worldwide, but the disease is seldom seen in horses at pasture and rarely in horses at constant work.
Colic Fig. 13-17	Horses	Improper feeding, working, or watering.	Excruciating pain; and, depending on the type of colic, other symptoms are: distended abdomen, increased intestinal rumbling, violent rolling and kicking, profuse sweating, constipation, and refusal of feed and water.	Worldwide.
Fluorine poisoning (Fluorosis)	All farm animals poultry, and man.	Ingesting excessive quantities of fluorine through either the feed or water.	Abnormal teeth (especially mottled enamel) and bones, stiffness of joints, loss of appetite, emaciation, reduction in milk flow, diarrhea, and salt hunger.	The water in parts of Arkansas, California, South Carolina, and Texas has been reported to contain excess fluorine. Occasionally throughout the U.S. high fluorine phosphates are used in mineral mixtures.
Founder Fig. 13-18	Horses Cattle Sheep Goats	Overeating, (grain; or lush legume or grass—known as "grass founder"), overdrinking, or from inflammation of the uterus following parturition. Also intestinal inflammation.	Extreme pain, fever (103° to 106° F.) and reluctance to move. If neglected, chronic laminitis will develop, resulting in a dropping of the hoof soles and a turning up of the toe walls.	Worldwide. Actual death losses from founder are not very great.

Treatment	Control and Eradication	Prevention	Remarks
Provide dietary sources of the nutrient or nutrients the deficiency of which is known to cause the condition.	When nutritional anemia is encountered, it can usually be brought under control by supplying dietary sources of the nutrient or nutrients known to cause the condition.	Supply dietary sources of iron, copper, cobalt, and certain vitamins. Keep suckling animals confined to a minimum and provide supplemental feeds at an early age.	Anemia is a condition in which the blood is either deficient in quality or quantity (a deficient quality refers to a deficiency in hemoglobin and/or red cells). Levels of iron in most feeds believed to be ample, since most feeds contain 40 to 400 mg/lb.
Absolute rest and quiet. While awaiting the veterinarian, apply heated cloths or blankets, or hot water bottles to the swollen and hardened muscles.	Azoturia is noncontagious. When trouble is encountered, decrease the ration and increase the exercise on idle days.	Restrict the ration and provide daily exercise when the animal is idle. Give a wet bran mash the evening before an idle day or turn the idle horses to pasture.	
Call a veterinarian. To avoid danger of inflicting self-injury, (1) place the animal in a large, well-bedded stable, or (2) take it for a slow walk. Most veterinarians use the stomach tube in the treatment of colic.	Proper feeding, working, watering, and parasite control.		Colic is also a symptom of abdominal pain that can be caused by a number of different conditions. For example, bloodworms cause a colic due to damage in the wall of blood vessels. This results in poor circulation to the intestine.
Any damage may be permanent, but animals which have not developed severe symptoms may be helped to some extent if the sources of excess fluorine are eliminated.	Discontinue the use of feeds, water, or mineral supplements containing excessive fluorine.	Avoid the use of feeds, water, or mineral supplements containing excessive fluorine. Not more than 65 to 100 ppm. fluorine should be present in dry matter of rations when rock phosphate is fed. Phosphorus sources should not contain more than 0.1% F.	
Pending arrival of the veterinarian, the attendant should stand the animal's feet in a cold-water bath.	Control the causes; namely, (1) overeating, (2) overdrinking, and/or (3) inflammation of the uterus following parturition.	Prevent the horse from overeating and overdrinking (especially when hot). Avoid retained afterbirth. After foaling, the afterbirth should pass out within 12 hours; otherwise call a veterinarian.	Unless foundered animals are quite valuable, it is usually desirable to dispose of them following a case of severe founder.

(Continued)

Table 13-13

Disease	Species Affected	Cause	Symptoms (and age or group most affected)	Distribution and Losses Caused by
Heaves Fig. 13-19	Horses Mules	Exact cause unknown, but it is known that the condition is often associated with the feeding of damaged, dusty, or moldy hay. It often follows severe respiratory infection such as strangles.	Difficulty in forcing air out of the lungs, resulting in a jerking of flanks (double flank action) and coughing. The nostrils are often slightly dilated and there is a nasal discharge.	Worldwide. Losses are negligible.
Iodine Deficiency (Goiter)	All farm animals, and man.	A failure of the body to obtain sufficient iodine from which the thyroid gland can form thyroxine (an iodine-containing compound).	Foals may be weak.	Northwestern U.S. and the Great Lakes region.
Osteomalacia	All farm animals.	Lack of vitamin D. Inadequate intake of calcium and phosphorus. Incorrect ratio of calcium and phosphorus.	Phosphorus deficiency symptoms are: depraved appetite (gnawing on bones, wood, or other objects, or eating dirt), lack of appetite, stiffness of joints, failure to breed regularly, decreased milk production, and an emaciated appearance. Calcium deficiency symptoms are: fragile bones, reproductive failures, and lowered lactations. Mature animals most affected. Most of the acute cases occur during pregnancy and lactation.	Southwestern U.S. is classed as a phosphorus-deficient area, whereas calcium-deficient areas have been reported in parts of Florida, Louisiana, Nebraska, Virginia, and W. Virginia.
Periodic Ophthalmia (Moon blindness) Fig. 13-20	Horses Mules Asses	(1) leptospirosis, (2) parasites—*Flaria equina* in the eye, or systemic parasitism, (3) eye reaction to repeated streptococcol infections, or (4) lack of riboflavin.	Periods of cloudy vision, in one or both eyes, which may last for a few days to a week or two and then clear up; but it recurs at intervals, eventually culminating in blindness in one or both eyes.	In many parts of the world. In the U.S., it occurs most frequently in the states east of the Missouri River.
Rickets	All farm animals, and man.	Lack of calcium, phosphorus, or vitamin D; or An incorrect ratio of the two minerals.	Enlargement of the knee and hock joints, and the animal may exhibit great pain when moving about. Irregular bulges (beaded ribs) at juncture of ribs with breastbone, and bowed legs. Rickets is a disease of young animals.	Worldwide. It is seldom fatal.

Treatment	Control and Eradication	Prevention	Remarks
Affected animals are less bothered if turned to pasture, if used only at light work, if fed an all-pelleted ration, or if the hay is sprinkled lightly with water at feeding. Antihistamine granules can be administered in feed to control coughing due to lung congestion.	(See Prevention.)	Avoid the use of damaged feeds. Feed an all-pelleted ration, thereby alleviating dust.	
Once the iodine-deficiency symptoms appear in farm animals, no treatment is very effective.	At the first signs of iodine deficiency, an iodized salt should be fed to all horses.	In iodine-deficient areas, feed iodized salt to all horses throughout the year. Salt containing 0.01% potassium iodide is recommended.	The enlarged thyroid gland (goiter) is nature's way of attempting to make sufficient thyroxine under conditions where a deficiency exists.
Increase the calcium and phosphorus content of feeds through fertilizing the soils. Select natural feeds that contain sufficient quantities of calcium and phosphorus. Feed a special mineral supplement or supplements. If the disease is far advanced, treatment will not be successful.	(See Treatment.)	Feed balanced rations, and allow animals free access to a suitable phosphorus and calcium supplement.	Calcium deficiencies are much more rare than phosphorus deficiencies in horses.
Antibiotics administered promptly are helpful in some cases.	If symptoms of moon blindness are observed, immediately (1) change to greener hay or grass or (2) add riboflavin to the ration at the rate of 20 mg per horse per day.	Feed high riboflavin green grass or well-cured green leafy hays; or Add riboflavin to the ration at the rate of 20 mg per horse per day. Control parasites.	This disease has been known to exist for at least 2,000 years.
If the disease has not advanced too far, treatment may be successful by supplying adequate amounts of vitamin D, calcium, and phosphorus, and/or adjusting the ratio of calcium to phosphorus.	(See Prevention.)	Provide (1) sufficient calcium, phosphorus, and vitamin D, and (2) a correct ratio of the two minerals.	Rickets is characterized by a failure of growing bone to ossify or harden properly.

(Continued)

Table 13-13

Disease	Species Affected	Cause	Symptoms (and age or group most affected)	Distribution and Losses Caused by
Salt Deficiency	All farm animals, and man.	Lack of salt (sodium chloride).	Loss of appetite, retarded growth, loss of weight, a rough coat, lowered production of milk, and a ravenous appetite for salt.	Worldwide, especially among grass eating animals.
Selenium Poisoning (Alkali disease)	All farm animals, and man.	Consumption of plants grown on soils containing selenium.	Loss of hair from the mane and tail in horses. In severe cases, the hoofs slough off, lameness occurs, food consumption decreases, and death may occur by starvation.	In certain regions of western U. S. —especially certain areas in South Dakota, Montana, Wyoming, Nebraska, Kansas, and perhaps areas in other states in the Great Plains and Rocky Mountains. Also, in Canada.
Urinary Calculi (Gravel, Stones, Water belly)	Horses Cattle Sheep Man	Unknown, but there is a higher incidence when there is: A high potassium intake, an incorrect Ca-P ratio, or A high proportion of beet pulp or grain sorghum in the ration.	Frequent attempts to urinate, dribbling or stoppage of the urine, pain and renal colic. Usually only males affected, the females being able to pass the concretions. Bladder may rupture, with death following. Otherwise, uremic poisoning may set in.	Worldwide. Affected animals seldom recover completely.
Vitamin A Deficiency (Night Blindness and Xerophthalmia)	All farm animals, and man.	Vitamin A deficiency.	Night blindness, the first symptom of vitamin A deficiency, is characterized by faulty vision, especially noticeable when the affected animal is forced to move about in twilight in strange surroundings. Xerophthalmia develops in the advanced stages of vitamin A deficiency. The eyes become severely affected, and blindness may follow.	Worldwide.

3. *Psychological stress* and *habit*, which contribute to the behavior of horses, and which have been accentuated by the unnatural environment to which man has subjected them.

Whatever the reason(s) for pica, the suspected causative factor(s) should first be rectified. When and where needed, the exercise should be stepped up; the eating time should be prolonged, and the interval between feedings shortened; nutritional deficiencies, imbalances, and physical form of ration should be corrected; and stress should be

(Continued)

Treatment	Control and Eradication	Prevention	Remarks
Salt-starved animals should be gradually accustomed to salt; slowly increase the hand-fed allowance until the animals may be safely allowed free access to it.	(See Treatment and Prevention.)	Provide plenty of salt at all times, preferably by free-choice feeding.	Common salt is one of the most essential minerals for grass-eating animals and one of the easiest and cheapest to provide. Excess salt intake can result in toxicity.
Although arsenic has been shown to counteract the effects of selenium toxicity, there appears to be no practical method of treating other than removal of animals from affected areas.	(Control measures based on prevention.)	Abandon areas where soils contain selenium, because crops produced on such soils constitute a menace to both animals and man.	Chronic cases of selenium poisoning occur when animals consume feeds containing 8.5 ppm. of selenium over an extended period; acute cases occur on 500 to 1,000 ppm. The toxic levels of selenium are in the range of 2.27-4.54 mg/lb. of feed.
Once calculi develops, dietary treatment appears to be of little value. Smooth muscle relaxants may allow passage of calculi if used before rupture of bladder.	Ammonium chloride has been effective as a control measure with cattle (1¼ to 1½ oz./head/day) and sheep (0.5% level of ration), but, to date, this treatment has not been studied experimentally with horses.	Avoid high phosphorus and low calcium. Keep the Ca:P ratio between about 2:1 and about 1:1. One to two percent salt in the concentrate ration may help (using the higher levels in the winter when water consumption is normally lower).	Calculi are stone-like concretions in the urinary tract which almost always originate in the kidneys. These stones block the passage of urine.
Treatment consists of correcting the dietary deficiencies.	(See Prevention and Treatment.)	Provide good sources of carotene (vitamin A) through green, leafy hays; silage; lush, green pastures; yellow corn or green and yellow peas; whole milk; fish oil; or add stabilized vitamin A to the ration.	

minimized. Even after these conditions have been rectified, it may be disconcerting to find that wood chewing, and perhaps various other forms of pica, persist among certain horses—perhaps due to habit. Thus, in the final analysis, there is only one foolproof way in which to prevent wood chewing; namely, to have no wood on which they can chew—to use metal, or other similar materials, for fences and barns.

Q. *Do you recommend the prolonged and continuous feeding of antibiotics to mature horses?*

A. No. Unless there is a low disease level, there is no evidence to warrant the continuous feeding of antibiotics to older horses. Such practice may even be harmful. Also, antibiotics are not approved by the Food and Drug Administration for continuous feeding to mature horses.

Q. *If the ration contains minerals, is it also necessary to self-feed them?*

A. Yes, people and horses have many things in common; among them, some individuals require more salt and other minerals than others. The ration should contain a reasonable level of minerals. Then, animals and feed differences (due to stage of maturity at harvest, weathering, and length in storage) should be met by free-choice mineral feeding. Allow free access to a double-compartment mineral box; with ground salt in one side, and in the other either (1) a mixture of 1/3 salt and 2/3 steamed bone meal (or di-calcium phosphate) or (2) a good commercial mineral.

Q. *Will alfalfa hay harm a horse?*

A. No, many horsemen actually prefer it over grass hay. If fed in large quantities, it may be somewhat laxative and horses may urinate more frequently, but without harm.

Q. *Can horses be self-fed on high energy rations?*

A. A few caretakers do self-feed high energy rations, but, sooner or later, those who do, usually founder a valuable horse. Except for the use of reasonably hard salt-protein blocks, salt-feed mixes in meal form, or high roughage rations, the self-feeding of horses is not recommended.

Q. *Is it possible to control the self-fed consumption of feed of horses through adding salt to a ration, without harm to horses?*

A. Yes, if the feed is in meal form—never pelleted, and if it is carefully and properly done. The practices and precautions are the same as those followed when self-feeding salt-feed mixtures to beef cattle and sheep (see *The Stockman's Handbook*, Sec. "Self-feeding salt-feed mixtures").

Q. *How can one control too rapid eating?*

A. This can be accomplished by spreading the concentrate thinly over the bottom of a large grain box, so that the horse cannot get a large mouthful; or by placing in the grain box a few smooth stones about the size of baseballs, so that the horse has to work to get feed.

Q. *How much roughage must a horse have?*

A. Actually, a horse does not have to have any hay. Also, more horses receive too much roughage than not enough, as evidenced by hay bellies (distended digestive tracts), quick tiring, and labored breathing.

Under most conditions, the roughage requirement of horses ranges from 0.5 percent to 1.0 percent of body weight, or from 5 to 10 pounds of roughage daily for a 1,000 pound horse.

Racehorses should receive a minimum of roughage, since they need a maximum of energy. Sometimes it is necessary to muzzle greedy horses to keep them from eating bedding when their roughage allowance is limited.

Q. *What is meant by the "tying up" syndrome?*

A. The "tying up" syndrome has been observed increasingly in recent years, particularly among racehorses, horses in endurance trials, and other horses in heavy exercise or training. It is characterized by muscle rigidity and lameness affecting the muscles of the croup and loin, accompanied by pain, disinclination to move, a variable temperature, and brownish colored urine.

Tying up differs from physiologic muscle fatigue in the conspicuous absence of hardness of muscle in the fatigue syndrome.

Some authorities feel that tying up and azoturia are one and the same, differing only in intensity. Both conditions result from exertion and present similar clinical signs and lesions. However, unlike azoturia, tying up seldom is characterized by kidney damage or high mortality.

Tying up appears to be more prevalent in mares than in geldings or stallions, more prevalent in young animals that are in high condition when put in training, and more prevalent following transportation of horses in vans or trailers. Yet, there are exceptions; tying up does occur in older animals and among those that have been in training for some time.

The cause is unknown, although it does seem to be associated with nervousness.

Affected animals usually recover in a short time. Treatment should be by a veterinarian. Among the specific treatments used are calcium borogluconate solution, insulin, thiamine, corticosteroids, tranquilizers, and selenium. The number of treatments within itself indicates a lack of basic knowledge and agreement relative to the disease.

Q. *What can you tell me about (1) "blood testing horses" (hematology) and (2) giving them "shots" or feeding iron?*

A. All body cells require oxygen. With strenuous exercise, as in racing, the oxygen requirement increases.

Oygen is transported by hemoglobin, the protein-iron coloring matter in blood.

It follows that any reduction in the hemoglobin content, or in total blood volume, will lower the oxygen-carrying capacity of the blood. When this condition is marked, anoxia, or anemia, develops, fatigue sets in, and there is lowered stamina and endurance.

Anoxia may be caused by many conditions. Usually it is due either to (1) nutritional deficiency, or (2) blood worms—both which may be aggravated by the stress and strain of racing, endurance trials, and showing.

Most trainers accept one or more of the following as indicative of the lack of "fitness": Loss of appetite, loss of weight, excessive "blowing" following work, a dry, harsh cough, rough coat, dull eye, watery instead of beady sweating, and "blowing up" over the loins. In an effort to be more exacting, some veterinarians who attend racing stables, endurance trials, and show strings now use blood examinations as a means of evaluating physical fitness.

It appears that, although there are breed differences, most horses which show consistent, good racing form have hemoglobin levels between 14 and 16 grams per milliliter, red cell counts between 9 and 11 million per cmm, and packed cell volumes between 40 percent and 45 percent. Also, other blood determinations are sometimes made. The blood testing approach is interesting and appealing. However, much more information on the subject is needed. Proof of this assertion, if any proof is needed, becomes evident when it is realized that all horses whose blood pictures fall within the above range are not necessarily good performers; neither are horses with blood pictures outside this range incapable of winning. Some horses do respond to treatment, but, generally, the results have been inconsistent and disappointing. One needs to know if horses which have lower blood values, but which do not respond to treatment, carry all of the red cells and hemoglobin that they are capable of developing—whether they have less potential for racing. Even more perplexing is the fact that this blood count can be too high, producing polycythemia. A horse with polycythemia frequently loses appetite, fails to thrive in the stable, performs unsatisfactorily, and may show cyanosis (dark bluish or purple coloration of the skin and mucous membrane due to lack of oxygen). It is also noteworthy that absolute polycythemia occurs at high altitudes or when there is heart disease or fibrosis of the lungs.

Racehorses with anemia are somtimes treated by either (1) injecting iron and/or vitamin B_{12}, or (2) giving orally (in the feed or water) one of several iron preparations. Sometimes vitamin C (ascorbic acid), folic acid, and the other B-complex vitamins are added.

At this time, there is insufficient knowledge of equine anemia, or of ways of stimulating hematopoiesis, to make a winner. The true role of therapy, if any, remains unknown.

The most that can be said at this time is that prevailing treatments usually satisfy the owner or trainer who insists that his charges "get the works." Most scientists are agreed, however, that "quickie" miracle shots or concoctions will never replace sound nutrition and parasite control on a continuous basis.

Selected References

Title of Publication	Author(s)	Publisher
Animal Nutrition	L. A. Maynard J. K. Loosli	McGraw-Hill Book Co., New York, N. Y. 1962.
Applied Animal Nutrition	E. W. Crampton L. E. Harris	W. H. Freeman & Co., San Francisco, Calif., 1969.
Comparative Nutrition of Farm Animals	H. R. Guilbert J. K. Loosli	Reprint from Journal of Animal Science, Feb. 1951, Vol. 10, No. 1, pp. 22-41, Pub. by National Res. Council, Washington, D. C.
Feeds and Feeding, Abridged	F. B. Morrison	Morrison Pub. Co., Clinton, Ia., 1958.
Feeds and Feeding, 22nd Ed.	F. B. Morrison	Morrison Pub. Co., Clinton, Ia., 1956.
Feeds Formulation Handbook	T. W. Perry	The Interstate Printers & Publishers, Inc., Danville, Illinois, 1966.
Fundamentals of Nutrition	E. W. Crampton L. E. Lloyd	W. H. Freeman & Co., San Francisco, Calif., 1959
Horseman's Handbook on Practical Breeding, A	J. F. Wall	Thoroughbred Bloodlines, Myrtle Beach, S. C., 1939.

Title of Publication	Author(s)	Publisher
Horse Science Handbook Volume 1......1963 Volume 2......1964 Volume 3......1966	Edited by M. E. Ensminger	Agriservices Foundation, 3699 East Sierra Avenue, Clovis, California.
Horse, The	D. J. Kays	Rinehart & Company, Inc., New York, N. Y., 1953.
Light Horses	M. E. Ensminger	Farmers' Bul. No. 2127, U. S. Department of Agricul- ture, Washington, D.C.
Merck Veterinary Manual, The		Merck & Co., Inc., Rahway, N. J.
Minerals for Livestock	Circ. 297 Gus Bohstedt	Extension Service, Uni- versity of Wisconsin, Madison, Wis., 1957.
Minerals for Livestock Feeding	H. H. Mitchell	Extension Service, Uni- versity of Illinois, Urbana, Ill., 1951.
Nutrient Requirements of Horses		National Research Council, 2101 Constitution Ave., N. W., Washington, D.C., 1966.
Nutrient Requirements of the Light Horse	Albert Wendell Nelson, DVM	American Quarter Horse Assn., Amarillo, Texas, 1961.
Nutritional Deficiencies in Livestock	R. T. Allman T. S. Hamilton	Food and Agri. Organiza- tion Studies No. 5, Rome, Italy.
Phosphate Fertilization of Alfalfa and Some Effects on the Animal Body	W. W. Heineman M. E. Ensminger W. E. Ham J. E. Oldfield	Tech. Bul. 24, 1957, Wash. Agri. Exp. Sta., Washing- ton State University, Pullman, Wash.
Proceedings of the Symposium of Mineral Nutrition		International Minerals and Chemicals, 20 N. Wacker Drive, Chicago, Ill.
Stockman's Hand- book, The	M. E. Ensminger	The Interstate Printers & Publishers, Inc., Danville, Ill., 1970.
Stud Manager's Handbook	December, 1961, 1962	Washington State Univer- sity, Pullman, Wash.
Stud Manager's Hand- book, Annual, begin- ning with Vol. 1 in 1965.	Edited by M. E. Ensminger	Agriservices Foundation, 3699 East Sierra Avenue, Clovis, Calif.

Title of Publication	Author(s)	Publisher
Study on the Breeding and Racing of Thoroughbred Horses Given Large Doses of Alpha Tocopherol, A	F. G. Darlington J. B. Chassels	Reprint from *The Summary*, Vol. 8, No. 1—February, 1956, London, Canada.
Your Shetland Pony	J. M. Kays	The American Shetland Pony Club, Lafayette, Ind.

14

In this chapter..

14

Buildings and Equipment
for Horses

THE EFFECTS of technological progress in buildings and equipment
are evident everywhere—in our homes, and in facilities used in meat
animal production. But altogether too many horsemen continue to
build and equip barns as grandfather did. Frequently, the accent is on
elaborateness for the purpose of impressing others. Also, there is a
paucity of experimental work pertaining to the basic requirements of
horse buildings. The most glaring deficiencies pertain to (1) labor-
saving devices,[1] (2) flexibility, (3) stress control—including temperature, (4) proper ventilation, (5) methods of handling excrement, (6)
sanitation, (7) safety of animals and caretakers, (8) fire-resistant construction, (9) materials,[2] and (10) cost.

ENVIRONMENTAL CONTROL FOR HORSES

Man achieves environmental control through clothing, vacations in
resort areas, and air-conditioned homes and cars.

Limited basic research has shown that animals are more efficient—
that they produce and perform better, and require less feed—if raised
under ideal conditions of temperature, humidity, and ventilation. The

---

[1] Seventy-five percent of horse work is still hand labor, one-third of which
could be eliminated by mechanization and modernization.

[2] Several horsemen complain that metal buildings are unsatisfactory, that they
must still be protected with wood, that moisture condensation is a problem, and
that they are too hot in the summer and too cold in the winter. Some express
preference for concrete blocks. However, the vast majority seem to favor conventional wood construction, despite the greater fire hazard.

primary reason for having horse buildings, therefore, is to modify the environment. Properly designed barns and other shelters, shades, insulation, ventilation, and air conditioning can be used to approach the environment that we wish. Naturally, the investment in environmental control facilities must be balanced against the expected increased returns; and there is a point beyond which further expenditures for environmental control will not increase returns sufficiently to justify the added cost. This point of diminishing returns will differ between sections of the country, quality of the horses (the more valuable the animals, the higher the expenditures for environmental control can be), and operators; and labor and feed costs will enter into the picture, also.

Environmental control is of particular importance in horse barn construction, because many horses spend the majority of their lives in stalls—for example, race and show horses may be confined as much as 95 percent of the time.

Heat Production by Horses

The heat produced by horses varies according to body weight, rate of feeding, environmental conditions, and degree of activity. Under average conditions, a 1,000-pound horse gives off about 1,790 Btu's[3] per hour, and a 1,500-pound horse 2,450 Btu's per hour.[4] The heat production of any animal is closely related to size and varies approximately as the $\frac{2}{3}$ power of the body weight.

Moisture Production by Horses

Most building designers are inclined to govern the amount of air change by the need for moisture removal. Table 14-1 gives the information necessary for determining the amount of moisture to be removed.

As shown in Table 14-1, a horse breathes into the air approximately 17.5 pounds, or about 2.1 gallons, of moisture per day. For 40 horses, there would be given off 700 pounds, or about 84 gallons, of

---

[3]British thermal unit (Btu) is the quantity of heat required to raise the temperature of one pound of water one degree Fahrenheit.

[4]*Farm Structures*, by H. J. Barre and L. L. Sammet, Table 6.2, p. 112, John Wiley and Sons, Inc., New York, 1950. By comparison, it is noteworthy that the same source reports that a 1,000 pound cow gives off about 3,000 Btu's per hour.

Table 14-1

VAPOR PRODUCTION[1]

Source	Grains/Hour	Lbs./Hr.	Lbs./Day
Horse	5,100	.729	17.50
Dairy cow	4,375	.625	15.00
300-lb. hog	729	.010	2.40
Sheep	486	.007	1.68
Hen	35	.0005	.12
Adult person	350	.005	1.20

[1]*Farm Buildings*, by John C. Wooley, McGraw-Hill Book Company, Inc., 1946, Table 25, p. 141. No weight was given for the farm horse, but most farm horses weigh from 1,200 to 1,500 pounds.

water per day. The removal of such a large quantity of moisture, especially in the winter when the barn is closed, is a difficult problem for the designer to solve.

Recommended Environmental Control for Horses

Because there is a paucity of experimental work on environmental control for horses upon which to base recommendations for barns for them, confinement systems in use for beef and dairy cattle, swine, and poultry were studied by the author as a means of arriving at the following recommendations:

1. *Temperature.*—The comfort zone of horses is within the range of 45° to 75°F., with 55°F. considered optimum.

Until they are dry, newborn foals should be warmed at 75° to 80°F., which can be accomplished by means of a heat lamp.

2. *Humidity.*—The preferred relative humidity is 60 percent, although a range of 50 to 75 percent is acceptable.

3. *Insulation and ventilation.*—These needs will vary from area to area. Where a wide spread between summer and winter temperature exists, and where horses are confined much of the time, proper insulation and ventilation are of prime importance. Under such circumstances, for moisture control in winter and temperature control in summer, horse barns should have at least 2 inches of insulation on the ceiling or roof, and the sidewalls should be insulated, also.

The design of the barn, and the temperature of the area, will determine the best type of ventilating system to use. Also, the requirements for summer and winter are so different that it is best to use two different ventilating systems—one for winter, and the other for summer. The author's recommendations follow:

a. *Winter ventilating system.*—Designed for a minimum of 60 cubic feet per minute (cfm) for each 1,000 pounds of horse.

b. *Summer ventilating system.*—Another system (in addition to the winter system), of 100 cubic feet per minute per 1,000 pounds of animal, should be available and used when needed.

During the summer, a satisfactory ventilating system can usually be achieved by opening (1) barn doors, and (2) high-up walls, or hinged panels, that swing down. Then, on extremely hot or quiet days, the natural ventilating system may be augmented with the summer and/or winter fan ventilating system (in the summer, reverse the winter fan(s) so that it will exhaust air).

A professional engineer should always be engaged to design the ventilating system. Generally, summer exhaust fans should be placed high, and winter exhaust fans low. Whatever the ventilating system, drafts on horses should be avoided.

4. *Light.*—Windows should be provided in the ratio of 1 square foot for each 30 square feet of floor area. They should be protected from horses and screened to keep flies out. Additionally, artificial light should be provided for the convenience of the caretaker. One 60-watt bulb, properly recessed and protected, in each stall, plus lighting in the aisle, should suffice.

5. *Water Temperature.*—In the winter months, water for the horse should be warmed to 40° to 45°F.; in the summer, it should be within the range of 60° to 75°F.

HORSE BARN POINTERS

Certainly, the care of horses differs from that accorded cattle, sheep, swine, or poultry; they require more individual attention. But just as the needs are unique, meeting them requires greater imagination and creativity.

Area Arrangement

Whether planning a new horse layout or altering an old one, all buildings, fences, corrals, and trees should be added according to a master plan, for once established they are usually difficult and expensive to move. The entire arrangement should make for the best use of the land and require a minimum of walking when caring for horses.

Location

The barn should be located so as to be:

1. *Accessible.*—It should be on an all-weather roadway or lane, thereby facilitating the use of horses, delivery of feed and bedding, and removal of manure. Also, it should be adjacent, or in near proximity, to a corral, paddock, or pasture.

2. *High and dry.*—It should be on high ground, with drainage away from it, thereby making for dryness.

3. *Expandable.*—There should be provision for easy expansion, if and when the time comes. Often a building can be expanded in length provided no other structures or utilities interfere.

4. *Convenient to water and electricity.*—Water should be available and plentiful, and electricity should be in near proximity.

Requisites of Horse Barns

All horse barns—regardless of kind, use, and purposes—should meet the following requisites:

1. *Environment control.*—Modify winter and summer temperatures for horses; protect them from rain, snow, sun, and wind; minimize stress.

2. *Reasonable cost, along with minimum maintenance.*—Initial cost is important, but consideration should also be given to durability and maintenance, and to such intangible values as pride and satisfaction, influence on the children, and advertising value.

3. *Adequate space.*—Too little space may jeopardize the health and well-being of horses, whereas more space than needed makes for unnecessary expense.

4. *Storage for feed bedding and tack.*—These are generally stored in the same building where used.

5. *Good ventilation.*—This refers to the changing of air—the replacement of foul air with fresh air. There should be a minimum of moisture and odor, and the barn should be free from drafts. Horse barn ventilation may be achieved through one or more of the following: opening under the roof, a ridge vent, hinged windows, dutch doors, and/or fans.

6. *Attractiveness.*—An attractive horse barn makes for a "heap of living" and enhances the sale value of the property. A horse barn that has utility value, is in good proportions, and is in harmony with the

natural surroundings, will have aesthetic value. Good design is never achieved by indulgence in fads, frills, or highly ornamental features.

7. *Minimum fire risk.*—The use of fire resistant materials gives added protection to horses. Also, fire retarding paints and sprays are available.

8. *Safety.*—Safety features should be observed, such as no projections on which horses may become injured, and arrangements for feeding and watering without walking behind horses.

9. *Saving of labor.*—This is a must in any commercial horse establishment. Also, where horses are kept for pleasure, it is well to minimize drudgery and eliminate unnecessary labor in feeding, cleaning, and handling.

10. *Horse health protection.*—Healthy horses are superior and efficient performers; hence, horse barns should provide healthful living conditions for the occupants.

11. *Rodent and bird control.*—Feed and tack storage areas should be rodentproof and birdproof.

12. *Suitable corrals and paddocks near by.*—Horse barns should be provided with well drained, safe, and durably and attractively fenced corrals or paddocks, either adjacent to or in close proximity.

13. *Flexibility.*—Both technological development and possible shifts in use make it desirable that horse barns be as flexible as possible—even to the point that they can be, cheaply and easily, converted into cabins, garages, storage buildings, and what not. Also for suburbanites and renters, permanent barns that are portable are advantageous.

Materials

Technology has evolved with new building materials and forced the improvement of old ones. In selecting horse barn building materials, consideration should be given to (1) initial cost, (2) durability and minimum maintenance, (3) attractiveness, and (4) fire resistance.

Among the materials available, and being used, are:

1. Wood, including plywood.
2. Metal.
3. Masonry; including concrete, concrete block, cinder, pumice block, brick, and stone.
4. Plastics.

Prefabricated Horse Barns

Pre-engineered and prefabricated horse barns are finding a place of increasing importance, especially on smaller horse establishments. Fabricators of such buildings have the distinct advantages of (1) price savings due to purchase of materials in quantity lots, (2) economical and controlled fabricating, and (3) well trained personnel for developing the best in plans and specifications.

Feed and Water Facilities

These are an important part of each barn. They may be either built-in or detached. For sanitary and flexibility reasons, as well as greater suitability, more and more good horsemen favor specialty feed and watering facilities, over old-time wood mangers and concrete or steel tanks. Bulk tank feed storage may well be considered on larger horse establishments, thereby eliminating sacks, lessening rodent and bird problems, and making it possible to obtain more favorable feed prices with larger orders.

KINDS OF HORSE BARNS

From the standpoint of intended use, horse barns are generally designed to serve (1) small horse establishments—the one- to a few-head owner, (2) large horse breeding establishments, or (3) riding academies and training and boarding stables. A summary of the kinds and plans of horse barns is presented later in this chapter, in Table 14-3.

When one or two riding horses are kept, they are usually stabled close to the house, which makes for greater convenience in their care and use. In most cases, there is provision made for limited feed and bedding storage and the tack used for such horses. Figures 14-1 and 14-2 show attractive small barns that are used as private stables.

With large horse breeding establishments, specially designed buildings are generally provided for different purposes. Because of the increasing importance of horses for recreation and sport—and the further fact that the same principles of building construction apply to the one- or two-riding-horse unit and the large breeding establishment —a brief discussion will be presented relative to each of the following types of buildings found on many of the larger breeding establishments throughout America: (1) broodmare and foaling barn, (2) barren mare barn, (3) stallion barn and paddocks, (4) breeding shed, (5) weanling

Fig. 14-1. Stable of Mrs. L. H. French, Hidden Valley, Calif. Note provision for plenty of fresh air, an essential for healthy horses. (Courtesy, *Sunset Magazine*)

and yearling quarters, and (6) isolation (quarantine) quarters.

Broodmare and Foaling Barn

The building designed as the broodmare barn may also be used for mares in foal, mares with suckling foals, weanlings, and barren mares. Whatever their size or style, there are two basic arrangements of multiple stall barns. The most common is a central aisle with a row of stalls along each side. The other is the "island" type, which consists of two rows of stalls, back to back, surrounded by an alley or runway. The island type is preferred when an indoor exercising ring is desired.

Maternity stalls should be 12 by 12 feet in size, or larger, and located so as to secure the most direct sunlight possible. When feasible, the maternity stalls should be adjacent to an office or some service room, so that at parturition time the caretaker may observe the mare through a peephole without being in sight. With this arrangement, it is preferable that the foaling stall have a double light switch, with one switch at the observation window and the other at the stall door.

For convenience and economy in operation, the broodmare barn

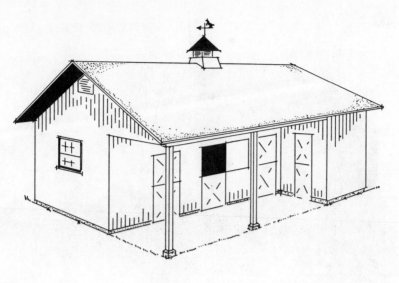

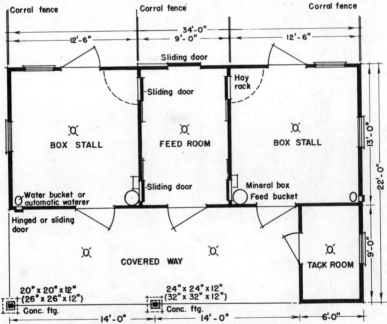

Corral fence   Corral fence   Corral fence

34'-0"

12'-6"   9'-0"   12'-6"

Sliding door

-Sliding door   Hay rack

BOX STALL   FEED ROOM   BOX STALL

13'-0"

22'-0"

-Sliding door   Mineral box
Feed bucket

Water bucket or
automatic waterer

Hinged or sliding
door

COVERED WAY   TACK ROOM

9'-0"

20" x 20" x 12"
(26" x 26" x 12")

24" x 24" x 12"
(32" x 32" x 12")

Conc. ftg.   Conc. ftg.

14'-0"   14'-0"   6'-0"

NOTE: 1. All swinging doors are Dutch.
    2. Hay racks deleted, when an all-pelleted ration is fed.
    3. Feed room partitions, 2" horizontal lumber to the ceiling.
    4. Windows open inward, protected by slats or wire grid.
    5. The feed and tack rooms will have ceilings and concrete floors.
    6. Box stall interior walls to be of 2" horizontal lumber to 5'-0" height, w/slatted
       wood or pipe or heavy wire above.

Fig. 14-2. A horse barn and plan. The barn contains two box stalls, plus feed and tack rooms.

Fig. 14-3. Broodmare loafing shed on the Morgan breeding establishment of Voorhis Farm, Red Hook, N. Y. (Courtesy, Fred Herrick, Manager, Voorhis Farm. Photo by Fred J. Sass, Red Hook, N. Y.)

Fig. 14-4. The main barn at Murrieta Stud, Murrieta, Calif., is an attractive structure built in a half circle, which faces a neat turfed centerpiece with the flag. (Courtesy, F. W. Koester, Editor, and B. K. Beckwith, Associate Editor, The Thoroughbred of California)

should have ample quarters for the storage of a considerable supply of hay, bedding, and grain. Usually, hay and straw are stored in an overhead mow, and grain may be stored either overhead or on the ground-floor level. In the latter case, extra precaution should be taken to prevent animals from taking advantage of an open grain-bin door; otherwise, founder probably will result.

A record or office room, toilet facilities, hot water supply, veterinary supply room, and tack room are usually an integral part of the broodmare barn. In many cases, a reception room for visitors is also provided.

Barren Mare Barn

The same type of barn as used for in-foal mares is entirely satisfactory for barren mares. Generally speaking, however, these mares do not require such careful attention or elaborate quarters. In large breeding establishments, usually they are run in bands of as many as twenty and are required to "rough it" to a considerable extent.

During inclement weather, a shelter should be available for barren mares. This may consist of either an open shed or a rectangular barn of the required size—allowing approximately 150 square feet per animal—with a combination hay rack and trough down the center or along either wall. If the barn is closed, it should have a large sliding door opening out, away from the direction of the prevailing winds. Ample hay, grain, and bedding should be stored in the barn.

Stallion Barn and Paddock

Stallion barns almost always face away from broodmare barns, and

Fig. 14-6. Stallion barn at Westerly Stud, Santa Ynez, Calif. It is comprised of three stalls, each 16 feet by 16 feet in size; and it is insulated and equipped with an overhead sprinkler system and infrared lamps. It faces three large stallion paddocks, each in permanent pasture.

preferably in the direction of prevailing winds. Some good horsemen prefer that the topography or plantings be such as to prevent the stallion from seeing mares or other mature horses at a distance. In general, English and French horsemen subscribe to this type of arrangement, keeping their stallions so they cannot see any other horses. On the other hand, many good horsemen in this country insist that such isolation usually makes for a mean, nervous horse. The latter advocates feel that stallions are better satisfied if they can see other horses off at a distance or even fairly close to them.

As in the broodmare barn, it is more practical and convenient to have feed and bedding storage within the stallion barn. Also, a small tack and equipment room should be provided.

Stallion paddocks and the stallion barn are a necessary adjunct to each other. The stallion barn may open directly into the paddock or be separated from it by a runway. The former arrangement is the more convenient and is quite desirable when a vicious stallion must be handled. Many good horsemen insist, however, that a paddock immediately adjacent to the stallion barn—where the horse can go in

Fig. 14-7. Stallion paddock on A. B. Hancock's Claiborne Farm, Paris, Kentucky. This illustrates the arrangement preferred by many stallion owners—high board fences and pasture paddocks separated by a 16-foot lane. (Courtesy, Horse Association of America)

and out of his quarters at will—encourages the animal to remain in the stall too much. These horsemen also believe that merely closing the stall door will not prevent the stallion from unnecessary loitering before the barn. Men of this school of thought insist that paddocks be located a short distance away from the stallion barn and be separated from it by runways.

Regardless of the proximity of the stallion paddock to the barn, a large paddock helps considerably in keeping in fit condition horses that are not otherwise exercised regularly. Although paddock exercise is not so good as that given under saddle or in harness, it helps to guard against filled hocks, azoturia, and other trouble.

Sodded paddocks that provide succulent and nutritious grass are also preferable to barren areas which merely serve as gymnasiums for stallions. A two- to four-acre area is desirable. Every effort should be made to build the stallion paddock at least 300 feet on a side.

Care should be taken to see that paddock fences are free from projections that might cause injury. Fences should be constructed of wood or metal, rather than wire. A double fence should separate nearby stallion paddocks, or a stallion paddock from a broodmare pasture. The paddock fence should be a minimum of six feet high and should be constructed of two by six inch lumber or good strong poles.

Water should be available in the stallion paddock at all times. Shade is also very desirable.

Breeding Shed and Breeding Corral

The breeding shed is nothing more than a large, roofed enclosure with a high ceiling in which mares may be handled and served under sanitary conditions. Most horsemen prefer to have the breeding shed in close proximity to the stallion barn, thus making for greater ease in handling nervous stallions.

The shed should be dustproof, high and without projections overhead that might possibly injure a rearing horse, well lighted, and have a clay or tanbark floor (preferably the latter, as it lessens the dust problem). Most breeding sheds are a minimum of 24 feet by 24 feet in size and have a 15- to 20-foot ceiling. The breeding shed should be served by two wide doors located on opposite sides of the shed. With this arrangement the stallion and mare can be taken out opposite doors. This will aid in preventing accidents when handling vicious or nervous animals.

The larger establishments generally include the following facilities

Fig. 14-8. Interior of large and high-ceilinged breeding shed at Westerly Stud, Santa Ynez, Calif. Note holding cage for foal in the corner. (Courtesy, F. W. Koester, Editor, and B. K. Beckwith, Associate Editor, The Thoroughbred of California.)

Fig. 14-9. Laboratory at Westerly Stud, Santa Ynez, Calif. (Courtesy, F. W. Koester, Editor, and B. K. Beckwith, Associate Editor, *The Thoroughbred of California*)

in addition to the center court which serves as the breeding shed: Laboratory for the veterinarian or technician, hot water facilities, and stalls in which mares are prepared for breeding. Formerly, many breeding sheds had a small stall for the young foal that usually accompanied the mare at the time of service. At the present time, however, these are seldom used, the foals being left at home.

When the cost of a breeding shed may be excessive, a high and spacious corral built of boards may be used satisfactorily.

Weanling and Yearling Quarters

The same type of quarters is adapted to both weanlings and yearlings. In all cases, however, the different age groups should be kept separated from each other, for older animals are likely to crowd the younger ones away from the feed or may inflict injury. It is also best to separate the sexes, at least by the January following foaling. Either small separate barns should be provided for the different age and

Fig. 14-10. An open shed for weanlings. This type of building furnishes a desirable place in which to winter young stock and idle horses unless the weather becomes too severe. (Courtesy, USDA)

sex groups of weanlings and yearlings or a larger building and adjacent paddocks may be adapted for such handling.

Weanlings or yearlings may be housed satisfactorily in either a stable or open shed; the main requisites being that the quarters are dry, sanitary, and well bedded and that they provide fairly good protection from winds. It must be remembered that in its native environment the horse is hardy and rugged and that diseases and unsoundnesses begin when there is too close confinement, improper feeding, and lack of exercise. This does not imply that such young animals should be neglected. Handling and gentling the animals at an early age is quite desirable.

It must be realized also that such animals will not develop and grow out satisfactorily unless they are well fed. The good horseman, therefore, seeks a happy medium between stabling and ranging in the handling of young stock; he realizes that there are benefits to be derived from each and that losses occur if either is carried to an extreme.

The main point to remember is that lots of fresh air and exercise are invaluable. Do not worry about young stock getting cold.

When stalls are used, two weanlings or two yearlings may be placed together.

Isolation (Quarantine) Quarters

New animals that have been brought into a stable should always be kept isolated for a minimum of 21 days before being taken into the herd. This applies to newly purchased animals, boarders, or animals being returned from showing or racing. Mares requiring treatment for infection of the genital tract should be quartered separately and run in special fields or paddocks.

A small barn designed for this purpose and with adjacent paddocks is considered an essential part of large breeding establishments. Separate feed and water facilities should also be provided for animals in

Fig. 14-11. Receiving barn at Gem State Stables, Tipton, Calif. Each stable opens into a small turnout area. (Courtesy, Harry W. and Velma V. Morrison, owners)

isolation. Moreover, the caretaker must use discretion in going from the quarantine quarters to the rest of the stables or herd. The quarters should be cleaned thoroughly and disinfected following the removal of each animal that has been stabled therein.

When possible, the isolation quarters should be so located that horses can be taken to them and removed without either the animals themselves or the vehicles in which they are transported passing through the rest of the breeding farm. It is also desirable that the drainage from the isolation quarters be away from the rest of the farm.

STALLS

Stalls are of two general types: (1) box stalls, and (2) tie, straight, standing, or slip stalls. As tie stalls differ primarily in the width of the area and their use is less common in breeding establishments, the discussion will be confined to loose or box stalls. The latter are preferred because they allow the horses more liberty, either when standing or lying down.

Adequate quarters for a horse should be: (1) ample in size and height for the particular type of animal; (2) properly finished and without projections; (3) dry with good footing; (4) equipped with suitable doors; (5) provided with ample windows for proper lighting; (6) well ventilated; (7) cool in summer and warm in winter; (8) equipped with suitable mangers, grain containers, watering facilities, and mineral boxes; and (9) easy to keep clean.

Floor of Stall

A raised clay floor covered with a good absorbent bedding, with proper drainage away from the building, is the most satisfactory flooring for horse stables. Clay floors are noiseless and springy, keep the hoofs moist, and afford firm natural footing unless wet; but they are difficult to keep clean and level. To lessen the latter problems, the top layer should be removed each year, replaced with fresh clay, and leveled. Also, a semi-circular concrete apron extending into each stall at the doorway will prevent horses from digging a hole in a clay floor at this point. This arrangement is particularly desirable in barns for yearlings, as they are likely to fret around the door.

Rough wooden floors furnish good traction for animals and are

Fig. 14-12. Box stalls in the stable of Mr. and Mrs. C. G. Furlong, Ojai, Calif. (Courtesy, Sunset Magazine)

warm to lie upon; but they are absorbent and unsanitary, they often harbor rats and other rodents, and they lack durability.

Concrete, asphalt, or brick floors are durable, impervious to moisture, easily cleaned, and sanitary; but they are rigid and without resilient qualities, slippery when wet, hazardous to horses, and cold to lie upon. It is noteworthy that concrete and asphalt, generously covered with bedding, are widely used for stable floors throughout Eastern and Western Europe.

There is great need for an improved stall floor covering material for horses—one which will lessen (1) the amount of bedding needed, and (2) the labor and drudgery of cleaning.[5]

---

[5]One such product now being tried on a limited basis is Tartan, developed by the 3M Company, St. Paul, Minn.

Concrete Footings

Concrete footings and foundation walls are recommended as they are both durable and non-corrosive. The foundation should be a minimum of 8 inches high, so as to be above the manure level.

Size and Height of Stall

Except for foaling mares and for stallions, there is no advantage in having box stalls larger than 12 feet square. The maternity stall should be at least 12 by 12 feet so that the attendant may get about the mare readily to accommodate the foal. Moreover, the stall should be without low hay racks (high hay racks may be used in a foaling stall), feed boxes, or other objects under which the mare might get caught or on which she might otherwise injure herself during parturition. The box stall for the stallion should be at least 14 by 14 feet in size.

It is also important that every part of a stall be of sufficient height so that the animal will not strike its head. A minimum clearance of eight feet is essential, and it is preferable that the ceiling over all stalls be nine feet or more in height.

Partitions and Interior of Stall

Regardless of the type of stall or the use made of it, there should be no projections (or ill-advised equipment) on which the horse may injure himself. Rough lumber, such as is commonly used in the construction of stables on ordinary farms, has no place in the finishing of stables for breeding establishments.

In general, the walls of the stable should be boarded up solid with smooth, hard lumber placed horizontally to a height of five feet, using either (1) durable plywood of adequate thickness and strength, or (2) two-inch, hard lumber (such as oak) placed horizontally. Hollow concrete blocks encourage stall kicking; hence, when used they should either be filled with concrete or lined with wood. Breaks in any part of the stall, caused by kicking, create a hazard for the animal. Stallion stalls are sometimes padded to a height of approximately five feet. All walls and partitions should be on concrete footings.

Above five feet, and extending up to a minimum of seven feet (or even to the ceiling), stall partitions and the hallway (or alleyway) front of the stall may be slatted, preferably with metal, to allow for better air circulation and companionship with other horses.

Fig. 14-13. Stall partition and door arrangement of the Al Blackburn Stable, Ojai, Calif. Note concrete footing of partition; walls boarded up solid with smooth, hard two-inch lumber placed horizontally to a height of five feet; and slatted upper portion of partition and alleyway front of vertical iron slats. (Courtesy, *Sunset Magazine*)

Most animals—especially stallions—are less nervous when they can see each other in their stalls. Some good horsemen object to slatted partitions for fillies and colts, arguing that young animals develop more self-reliance if stabled where partitions are solid. They cannot see and watch one another and will not worry if they are not turned out simultaneously.

The slatted upper portion of the stall (partitions and alleyway front) may consist of vertical iron slats, durable vertical wood slats, or a heavy "cyclone-type" fence placed on iron or wood frame. A two-inch or smaller mesh is preferable. Whatever the material, it should be durable and strong, and the openings should be sufficiently close so that there can be no danger of animals biting the tongue or lips of each other.

A smooth ceiling should finish the interior of every stall. If electric lights are installed, they should be placed under protective cover and flush with the ceiling.

Tail boards are necessary for certain horses.

Stall doors may be either (1) the sliding type suspended by overhead rollers or rails (preferably sliding within the stall, so horses cannot push them out), or (2) the swinging Dutch type, with the top part swinging down or to the side.

Weather protection over the stall door is important. It can be easily and simply achieved by an overhanging roof.

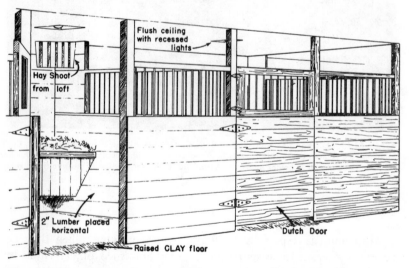

Fig. 14-14. A satisfactory type of box stall for horses. (Drawing by Steve Allured)

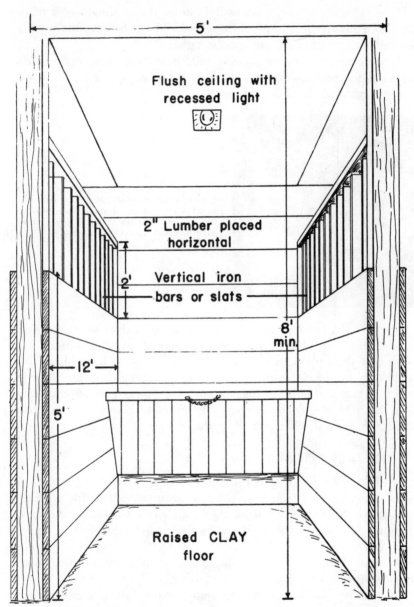

Fig. 14-15. A satisfactory type of tie stall for horses. (Drawing by Steve Allured)

HALLWAYS OR ALLEYWAYS

The hallways or alleyways of light-horse stables should be a minimum of eight feet in width[6] and height. Unlike stalls, they are usually not ceiled over, and they are usually higher.

The numerous types of flooring used in stalls are also used in hallways. In general, however, a clay floor is less popular than the hardsurfaced materials for this purpose.

Fig. 14-16. Hallway in the stable of L. Chase Grover, Woodside, Calif. Note that the traditional wide hallway separates two rows of stables, and that the hallway is not ceiled over. (Courtesy, *Sunset Magazine*)

Usually the hallway separates two rows of stables on either side. In northern areas, however, very often a hallway goes around the outside of the barn with two rows of stalls, back to back, down the center. In this arrangement, the alleyway is a very desirable place in which to exercise horses during inclement weather. This system, however, has one real disadvantage: It is difficult to arrange for direct sunlight in stalls that are located on the interior of the barn.

THE TACK ROOM

A tack room is an essential part of any barn. With one or two stall units, a combination tack and feed room is usually used, for practical reasons. On large establishments, the tack room is frequently the show place of the stable. As such, the owner takes great pride in its equipment and arrangement. Also, depending upon the use of the horses, the tack room takes on an air and personality that represents the horses in the stalls.

Generally, the tack rooms in stables where there are American

---

[6]The width should be increased if wide vehicles are to be accommodated. With wide trucks, 10 to 12 feet may be desirable.

Fig. 14-17. The impeccable formal tack room of the J. A. Smith stable, El Monte, California, contains special tack for Hackney and harness show ponies of different sizes and classifications. Since appointments in harness show classes are very important, each set of harness is made for a particular class and rig. The bugle on the table is used to call classes at the shows. (Photo by John H. Williamson, Arcadia, Calif.)

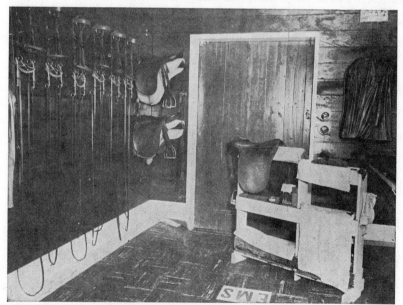

Fig. 14-18. The tack room of the Ella Mae Shofner stable, Montebello, California, is both attractive and practical for serving saddle horses. Note plastic harness cover on the wall, and the convenient saddle cleaning stand that holds all the necessary equipment for saddles, harness, and bridles. (Photo by John H. Williamson, Arcadia, Calif.)

Fig. 14-19. The tack room of the C. M. Deardorff stables, Santa Ana, California. This tack room presents an interesting and attractive display of pictures of winning horses, trophies and ribbons won in shows, and beautiful silver saddles used for parade. This tack room has been in active service for 59 years. (Photo by John H. Williamson, Arcadia, Calif.)

Fig. 14-20. Tack room of Dwight Murphy's San Marcos Ranch, Santa Ynez Valley, California. Note the large natural color paintings by Nicholas S. Ferfires, depicting the different costumes and saddles of riders and the beautiful silver decorated saddles used in parades on the noted Palominos of San Marcos Ranch. (Photo by John H. Williamson, Arcadia, Calif.)

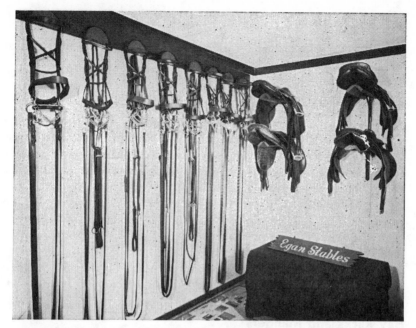

Fig. 14-21. The tack room of the Bob Egan stable, Pacific Palisades, California, is rather typical for owners of hunters, jumpers, and polo ponies. The tack box holds coolers, rub rags, cleaning equipment, hammers, nails, and other gear necessary in taking the horses to the shows. (Photo by John H. Williamson, Arcadia, Calif.)

Saddle Horses, harness horses, or hunters are rather formal. In the vernacular of the "horsey set," they maintain the "Boston touch." On the other hand, where western style riding prevails, generally the formal tack rooms have been replaced by more practical, simple rooms.

Tack rooms should be floored, rodentproof and birdproof, and ceiled over.

Figures 14-17 through 14-21 present some tack rooms that are rather characteristic of stables wherein there are different types and classes of light horses.

FIRE PROTECTION

Barns in which valuable horses are stabled should be posted with "no smoking" signs. Additionally, they should be equipped with (1) fire hoses in recessed areas, (2) an automatic fire alarm system, and (3) an automatic sprinkler system. In areas subject to electrical storms, barns should also be equipped with lightning rods.

The fire hazard can also be minimized by storing nothing but properly cured hay and by making sure that all wiring is in accord with strict electrical codes.

HORSE EQUIPMENT

Although the design of horse equipment is likely to be dominated by the fads and fancies of the owner, the basic needs are merely for simple but effective equipment with which to provide hay, concentrates, minerals, and water—without waste, and without hazard to the horse. Whenever possible, it is desirable that feed and water facilities be located so that they can be filled without necessitating that the caretaker enter the stall or corral, from the standpoint of both convenience and safety. In any event, it should not be necessary to walk behind horses in order to feed and water them.

Table 14-4 lists the kind, size, and location of the most common horse feed and water equipment; and a discussion of each type follows.

Hay Racks and Mangers

Some authorities advocate feeding the hay from the floor, inasmuch as horses feed from the ground while grazing. This system has the

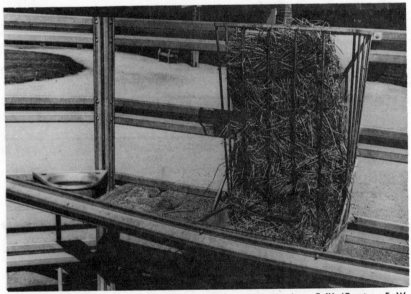

Fig. 14-22. Steel hay rack in paddock at Murrieta Stud, Murrieta, Calif. (Courtesy F. W. Koester, Editor, and B. K. Beckwith, Associate Editor, *The Thoroughbred of California*)

Fig. 14-23. A good outdoor hay rack. (Courtesy, *Western Horseman*, Colorado Springs, Colo.)

Fig. 14-24. A good outdoor hay rack in a well-fenced horse paddock. (Courtesy, *Sunset Magazine*)

advantage of reducing the cost of construction, economizing in stall space, and enhancing the security of the horse in the stable. But it requires a careful allotment of hay in order to prevent waste. Moreover, some horses acquire the habit of pawing whatever is in front of them, so that they either eat contaminated hay or waste a considerable part of it.

The author favors the use of hay racks because they (1) alleviate the problem of contaminated hay and lessen parasitic infection, and (2) lessen pawing and waste. In barns with hay lofts, there should be a chute above each hay rack, so that the hay can be dropped directly from the loft. Racks should open at the bottom so that dirt, chaff, and trash may be removed or will fall out. For stallions and broodmares, high racks should be used to eliminate injury hazards.

Grain Containers

There is hardly any limit to the number of types of grain containers, both patented and homemade, that are used by horsemen. These containers range all the way from very simple, inexpensive boxes to elaborate and costly equipment. Regardless of the type, the concentrate containers should be removed easily and cleaned by scrubbing. Such cleaning is especially important after a wet mash has been fed. Also, they should not constitute a hazard to horses.

Fig. 14-25. Feed bucket with snap hook, used in the stable of Mr. and Mrs. Edwin Knowles, Montecito, California. (Courtesy, *Sunset Magazine*)

A very popular and practical feed container consists of a triangular metal pan set in a wooden shelf, arranged so that the pan can be slid out through a slot in the stall wall for the feed to be put into, or for cleaning without requiring the attendant to go into the stall.

Watering Facilities

As in feed containers, there is a bountiful supply of types of watering facilities from which to select; some stationary, and other removable. Whatever the type, the water container should be one that can be drained and cleaned frequently. All animals in stalls should be provided with water, and each paddock should have a suitable tank or trough. In cold areas, stationary waterers should be provided with heaters.

Fig. 14-26. Automatic waterer, placed at one side of manger. (Courtesy, *Sunset Magazine*)

Mineral Boxes

All horses should have access to suitable minerals at all times. Salt and other minerals should be placed in separate compartments of a small wood box, located in a corner of the stall at a sufficient height so that the animal cannot rub upon it; or minerals should be incorporated in the ration.

Other Horse Equipment

In addition to the basic equipment needed for feeding and watering

Fig. 14-27. Horse watering tank set in the fence so that there are no protruding corners that might cause injury. (Courtesy, Major C. B. Team, USDA)

Fig. 14-28. Many stallion owners make use of a breeding chute in the breeding operations. This shows a satisfactory type of breeding chute. (Courtesy, Major C. B. Team, USDA)

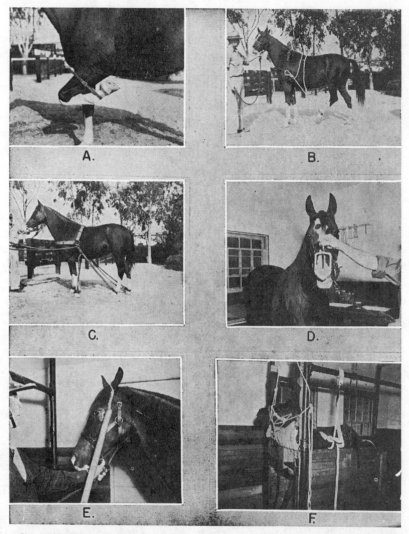

Fig. 14-29. Various means of restraining a horse: A, knee strap; B, side sling; C, casting harness; D, humane nose twitch; E, ear twitch; and F, stocks. The essential features of such methods and equipment are: (1) thorough restraint of the animal, without the hazard of injury, and (2) convenience and protection for the operator. (Courtesy, Major C. B. Team, USDA)

horses, there is hardly any limit to the other kinds of ingenious equipment used in the care and management of breeding establishments. Some of these items of equipment, with illustrated methods of use in some cases, are presented in figures 14-28 and 14-29.

FENCES FOR HORSES

Good fences (1) maintain boundaries, (2) make horse operations possible, (3) reduce losses to both animals and crops, (4) increase property values, (5) promote better relationships between neighbors, (6) lessen accidents from animals getting on roads, and (7) add to the attractiveness and distinctiveness of the premises.

Large pastures, in which the concentration of horses is not too great, may be fenced with woven wire. But corrals, paddocks, and smaller pastures require more rigid materials. The deficiencies of board and pole fences are generally recognized: They are chewed by horses; they splinter and break, which may injure a horse; they must be painted and repainted; they're expensive to maintain; and they rot.

Until recently, metal fences—conventional steel, aluminum, wrought iron, chain link, cable, and others—possessed one or more deficiencies; to most people all of them were cold, unimaginative and unattractive in color; some could not be painted; some sagged from side to side; some corroded; some lack resilience—when bumped they stayed bent—;

Fig. 14-30. Pasture paddock at Gem State Stables, enclosed with a well built metal fence. (Courtesy, Harry W. and Velma V. Morrison, owners, Tipton, Calif.)

Table 14-2

HANDY HORSE FENCE CHART

Material	Material Specifications		Construction Details			Comments
	Post	Line Fence or Rails	Fence Height	Number and Spacing Rails or Mesh of Wire	Distance between post on centers	
Steel or Aluminum Fence	7½' 7½' 8½'	10' or 20' rail 10' or 20' rail 10' or 20' rail	60" 60" 72"	3 rails; 20" centers 4 rails; 15" centers 4 rails; 18" centers	10' 10' 10'	Because of the strength of most metal rails, fewer rails and posts are necessary than where wood is used.
Board	7½', 4"-8" diameter 8½', 4"-8" diameter	2" x 6", or 2" x 8" 2" x 6", or 2" x 8"	60" 72"	4 Boards 5 Boards	8' 8'	
Poles	7½', 4"-8" diameter 8½', 4"-8" diameter	4"-6" diameter 4"-6" diameter	60" 72"	4 poles 5 poles	8' 8'	
Woven Wire	7½', 4"-8" diameter	9 or 11 gauge stay wire	55"-58"	12" mesh	12'	Woven wire is satisfactory for larger areas where the concentration of animals is not too great. But it is not recommended for corrals, paddocks, or small pastures. Use 1 or 2 strands of barbed wire (with points 3" to 4" apart) on top.

Fig. 14-31. A suitable wire fence for horses where the concentration of animals is not too great. The woven wire should be 55 or 58 inches high, with No. 9 top and bottom wire and No. 9 or 11 stay wire, and 12-inch mesh. This type of fence is also satisfactory for all other farm animals except young pigs.

Fig. 14-32. An electric fence for horses, showing the proper height above the ground. Where a temporary enclosure is desired or where existing fences need bolstering from roguish or breachy animals, it may be desirable to install an electric fence, which can be done at a minimum cost. Remember that *an electric fence can be dangerous;* thus (1) necessary safety precautions should be taken, and (2) one should first check into the state regulations relative to their installation and use.

Fig. 14-33. A strong pole fence. Fences for valuable horses should always be constructed of metal poles or two-inch lumber, and there should not be any projections that might cause injury. Barbed wire fence is always hazardous for horses. (Courtesy, *Sunset Magazine*)

and most of them were difficult to construct. But metal fences have been greatly improved in recent years.

Table 14-2 lists the common materials for horse fences and gives the specifications for their use.

SPACE REQUIREMENTS

One of the first, and frequently one of the most difficult problems, confronting the horseman who wishes to construct a building or item of equipment is that of arriving at the proper size or dimensions.

Space Requirements of Buildings and Equipment for Horses

Some conservative average figures of the building and equipment space requirements of horses are herewith presented. Table 14-3 shows the space requirements for buildings, and Table 14-4 shows the space requirements for feed and water. In general, less space than indicated may jeopardize the health and well-being of animals, whereas more space may make the buildings and equipment more expensive than necessary.

Recommended Minimum Width of Service Passages

In general, the requirements for service passages are similar, regardless of the kinds of animals. Accordingly, the suggestions contained in Table 14-5 are equally applicable to horse, sheep, cattle, and swine barns.

Storage Space Requirements for Feed and Bedding

The space requirements for feed storage for horses vary so widely that it is difficult to provide a suggested method of calculating space requirements applicable to such diverse conditions. The amount of feed to be stored depends primarily upon: (1) the length of pasture season, (2) the method of feeding and management, (3) the kind of feed, (4) the climate, (5) the proportion of feeds produced on the farm or ranch in comparison with those purchased, and (6) the number of horses. Normally, the storage capacity should be sufficient to handle all feed grain grown on the farm and to hold purchased supplies.

Table 14-6 gives the storage space requirements for feed and bedding. This information may be helpful to the individual operator who desires to compute the barn space required for a specific horse enterprise. This table also provides a convenient means of estimating the amount of feed or bedding in storage.

Table 14-3

SPACE REQUIREMENTS OF BUILDINGS FOR HORSES; KINDS AND PLANS

Kinds, Uses, and Purposes	Recommended Plan	Box Stalls or Shed Areas				Tie Stalls (size)
		Size	Height of Ceiling	Height of Doors	Width of Doors	
Smaller Horse Establishments: Horse barns for pleasure horses, ponies, and/or raising a few foals.	12' x 12' stalls in a row; combination tack-feed room for 1- and 2-stall units; separate tack and feed rooms for 3-stall units or more. Generally, not more than a month's supply of feed is stored at a time. Use of all-pelleted rations (hay and grain combined) lessens feed storage space requirements.	Horses: 12' x 12' Ponies:[1] 10' x 10'	8' - 9'	8'	4'	5' wide; 10 - 12' long
Larger Horse Breeding Establishments: The following specially designed buildings may be provided for different purposes: Broodmare and Foaling Barn	A rectangular building, either (1) with a central aisle, and a row of stalls along each side, or (2) of the "island" type, with two rows of stalls, back to back, surrounded by an alley or runway. Ample quarters for storage of hay, bedding, and grain. A record or office room, toilet facilities, hot water supply, veterinary supply room, and tack room are usually an integral part of a broodmare barn.	12' x 12' to 16' x 16'	9'	8'	4'	
Stallion Barn	Quarters for one or more stallions, with or without feed storage. A small tack and equipment room. Stallion paddocks, at least 300 ft. on a side, adjacent to or in close proximity.	14' x 14'	9'	8'	4'	
Barren Mare Barn	An open shed or rectangular building, with a combination rack and trough down the center or along the wall. Storage space for ample hay, grain, and bedding.	150 sq. ft. per animal	9'	8'	4'	
Weanling or Yearling Quarters	Open shed or stalls. The same type of building is adapted to both weanlings and yearlings; but different ages and sex groups should be kept separate. When stalls are used, two weanlings or two yearlings may be placed together.	10' x 10'	9'	8'	4'	

(Continued)

Footnote on last page of table.

Table 14-3 (Continued)

Kinds, Uses, and Purposes	Recommended Plan	Box Stalls or Shed Areas			Tie Stalls (size)
Breeding Shed	A large, roofed enclosure with a high ceiling; should include laboratory for the veterinarian, hot water facilities, and stalls for preparing mares for breeding and holding foals.	24' x 24'	15' - 20'	8'	9'
Isolation (quarantine) Quarters	Small barn, with feed and water facilities and adjacent paddock; for occupancy by new or sick animals.	12' x 12'	9'	8'	4'
For Riding Academies and Training and Boarding Stables	Either (1) stalls constructed back to back in the center of the barn, with an indoor ring around the outside; (2) stalls around the outside and a ring in the center; or (3) stalls on either side of a hallway or alleyway, and an outdoor ring.	12' x 12'	9'	8'	4'	5' wide; 10' - 12' long

[1]Even for ponies, a 12' x 12' stall is recommended since (1) it costs little more than a 10' x 10', and (2) it affords more flexibility—it can be used for bigger horses when and if the occasion demands.

Table 14-4

KIND, SIZE, AND LOCATION OF FEED AND WATER EQUIPMENT

Equipment for	Kind of Equipment	Materials and Design	Sizes for — Horses	Sizes for — Ponies	In Stall — Location	In Stall — Height	In Corral — Location	In Corral — Height	Remarks
Concentrates	Pail; tub	Metal, plastic, or rubber; usually with screw eyes, hooks, or snaps for suspending.	16-20 qts.	14-16 qts.	Front of stall.	2/3 height of animal at withers; or 38"-42" for horses, and 28"-32" for ponies.	Along fence line	Same height as stall	For sanitary reasons, removable concentrate containers are preferable, so that they can be taken out and easily and frequently cleaned—which is especially important after a wet mash has been fed.
	Box	Wood	Width 12"-16" / Length 24"-30" / Depth 8"-10"	Width 10"-12" / Length 20"-24" / Depth 6"-8"	"	"			If desired, a pie-shaped metal pan set in a wooden shelf can be mounted in a front corner of the stall and pivoted in such manner that it can be pulled outward for filling and cleaning, then returned into the stall and locked in place.
Hay	Stall rack	Metal, fiber, or plastic	25-30 lbs.	10-15 lbs.	Corner of stall; in trailer or van.	Bottom of rack same height as horse or pony at withers.			Hay racks (1) eliminate contaminated hay and lessen parasitic infestation, and (2) lessen pawing and waste. Racks should be open at bottom so that dirt, chaff, and trash may be removed or will fall out. For stallions and broodmares, always use high racks to avoid injury hazards.
	Manger	Wood	Width 30" / Length 24"-30"	Width 20" / Length 20"	Front or corner of stall.	30"-42" for horses; 20"-24" for ponies.			
	Corral rack	Wood	Large enough to provide one day's supply of hay for intended number of horses.				In fence line if it feeds from one side only. On high ground if it feeds from both sides.	Top of rack may be 1' to 2' higher than height of horse at withers.	Corral hay racks that feed from both sides should be portable.
Mineral	Box	Wood			Corner of stall.	Same height as concentrate box.	Fence corner	2/3 height of horse at withers.	If mineral container is stationed in the open—in a corral, or in a pasture—it should be protected from wind and rain. Mineral containers should have two compartments—one for mineral mix, and the other for salt.
	Self-feeder	Metal or wood				"	Fence corner		

(Continued)

Table 14-4 (Continued)

Equipment for	Kind of Equipment	Materials and Design	Sizes for Horses	Sizes for Ponies	In Stall — Location	In Stall — Height	In Corral — Location	In Corral — Height	Remarks
Water	Stall, automatic	Metal; one cup or two cups.			Front corner of stall	24" - 30"			The daily water requirements are: Mature horse, 12 gals.; foals to 2-year-olds, 6-8 gals.; and ponies 6-8 gals. In colder areas, waterers should be heated, and equipped with thermostatic controls. A satisfactory water temperature range in the winter is 40°-45° F.; in summer, 60°-80° F. Watering facilities should be designed so as to facilitate draining and cleaning. Water facilities should be located proper distance from feed containers; otherwise, horses will (1) carry feed to the waterer, or (2) slobber water into the concentrate container. A 20" x 30" automatic waterer will accommodate about 25 horses, and a two-cup waterer will serve 12 head. Automatic waterers should be checked daily.
	Corral, automatic				In fence corner of line fence	24" - 30"			
	Pail	Metal, plastic, or rubber			Front of stall	2/3 height of horse at withers; or 38" - 42" for horses, and 28" - 32" for ponies.			
	Tank	Concrete; steel					Set in fence so that there are no protruding corners; or painted white out in corral or pasture.	30" - 36"	One linear foot of tank space should be allowed for each five horses. Tanks should be equipped with a float valve, which should be protected.

Table 14-5

RECOMMENDED MINIMUM WIDTHS FOR SERVICE PASSAGES

Kind of Passage	Use	Minimum Width
Feed alley	For feed cart	4'
Driveway	For wagon, spreader, or truck	9'-12'
Doors and gate	Drive-through	8'- 9'

Table 14-6

STORAGE SPACE REQUIREMENTS FOR FEED AND BEDDING

Kind of Feed or Bedding	Pounds per Cubic Feet (approx.)	Cubic Feet per Ton (approx.)	Pounds per Bushel of Grain	Cubic Feet per Bushel
Hay[1]—				
Timothy, loose	3	625-640		
Wild hay, loose	3-4	450-600		
Alfalfa, loose	4	470-485		
Clover, loose	4	500-512		
Chopped hay	10	210-225		
Baled hay (closely stacked)	10	150-200		
Straw and Shavings—				
Straw, baled	10	200		
Straw, loose[1]	2-3	600-1,000		
Shavings, baled	20	100		
Silage—				
Corn or sorghum silage in tower silos	40	50		
Corn or sorghum silage in trench silos	35	57		
Mill Feed—				
Bran	13	154		
Middlings	25	80		
Linseed or soybean meal	35	57		
Grain—				
Corn, shelled	45	45	56	1.25
Corn, ear	28	72	70	2.50
Corn, snapped	25	81	80	3.25
Oats	26	77	32	1.25
Barley	39	51	48	1.25
Wheat	48	42	60	1.25
Rye	45	44	56	1.25
Grain sorghum	45	44	56	1.25

[1]From *Doane Agricultural Digest*, Table 1, p. 532 (Courtesy, Mr. Howard Doane). Under hay and loose straw, a range is given under the columns for "pounds per cubic feet" and "cubic feet per ton" the higher figures being for hay and loose straw settled one to two months, and the lower figures for hay or loose straw settled over three months.

SHOW-RING

There are no standard specifications relative to size, type of construction, and maintenance of show-rings. Yet, all the better rings meet certain basics.

For most purposes, the author recommends a ring 125 feet by 250 feet in size. It is recognized, however, that many good show-rings are either smaller or larger than these dimensions.

In order to allow plenty of room for such classes as working hunters and jumpers, in which as many as 12 separate jumps may be used, a number of shows have copied the famous Devon Horse Show for ring size. It measures 150 feet by 300 feet. But some horsemen consider it too big.

Those favoring smaller rings point out that the Spanish Riding School ring, in Vienna, in which the Lipizzans perform, is only 180 feet long, 59 feet wide, and 56 feet high; and that New York's Madison Square Garden ring, in which the National Horse Show is held, is slightly under 100 feet wide.

In addition to ring size, consideration must be given to proper footing—to achieving resilience, yet firmness and freedom from dust. With an outdoor ring, establishing proper drainage and constructing a good track base are requisite to all-weather use. Drainage is usually secured by (1) locating the ring so that it is high, with the run-off away from it, and (2) installing a perforated steel pipe (with the perforations toward the bottom side), or drainage tile, underneath the track if necessary.

Resilience, with firmness, is usually secured by mixing organic matter with dirt or sand. For example, the entire ring at the Spanish Riding School is covered with a mixture of two-thirds sawdust and one-third sand, which is sprinkled at intervals to keep the dust down.

In many indoor rings of the United States, 6 to 8 inches of tanbark on a dirt base are used. Unless tanbark is wet down at frequent intervals, it tends to pulverize and give poor footing. Others mix shavings and/or sawdust with dirt or sand to obtain a covering of 18 to 24 inches of the material. One good ring with which the author is familiar was prepared by laying down 9 inches of wood shavings, 2 inches of sawdust, and 4 inches of sand—all of which were mixed together, then oiled. Still others add a bit of salt, because it holds moisture when wetted down, thereby minimizing dust.

For outdoor rings, needed organic matter for resilience is some-

Fig. 14-34. Indoor arena in Rex C. Cauble's Cutter Bill Championship Arena (named after Cutter Bill, the World Champion Cutting Horse of 1962), Denton, Tex. This working arena is 360 feet long and 80 feet wide. It is illuminated with Mercury Vapor lights. The floor is made of 4 inches of sand over a hard clay base. (Courtesy Roy Davis, Editor, *Quarter Horse Journal*)

times secured by seeding rye, or other small grain, on the track during the off-season, then disking the green crop under.

No matter how good the construction, a show-ring must be maintained, both before the show and between events. It must be smoothed and leveled, and holes must be filled; and, when it gets too hard, it must be penetrated. A flexible, chain-type harrow is recommended for show-ring maintenance.

In addition to ring size, construction, and maintenance, consideration must be given to layout for facilitating reversing a performance class in a ring that has turf or other decorative material in the center; and to the attractiveness of the ring; spectator seating capacity, comfort, and visibility; nearby parking; and handling the crowd.

Fig. 14-35. Jumps in the attractive ring at Ribbonwood Arabian Ranch, Mountain Center, Calif. (Photo by Miss Gloria Rawcliffe, Clovis, Calif.)

Selected References

Title of Publication	Author(s)	Publisher
Light Horses	Farmers' Bul. No. 2127	U. S. Department of Agriculture, Washington, D. C.
Stockman's Handbook, The	M. E. Ensminger	Interstate Printers & Publishers, Inc., Danville, Ill., 1970.

15

In this chapter . . .

15

Horse Health, Disease Prevention, and Parasite Control[1]

by

DR. ROBERT F. BEHLOW, DVM, Professor and Extension Veterinarian, North Carolina State University, Raleigh, North Carolina,

and

DR. M. E. ENSMINGER, Ph.D., Distinguished Professor, Wisconsin State University, and Collaborator, U. S. Department of Agriculture.

AS LIGHT HORSES ARE, in most instances, quite valuable and, in the case of running horses, must be in top shape, they merit well-informed owners. When disease is encountered, they require the best of care and treatment that a competent veterinarian can give them.

Of course, with the advent of the automobile and truck, many horses were automatically quarantined on the farm or ranch where they had less opportunity to rub noses, less need to eat out of con-

---

[1] In the initial preparation of this chapter, an authoritative review was accorded by and many helpful suggestions were received from Dr. J. H. Drudge, Parasitologist, Department of Animal Pathology, University of Kentucky, Lexington, Ky.; Dr. W. R. McGee, DVM, equine veterinarian, of Hagyard-Davidson-McGee, Lexington, Ky.; Dr Jerry Harsch, DVM, equine practitioner, Goldendale, Wash.; and Dr. Jack Dunlap, DVM, Parasitologist, Washington State University, Pullman, Wash.

In the preparation of this fourth edition, Dr. J. H. Drudge, now Professor, Department of Veterinary Science, University of Kentucky, Lexington, reviewed the material on Internal Parasites of Horses; and Dr. Fred W. Knapp, Department of Entomology, of the same institution, reviewed the section on External Parasites of Horses.

It is to be emphasized that the review accorded by these eminent authorities does not constitute either full approval or full agreement of the reviewers and the authors on the contents of this chapter.

The material presented in this chapter is based on factual information believed to be accurate, but is not guaranteed. Where the instructions and precautions given herein are in disagreement with those of competent local authorities or reputable manufacturers, always follow those of the latter two.

523

taminated livery stable mangers and feed boxes, and none of the hazards of the community hitching post and the town watering tank. Certainly, the decreasing numbers of draft horses and mules is self-evident, but there is great interest in the use of horses for recreation and sport; and the same diseases, parasites, and ailments still plague horses.

In the past two decades, science has moved with rapid and far-reaching strides in the field of horse health, disease prevention, and parasite control; and new and important advances are being made almost daily. Progressive horsemen and veterinarians will wish to follow these modern developments with care, constantly improving upon present information and recommendations.

Currently, some parasites are being used to carry out their own self-destruction (for example, male screwworms are being sterilized by gamma rays from radioactive cobalt, then when normal screwworm females, which mate only once, mate with these sterile males, their eggs do not hatch; and diseased insects and insects with lethals are being released) and new chemicals are being used in parasite control. Eventually, parasites will be practically eliminated—they will no longer depress the health and well-being of animals.

NORMAL TEMPERATURE, PULSE RATE, AND BREATHING RATE OF FARM ANIMALS

Table 15-1 gives the normal temperature, pulse rate, and breathing rate of farm animals. In general, any marked and persistent deviations from these normals may be looked upon as a sign of animal ill health.

Table 15-1

NORMAL TEMPERATURE, PULSE RATE, AND BREATHING
RATE OF FARM ANIMALS

| Animal | Normal Rectal Temperature | | Normal Pulse Rate | Normal Breathing Rate |
	Average	Range		
	(degrees F.)	(degrees F.)	(rate/minute)	(rate/minute)
Horses-----------------	100.5	99 -100.8	32-44	8-16
Cattle-----------------	101.5	100.4-102.8	60-70	10-30
Sheep-----------------	102.3	100.9-103.8	70-80	12-20
Goats -----------------	103.8	101.7-105.3	70-80	12-20
Swine-----------------	102.6	102 -103.6	60-80	8-13

Every horseman should provide himself with an animal thermometer, which is heavier and more rugged than the ordinary human thermometer. The temperature is measured by inserting the thermometer full length in the rectum, where it should be left a minimum of three minutes. Prior to inserting the thermometer, a long string should be tied to the end.

In general, infectious diseases are ushered in with a rise in body temperature, but it must be remembered that body temperature is affected by stable or outside temperature, exercise, excitement, age, feed, etc. It is lower in cold weather, in older animals, and at night.

The pulse rate indicates the rapidity of the heart action. The pulse of a horse is taken either at the margin of the jaw where an artery winds around from the inner side, at the inside of the elbow, or under the tail. It should be pointed out that the younger, the smaller, and the more nervous the animal, the higher the pulse rate. Also, the pulse rate increases with exercise, excitement, digestion, and high outside temperature.

The breathing rate can be determined by placing the hand on the flank, by observing the rise and fall of the flank, or, in the winter, by watching the breath condensate in coming from the nostrils. Rapid breathing due to recent exercise, excitement, hot weather, or poorly ventilated buildings should not be confused with disease. Respiration is accelerated in pain and in febrile conditions.

A PROGRAM OF HORSE HEALTH, DISEASE PREVENTION, AND PARASITE CONTROL

In addition to following a program embracing superior breeding, sound management, and scientific feeding, the good horseman will adhere to a strict sanitation and disease-prevention program designed to protect the health of his animals. Although the exact program will differ from farm to farm, the basic principles will remain the same. With this thought in mind, the following program of horse health, disease prevention, and parasite control is presented with the hope that the horseman will use it (1) as a yardstick with which to compare his existing program, and (2) as a guidepost so that he and his local veterinarian, and other advisors, may develop a similar and specific program for his own enterprise.

I. General Horse Program

1. If encephalomyelitis was present in a given community the preceding year, vaccinate all horses prior to May 1.

2. Vaccinate all valuable horses with tetanus toxoid and provide proper wound treatment; also give a booster shot each spring and/or when a wound is inflicted.

3. To control the virus respiratory-abortion complex, or epizootic abortion (rhinopneumonitis), in edemic areas, vaccinate all horses on the farm against rhinopneumonitis in July and October, using the hamster-modified virus intranasally.

4. Avoid public feeding and watering facilities.

5. Prevent or control parasites by adhering to the following program:

a. Provide good sanitary practices and a high level of nutrition.

b. Have adequate acreage; use temporary seeded pasture rather than permanent pasture, and practice rotation grazing.

c. Pasture young stock on clean pastures, never allowing them to graze on an infested area unless the area has been either plowed or left idle for a year in the interim.

d. Do not spread fresh horse manure on pastures grazed by horses; either store the manure in a suitable pit for at least two weeks or spread it on fields that are to be plowed and cropped.

e. When small fields or paddocks must be used, pick up the droppings at frequent intervals.

f. Keep pastures mowed and harrowed (use a chain harrow).

g. Prevent fecal contamination of feed and water.

h. When internal parasites are present, administer suitable vermifuges and later move to a clean area.

i. When external parasites are present, apply the proper insecticide.

j. If cattle are on the farm, alternate the use of pastures between cattle and horses, since horse parasites will die in cattle.

k. Avoid overgrazing, because there are more parasites on the bottom inch of the grass.

6. When signs of infectious disease are encountered, promptly isolate affected animals, provide them with separate water and feed containers, and follow the instructions and prescribed treatment of the veterinarian.

II. Breeding and Foaling

1. Mate only healthy mares to healthy stallions and observe scrupulous cleanliness at the time of service and examination. Never breed a mare from which there is a discharge.

2. Provide plenty of exercise for the stallion and the pregnant mare, either in harness or under the saddle or in roaming over a large pasture in which plenty of shade and water are available.

3. During the spring and fall months when the weather is warm, allow the mare to foal in a clean, open pasture, away from other livestock. During inclement weather, place the mare in a roomy, well-lighted, well-ventilated box stall—which first should be cleaned carefully, disinfected thoroughly with a lye solution (made by adding 1 can of lye to 12 to 15 gallons of water), and provided with clean bedding for the occasion. After foaling, all wet, stained, or soiled bedding should be removed and the floor lightly dusted with lime (excessive lime is irritating to the eyes and nasal passages of foals). The afterbirth should be examined for completeness, and after ascertaining that all of it has been discharged it should be burned or buried in lime; and the mare should be kept isolated until all discharges have ceased.

4. To lessen the danger of navel infection, promptly treat the navel cord of the newborn foal with tincture of iodine.

5. As a precaution against foaling diseases and other infectious troubles, the veterinarian may administer antibiotics to both the mare and foal on the day of foaling.

III. New Horses and Visiting Mares

1. Isolate new animals for a period of three weeks before adding them to the herd. During this period, the veterinarian may (a) administer sleeping sickness vaccine (in season) and tetanus toxoid, (b) make a thorough general and parasitic examination, and (c) give a genital examination of breeding animals, and treat where necessary.

2. Require that mares brought in for breeding be accompanied by a health certificate issued by a veterinarian. Beware of mares that have had trouble in foaling or have lost foals.

3. If feasible, cover visiting mares near their own isolation quarters, using tack and equipment that is not interchanged with that used for mares kept on the establishment.

DISEASES OF HORSES

Every good horseman knows that keeping animals healthy is a major responsibility. In the discussion that follows, an attempt is made to give a combination of practical and scientific information relative to the most important diseases affecting horses. It is intended that this should enhance the services of the veterinarian; for the horseman can do a better job in controlling animal diseases if he has enlightened information at his disposal. Effective animal health programs call for full cooperation between the horseman and the veterinarian. Perhaps it is also a fair statement of fact to add that superstition, myth, and secret formulae are used more extensively in treating the diseases of horses than in treating ailments of any other class of livestock.

Anthrax (or; Splenic fever, Charbon)

Anthrax, also referred to as splenic fever or charbon, is an acute infectious disease affecting horses and other warm-blooded animals and man; but cattle are most susceptible. It usually occurs as scattered outbreaks or cases, but hundreds of animals may be involved. Certain sections are known as anthrax districts because of the repeated appearance of the disease. Grazing animals are particularly subject to anthrax, especially when pasturing closely following a drought or pasturing land that has been recently flooded. In the United States, human beings get the disease mostly from handling diseased or dead animals on the farm or hides, hair, and wool in factories.

Historically, anthrax is of great importance. It is one of the first scourges to be described in ancient and Biblical literature; it marks the beginning of modern bacteriology, being described by Koch in 1876; and it is the first disease in which immunization was effected by means of an attenuated culture, Pasteur having immunized animals against anthrax in 1881.

SYMPTOMS AND SIGNS[2]

The mortality is usually quite high. It runs a very short course and is characterized by a blood poisoning (septicemia). The first indication of the disease may be the presence of severe symptoms of colic accompanied by high temperature, loss of appetite, muscular weak-

---

[2]Currently, many veterinarians prefer the word "signs" rather than "symptoms," but throughout this chapter the author accedes to the more commonly accepted terminology among horsemen and includes the word "symptoms."

ness, depression, and the passage of bloodstained feces. Swellings may be observed over the body, especially around the neck region; and in the horse they may appear around the mammary gland or sheath. Milk secretion may turn bloody or cease entirely, and there may be a bloody discharge from all body openings. In very acute anthrax, the animal may die without having shown any symptoms.

CAUSE, PREVENTION, AND TREATMENT

The disease is identified by a microscopic examination of the blood in which will be found *Bacilli anthracis*, the typical, large rod-shaped organism causing anthrax. These bacilli can survive for years in a spore stage, resisting all destructive agents. As a result, they may remain in the soil for extremely long periods.

This disease is one that can be prevented largely by immunization. In the so-called anthrax regions, vaccination should be performed well in advance of the time when the disease normally makes its appearance. At least nine types of biologics (serums, bacterins, and vaccines) are now available for use in anthrax vaccination, and the choice of the one to be used should be left to the local veterinarian or state livestock sanitary officials. In infested areas, vaccination should be repeated each year. Herds that are infected should be quarantined, and all milk and other products should be withheld from the market until the danger of disease transmission is past. The horseman should never open the carcass of a dead animal suspected of having died from anthrax; instead, the veterinarian should be summoned at the first sign of an outbreak.

When the presence of anthrax is suspected or proved, all carcasses and contaminated materials should be completely burned or deeply buried, preferably on the spot. This precaution is important because the disease can be spread by dogs, coyotes, buzzards, and other flesh eaters and by flies and other insects.

When an outbreak of anthrax is discovered, all sick animals should be isolated promptly and treated. All exposed healthy animals should be vaccinated; pastures should be rotated; the premises should be quarantined; and a rigid program of sanitation should be initiated. These control measures should be carried out under the supervision of a veterinarian.

Treatment generally involves the administration of large quantities of antibiotics (3 to 12 million units of antibiotics) and good nursing

care. If used in the early stages, 50 to 100 milliliters of antianthrax serum
may also be helpful.

Distemper (or Strangles)

This is a widespread communicable disease of horses and mules, prevailing especially among young animals. It is also referred to as
strangles or infectious adenitis.

Animals that have had the disease are usually immune for life.

SYMPTOMS AND SIGNS

In a week or less following exposure, the disease may manifest
itself suddenly in the form of depression and loss of appetite. There
will be high fever followed by a discharge of pus from the nose. By
the third or fourth day of the disease, the glands under the jaw start
to enlarge, become sensitive, and eventually break open and discharge
pus. Because the pharynx is also involved, a cough is present that is
easily initiated. The disease may spread to other lymph glands of the
body and is then called bastard strangles. As soon as the abscesses are
drained, healing usually takes place.

CAUSE, PREVENTION, AND TREATMENT

The essential cause of the disease is a bacterium called *Streptococcus equi*. Transmission is usually by the ingestion or inhalation
of the infected discharges. The disease seems to spread rapidly when
so-called "green" horses are brought together. The organism is capable
of existence outside the animal's body for as long as six months.

Prevention consists of avoiding contact with infected animals or
contaminated feeds, premises, or equipment. Public stables and watering troughs are to be avoided. At the first sign of symptoms, the
affected animal should be put in strict quarantine. The contaminated
quarters and premises should be thoroughly cleaned and disinfected.
All excreta and contaminated bedding should be burned or buried.

The injection of animals with bacterin containing killed *Streptococcus equi* will help raise the level of immunity and may prevent the
disease. However, the use of bacterins is not always beneficial. If given
during a distemper outbreak, they may cause purpura hemorrhagica, a
disease that results from a sequel of streptococcus infections.

As far as treatment is concerned, good nursing appears to be most
important. This includes clean, fresh water, good feed, and shelter

with uniform temperature away from drafts. Antibiotics and/or sulfa drugs administered by a veterinarian are definitely indicated. It must be stressed that immediate action is of the utmost importance in this disease.

Encephalomyelitis (or; Sleeping sickness, Eastern, Western encephalitis)

This brain disease of horses and mules is also known as "sleeping sickness" or "brain fever." It is known as encephalitis or "sleeping sickness" in humans. Both the horse and man are "dead-end" hosts, infected only by the mosquito.

Since 1930, this infectious disease of horses has assumed alarming proportions in the United States. It is seasonal in character, extending from early summer until the first sharp frost of fall, when it invariably disappears.

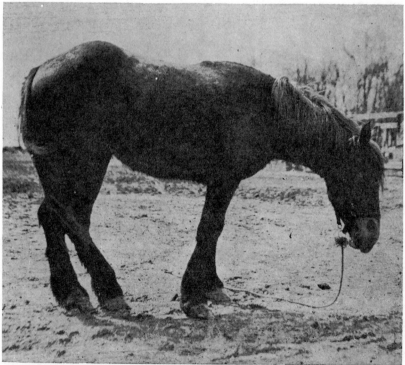

Fig. 15-1. Horse with encephalomyelitis (sleeping sickness). Note the sleepy attitude and the depressed head. (Courtesy, Department of Veterinary Pathology and Hygiene, College of Veterinary Medicine, University of Illinois)

Encephalomyelitis causes estimated average annual losses of $750,000.[3]

SYMPTOMS AND SIGNS

In the early stages, the horse walks aimlessly about, crashing into objects. Later, the animal may appear sleepy, standing with a depressed head. Grinding of the teeth may be noted. Local paralysis may develop, causing the animal to go down. Inability to swallow, paralysis of the lips and bladder, and blindness may be observed. If the affected animal does not recover, death usually occurs in two to four days following the onset of symptoms. Those animals which recover but are unable to react to normal stimuli are referred to as "dummies." Some animals make full recovery.

In mild cases, the horse may merely yawn a few times; this is the only clinical sign of the disease.

CAUSE, PREVENTION, AND TREATMENT

The disease is caused by four immunological, distinct filtrable viruses. The two most important ones in the United States are spoken of as eastern and western types, so named because of the geographic location of the first outbreaks. Generally speaking, mortality from the western type does not exceed 50 percent, whereas that from the eastern type is 90 percent or higher. The disease can be transmitted by nasal instillation, by at least thirteen members of three genera of mosquitoes, by the assassin bug, and by the spotted fever tick. The mosquito *Culex tarsalis* appears to be the most likely carrier. It is suspected that fowl may be virus reservoir, as, in one investigation, 26 to 57 percent of birds examined in Washington and California showed neutralizing antibodies. The infection usually does not exceed 20 percent, with considerable time lapse between cases on the same premises. In infected regions, most older horses seem to have acquired some degree of immunity.

Prevention entails vaccination of all horses as soon as the disease makes its appearance in a community or vaccination before May if the disease has been present in a community the previous year. The latter is the recommended procedure. Vaccination consists of one and preferably two injections intradermally (in the skin) of a vaccine

---

[3]*Losses in Agriculture*, Agriculture Handbook No. 291, ARS, U. S. Department of Agriculture, 1965, p. 76.

that consists of artificially infected chick-embryo tissue, in which the power of the virus to produce the disease has been destroyed by formalin. When two injections are made, they should be spaced seven to ten days apart. A veterinarian should administer the vaccine. Immunity lasts about six months. Other preventive measures include the isolation of infected animals in screened cages or the application of insect repellent to them; prompt disposal of all infected carcasses; destruction, if possible, of insect breeding grounds; and discouragement of movement of animals from an epizootic area to a clean one.

The use of specific immune serum in protecting animals which might be exposed to the virus may be indicated under certain circumstances. However, this serum is no longer readily available.

Careful nursing is perhaps the best and most important treatment. Feed and water should be available at all times. Some resort should be made to intravenous supportive medication.

Equine Abortion

Abortion is, strictly speaking, the expulsion of the impregnated ovum at any period prior to the time that the foal can survive out of the uterus. If the foal is advanced enough to live, it is known as premature parturition, and in the mare this may occur as early as the tenth month.

Of all mares that become pregnant, it is estimated that two-thirds will have normal, healthy foals; and one-third will either abort or produce weak, infected foals. The financial loss can be readily understood when one realizes that stud fees alone may range from $50 to $20,000, not to mention the investment in the mares and other production factors involved in the breeding establishments.

SYMPTOMS AND SIGNS

Abortion symtoms vary according to the stage of pregnancy in which abortion occurs, whether it is early or late. Sometimes, especially during the first two months of pregnancy, the mare may miscarry without observable symptoms, and the fact only becomes known by her coming in heat. At other times, a small clot of blood, containing the rudiments of the foal, may be found behind the mare if she is under close observation. If the occurrence is somewhat later in gestation, there will be some general disturbance, loss of appetite, neighing, and straining; and the small body of the fetus is expelled, enveloped in its membranes. In later stages of pregnancy, abortions are attended by greater constitutional disturbance; and the process resembles normal parturition, with the aggravation that more effort and straining is required to force the fetus through the comparatively undilatable mouth of the uterus. The vulva becomes swollen, with mucus or even bloody discharge; the abdomen droops; the udder fills; the mare paws with the forefeet and kicks with the hind feet, switches the tail, moves around uneasily, lies down and rises, strains, and, as in natural foaling, expels first mucus and blood then "the waters," and finally the fetus. These signs of approaching abortion may last an hour or two, or they last for a day or more. The symptoms subside for a time, only to reappear with renewed energy.

CAUSE, PREVENTION, AND TREATMENT

Causes of abortion in mares may be grouped under five headings, as follows: (1) *Salmonella abortivoequina*, (2) streptococcic abortion, (3) virus or epizootic abortion (rhinopneumonitis), (4) viral arteritis, and (5) miscellaneous causes of abortion.

1. *Salmonella abortivoequina* is an infectious disease of mares of an acute nature. It is commonly referred to as contagious abortion. Evidence indicates that the organisms probably gain entrance into the body by ingestion and have an incubation period of two to four weeks. Within thirty days following abortion, the organisms usually disappear from the uterus of the mare. The genital tract returns to normal within a short time, barring the entrance of other organisms. In a majority of the cases a normal foal is produced by the aborting mare the following year. *Salmonella abortivoequina* may be diagnosed through the use of the agglutination test or by the isolation of the organism from the aborted fetus, from the afterbirth, or from the uterine secretion. Abortions of this type occur most frequently in the latter half of the gestation period. A salmonella bacterin has been used with great success in the control of equine contagious abortion. Vaccination should be repeated every year where this disease is prevalent. Where premises are infected with the organism, it is a good practice to vaccinate each mare early in the fall with three injections, subcutaneously, one week apart. The vaccination program has eliminated this disease in Kentucky. As a result, few farms in that area vaccinate mares against this disease at the present time.

2. *Streptococcic abortion infection*, which gains entrance through

the genital tract, is said to be responsible for 17 percent of the abortions in mares. The streptococcus is either in the genital tract of the mare before she is bred or is introduced at the time of service. A diagnosis may be made on the basis of isolation of streptococci from the fetus. The afterbirth is usually found to be badly diseased. Usually the mare develops metritis and cervicitis, returning to normal only after treatment.

Streptococcic abortion may be suggested when the placenta is retained more than three hours, when the placenta is abnormally large, and when the foal is weak or diseased at birth or dies shortly thereafter. This type of abortion usually occurs early in pregnancy, generally prior to the fifth month. Mares bred on the ninth day have abortion rates four times higher than mares bred later. There is no known preventive for this type of abortion. However, adherence to the following general rules will materially reduce streptococci abortions:

a. Breed mares only when the genital tract has returned to normal.
b. Mate only healthy (bacteriologically clean) mares to healthy stallions and be scrupulously clean at the time of breeding.
c. Give a mare foaling abnormally in any respect plenty of time to return to the normal state.
d. Remember that infection is ever present in the filth of the external genitals of both stallion and mare.
e. Suturing the lips of the vulva will control this type of abortion in many mares. But this should be done by and on the advice of the veterinarian.

When a mare is found to have a severe genital infection, she should be treated properly and should have sexual rest for from six months to a year.

3. *Virus or epizootic abortion (rhinopneumonitis)* is a highly contagious respiratory disease (sometimes referred to as a cold) of horses, caused by a filtrable virus. Outbreaks can assume serious proportions. Although not all mares in a group may abort, a sufficient number are affected to indicate that the disease is infectious. The name epizootic, which is applied to this type of abortion in equines, has the same implication as the term epidemic in humans. The mares generally expel the fetuses late in gestation, mostly after the fifth month; however, some foals are born alive with rhinopneumonitis and die at 2 to 3 days of age. The fetal membranes are seldom retained. The genital tract returns to normal quite as promptly as it does following normal parturi-

tion. As the mare suffers no apparent physical reaction, she may be bred the same season and will usually produce a normal foal the following year. Aborted fetuses will have gross pathology that is rather uniform, consisting of lesions not observed thus far in abortion due to other causes. This particular virus abortion is known as fetal rhinopneumonitis, to distinguish it from other virus abortions. Control consists of the intranasal inoculation with hamster-adapted virus of *all* horses of each sex and all ages on the farm twice annually, in July and in October.

Equine rhinopneumonitis causes estimated average annual losses of $5,000,000.[4]

4. *Viral arteritis* is an acute infectious disease characterized by fever, catarrhal inflammation of the mucosa of the respiratory tract, or edema of the eyelids and legs. When pregnant mares are infected, 50 to 80 percent of them may abort. The virus is not affected by antibiotics or sulfonamides, and there is no evidence that either influences the course of the viral infection. Good nursing will help. No vaccines are available for immunization. New horses should be isolated as a preventive measure, and affected horses should be quarantined.

5. *Miscellaneous causes* include all cases of abortion that cannot be definitely classified as *Salmonella*, streptococcic, virus, or viral arteritis abortions. In some breeding establishments, as many as 50 percent or more of the mares may abort without showing any signs of illness, and bacterial cultures from the fetus and mare may be negative. In the category of miscellaneous causes of abortions are those due to nutritional disturbances, to functional disturbances of the ovaries, and probably in some cases to an unbalanced condition of the whole endocrine system. Also included under this heading are twin pregnancies, accidents and injury, defective development or malnutrition of the fetus, noninfectious pathological lesions in the uterus of the mare, and occasionally bacteria. Causes of this type are so numerous and general that aside from good feeding, breeding, and management practices not much can be done to prevent them; but these three practices are vital in prevention of abortion as well as other diseases. The mare may abort from almost any cause that very profoundly disturbs the system.

It is important to recognize an impending abortion as early as possible; for sometimes it may be prevented. Otherwise, certain precautions may be taken in order to prevent the spread of

---

[4]*Losses in Agriculture*, Agriculture Handbook No. 291, ARS, U. S. Department of Agriculture, 1965, p. 76.

infection. When a pregnant mare shows any general indefinable illness, she should be examined closely for abortion indications. Any suggestive indications should prompt the horseman to call a veterinarian immediately.

Preventive measures embrace avoidance of all possible causes. Where abortions have already occurred in the broodmare band, the special cause in the matter of feed, water, exposure to injuries, overwork, lack of exercise, and so forth may often be identified and removed. Avoid all causes of constipation, diarrhea, indigestion, bloating, violent purgatives or other potent medicines, painful operations, and slippery roads.

There are four important considerations in controlling abortion in any band of broodmares. These are:

1. All the pregnant mares should be vaccinated each year against *Salmonella* abortion on premises known to be contaminated.

2. To control and prevent streptococci abortion, mate only healthy mares to healthy stallions and observe scrupulous cleanliness at the time of service and examination. Suture mares where necessary.

3. To prevent rhinopneumonitis, follow a planned program under the direction of a veterinarian. A modified live virus is administered to all horses on the farm by intranasal inoculation twice annually—in July, and again in October.

4. Keep the broodmares healthy and in good flesh, and feed a ration of hay and grain that contains all the essential elements of nutrition.

When a case of abortion is encountered, the following procedure is recommended: (1) Gather up the fetus and afterbirth with great care and arrange through the local veterinarian for a diagnosis by a state diagnostic laboratory; (2) isolate the mare in a place where she can be kept in quarantine; (3) burn or bury the bedding; and (4) thoroughly disinfect the stall with a five percent lysol solution.

One of the most important factors to remember about abortion is that a veterinarian should be called for diagnosis, prevention, treatment, and cure. To forget this is to invite trouble and to pave the way for possible spreading of the infection.

Equine Infectious Anemia (or Swamp fever)

Equine infectious anemia is a very serious blood disease of horses and mules. It is sometimes referred to as swamp fever, mountain fever, slow fever, or malarial fever. Very early, the name swamp fever was given to the disease in the United States because of its prevalence in moist locations—such as on the coastal plains of Texas, and in the lowlands of the Platte and Mississippi Rivers—but it is now known that altitude is not a factor. The disease is found in the higher altitudes, far removed from any swamps. This infectious disease was first reported in France as early as 1843, and it has existed in the United States for at least sixty years. It is characterized by a great variation in symptoms and course. There is a marked tendency for the disease to localize on certain farms or areas, and it does not spread rapidly.

SYMPTOMS AND SIGNS

Symptoms vary, but some of the following are usually seen: high and intermittent fever, depression, stiffness, and weakness (especially in the hind quarters), anemia, jaundice, edema and swelling of the lower body and legs, unthriftiness, and loss of condition and weight—even though the appetite remains good. Most affected animals die within two to four weeks.

It is an unfortunate truth, however, that neither the symptoms nor the post-mortem findings relative to infectious anemia are suffi-

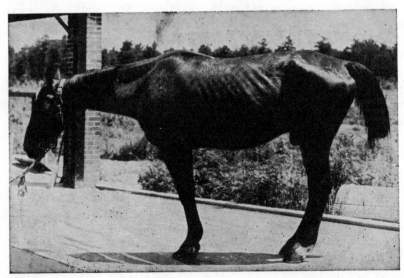

Fig. 15-2. Horse with equine infectious anemia (or swamp fever), five days before death. (Courtesy, USDA)

ciently characteristic to make a definite diagnosis possible. For certainty in diagnosis, it may be necessary to employ transmission tests by inoculating susceptible horses.

CAUSE, PREVENTION, AND TREATMENT

This disease is caused by a specific virus. The virus is commonly carried in the blood of infected animals over long periods of time, even though these carrier animals may have made a temporary or even a rather lasting apparent recovery. It is spread chiefly by biting insects, especially flies, but it may also be spread by contaminated hypodermic needles. Studies show that any debilitating factors that lower the animal's resistance not only may predispose the animal to disease but may greatly influence its progress.

There is no vaccination. The following preventive measures are recommended:

1. Use disposable hypodermic needles (one needle to one horse) and sterilize all other skin-penetrating instruments by boiling at least 15 minutes.

2. Practice good sanitation and eliminate or reduce biting insects as much as possible.

3. Be on the alert for sick horses and get a veterinary diagnosis on them.

4. Use tack equipment on one horse only.

5. At race tracks and shows, keep stalls, starting gates, and other facilities clean.

When a positive diagnosis has been made, it is advisable to kill the animal and properly destroy the carcass. Infected mares or stallions should not be used for breeding purposes. To date, there is still no expeditious method of diagnosis; and until such time as one exists, the control will be very difficult.

The treatment of the disease has been unsuccessful because at the present time no method is known to destroy the virus in the blood stream.

Equine Influenza

Equine influenza is a highly contagious disease which has been recognized for many years and which is widespread throughout the world. It frequently appears where a number of horses are assembled, such as at race tracks, sales, and shows.

While the mortality or death rate from influenza is low, the economic loss is high. The disease may interrupt training programs and racing schedules for weeks or months; and it may force the withdrawal of animals from sales, thereby delaying and/or making for less favorable disposal.

Although horses, swine, and man are subject to influenza and the clinical symptoms are similar in the different species, there appears to be no transmission of the disease between species.

SYMPTOMS AND SIGNS

Young animals (except for very young foals, which have passive immunity from the dam's milk) are particularly suspectible to influenza. For this reason, outbreaks of epidemic proportions are rather common at race tracks where large numbers of yearlings and two-year-olds are shipped for training and racing purposes. Older animals are usually immune, probably due to repeated exposure to the disease. Symptoms develop as early as two days or as late as ten days after exposure.

The onset of influenza in horses is marked by rapidly rising temperature, which may reach 106° F. and persist for two to ten days. Other signs include loss of appetite, extreme weakness and depression, rapid breathing, a dry cough, and water discharges from the eyes and nostrils, which are followed by a white- to yellow-colored nasal discharge.

Since one of the first symptoms of equine influenza is a rapidly rising temperature, it is recommended that the temperature of young horses be taken twice daily under the following circumstances:

1. For a period of four to five days prior to shipment.
2. For two to ten days after arrival at a new location.
3. When horses are stabled in an area where influenza, coughs, and colds are known to exist.

CAUSE, PREVENTION, AND TREATMENT

Influenza is caused by a nyxovirus with properties of the Type A influenza viruses.

Conditions incident to shipment, exposure to cold, sudden changes of climate, and fatigue appear to lower the resistance of horses so as to make them more susceptible to the disease.

It is believed that the most common method of transmission of influenza is by way of the respiratory tract, and that the virus itself is carried on contaminated feed, bedding, water, buckets, brooms, on the clothing and hands of attendants, and on transportation facilities.

Effective prevention is obtained by vaccination with a killed virus, using two doses, and following the manufacturer's directions on the time of the second dose. For continued protection, each vaccinated animal must receive (1) an annual booster, or (2) a booster when there is exposure or an epizootic condition. Also, all new animals should be isolated for three weeks, and sick animals should be quarantined.

Treatment should be handled by the veterinarian. No exercise, no matter how mild, should be permitted during the period of elevated temperature. The early use of antibiotics and/or sulfa drugs will prevent secondary bacterial complications.

Glanders (Farcy)

This very old disease, commonly referred to as farcy or *malleus*, has worldwide distribution, though it is not important in the United States at the present time. Glanders was described as early as 400 B. C., and it received the Greek name *malleus* from Aristotle. It is an acute or chronic infectious disease of horses, mules, and donkeys; but it can be transmitted to other animals and to human beings through close contact.

SYMPTOMS AND SIGNS

The disease usually manifests itself either in the acute or chronic form. The chronic form is most often observed in the horse, while the acute form is seen more in mules and donkeys. The incubation period varies from weeks to months. The chronic symptoms may be manifested in the lungs, skin, or nasal passages. In the nasal form, there is a nasal discharge which later becomes pus. Hard red nodules, which break down into abscesses and then ulcers, will be seen. When the ulcers heal, they leave a star-shaped scar. The skin form is often seen with the nasal form. It is characterized by the development of nodules and ulcers in the skin and subcutaneous tissue. Both the skin and nasal forms are thought to originate in the lungs. The lungs are the most common location for the lesions of glanders. Evidence of infection consists of a loss in condition and lack of endurance, with sudden bleeding from the nose. Coughing followed by a mucous discharge may be noted. At this stage, there are nodules and abscesses in the lung tissue. In the acute form of the disease, death usually occurs within a week after many or all of the symptoms noted above have been in evidence.

CAUSE, PREVENTION, AND TREATMENT

The cause of this disease is the bacterium *Malleomyces mallei*. It is transmitted by inhalation or ingestion of the exudate containing the causative organism.

Any suspected animal should be subjected to the "mallein test." Positive diagnosis is cause for immediate destruction of the animal and the careful cleaning and disinfection of the contaminated equipment and premises. All exposed animals should be tested at frequent intervals.

To date, it has been impossible to obtain glanders immunity in an animal, and no cure is known.

Navel Infection (Joint-ill, Navel-ill, Actinobacillosis, or Streptococcus)

Navel infection is an infectious disease of newborn foals, calves, and lambs, although it occurs less frequently in calves and lambs than in foals.

SYMPTOMS AND SIGNS

Navel infection is characterized by loss of appetite, by swelling, soreness and stiffness in the joints, by umbilical swelling and discharge, and by general listlessness. There are slowly developing cases that do not become apparent until four to six months of age. These foals usually succumb.

CAUSE, PREVENTION, AND TREATMENT

Navel infection is caused by several kinds of bacteria.

The recommended preventive measures are: sanitation and hygiene at mating and parturition, painting the navel cord of the newborn animal with iodine, and bacterins. Lack of sanitation is the most important factor in the cause of this disease.

For treatment, the veterinarian may give a blood transfusion, and he may administer a sulfa drug or an antibiotic.

Rabies (Hydrophobia, or Madness)

Rabies is an acute infectious disease of horses and all other warm-blooded animals and man. It is characterized by deranged consciousness and paralysis, and it terminates fatally. This disease is one that is far too prevalent, and, if present knowledge were applied it could be controlled and even eradicated.

When a human being is bitten by a dog that is suspected of being rabid, the first impulse is to kill the dog immediately. This is a mistake. Instead, it is important to confine the animal under the observation of a veterinarian until the disease, if it is present, has a chance to develop and run its course. If no recognizable symptoms appear in the animal within a period of two weeks after it inflicted the bite, it is safe to assume that there was no rabies at the time. Death occurs within a few days after the symptoms appear, and the dog's brain can then be examined for specific evidence of rabies. With this procedure, unless the bite is in the region of the neck or head, there will usually be ample time in which to administer treatment to exposed human beings. As the virus has been found in the saliva of a dog at least five days before the appearance of the clinically recognizable symptoms, the bite of a dog should always be considered potentially dangerous until proved otherwise. In any event, when people are bitten or exposed to rabies, they should see their local doctor. He may use a vaccine made of (1) killed virus, nervous tissue origin, or (2) killed virus, duck embryo or chick embryo origin. Also, new and promising vaccines have been developed and are being tested experimentally.

SYMPTOMS AND SIGNS

Less than ten percent of the rabies cases appear in horses, cattle, swine, and sheep. The disease usually manifests itself in two forms: the furious, irritable, or violent form, or the dumb or paralytic form. It is often difficult to distinguish between the two forms, however. The furious type usually merges into the dumb form because paralysis always occurs just before death.

In comparison with other animals, the horse may resort to more violence and is exceedingly dangerous.

CAUSE, PREVENTION, AND TREATMENT

Rabies is caused by a filtrable virus which is usually carried into a bite wound by the infected saliva. The malady is generally transmitted to farm animals by dogs and certain wild animals such as the fox, skunk, and bat.

Rabies can best be prevented by attacking it at its chief source, the dog. With the advent of an improved anti-rabies vaccine for the dog, it should be a requirement that all dogs be immunized. This should be supplemented by regulations governing the licensing, quarantine, and transportation of dogs. Also, the control of wild carnivores and bats is of increasing importance in the eradication of rabies.

When horses are bitten or exposed to rabies, they should be seen by a veterinarian. The older vaccine, used for rabies control in all animals, was a killed vaccine of brain origin. Killed virus tissue (duck embryo) culture origin is now being used on some animals, but there is little information on its use for horses.

Tetanus (Lockjaw)

Tetanus is chiefly a wound-infection disease that attacks horses (and other equines) and man, although it does occur in swine, cattle, sheep, and goats. It is generally referred to as lockjaw.

Fig. 15-3. Horse with tetanus. Notice the stiff-legged condition and partly raised tail. (Courtesy, Department of Veterinary Pathology and Hygiene, College of Veterinary Medicine, University of Illinois)

In the United States, the disease occurs most frequently in the South, where precautions against tetanus are an essential part of the routine treatment of wounds. The disease is worldwide in distribution.

SYMPTOMS AND SIGNS

The incubation period of tetanus varies from one to four weeks, but may be from one day to many months. It is usually associated with a wound but may not directly follow an injury. The first noticeable sign of the disease is a stiffness first observed about the head. The animal often chews slowly and weakly and swallows awkwardly. The third eyelid is seen protruding over the forward surface of the eyeball (called "haws"). The animal then shows violent spasm or contractions of groups of muscles brought on by the slightest movement or noise. It usually attempts to remain standing throughout the course of the disease. If recovery occurs, it will take a month or more. In over 80 percent of the cases, however, death ensues—usually because of sheer exhaustion or paralysis of vital organs.

CAUSE, PREVENTION, AND TREATMENT

The disease is caused by an exceedingly powerful toxin (more than one hundred times as toxic as strychnine) liberated by the tetanus organism (*Clostridium tetani*). This organism is an anaerobe (lives in absence of oxygen) which forms the most hardy spores known. It may be found in certain soils, horse dung, and sometimes in human excreta. The organism usually causes trouble when it gets into a wound that rapidly heals or closes over it. In the absence of oxygen, it then grows and liberates the toxin which follows up nerve trunks. Upon reaching the spinal cord, the toxin excites the symptoms noted above.

The disease can be prevented through the use of tetanus toxoid. Two doses should be given at six-week intervals, followed by a booster injection annually. If wound infections occur in vaccinated animals, it is wise to give a dose of tetanus toxoid as the rise in antitoxin titer will occur more promptly than the development of clinical signs.

Once the disease develops, the horse should be placed under the care of a veterinarian. Early in the course of the disease, massive doses of antitoxin—100,000 to 200,000 units or more—may be effective. Also, tranquilizing drugs are effective in reducing the extent and severity of muscular spasms, and antibiotics are helpful.

Horses with tetanus should be confined to darkened box stalls in which the feeding and watering facilities are placed high enough so that the animal is capable of gaining access to them without lowering its head. Support by slinging should be given wherever possible.

PARASITES OF HORSES

The term parasite refers to a form of animal life that lives in or on the body of a host animal, deriving its food therefrom. Parasites kill some horses, but, by and large, the main damage is insidious and results in lowered efficiency—i.e., something less than the best performance a horse is capable of showing.

Internal Parasites of Horses[5]

Some 150 different kinds of internal parasites infect horses throughout the world,[6] and probably no individual animal is ever entirely free of them. Although equines are not unique among herbivorous animals in their susceptibility to parasitism, they do harbor many diverse species of pests. Probably this can be attributed to the fact that horses, perhaps more than other domestic animals, have been transported widely for service in war and colonizing enterprises and for racing and breeding purposes. Fortunately, comparatively few of these parasites inflict serious damage upon their host; but those few can be extremely harmful and even deadly.

As would be expected, the kinds of parasites and the degree of infection in horses vary in different parts of the world, and also among individual horses. Then, too, some of the parasites are distributed more or less regionally, primarily because of differences in developmental cycles.

The internal parasites may be located in practically every tissue and cavity of the body. However, most of them locate in the alimentary tract, lungs, body cavity, or bloodstream. Those which inhabit the digestive system usually become localized in specific parts of it. Still others are migratory or wandering in their habits, traveling throughout different parts of the body.

---

[5]The material on Internal Parasites of Horses was authoritatively reviewed by Dr. J. H. Drudge, Professor, Department of Veterinary Science, University of Kentucky, Lexington.

[6]Some 57 species parasitize horses in this country.

Fig. 15-4. Same horse before (upper picture) and after (bottom picture) treatment for internal parasites. Parasites retard the foal's development and lower the efficiency of mature horses. Also, feed is always too costly to give to parasites. (Courtesy, College of Veterinary Medicine, University of Illinois)

GENERAL SYMPTOMS

Usually the symptoms of parasitism are marked by a slowly progressive chain of events that the owner may overlook entirely or confuse with other conditions. The general symptoms of parasitic infections in the horse are: weakness, unthrifty appearance and emaciation, tucked up flanks, distended abdomen ("potbelly"), rough coat, paleness of the membranes of the eyes and mouth, in some cases frequent colic and diarrhea, and stunted growth and development in young animals. Affected animals usually eat well, and the temperature remains normal; but there is always a loss in the functional efficiency of the individual as a working unit.

With certain types of parasitic infections, the specific effects are very pronounced. This is true, for example, of the protozoan parasite *Trypanosoma equiperdum*, which causes dourine.

GENERAL PREVENTIVE AND CONTROL MEASURES

Most parasitic infections of equines may be attributed to the fact that, under domestication, horses (as well as all other animal species) have been forced to sleep and eat in close proximity to their own feces —being either confined and fed in a stall or fenced within limited grazing areas or pastures. By contrast, in the wild state animals roved over vast areas, seldom eating, watering, or sleeping in the same spot.

As the feces of the horse are the primary source of infection of internal parasites, it should be obvious that the most important requisite of successful control measures is that they be designed to separate the animal from its own excrement. The following control measures are recommended to the horseman:

1. Provide good sanitary measures and a high level of nutrition.
2. Provide temporary seeded pastures rather than permanent native pastures. These should be plowed, cropped, and reseeded to grasses or legumes at regular intervals, usually every three to five years.
3. Practice rotation grazing so as to keep horses off the pasture for an entire year at regular intervals, during which time the pasture may be either left idle or grazed by some other class of livestock.
4. Provide for greater acreage per animal, thus lessening the degree of exposure to contamination.
5. Pasture young stock on clean pastures; never allow them to follow horses unless the area has been either plowed or left idle for a year in the interim.

6. Do not spread fresh horse manure on pastures grazed by horses. Either store the manure in a suitable tightly constructed pit for at least a two-week interval prior to spreading, allowing the spontaneously generated heat to destroy the parasites,[7] or spread the fresh manure on those fields that will be plowed and cropped prior to reseeding.

7. Pick up the droppings in the paddocks and fields, especially in those areas where temporary pastures are not available and a system of rotation grazing cannot be followed. Handle these droppings as indicated in point No. 6.

8. Treat infected animals prior to turning them out to a clean area.

9. Follow rigid stable sanitation in order to prevent fecal contamination of feed and water. This requires a clean stall and properly constructed and sanitary grain boxes, hay racks, and watering facilities.

10. Frequent mowing and raking of pastures, followed by harrowing with a chain harrow is desirable, for it tends to expose bottom grass and fecal matter to the sunlight.

11. Consult your veterinarian as to treatment, dosage, interval between treatments, and method of fecal examination; and then treat all horses regularly and precisely as directed.

COMMON INTERNAL PARASITES

As there are so many kinds of internal parasites, only the most common and damaging ones will be discussed herein. Strongyles, ascarids, and bots are generally the most injurious of internal parasites, although other kinds are capable of producing severe injury on occasion and generally contribute to the over-all picture of parasitism wherever they occur.

Ascarids (Large roundworms, or White worms)

The ascarid, *Parascaris equorum*, is found in the small intestines of equines. The female roundworm varies from 6 to 22 inches in length and the male from 5 to 13 inches. When full-grown, both are about the diameter of a lead pencil.

---

[7]Steam under pressure in an insulated manure box will accomplish the same results in about two hours' time. When steam is not used, and the heat of the manure is relied upon, the outside fecal material should remain for further heating.

DISTRIBUTION AND LOSSES CAUSED BY ASCARIDS

Roundworms are fairly widely distributed throughout the United States. They especially affect foals and young animals, but are rarely important in horses over five years of age. This decreased susceptibility as age increases is credited to an acquired immunity resulting from earlier infections. Roundworms are particularly damaging to their equine host because of the destruction that the migrating larvae inflict

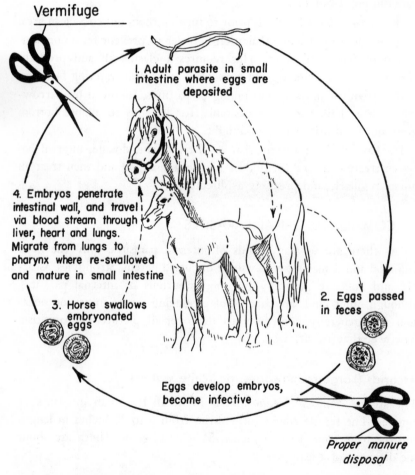

Vermifuge

1. Adult parasite in small intestine where eggs are deposited

4. Embryos penetrate intestinal wall, and travel via blood stream through liver, heart and lungs. Migrate from lungs to pharynx where re-swallowed and mature in small intestine

3. Horse swallows embryonated eggs

2. Eggs passed in feces

Eggs develop embryos, become infective

Proper manure disposal

Fig. 15-5. Diagram showing the life history and habits of the ascarid (or large roundworm). As noted (see scissors), effective control and treatment (cutting the cycle of the parasite) consist of (1) proper manure disposal, and (2) administering an effective vermifuge. (Drawing by R. F. Johnson)

upon the liver and lungs and the partial or complete obstruction of the small intestine caused by the large size and numbers of worms.

LIFE HISTORY AND HABITS

Although it pursues a migratory route in the host, the roundworm usually comes to rest in the upper part of the small intestines; but sometimes it is found in the middle and terminal portions of the small intestine. The complete life cycle of this parasite may be summarized as follows:

1. In the small intestine, the female worms deposit thousands of eggs which pass to the outside with the feces. Ascarid eggs are very resistant to environmental conditions and may live for years in stalls, paddocks, and pastures. Thus, the source of infection for young horses is the contaminated ground that was seeded down by ascarid eggs by preceding crops of infected foals. These eggs are not infective.

2. Under favorable conditions—warm weather and dampness—the eggs develop embryos and are infective to horses in 10 to 14 days.

3. The infective eggs are swallowed with feed and water, especially by grazing horses, and the larvae are liberated in the intestines.

4. The larvae then take the following migratory route: They penetrate the intestinal wall and enter the blood stream, thence travel via the blood through the liver, heart, and lungs, leave the bloodstream of the lungs and migrate up the trachea to the pharynx, and finally are again swallowed and develop to maturity in the small intestine.

DAMAGE INFLICTED; SYMPTOMS AND SIGNS OF AFFECTED ANIMALS

The injury produced by ascarids covers a wide range, from light infections producing moderate effects to heavy infections which may be the essential cause of death. Death from ascarid infection is usually due to a ruptured intestine. Serious lung damage caused by migrating ascarid larvae may result in pneumonia. More common, and probably more important, are retarded or impaired growth and development manifested by potbellies, rough hair coats, and digestive disturbances.

PREVENTION, CONTROL, AND TREATMENT

Prevention consists primarily of sanitary measures. The foaling barn and paddocks must be kept clean, manure must be disposed of properly, and clean feed and water must be supplied. Young foals should be placed on clean pasture.

Over the past years, several new drugs have come along for ascarid control. Some of these are fast replacing carbon disulfide, which was first introduced in 1917. Nevertheless, both the old and the new drugs and treatments follow:

1. *Carbon disulfide,* administered by a stomach tube or capsule, preferably following an 18- to 24-hour fast. It is given at the rate of about 6 cubic centimeters for each 250 pounds body weight, with a maximum dose of 24 cubic centimeters for an adult horse; although some variation should be made according to the physical condition of the animal.

2. *Parvex (or piperazine-carbon disulfide complex),* at doses delivering 20 milligrams piperazine base per pound body weight of horse, administered at 8-week intervals, beginning at 8 to 10 weeks of age. It is best administered by stomach tube, but care must be taken to avoid injury to the horse from the tubing itself. Parvex is also effective against bots, small strongyles, and pinworms.

3. *Piperazine* salts administered by a stomach tube, syringe, or mixed in the feed. These drugs should be used at the rate of 40 milligrams of piperazine base per pound of body weight. Manufacturer's directions should always be followed, because different salts have different piperazine base contents.

4. *Equizole (or Thiabendazole),* at 100 milligrams per kilograms body weight. This is twice the dosage level used in treating strongyles; hence, when used at this level it is rather expensive for ascarid control. In addition to being effective in ascarid control, Equizole is effective in the control of the other roundworms—large strongyles, small strongyles, and pinworms.

5. *Dyrex,* which should be administered according to the manufacturer's directions.

6. *Dizan-piperazine,* given according to manufacturer's directions.

7. *Dichlorvos (Equigard)* pellets at the rate of 40 mg/2.2 lbs. (1 kg) body weight.

In addition to selecting the particular wormer(s) for ascarid control, the horseman should set up a definite treatment schedule, then follow it. The advice of the veterinarian should be sought on both points. Also, to preclude the possibility that worms may become resistant to a drug that is used continuously, the veterinarian may use a different vermifuge at intervals.

The first ascarid infections in foals mature when the foals are about

11 weeks of age; hence, the first treatment should be given at 8 to 10 weeks of age so as to remove the initial infection just before the ascarids mature. In most areas, treatments for ascarid control should be repeated at 8-week intervals, at least during the summer months. Mares should be wormed 30 days before foaling.

Bots

Horse bots are highly specialized parasites—attacking horses, mules, asses, and perhaps zebras, but not molesting other classes of livestock. Although four distinct species of bots have been found in the United

Fig. 15-6. The nose bot fly. Gastrophilus hemorrhoidalis. (Courtesy, USDA)

Fig. 15-7. Horses rubbing their noses on each other in an effort to avoid the nose bot fly (G. hemorrhoidalis). Though the bot fly does not sting the animal, deposition of the eggs on the lips causes a tickling sensation. (Courtesy, USDA)

States, only three are serious pests of horses; namely, the common horse bot or nit fly *(Gastrophilus intestinalis)*, the throat bot or chin fly *(G. nasalis)*, and the nose bot or nose fly *(G. hemorrhoidalis)*.

DISTRIBUTION AND LOSSES CAUSED BY BOTS

As horse bots are found in different sections of the world, it is reasonable to surmise that they were introduced to this country with the first horses imported from Europe. The common horse bot or nit fly and the throat bot or chin fly are now distributed throughout the United States wherever horses are found, but the latter are much more numerous in the drier areas of the country and at higher altitudes.

Broadly speaking, the losses inflicted by horse bots are of three types; namely, (1) the annoyance to the animal caused by the flies at the time they deposit the eggs, (2) the burrowing of the bots into the lining of the alimentary canal, resulting in irritation and a place of

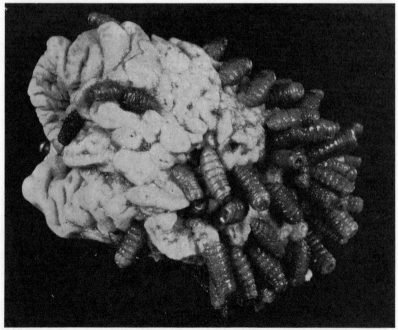

Fig. 15-8. Bots attached to the stomach wall of a horse. At this stage they remain attached to the lining of the stomach and intestines for several months, feeding on blood until they are about ¾ inch in length, after which they release their hold and pass out with the feces. (Courtesy, Department of Veterinary Pathology and Hygiene, College of Veterinary Medicine, University of Illinois)

entry for microorganisms, and (3) the sapping of blood. Contrary to the common belief of many persons, bot flies do not sting the animal.

LIFE HISTORY AND HABITS

Like other flies, the four distinct stages of the horse bot are: the egg, the larva (bot), the pupa, and the adult. It requires one year in

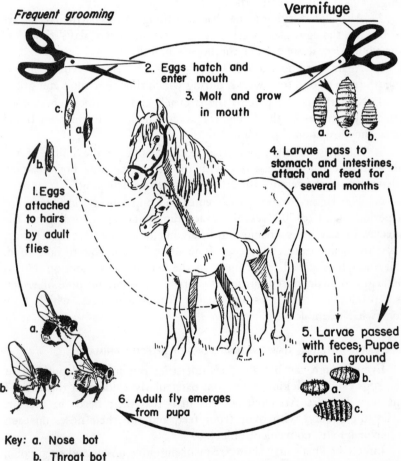

Frequent grooming

Vermifuge

2. Eggs hatch and enter mouth

3. Molt and grow in mouth

c.

a.

4. Larvae pass to stomach and intestines, attach and feed for several months

b.

1. Eggs attached to hairs by adult flies

a.

b.

c.

5. Larvae passed with feces; Pupae form in ground

6. Adult fly emerges from pupa

b.

a.

c.

Key: a. Nose bot
 b. Throat bot
 c. Common bot

Fig. 15-9. Diagram showing the life history and habits of horse bots, of which three species are serious pests. As noted (see scissors), effective control and treatment (cutting the cycle of the parasite) consist of (1) frequent grooming, washing, and clipping to remove the eggs that are attached to the hairs of the host; and (2) administering an effective vermifuge. (Drawing by R. F. Johnson)

which to complete the entire life cycle of the horse bot. Further details concerning the habits and life histories of the bot are as follows:

1. The eggs are attached to the hairs of the host. The common bot fly may deposit its eggs on various parts of the animal, but particularly about the fetlocks and on the inside of the knees; the throat bot fly attaches its eggs on the hairs beneath the jaws; and the nose bot fly deposits its eggs on the short hairs of the lips. Usually only a single egg is laid at each strike.

2. Although varying somewhat according to the particular species of bot fly, the eggs usually hatch within two to seven[8] days' time, and the young larvae soon enter the horse's mouth.

3. Again varying according to species, the larvae remain in the mouth from two to four weeks, during which time they molt and grow.

4. Next the larvae pass to the stomach and intestines where they attach themselves to the lining for several months, feeding on blood until they are about ¾ inch in length.

5. When grown, the bots release their hold on the lining of the alimentary canal and pass out with the feces; the nose bots reattach themselves to the rectum for a few days before dropping.

6. The larvae, or bots, then enter the pupal or resting stage for a period of 20 to 70 days, the exact time varying according to the species. Finally, they change into the adult or fly stage at which time they are again ready to lay eggs. The adult fly is unable to take food, but enough is stored in its body in the bot stage to develop 150 to 300 eggs to be deposited during its short life, the sole purpose of which is reproduction. The flies are smaller than honey bees, which they somewhat resemble.

DAMAGE INFLICTED; SYMPTOMS AND SIGNS OF AFFECTED ANIMALS

Even though the bot fly does not sting the animal, deposition of the eggs causes a tickling sensation, particularly evident in the case of the nose bot fly. Attacked animals may toss their heads in the air, strike the ground with their front feet, and rub their noses on each other or on any convenient object.

Infected animals may show frequent digestive upsets and even colic, lowered vitality and emaciation, and reduced work output. The most serious effect is general debility of the animal caused by toxic excre-

---

[8] As the eggs of the common bot fly must be rubbed first by the warm lips of the horse in order to hatch, they may lie quietly in the egg stage for as long as 90 days.

tions from the parasites. Occasionally, heavy infections have caused rupture of the stomach.

PREVENTION, CONTROL, AND TREATMENT

Working animals may be given fair protection against the annoyance resulting from the deposition of eggs by throat and nose bots through the application of a cover to the jaws and nose, respectively. Frequent grooming, washing, and clipping are also helpful control measures.

Horses should be treated for bots as follows:

1. In the late fall or early winter, at least one month after the first killing frost, administer one of the recommended vermifuges according to directions.

2. Thirty days prior to administering a vermifuge, the eggs of the common bot fly, which may be clinging to the body, should be destroyed by either (a) vigorously applying warm water at 120° F., or (b) clipping the hair of the horse. The insides of the knees and the fetlocks especially should be treated in this manner.

3. Prevention of reinfection is best assured through community campaigns in which all horses within the area are thus treated.

The following drugs are used in bot control:

1. *Carbon disulfide,* which has been used for half a century for the control of bots. It is given at the rate of 6 cubic centimeters for each 250 pounds body weight, with a maximum dose of 24 cubic centimeters for an adult horse. Carbon disulfide is highly effective in bot control. However, it is toxic and care must be exercised to insure its safe administration. It is best given via stomach tube, and by a veterinarian.

2. *Parvex (piperazine-carbon disulfide complex),* which is quite effective against bots, although it is somewhat less effective than carbon disulfide. If Parvex is used in ascarid and strongyle control, bots will be taken care of automatically.

3. *Trichlorfon (Neguvon),* which is available in different forms and under different trade names. The USDA (a) recommends (in *Stud Managers' Handbook,* Vol. 3, p. 138) that the rate of administration of trichlorfon be within the range of 1.2 to 1.8 grams per 100 pounds body weight (the lower amounts being for Thoroughbreds and other sensitive horses), with a single dose given after the first killing frost; and (b) gives (in USDA Agric. Handbook 331, 1967) the following safety restrictions relative to the use of trichlorfon: Do not treat sick

or debilitated horses, foals less than 4 months old, or mares in the last month of pregnancy. Do not administer trichlorfon in conjunction with (or 10 days after treatment with) other organic phosphates or cholinesterase inhibitors. Do not repeat more often than every 30 days. Do not administer intravenous anesthetics, especially muscle relaxants, for a period of two weeks after using trichlorfon. Do not treat horses that are to be used for food.

Trichlorfon is the generic name (the common name, not protected by trademark registration) for the organic phosphate Bayer L 13/59, which is available commercially, and is the active ingredient in the following trade name products:

a. *Anthon* (manufactured by Chemagro Corporation), which is in granules and can be given in the feed. This makes it advantageous for use in horses that fight the passage of the stomach tube or balling gun. In addition to its efficacy in bot control, Anthon also removes ascarids and pinworms.

b. *Dyrex* (manufactured by Ft. Dodge Laboratories), which is available (1) in granules, for administration in the feed; (2) in boluses, for balling gun administration; and (3) in T.F. (tube formulation), for stomach tube administration.

Anthon and Dyrex should be used according to the directions of the manufacturers. Both products have essentially the same efficacy on bots.

4. *Dichlorvos (Equigard)*—This formulation in resin pellets should be added to the feed according to the manufacturer's (Shell Chemical) directions. Restriction of water intake 4 to 6 hours prior to administration and 3 hours after treatment is quite important for most effective bot control.

Dourine

This is a chronic venereal disease of horses and asses, caused by the microscopic parasite *Trypanosoma equiperdum*. It is also referred to as "mal du coit" or equine syphilis, because it is similar to syphilis in man.

DISTRIBUTION AND LOSSES CAUSED BY DOURINE

It is still quite frequent in many countries, but now rare in the United States.

LIFE HISTORY AND HABITS

The causative parasite is transmitted from animal to animal by the act of copulation. Following an incubation period of eight days to two months, the characteristic symptoms appear in infected animals.

DAMAGE INFLICTED; SYMPTOMS AND SIGNS OF AFFECTED ANIMALS

There are two stages usually described for the disease. The primary symptoms are a redness and swelling of the external genitalia of both the mare and stallion. There are frequent attempts at urination, and increased sexual excitement is observed in both sexes. A pussy discharge may be noted. The secondary stage is initiated by the appearance of firm, round, flat swellings (dollar plaques) on the body and neck. In the advanced stages, nervous symptoms may also be manifest. They consist of paralysis of the face, knuckling of the joints of the hind limbs, and dragging of the feet.

PREVENTION, CONTROL, AND TREATMENT

The infective agent is a protozoan. It is spread mostly through mating, but may be transmitted by biting insects. The complement fixation test is used in diagnosis.

The most effective method of eradication is the prompt destruction of all the infected animals. Often in areas of heavy infection, the castration of stallions and spaying of mares is practiced with only a small degree of success. The most effective prevention consists of avoiding coition with infected animals, and in the application of modern hygiene.

No successful treatment is known.

Equine Piroplasmosis (or Babesiases)

This disease is tick-borne and caused by either of two protozoans, *Babesia caballi* or *B. equi*, which invade the red blood cells.

DISTRIBUTION AND LOSSES CAUSED BY EQUINE PIROPLASMOSIS

The disease is worldwide. It was first diagnosed in the United States in 1961, in Florida. Death rate is between 10 and 15 percent.

LIFE HISTORY AND HABITS

Horses usually acquire the infection from ticks, although occasionally it is introduced through intra-uterine infection.

After the tick attaches itself to the host horse, the protozoan leaves it, enters the bloodstream, invades a red blood cell, multiplies (by simple division) and destroys the invaded red blood cell, following which each new protozoan invades different blood cells and repeats the performance.

DAMAGE INFLICTED; SYMPTOMS AND SIGNS OF AFFECTED ANIMALS

The signs are very similar to equine infectious anemia (or swamp fever), but a positive diagnosis can be made by demonstrating the presence of the protozoa in the red blood cells. Clinical signs include fever (103° to 106° F.), anemia, icterus, depression, thirst, and lacrimation and swelling of the eyelids. Constipation and colic may occur. The urine is yellow to reddish colored. The incubation period is one to three weeks.

PREVENTION, CONTROL, AND TREATMENT

Tick control is the most effective approach to the prevention of equine piroplasmosis. Fifteen species of ticks are considered vectors; among them, the brown dog tick, *Rhipicephalus sanguineus*, and the tropical horse tick, *Dermacentor nitens*, both of which are found in the United States.

Also, extreme caution should be exercised in the use of all syringes, needles, and medical instruments. Recovered animals remain carriers for 10 months to 4 years; hence, they should be isolated.

A number of treatments are used, each with varying degrees of success; hence, the choice of treatment should be left with the veterinarian. Among the common treatments are: (1) A subcutaneous dose of 15 milliliters of a 40 percent solution of phenamidine isethionate per 1,000 pounds body weight, or (2) 1 percent aqueous solution of trypan blue at the level of 0.5 to 0.6 grams per 100 kilograms body weight.

Intestinal Threadworms (Strongyloides)

Infections by the small intestinal threadworm *(Strongyloides westeri)* are quite common in foals. Little is known of the actual effects of this worm on foals other than the association of diarrhea with infection and the self-limiting aspects in which the worms disappear by the time the foals are six months of age. Thiabendazole (Equizole) is effective in removing intestinal threadworms. The usual dose is 2 grams per 100 pounds body weight.

Pinworms (Rectal worms)

Two species of pinworms are frequently found in horses; namely, *Oxyuris equi* and *Probstmyria vivipara*. The former are whitish worms with long, slender tails, whereas the latter are so small as to be scarcely visible to the naked eye.

DISTRIBUTION AND LOSSES CAUSED BY PINWORMS

Pinworms are quite widely distributed in horses throughout the United States. The large species, *Oxyuris equi*, are the most damaging to the host.

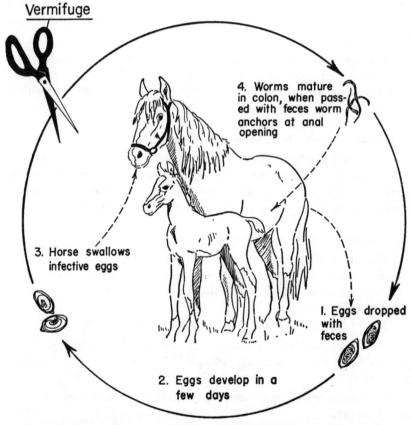

Vermifuge

4. Worms mature in colon, when passed with feces worm anchors at anal opening

3. Horse swallows infective eggs

1. Eggs dropped with feces

2. Eggs develop in a few days

Fig. 15-10. Diagram showing the life history and habits of the pinworm. As noted (see scissors) the common treatment for the removal of pinworms consists of administering a suitable vermifuge, thus cutting the cycle of the parasite. Prevention and control involve sanitation and keeping the animal separated from its own excrement. (Drawing by R. F. Johnson)

LIFE HISTORY AND HABITS

The life history of the larger of the two species of pinworms, *Oxyuris equi*, may be summarized as follows:

1. The female worms pass out with the feces, either depositing their eggs with the droppings or around the anal region. The latter type of deposition results when the female worms of *O. equi* anchor themselves at the anal opening and deposit their eggs.

2. Outside the body, the eggs develop and reach the infective stage in a few days.

3. Horses become infected by swallowing the eggs with feed or water.

4. The worms mature in the large intestine, principally in the dorsal colon.

The small pinworm, *Probstmyria vivipara*, are—as the name indicates—viviparous worms. Their young are produced alive, and presumably they can complete their entire cycle of development within the ventral colon of the host.

DAMAGE INFLICTED; SYMPTOMS AND SIGNS OF AFFECTED ANIMALS

Frequently the best evidence of the presence of the larger pinworms is that the worms are seen in the feces of heavily infected animals. Irritation of the anus and tail rubbing are also symptoms. Heavy infections may also cause digestive disturbances and produce anemia.

PREVENTION, CONTROL, AND TREATMENT

The prevention and control of pinworms are similar to measures for the large intestinal roundworms and strongyles. Chiefly, this involves sanitation and keeping the animal separated from its own excrement.

The preferred treatments for the removal of pinworms are:

1. *Thiabendazole (Equizole)*; two grams of Equizole per 100 pounds body weight is nearly 100 per cent effective against mature pinworms.

2. *Piperazine*; 4.0 grams per 100 pounds of horse, at one- to two-month intervals.

3. *Phenothiazine and parvex, or other piperazines*; 1.25 grams phenothiazine and 4.0 grams piperazine base per 100 pounds of horse, at six- to eight-week intervals.

4. *Dizan suspension, with piperazine citrate*; 1.0 oz. per 100 pounds of horse, at one- to two-month intervals.

5. *Dyrex captabs*; 3.6 grams per 100 pounds of horse, twice per year.

6. *Dichlorvos (Equigard)*, resin pellets added to the feed according to manufacturer's (Shell Chemical) directions.

In case of severe itching, blue ointment may be applied around the tail beneath the anus. Some horsemen administer an enema as a means of relieving the symptoms.

Stomach Worms

Stomach worms of horses consist of a group of different kinds of parasitic worms that are responsible for inflammation in the stomach or for a condition referred to as "summer sores." Three species of large stomach worms are capable of producing severe gastritis in horses. Diagnosis is difficult because the eggs are not ordinarily detected by flotation examination of feces, thus the importance of these worms tends to be minimized.

The minute stomach worm *(Trichostrongylus axei)* is a common parasite of cattle, sheep, and a number of other hosts, in addition to the horse; and there is cross infection between different species of animals.

DISTRIBUTION AND LOSSES CAUSED BY STOMACH WORMS

Workers in both Europe and the United States have expressed the opinion that probably no other ailment of horses is so regularly associated with a sudden loss of condition as is infection with stomach worms. Wasted feed and lowered efficiency are the chief losses when horses are infected with stomach worms.

LIFE HISTORY AND HABITS

The life history of the horse stomach worm varies somewhat, according to the particular kind. The cycle of the large stomach worm, *Habronema muscae*, is as follows:

1. The mature worms in the stomach lay many eggs.

2. The eggs containing young worms are expelled from the digestive tract with manure.

3. The eggs are swallowed by fly maggots; the young worms de-

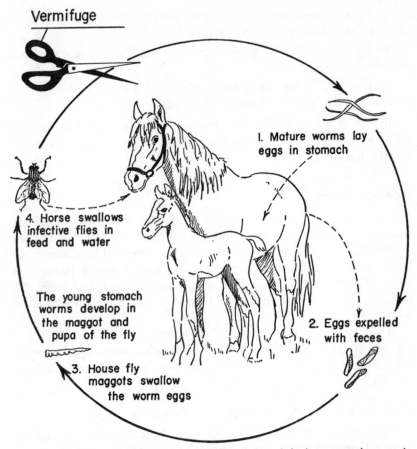

Vermifuge

I. Mature worms lay
eggs in stomach

4. Horse swallows
infective flies in
feed and water

The young stomach
worms develop in
the maggot and
pupa of the fly

2. Eggs expelled
with feces

3. House fly
maggots swallow
the worm eggs

Fig. 15-11. Diagram showing the life history and habits of the large stomach worm. As noted (see scissors) a suitable anthelmintic may be used for removal of stomach worms, thus cutting the cycle of the parasite. (Drawing by R. F. Johnson)

velop in the maggot and in the pupa and are infective when the adult fly emerges.

4. Horses become infected after swallowing infected flies or the larvae that escape from flies while the latter are feeding on the moisture of the lips.

DAMAGE INFLICTED; SYMPTOMS AND SIGNS OF AFFECTED ANIMALS

Sometimes, the larvae of the larger stomach worms are responsible in part for a relatively common skin disease of horses called summer sores.

Heavy infections may cause a rapid loss of condition associated with extensive and severe catarrhal gastritis. Long-standing infections result in chronic inflammatory changes.

PREVENTION, CONTROL, AND TREATMENT

Preventive measures are similar to those already discussed for other internal parasites of horses.

The recommended drug treatments and schedules as given in this book for the control of ascarids and bots are effective also against stomach worms; hence, repetition at this point is unnecessary.

Dilute formaldehyde and astringents are commonly used in the treatment of summer sores.

Strongyles (Bloodworms)

Of the several hundred parasites affecting horses, without question the most serious threat to the health and life of the horse kept under conditions found on breeding farms the world over is the strongyle.

Out of a total of 140 horses autopsied by Dr. Robert F. Behlow, DVM (co-author of this chapter) at the University of Kentucky in 1960, 22 died of verminous aneurysm, the most harmful effect of parasitism in the horse, caused by the bloodworm parasite *Strongylus vulgaris*.[9] Most of the 22 losses were young animals (sucklings and weanlings), and one or more of them might have been million dollar horses.

There are approximately 60 different species of strongyles. Although not all of these kinds have ever been found in any one horse, almost every animal that has had access to pasture, and has not been treated at intervals for their removal, harbors several of them. The different species vary considerably in size, some being scarcely visible to the naked eye; whereas others reach a length of 2 inches.

The large strongyles—also variously referred to as palisade worms, bloodworms, sclerostomes, and red worms—include only three species, but these forms are the most injurious parasites of the horse. The balance of the species—the vast majority of strongyles (about 40 species) —are the small strongyles. The latter are generally regarded as being much less pathogenic than the large strongyles. In a heavily infected

---

[9]Personal communication to the author dated January 9, 1961, from Dr. J. H. Drudge, Parasitologist, University of Kentucky, Lexington, Ky.

animal, 1 or more of the 3 species of large strongyles may be present, along with 10 to 12 species of small strongyles.

DISTRIBUTION AND LOSSES CAUSED BY STRONGYLES

Strongyles are found throughout the United States wherever horses are pastured. Naturally, the degree of infection varies according to the extent of exposure; and this in turn depends upon the sanitation, feeding, medication, season, and climate. Heavy infections with strongyles may result in marked unthriftiness, loss in capacity to perform work, and even death. The harmful effects are greatest with younger animals.

As a single deposit of manure from an infected horse may contain hundreds of thousands of microscopic strongyle eggs, and with the life cycle of the parasite being what it is, it is easy to understand why pastured horses are almost always infected.

The life cycle of *Strongylus vulgaris* follows:

1. The eggs are passed in the feces.
2. The eggs embryonate on the ground.
3. The eggs hatch into the first stage larvae, thence they develop to second stage larvae, and finally to third stage infective larvae. This process takes about seven days under favorable temperature and moisture conditions.
4. The larvae crawl onto vegetation.
5. The infective larvae are ingested in feed and water.
6. As yet, there is no general agreement about the migratory route of the parasite from this point on, but recent findings support the following for *Strongylus vulgaris*: The larvae penetrate the wall of the small intestine, cecum, and ventral colon; thence they invade the walls of the small arteries and migrate toward the anterior mesentric artery; thence, the larvae break out of the endothelium of the artery and produce thrombosis and aneurysm; thence the larvae break out of the thrombus and are carried by the bloodstream to the ventral colon and cecum; thence they migrate back through the walls and become attached to mucosa of the cecum and colon, where they grow to adults. All this migration and development takes four to five months, during which time the larvae are inaccessible to drug therapy.

The small strongyles appear to be less migratory, passing directly to the large intestine after being swallowed. Some of them attach themselves to the wall of the large intestine, much in the same manner as

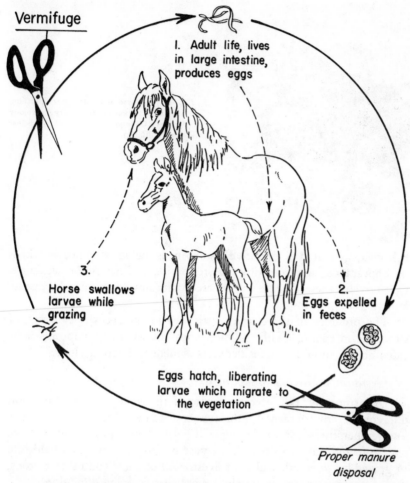

Vermifuge

1. Adult life, lives in large intestine, produces eggs

3. Horse swallows larvae while grazing

2. Eggs expelled in feces

Eggs hatch, liberating larvae which migrate to the vegetation

Proper manure disposal

Fig. 15-12. Diagram showing the life history and habits of strongyles. As noted (See scissors) a vermifuge may be used for removing strongyles, thus cutting the cycle of the parasite. First and foremost, however, it is important that there be a barrier between the horse and its excrement. (Drawing by R. F. Johnson)

the large strongyles. Most of them, however, are usually found free and unattached in the large intestine, cecum, or small intestine.

DAMAGE INFLICTED; SYMPTOMS AND SIGNS OF AFFECTED ANIMALS

Severe infections with large and small strongyles—and such infections are especially common with animals grazed on permanent pastures—result in lack of appetite, anemia, progressive emaciation, a rough

Fig. 15-13. Horse with strongyle infection. (Courtesy, Department of Veterinary Pathology and Hygiene, College of Veterinary Medicine, University of Illinois)

hair coat, sunken eyes, digestive disturbances including colic, a tucked-up appearance, and sometimes posterior incoordination or weakness. Collectively, these diverse and severe symptoms constitute the disease known as strongylosis.

The presence of the characteristic ova in the feces is evidence of strongyle infection, and, combined with the marked symptoms indicated above, should be considered as evidence of strongylosis.

PREVENTION, CONTROL, AND TREATMENT

Unfortunately, the infective larvae of the strongyle can withstand unfavorable environmental influences to a remarkable degree. Neither low temperatures nor air drying will harm them. As a result, pasture once infected will remain so for a year or more, even when held idle or grazed by some other class of livestock. For these and other reasons, the control of strongyles involves more than average difficulties.

All the general control measures previously recommended for parasites of all kinds may well be applied to the control of strongyles. First and foremost, it is important that there be a barrier between the horse and its excrement. Gathering up manure daily from pastures and barns and storing it in a pit for two or three weeks, allowing it to be subjected to its own generated heat, is a sure way to reduce infections. Moist pastures and overstocking should be avoided. Pasture rotation or rotation of stock is effective, as these parasites are not transmissible to ruminants or swine. Medication should supplement rather than replace wholesome feed and water and clean surroundings.

The commonly used treatments for the removal of strongyles are:

1. *Equizole (Thiabendazole)*; given at the rate of 50 milligrams per kilogram of weight of horse (2 grams per 100 pounds body weight). Most successful strongyle control programs call for giving Equizole every six to eight weeks except during cold weather, when it is needed less often.

2. *Phenothiazine + Parvex (Parvex plus)*; 1.25 grams phenothiazine and 7.5 grams parvex (7.5 grams of parvex contains the equivalent of 4.0 grams of piperazine base) per 100 pounds of horse, at six- to eight-week intervals.

3. *Dizan suspension with piperazine citrate*; 1 ounce per 100 pounds of horse, at one- to two-month intervals.

4. *Dyrex captabs*; 3.6 grams per 100 pounds of horse, two times per year.

5. *Phenothiazine in therapeutic dose*; where there is a heavy infection, a therapeutic dose of phenothiazine may be used (for mature horses, 25 grams in a capsule or drench; one-half this amount for sucklings, weanlings, or yearlings).

6. *Phenothiazine at low-level*; phenothiazine, which was first introduced in 1941, is especially recommended, after therapeutic treatment,[10] where there is heavy infection of mares, which serve as the most important source of strongyle infection for foals. As is true in using any of the drugs against internal parasites, the safe and effective medication with phenothiazine requires close adherence to the recommended dosages and methods of administration. The low-level phenothiazine control for weanlings or older horses consists in *thoroughly mixing* and feeding in the grain ration 2 grams of phenothiazine daily for the first 21 consecutive days of each month, skipping the phenothiazine the rest of the month, and repeating each month throughout the year. *Avoid sweet feeds during the phenothiazine treatment.* Give treatment to both sexes and all ages. Sucklings should be limited to 1 gram of phenothiazine daily for the first 21 days of each month from the time they are started on a grain ration to 4 months of age. All animals above 4 months in age (weanlings or older) should get the 2 grams daily as indicated.

7. *Dichlorvos (Equigard)*, resin pellets added to feed according to manufacturer's (Shell Chemical) directions.

---

[10]Phenothiazine is not recommended under some circumstances, as when horses are anemic; thus, the veterinarian should be consulted about its use.

Tapeworms

There are three species of horse tapeworms, but *Anoplocephala perfoliate* is both the most common and most damaging of the three. It tends to form clusters at the ileocecal valve region of the cecum and produce ulcerative lesions, which may perforate.

Treatment is not ordinarily suggested, primarily because only light infections are encountered. Among the traditional tapeworm treatments are: areca nut, kamala, and oleoresin of male fern. Recent evidence indicates that Di-phenthane-70 (Teniatol) at 40 milligrams per kilogram is well tolerated and effective.

External Parasites of Horses[11]

Horses are subject to attack by a variety of external parasites, just as are other animals. Biting and sucking lice *(Mallophaga* and *Anaplura)*, three species of mites *(Sarcoptes, Psoroptes,* and *Chorioptes)*, and one or more species of ticks *(Ixodidae)* infest horses the year round. During the warmer months, stable flies *(Stomoxys calcitrans)* (L.) and numerous species of horse flies and deer flies *(Tabanidae)* are a constant annoyance. The face fly *(Musca autumnalis* De Geer*)* is a serious pest whenever found in large numbers. The horn fly *(Haematobia irritans)* is not regarded as an important pest of horses, yet horses sometimes suffer intensely from light to moderate infestations of them. Also horses are subject to infestation by three species of bots *(Gasterophilus* spp., Family *Oestridae)* which winter as larvae in the alimentary canal. In some areas, cattle grubs *(Hypoderma* spp.*)* occur in horses and are a serious problem, because one or two grubs in the back make the animal unfit for riding until they are removed and the wound heals. All of these pests lower the vitality of horses, mar the hair coat and skin, and produce a general unthrifty condition.

External parasites are also responsible for the spread of several serious diseases of horse which exact a heavy toll each year in sickness and deaths. Thus, Equine piroplasmosis *(or Babesiases)* is transmitted by a tick *(Dermacentor nitens* Neumann*)*. Mosquitoes *(Culicidae)* are vectors of equine infectious anemia (swamp fever) and equine encephalomyelitis (sleeping sickness).

A large number of insecticides have been registered by the U. S.

[11]The material under this section was authoritatively reviewed by Dr. Fred W. Knapp, Department of Entomology, University of Kentucky, Lexington.

Department of Agriculture and are in use to control various external parasites of cattle, sheep, and hogs. However, many of these materials have not been registered for use on horses, or they are registered for use against only certain species of external parasites. There are two reasons for this: (1) The erroneous impression that an insecticide that is registered for use on cattle can also be used on horses; and (2) the feeling among some insecticide companies that the potential market is not sufficient to justify the heavy expense of the toxicological and residue studies necessary to obtain the data required for registration. The latter reason has largely disappeared with recent increases in light horse numbers and prices.

GENERAL SYMPTOMS

A heavy infestation of common external parasites may result in severe irritation, restlessness, rubbing, loss of hair, and an unthrifty condition.

GENERAL PREVENTIVE AND CONTROL MEASURES

Sanitation, good grooming, avoiding too heavy concentration of horses, and spraying or dusting as required are the common measures employed in preventing and controlling external parasites of horses.

COMMON EXTERNAL PARASITES

Flies and lice are the most common external parasites of horses, although some of the others are capable of producing more severe injury when they occur.

Blowflies

The flies of the blowfly group include a number of species that find their principal breeding ground in dead and putrifying flesh, although sometimes they infest wounds or unhealthy tissues of live animals and fresh or cooked meat. All the important species of blowflies except the flesh flies, which are grayish and have three dark stripes on their backs, have a more or less metallic luster.

DISTRIBUTION AND LOSSES CAUSED BY BLOWFLIES

Although blowflies are widespread, they present the greatest problem in the Pacific Northwest and in the South and southwestern states. Death losses from blowflies are not excessive, but they cause much discomfort to affected animals, and they lower production.

LIFE HISTORY AND HABITS

With the exception of the group known as gray flesh flies, which deposit tiny living maggots instead of eggs, the blowflies have a similar life cycle to the screwworm, except that the cycle is completed in about one-half the time.

DAMAGE INFLICTED; SYMPTOMS AND SIGNS OF AFFECTED ANIMALS

The blowfly causes its greatest damage by infesting wounds and the soiled hair of living animals. Such damage, which is largely limited to the black blowfly (or wool-maggot fly), is similar to that caused by screwworms. The maggots spread over the body, feeding on the dead skin and exudates, where they produce a severe irritation and destroy the ability of the skin to function. Infested animals rapidly become weak and fevered; and, although they recover, they may remain in an unthrifty condition for a long period.

PREVENTION, CONTROL, AND TREATMENT

Prevention of blowfly damage consists of eliminating the pest and decreasing the susceptibility of animals to infestation.

As blowflies breed principally in dead carcasses, the most effective control consists in promptly destroying all dead animals by burning or deep burial. The use of traps, poisoned baits, and electrified screens is also helpful in reducing trouble from blowflies. Suitable repellents, such as pine tar oil, help prevent the fly from depositing its eggs.

Sprays containing 0.25 percent coumaphos are registered and are the most effective means of controlling blowfly larvae infesting soiled hair and wounds. Although diphenylamine (Smear 62) and lindane (EQ 335) smears have not been registered for use on horses, they have long been effectively used on equines, as well as other farm animals, for treating wounds infested with blowfly maggots.

Cattle Grubs

None of the systemic treatments used to control grubs in cattle has been registered for control of these pests in horses. However, dusts containing 1.5 percent Rotenone or washes consisting of 12 ounces of

5 percent Rotenone wettable powder per gallon of water applied thoroughly to the backs of horses will kill grubs that have cut through the hide. Hand removal of occasional grubs in the backs of horses is probably the most practical method where only a few horses are involved.

Flies

Flies are probably the most important insect pests of horses. Biting stable flies, many species of horse flies and deer flies, and horn flies are, without doubt, the most annoying species affecting horses. Nonbiting house flies *(Musca domestica L.)* and the face fly are great nuisances. Because of their varying habits, different materials and methods are required for the control of different species of flies.

HOUSE FLIES AND STABLE FLIES

The control of house flies and stable flies on the horse establishment is made easier by good sanitation practices, including proper collection and disposal of manure, waste feed, and other fly-breeding media. However, insecticides are usually needed, also.

The organophosphates are the most effective sprays now available

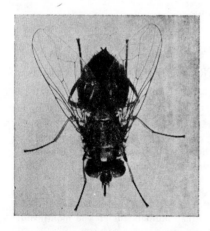

Fig. 15-14. Stablefly, Stomaxys calcitrans. (Courtesy, USDA)

for fly control. The insecticides now recommended, along with the concentration and application rate of each, are given in Table 15-2.

Dichlorvos at 0.5 to 1.0 percent, and naled at 1.0 percent may also be applied as space sprays or fogs in farm buildings. Pyrethrin sprays, containing 0.1 to 0.25 percent pyrethrins and 1.0 to 2.0 percent synergist, are also effective for such use. Any of the materials listed in Table 15-2 may be used as outdoor sprays.

Table 15-2

HOUSE FLY AND STABLE FLY CONTROL SPRAYS FOR HORSES[1]

Insecticide and Concentration	Sprays and Amount/Animal
Carbaryl 0.5%	1 qt. wet spray
Ciodrin 0.15%-1.0%® [2]	1-4 qts. wet spray
Ciodrin 2.0%	1-2 ozs. mist spray (or automatic sprayer)
Coumaphos 0.125%	1-2 qts. wet spray
Dioxathion 0.15%-0.6%	1-2 qts. wet spray
Dichlorvos 1.0%	1-2 ozs. mist spray (or automatic sprayer)
Malathion 0.5%	2 qts. wet spray
Methoxychlor 0.5%	1-4 qts. wet spray
Ronnel 0.25%	1-2 qts. wet spray
Ruelene ® [2] 0.5%[3]	1-4 qts. wet spray
Toxaphene 0.5%	1-4 qts. wet spray
Pyrethrins + synergist (0.05%-0.1%	1-2 qts. wet spray
+	or
.05%-1.0%	1-2 ozs. mist spray

[1]From: *Stud Managers' Handbook,* Vol. 3, p. 136, pub. by Agriservices Foundation, Clovis, Calif., 1967. Table prepared by Insects Affecting Man and Animals Research Branch, Entomology Research Division, ARS, USDA, Washington, D.C.
[2]Alpha-methylbenzyl 3-hydroxy-crontonate dimethy phosphate.
[3]4-tert-butyl 2-chlorophenyl methyl methylphosphoramidate.

Table 15-3

HORN FLY CONTROL SPRAYS FOR HORSES[1]

Insecticide and Concentration	Remarks
Carbaryl 0.5% spray	Do not treat more often than every four days.
Ciodrin 0.3%	Do not treat more often than every seven days.
Coumaphos 0.6%	Spray backs every three weeks or as needed.
Dioxathion 0.15%	Spray only at two-week intervals. Do not spray foals.
Lindane 0.03%-0.06% spray	—
Malthion 4.0%-5.0% dust	Do not treat animals under one month old.
Malathion 0.5% spray	Do not treat animals under one month old.
Methoxychlor 0.5% spray	—
Ronnel 0.5% spray	—
Pyrethrins (0.05%-0.1%) and synergist (0.5%-1.0%)	Mist or wet spray as needed.

[1]From: *Stud Managers' Handbook,* Vol. 3, p. 137, pub. by Agriservices Foundation, Clovis, Calif., 1967. Table prepared by Insects Affecting Man and Animals Research Branch, Entomology Research Division, ARS, USDA, Washington, D.C.

Several baits are effective in house fly control, but they are not effective against stable flies. These house fly control baits consist of (1) 0.5 to 2.0 percent of an organophosphate toxicant such as dichlorvos, diazinon, malathion, naled, or trichlorfon, and (2) a food attractant such as sugar or syrup. The preparations may then be mixed with water and sprinkled on surfaces or formulated as granular baits with corn meal, grits, or sand and broadcast over surfaces where flies congregate.

Also, treated cotton cord impregnated with 10 percent parathion or 25 percent diazinon and suspended from the ceiling will give prolonged and effective control of house flies, but not stable flies. Such cord may be purchased, ready for use. It should be suspended from the ceiling at the rate of 300 feet of cord per 1,000 square feet of floor space.

HORN FLIES

Although horn flies are primarily pests of cattle, sometimes they seriously annoy horses. Any of the materials recommended for the control of horn flies on cattle will also provide effective control on horses. However, only the materials listed in Table 15-3 are specifically registered for horn fly control on horses.

HORSE FLIES, STABLE FLIES, AND MOSQUITOES

The residual sprays used for horn fly control are ineffective against biting flies and mosquitoes. Repellent sprays containing 0.05 to 0.1 percent pyrethrins, with or without 0.5 to 0.1 percent synergist, are the best means of combatting horse flies, stable flies, and mosquitoes. Mist or wet sprays of such formulations will minimize the attacks of biting insects for several hours to a full day. Sprays containing 0.3 percent ciodrin will also provide short-time protection from biting flies and mosquitoes. Dichlorvos is effective in protecting cattle against biting insects, but it is not registered for use on horses.

FACE FLIES

Face flies are very important pests of horses in certain areas. Currently, the only treatments registered for face fly control on horses are a 0.3 percent ciodrin spray and a syrup bait containing 0.5 percent dichlorvos (Vapona). The bait should be brushed lightly (3 to 5 milliliters) on the forehead. The treatments are effective for only a short time and may have to be applied almost daily.

Lice and Ticks

The louse is a small, flattened, wingless insect parasite of which there are several species. The two main types are sucking lice and biting lice. Of the two groups, the sucking lice are the most injurious.

Most species of lice are specific for a particular class of animals. Lice are always more abundant on weak, unthrifty animals and are more troublesome during the winter months than during the rest of the year.

Several kinds of ticks may be found on horses; among them (1) the winter tick [*Dermacentor albipictus* (Pack)], and (2) the lone star tick [*Amblyomma americanum* (L.)].

DISTRIBUTION AND LOSSES CAUSED BY LICE AND TICKS

The presence of lice upon animals is almost universal, but the degree of infestation depends largely upon the state of animal nutrition and

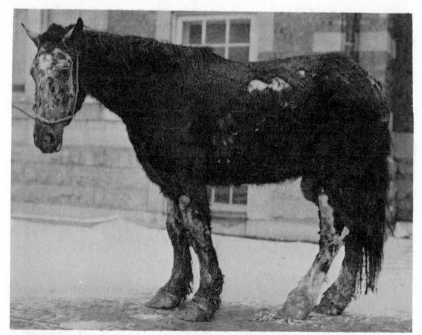

Fig. 15-15. Horse with a severe infestation of lice. Note the rough coat and loss of hair caused by gnawing and rubbing. Infestation shows up most commonly in winter and in poorly-fed and neglected animals. (Courtesy, Department of Veterinary Pathology and Hygiene, College of Veterinary Medicine, University of Illinois)

the extent to which the owner will tolerate parasites. The irritation caused by the presence of lice on horses retards growth, gains, and/or production of milk.

In the southern and western parts of the United States, ticks may become a serious problem by reducing the vitality of the animals through constant irritation and the blood loss during severe infestations.

LIFE HISTORY AND HABITS

Lice spend their entire life cycle on the host's body. They attach their eggs or "nits" to the hair near the skin where they hatch in about two weeks. Two weeks later the young females begin laying eggs, and after reproduction they die on the host. Lice do not survive more than a week when separated from the host; but, under favorable conditions, eggs clinging to detached hairs may continue to hatch for two or three weeks.

The life history and habits of ticks differ, according to species.

DAMAGE INFLICTED; SYMPTOMS AND SIGNS OF AFFECTED ANIMALS

Lice infestation shows up most commonly in winter on ill-nourished and neglected animals. There is intense irritation, restlessness, and loss of condition. As many lice are blood suckers, they devitalize their host. There may be severe itching and the animal may be seen scratching, rubbing, and gnawing at the skin. The hair may be rough and thin, and lack luster; and scabs may be evident. In horses,

Table 15-4

LICE AND TICK CONTROL FOR HORSES[1]

Insecticide and Concentration	Remarks
Carbaryl 0.5% spray	Do not treat more often than every four days.
Ciodrin 0.3% spray	Do not treat more often than every seven days.
Coumaphos 0.125%	Treat every three weeks.
Dioxathion 0.15% spray	Treat only at two-week intervals. Do not treat foals.
Lindane 0.03%-0.06% spray	——
Malathion 0.5% spray	Do not treat animals under one month old.
Malthion 4%-5% dust	Do not treat animals under one month old.

[1]From: *Stud Managers' Handbook*, Vol. 3, p. 138, pub. by Agriservices Foundation, Clovis, Calif., 1967. Table prepared by Insects Affecting Man and Animals Research Branch, Entomology Research Division, ARS, USDA, Washington, D.C.

favorite locations for lice are the root of the tail, on the inside of the thighs, over the fetlock region, and along the neck and shoulders. In some cases, the symptoms may resemble those of mange; and it must be kept in mind that the two may occur simultaneously. With the coming of spring, when the hair sheds and the animals go to pasture, lousiness is greatly diminished.

Ticks lower the vitality of animals through irritation and loss of blood.

PREVENTION, CONTROL, AND TREATMENT

The materials registered and approved for horse lice and tick control are given in Table 15-4.

Mites (Mange)

Mites produce a specific contagious disease known as mange (or scabies, scab, or itch). These small insect-like parasites, which are almost invisible to the naked eye, constitute a very large group. They attack members of both the plant and animal kingdom.

Each species of domesticated animals has its own peculiar species of mange mites; and, with the exception of the sarcoptic mites, the mites from one species of animals cannot live normally and propagate permanently on a different species. The sarcoptic mites are transmissible from one class of animals to another and, in the case of the sarcoptic mite of the horse and cow, from animals to man. There are two chief forms of mange: sarcoptic mange, caused by burrowing mites, and psoroptic mange, caused by mites that bite the skin and suck blood but do not burrow. The sarcoptic form is most damaging; for, in addition to their tunneling, the mites secrete an irritating poison. This combination results in severe itching.

Mites are responsible for the condition known as mange (scabies) in horses, sheep, cattle, and swine. The disease appears to spread most rapidly among young and poorly nourished animals.

DISTRIBUTION AND LOSSES CAUSED BY MITES

Injury from mites is caused by irritation and blood sucking and the formation of scabs and other skin affections. In a severe attack, the growth of young animals may be retarded.

Fig. 15-16. Horse with a severe infestation of sarcoptic mites, producing a condition commonly known as mange (or scabies, scab, or itch). The only certain method of diagnosis is to demonstrate the presence of mites. (Courtesy, USDA)

LIFE HISTORY AND HABITS

The mites that attack livestock and poultry breed exclusively on the bodies of their hosts, and they will live for only two or three weeks when removed therefrom. The female mite which produces sarcoptic mange—the most severe form of scabies—lays from 10 to 25 eggs during the egg-laying period, which lasts about two weeks. At the end of another two weeks, the eggs have hatched and the mites have reached maturity. A new generation of mites may be produced every 15 days.

The disease is more prevalent during the winter months, when animals are confined and in close contact with each other.

DAMAGE INFLICTED; SYMPTOMS AND SIGNS OF AFFECTED ANIMALS

When the mite pierces the skin to feed on cells and lymph, there is marked irritation, itching, and scratching. Exudate forms on the surface, and this coagulates, crusting over the surface. The crusting is often accompanied or followed by the formation of thick, tough, wrinkled skin. Often there are secondary skin infections. The only certain method of diagnosis is to demonstrate the presence of the mites.

PREVENTION, CONTROL, AND TREATMENT

Prevention consists of avoiding contact with diseased animals or infested premises. In the case of an outbreak, the local veterinarian or livestock sanitation officials should be contacted.

Mites can be controlled by spraying or dipping infested animals with suitable insecticidal solutions and by quarantine of affected herds. Dips containing 0.06 percent lindane or 0.5 percent toxaphene are recommended for the control of mites. Sprays containing 0.5 percent malathion are also effective. Lime-sulfur and nicotine dips were once the standard remedies for controlling mange mites, but they are little used today.

Ringworm

Ringworm, or barn itch, is a contagious disease of the outer layers of skin. It is caused by certain microscopic molds or fungi *(Trichophyton, Achorion,* or *Microsporon)*. All animals and man are susceptible.

DISTRIBUTIONS AND LOSSES CAUSED BY RINGWORM

Ringworm is widespread throughout the United States. Though it may appear among animals on pasture, it is far more prevalent as a stable disease. It is unsightly, and affected animals may experience considerable discomfort; but the actual economic losses attributed to the disease are not too great.

LIFE HISTORY AND HABITS

The period of incubation for this disease is about one week. The fungi form seed or spores that may live 18 months or longer in barns and elsewhere.

DAMAGE INFLICTED; SYMPTOMS AND SIGNS OF AFFECTED ANIMALS

Round, scaly areas almost devoid of hair appear mainly in the vicinity of the eyes, ears, side of the neck, or the root of the tail. Crusts may form, and the skin may have a gray, powdery, asbestos-like appearance. The infested patches, if not checked, gradually increase in size. Mild itching usually accompanies the disease.

PREVENTION, CONTROL, AND TREATMENT

The organisms are spread from animal to animal or through the medium of contaminated fence posts, curry combs, and brushes. Thus, prevention and control consist of disinfecting everything that has been in contact with infested animals. The affected animals should also be isolated. Strict sanitation is an essential in the control of ringworm.

The hair should be clipped, the scabs removed, and the area sand-papered and washed with soap. The diseased parts should be painted with tincture of iodine or salicylic acid and alcohol (1 part in 10) every three days until cleared up. Certain proprietary remedies available only from veterinarians have proved very effective in treatment.

Screwworm

Among all the insect pests on this earth, those which raise their maggots in the living flesh of animals—such as the screwworm—are peculiarly loathsome. True screwworms seldom get through the unbroken skin, but will penetrate moist pockets like the prepuce of a gelding. They are not found in cold-blooded animals such as turtles, snakes, and lizards.

Man-made wounds resulting from branding and castrating horses afford a breeding ground for this parasite. Add to this the wounds from some types of vegetation, from fighting, and from blood-sucking insects; and ample places for propagation are provided.

DISTRIBUTION AND LOSSES CAUSED BY SCREWWORMS

Normally, the primary screwworm fly is confined to the southern and southwestern states, including Arizona and the southern half of California. Occasionally, under exceptionally favorable weather conditions or through the shipping of infested animals from further south, destructive outbreaks of the pest have occurred in some of the Corn Belt states.

In infested areas, the screwworm is undoubtedly the greatest enemy of all the insect species with which the livestock owner must contend. For example, in the Southwest, where it inflicts the most injury, many ranchmen report that 50 percent of their normal annual livestock losses are caused by this parasite.

LIFE HISTORY AND HABITS

The primary screwworm fly is bluish green in color, with three dark stripes on its back and reddish or orange color below the eyes. The fly generally deposits its eggs in shingle-like masses on the edges or the dry portion of wounds. From 50 to 300 eggs are laid at one time, with a single female being capable of laying about 3,000 eggs in a lifetime. Hatching of the eggs occurs in 11 hours, and the young whitish worms (larvae or maggots) immediately burrow into the living flesh. There they feed and grow for a period of four to seven days, shedding their skin twice during this period.

When the larva has reached its full growth, it assumes a pinkish color, leaves the wound, and drops to the ground, where it digs beneath the surface of the soil and undergoes a transformation to the hard-skinned, dark-brown, motionless pupa. It is during the pupa stage that the maggot changes to the adult fly.

After the pupa has been in the soil from 7 to 60 days, the fly emerges from it, works its way to the surface of the ground, and crawls up on some nearby object (bush, weed, etc.) to allow its wings to unfold and otherwise to mature. Under favorable conditions, the newly emerged female fly becomes sexually mature and will lay eggs five days later. During warm weather, the entire life cycle is usually completed in 21 days, but under cold, unfavorable conditions, this cycle may take as many as 80 days or longer.

DAMAGE INFLICTED; SYMPTOMS AND SIGNS OF AFFECTED ANIMALS

The injury caused by this parasite is inflicted chiefly by the maggots. Unless proper treatment is administered, the great destruction of tissues kills the host in a few days.

PREVENTION, CONTROL, AND TREATMENT

Prevention in infested areas consists mainly of keeping animal wounds to a minimum and of protecting those that do materialize.

As the primary screwworm must have living warm-blooded animals in which to breed and so that it may survive, it must produce a new generation during each four-month period. It is evident, therefore, that the most effective control measures can be effected during the winter months. During this season, the life cycle is slowed down, and it is difficult for the fly to live and breed. Thus, the most effective control consists of preventing infestation of wounds and of killing all possible maggots during the winter and spring months. Additional control is effected through timing, as much as possible, those farm and ranch operations that necessarily produce wounds. The winter season is preferable, being the time when the flies are least abundant and least active. The eradication of plants that cause injuries, breeding so that young will arrive during the season of least fly activity, and avoidance of anything else that might produce wounds will all aid greatly in screwworm control. In brief, the elimination of wounds or injuries to the host constitutes effective control.

If possible, there should be facilities available for handling and treating wounded or infested animals. A screened, fly-proof area is highly desirable.

The common screwworm treatment consists in the application (brush or smear) on the wound of either Smear 62 or EQ 335—twice the first week and then weekly until healed.

The screwworm eradication program, by sterilization, has been very effective. This consists in sterilizing male screwworms, in the pupal stages with X rays or gamma rays. Male screwworms mate repeatedly, but females mate only once. Thus, when a female mates with a sterilized male, only infertile eggs are laid. The release of millions of sterilized males has led to the near eradication of screwworms from most of the United States.

USE CHEMICALS SAFELY

Agricultural chemicals are as vital to the health of animals as modern medicines are to the health of people. Horsemen depend on chemicals—insecticides, herbicides, fungicides, and similar materials—to control the pests that attack their animals or damage their feed crops; and, when necessary, they use biologics for the prevention or treatment of animal diseases.

Registered materials for the protection of livestock and feed crops are safe when used as recommended. But some of them can be hazardous if they are improperly applied or administered. Misuse can bring serious financial loss and/or lower the quality of products.

Observance of the following guidelines will assure the profitable and safe use of chemicals: [12]

1. *Use chemicals economically.*

    a. Don't use more than the recommended amount of pesticide. Follow directions on the container label. Most of the materials are expensive. Overdosage is wasteful and often hazardous.

    b. Use only the chemicals that competent authorities recommend as both safe and effective for your specific purpose.

[12]These guidelines were prepared by the Agricultural Research Service, USDA, and issued June, 1966, in USDA PA-727.

c. Store chemicals carefully, for safety and economy. Avoid spillage.

d. Prevent waste of chemicals by keeping application equipment in perfect working condition. Calibrate the equipment so it will dispense the recommended dosage.

2. *Don't poison livestock.*

a. Be sure chemicals are always properly labeled. Prevent misuse by referring to the label each time a chemical is used. Don't transfer chemicals from the original containers to unlabeled containers.

b. Use only chemicals that are registered or licensed as suitable for the particular purpose intended.

c. Place covers over feed and water containers when applying chemicals on or near areas occupied by livestock.

d. Keep chemicals thoroughly mixed when applying them to livestock. Otherwise, some animals may receive too much of the active ingredient for safety, or too little to accomplish the desired purpose.

e. Don't use a spray or dip if an oily or gummy film appears on its surface after it has been mixed; the chemical may have deteriorated, and consequently the active ingredient may not be evenly distributed in the mixture.

f. Don't use food or drink containers for measuring or storing pesticides.

3. *Don't contaminate products.*

The residues of some chemicals may accumulate in the bodies of animals. Under Federal and state laws, meat containing illegal pesticide residue is condemned and may not be sold as human food. To prevent illegal residues from being present in the meat of slaughtered animals, observe these measures where horses are slaughtered for human food, as they are in many parts of the world:

a. Follow label directions when treating animals with pesticides.

b. When soils are treated on which will be grown feed or forage, use only a chemical that will not contaminate the crop.

c. Clean application equipment thoroughly before using it to apply a different pesticide.

d. Don't feed animals wastes from canneries or food processing plants unless it is ascertained that these wastes will not cause illegal pesticide residues in the meat.

e. Allow the prescribed number of days to elapse between the last application of a chemical and the harvesting or grazing of feed crops.

f. After spraying, dipping, or dusting animals with pesticides, observe the prescribed number of days' interval between the last treatment and slaughter. Refer to the container labels for the information; and see Table 15-5.

4. *General pesticide precautions.*

a. Follow the directions and heed all precautions on pesticide container labels.

b. Keep pesticides in closed, well-labeled containers in a dry place. Store them where they will not contaminate food or feed, and *where children and animals cannot reach them.* Keep empty containers away from children and animals; dispose of containers as promptly as possible.

c. When handling a pesticide, wear clean, dry clothing.

d. Avoid repeated or prolonged contact of pesticide with your skin.

e. Wear protective clothing or equipment if the container label states that it is needed. Avoid prolonged inhalation of pesticide dusts or mists. Don't spray into the wind.

f. Avoid spilling pesticide concentrate on your skin, and keep it out of your eyes, nose, and mouth. If you spill any on your skin, wash it off immediately with soap and water. If you get it in your eyes, flush the eyes with water for 15 minutes; get medical attention. If you spill it on your clothing, change the clothing at once and launder it before wearing it again.

g. After handling a pesticide, don't eat, smoke, or drink, until you have washed your hands and face. Wash your hands and face and any other exposed skin immediately after applying pesticide.

h. To protect water resources, fish, and wildlife, don't contaminate lakes, streams, or ponds with pesticides. Don't clean spraying equipment or dump unwanted spray material near such water.

i. To protect honey bees and other pollinating insects that are necessary in the production of many crops, treat crops at times when these insects are not visiting the plants. This may be before or after flowering, or it may be at night.

j. Avoid drift of pesticide to nearby livestock, crops, or bee yards. Ground sprayers do not permit so much drift as other types of application equipment.

k. Dispose of empty pesticide containers at a sanitary land-fill dump, or bury them at least 18 inches deep in a level, isolated place where they will not contaminate water supplies. If you have trash collection service, you may wrap small containers in heavy layers of newspapers and place them in the trash can.

Observe Tolerances and Withdrawal Periods

The insecticide recommendations given in this chapter are for horses not used for food. Where horses are to be slaughtered for food, the tolerance levels and withdrawal periods shown in Table 15-5 must be observed:

Table 15-5

INSECTICIDE TOLERANCES AND WITHDRAWAL PERIODS
ON HORSES SLAUGHTERED FOR FOOD

Insecticide	Tolerance (ppm. in fat)	Minimum Days from Last Application to Slaughter
	(ppm.)	*(days)*
DDT	7	30
Dioxathion (Delnav)	1	—
Lindane (0.03%)	7	30
Lindane (0.03%-0.05%)	7	60
Methoxychlor	3	—
Toxaphene	7	28

DISINFECTANTS[13]

A disinfectant is an agent which is intended to destroy microorganisms on inanimate surfaces. It should be distinguished from an

---

[13]In the preparation of this section and Table 15-6, the author had the benefit of the authoritative review and suggestions of the following: Dr. George F. Reddish, Professor of Microbiology and Public Health, St. Louis College of Pharmacy, St. Louis, Mo.; and Dr. R. W. H. Gillespie, Professor of Veterinary Microbiology, College of Veterinary Medicine, Washington State University, Pullman, Wash.

Table 15-6

HANDY DISINFECTANT GUIDE

(Chemical agents should not be relied upon to destroy spores; controlled and prolonged heat is required for this purpose.)

Kind of Disinfectant	Usefulness	Strength	Limitations and Comments
Alcohol	Effective against the less resistant disease germs provided there is adequate exposure.	70% alcohol—the content usually found in "rubbing" alcohol.	Limited application. Not recommended for general use. Often used as a local antiseptic in obtaining blood samples or making hypodermic injections. Not reliable for sterilization of instruments.
Bichloride of Mercury (mercuric chloride; corrosive sublimate)	Destroys less resistant bacteria under favorable conditions. Tends to prevent growth rather than actually destroy bacteria. Organic mercurials, sometimes used as a local antiseptic, are less poisonous and more reliable.	Tablets used in a dilution of 1 to 1,000.	Unreliable as a germ killer in the presence of organic matter. Also, cattle are especially susceptible to mercury poisoning. For farm disinfection, bichloride of mercury is inferior to synthetic phenols, lye, saponified cresols, and the new cationic bactericides.
Boric Acid[1]	As wash for eyes, and other sensitive parts of the body.	1 oz. in 1 pt. water (about 6% solution).	It is a weak antiseptic. It may cause harm to the nervous system if absorbed into the body in large amounts. For this and other reasons, antibiotic solutions and saline solutions are fast replacing it.
Cationic Bactericides (Many commercial products available, including QAC, i.e., quaternary ammonium compounds)	Primarily detergents but some are actively bactericidal. Often used in sanitizing dairy or other equipment and utensils. Use only as recommended by a sanitarian.	Concentration varies with different products and under different conditions. Follow authoritative recommendations.	They have only a slight toxicity and are non-irritant and odorless. They are neutralized by soap, anionic detergents and even by mineral content of some waters. Superior to chlorine compounds in the presence of organic matter. They are not effective against TB organisms and spores.

Footnote on last page of table.

(Continued)

Table 15-6 (Continued)

Kind of Disinfectant	Usefulness	Strength	Limitations and Comments
Cresols (Many commercial products available)	A generally reliable class of disinfectant. Effective against brucellosis, shipping fever, swine erysipelas, and tuberculosis.	4 oz. per gal.; or according to the directions found on the container.	Cannot be used where odor may be absorbed, and, therefore, not suited for use around milk and meat.
Heat (by steam, hot water, burning, or boiling)	In the burning of rubbish or articles of little value, and in disposing of infected body discharges. The steam "jenney" is effective for disinfection if properly employed—particularly if used in conjunction with a phenolic germicide.	10-min. exposure to boiling water is usually sufficient.	Exposure to boiling water will destroy all ordinary disease germs, but sometimes fails to kill the spores of such diseases as anthrax and tetanus. Moist heat is preferred to dry heat, and steam under pressure is the most effective. Heat may be impractical or too expensive.
Hypochlorites (chlorine compounds)	For deodorizing manure, sewers and drains, and for disinfecting milk cans and bottles and around dairy barns.	200 parts available chlorine per million of water. Unstable; replace solution frequently as recommended.	Excellent for disinfection, but with following limitations: Not effective against the TB organism and spores. Its effectiveness is greatly reduced in presence of organic matter, such as milk, even in small quantities. Hypochlorites deteriorate rapidly when exposed to air.
Iodine[1]	Extensively used as skin disinfectant, for minor cuts and bruises.	Generally used as a tincture of iodine 2% or 7%.	Never cover with a bandage. Clean skin before applying iodine.

Footnote on last page of table.

(Continued)

Table 15-6 (Continued)

Kind of Disinfectant	Usefulness	Strength	Limitations and Comments
Iodophor (iodine complexed with a detergent which releases free iodine at a controlled rate)	For disinfecting milk cans and bottles around dairy barns and for area disinfection where large quantities of organic soil are not present.	75 parts available iodine per million is minimum under ideal circumstances. 150 ppm. is recommended for most practical uses. Unstable—replace solution frequently.	An excellent disinfectant but with the following practical limitations: Germicidal agent rapidly consumed by organic matter, necessitating frequent replacement. Functions best in a highly acid range. Solution strength must be increased to get necessary available iodine when mixture is made with alkaline water. Iodine slowly volatilizes from solution. Considerable control should be exercised.
Lime (quicklime; burnt lime; calcium oxide)	As a deodorant when sprinkled on manure and animal discharges; or as a disinfectant when sprinkled on the floor or used as a newly-made "milk of lime" or as a whitewash.	Use as a dust; as "milk of lime"; or as a whitewash but use fresh.	Not effective against organism of TB and the spore formers. Wear goggles when adding water to quicklime.
Lye (sodium hydroxide or caustic soda)	On concrete floors; in milk houses because there is no odor; against microorganisms of brucellosis and the viruses of foot-and-mouth disease, hog cholera, and vesicular exanthema. In strong solution (5%) effective against anthrax and blackleg.	1 can (13-oz.) to 12 to 15 gals. water. To prepare a 5% solution, add 5 cans (13-oz.) to 10 gals. water.	Damages fabrics, aluminum, and painted surfaces. Be careful, for it will burn the hands and face. Not effective against organism of TB, or Johne's disease, or strangles, or most spores. When used in hog houses, lye should be mixed with hot water, as the heat of the water will destroy the worm eggs. *Diluted vinegar can be used to neutralize lye.*

Footnote on last page of table.

(Continued)

Table 15-6 (Continued).

Kind of Disinfectant	Usefulness	Strength	Limitations and Comments
Phenolic Germicides, Synthetic (those containing odorless nontoxic phenols such as orthophenyl phenol or orthobenzyl parachlorophenol)	A very reliable class of disinfectants effective against all disease-producing fungi and bacteria including the TB organism.	Varies with different formulations; follow directions on manufacturer's label.	Excellent for disinfection. They are not inactivated by soap, anionic detergents, hard water or organic matter. They are effective against all bacteria and fungi including the TB organism but not the spores of anthrax and tetanus.
Sal Soda	It may be used in place of lye against foot-and-mouth disease and vesicular exanthema.	10.5% solution (13½ ozs. to 1 gal. water).	
Soap	Its power to kill germs is very limited. Greatest usefulness is in cleansing and dissolving coatings from various surfaces, including the skin, prior to application of a good disinfectant.	As commercially prepared.	Although indispensable for sanitizing surfaces, soaps should not be used as disinfectants. They are not regularly effective; staphylococci and the organisms which cause diarrheal diseases are resistant.
Soda Ash (or sodium carbonate)	It may be used in place of lye against foot-and-mouth disease and vesicular exanthema.	5% solution (1 lb. to 3 gals. water). Most effective in hot solution.	Commonly used as a cleansing agent, but has disinfectant properties, especially when used as a hot solution.

¹Sometimes loosely classed as a disinfectant but actually an antiseptic and practically useful only on living tissue.

antiseptic, which is intended for destruction or reduction of micro-organism populations on living tissue. (Two common antiseptics—boric acid and iodine—are listed in Table 15-6.)

Under ordinary circumstances, proper cleaning of barns removes most of the microorganisms present along with the filth. However, those remaining may be capable of causing an outbreak of disease. Therefore, a good disinfectant should be employed in the cleaning program as a preventive measure. In case of a disease outbreak, the premises must be thoroughly disinfected.

Effective disinfection depends on four things:

1. Thorough cleaning with a good detergent-germicide.

2. A very close adherence to the manufacturer's directions for use, especially with reference to making the dilution.

3. The temperature; most disinfectants are much more effective if applied hot.

4. Thoroughness of application, and time of exposure.

Disinfection must in all cases be carried out in a very thorough manner because any area that is not thoroughly cleaned with a disinfectant is capable of harboring disease germs.

Sunlight possesses disinfecting properties, but it is variable and superficial in its action. Heat and some of the chemical disinfectants are more effective. The application of heat by burning or by boiling is an effective method of disinfection. In the case of such surfaces as walls and floors, however, it should be remembered that heat requires some time for action and that the surface for treatment itself should become hot. Simply spraying a surface with boiling water or with steam will not necessarily disinfect it. The hot solution cools too rapidly on most surfaces. It is usually more practical to use a good detergent-germicide, and when possible to apply it hot.

In choosing a chemical disinfectant it should be realized that not all disease-producing bacteria are subject to the same chemical agents. Of the many chemical disinfectants available, the synthetic phenolics have generally been considered most practical and most broadly effective, followed by the cresols, the quaternary ammonium compounds, and the hypochlorides.

Table 15-6 gives a summary of the limitations, usefulness, and strength of some common disinfectants.

Selected References

Title of Publication	Author(s)	Publisher
Anatomy and Physiology of Farm Animals	R. D. Frandson	Lea & Febinger, Philadelphia, Pa., 1965.
Animal Diseases	Yearbook of Agriculture, 1956	U. S. Department of Agriculture, Washington, D. C.
Animal Sanitation and Disease Control	R. R. Dykstra	The Interstate Printers & Publishers, Inc., Danville, Ill., 1961.
Diseases of the Horse	Bureau of Animal Industry	U. S. Department of Agriculture, Washington, D. C., 1942.
Dourine of Horses	Farmers' Bul. No. 1146	U. S. Department of Agriculture, Washington, D. C., 1935.
Equine Medicine & Surgery	68 Authors	American Veterinary Publications, Inc., Wheaton, Ill., 1963.
Farmer's Veterinary Handbook, The	J. J. Haberman	Prentice-Hall, New York, N. Y., 1953.
Home Veterinarian's Handbook, The	E. T. Baker	Macmillan Co., New York, N. Y., 1949.
Horse Science Handbooks	Edited by M. E. Ensminger	Agriservices Foundation, 3699 East Sierra, Clovis, Calif.
Horsemanship and Horsemastership	Vol. II, Part Three, Animal Management	The Cavalry School, Fort Riley, Kansas, 1944.
Infectious Anemia (Swamp Fever)	Farmers' Bul. No. 1819	U. S. Department of Agriculture, Washington, D. C., 1938.
Infectious Diseases of Domestic Animals, The	W. A. Hagan D. W. Bruner	Comstock Publishing Associates, Ithaca, N. Y., 1957.
Insecticide Recommendations	Agri. Handbook (annual)	U. S. Department of Agriculture, Washington, D. C.
Keeping Livestock Healthy	Yearbook of Agriculture, 1942	U. S. Department of Agriculture, Washington, D. C.
Livestock Health Encyclopedia	Rudolph Seiden	Springer Publishing Co., New York, N. Y., 1951.
Merck Veterinary Manual, The		Merck & Co., Rahway, N. J., 1967.

Title of Publication	Author(s)	Publisher
Parasites and Parasitic Diseases of Horses	Benjamin Schwartz Marion Imes A. O. Foster	Circ. No. 148, U. S. Department of Agriculture, Washington, D. C., 1948.
Principles of Veterinary Science	F. B. Hadley	W. B. Saunders Co., Philadelphia, Pa., 1949.
Progress in Equine Practice	Edited by E. J. Catcott J. F. Smithcors	Am. Vet. Publications, Inc., 114 North West St., Wheaton, Ill., 1966.
Stockman's Handbook, The	M. E. Ensminger	The Interstate Printers & Publishers, Inc., Danville, Ill., 1970.
Stud Manager's Handbook	December, 1961, 1962	Washington State University, Pullman, Wash.
Stud Managers' Handbooks	Edited by M. E. Ensminger	Agriservices Foundation, 3699 East Sierra Ave., Clovis, Calif.
Veterinary Guide for Farmers	G. W. Stamm	Windsor Press, Chicago, Ill., 1950.
Veterinary Medicine	D. G. Blood J. A. Henderson	The Williams and Wilkins Co., Baltimore, Md., 1960.
Veterinary Notebook	W. R. McGee	*The Blood-Horse*, Lexington, Ky., 1958.
Veterinary Notes for the Standardbred Breeder	W. R. McGee	The United States Trotting Association, 1349 East Broad Street, Columbus, Ohio.

16

In this chapter . . .

16

Horsemanship[1]

RIDING HAS BECOME increasingly popular in recent years because it offers pleasant and healthful outdoor recreation, beneficial to both body and mind. Furthermore, it is a sport that can be indulged in at any time by those who like it. Also, it can be enjoyed alone or with groups. Nor is it confined to any age, rank, or profession. Businessmen value riding because they can get vigorous exercise and obtain relaxation from professional troubles. A good horse is companion enough, is always good humored, and has no worries or business troubles to talk about.

Women can ride at such times as may suit their convenience. For the housewife, this may be an important consideration.

Children build character through riding, automatically acquiring confidence, self-control, and patience—all through companionship with their good friend and stout companion, the horse.

For greatest enjoyment, one should learn to ride correctly. It is an unfortunate truth that many people think they can ride if only they can stick on a horse. Although these same people may pay well for instruction in golf, swimming, tennis, and other sports, it never occurs to them that a competent riding master may be essential in learning to ride. The word competent is used with reference to riding

[1]Acknowledgment, with sincere thanks, is given to the following competent equestrians and equestriennes who reviewed Chapter 16. Mrs. Frances Reker, Owner and Riding Director, Frances Reker School of Horsemanship and Happy Horse Stables, Rockford, Minn.; Mrs. Fern Palmer Bittner, Lindenwood College, St. Charles, Mo.; Mrs. Claud H. Drew, Columbia, Mo.; Mr. Allen I. Ross, Stanford Riding School, Stanford University, Calif.; Col. F. W. Koester, U. S. Army, retired; Major Charles B. Team, formerly Q.M.C., Pomona Remount Station, Pomona, Calif.; and Professor Byron H. Good, Department of Animal Husbandry, Michigan State University, East Lansing, Mich.

masters; for, what is even more tragic, many people think that they are qualified to instruct others as soon as they have learned a few things about riding.

Equitation is a very difficult subject to teach. In the first place, no two horses nor two riders are alike. Then there is hardly any limit to the types of available equipment, and there are the different gaits; and, in addition, riding to hounds and riding on a city bridle path present entirely different problems. Moreover, riding cannot be taught by merely reading a set of instructions. It can be mastered only after patient practice under a competent instructor. The amateur, therefore, should be under no illusions about achieving horsemanship and horsemastership merely through reading what follows. Rather, it is proposed to present here some of the basic principles of equitation and information pertaining to equipment, with the hope that the beginner may better understand the why and wherefore of the instructions given him. Also, through reading this presentation it is hoped that the experienced equestrian may be less likely to suffer relapse.

It must be recognized also that there are many schools of riding, and each riding master will proceed along different lines. Yet, the end result will always be the same—training the rider to get the maximum pleasure with the least exertion to himself and his mount. Regardless of the method of instruction, the first requisite is that of instilling confidence in the amateur. Confidence is usually obtained through first becoming familiar with the horse and equipment and then by riding a gentle and obedient horse at the walk in an enclosed ring, while keeping the mount under control at all times.

In instructing the beginner, the author favors a simple approach of first becoming familiar with the horse and equipment and then learning to use that equipment properly. Knowledge of correct grooming and care of the horse, care of equipment, saddling, bridling, and leading is also essential.

SELECTION OF THE MOUNT

The mount should be carefully selected by a competent horseman. In addition to obtaining a sound horse of desirable conformation, one should give the following points careful consideration:

1. The mount should be purchased within a price range that the rider can afford.

2. The amateur or child should have a quiet, gentle, well-broken horse that is neither headstrong nor unmanageable. The horse should

Fig. 16-1. The mount should be selected carefully for the individual rider—keeping in mind (1) the purchase price that the rider can afford, (2) the skill of the rider, (3) the size of the rider, and (4) the type of work to be performed.

never be too spirited for the rider's skill. It is best that the beginner select a horse (a) with manners, rather than looks, and (b) that is older, rather than a two- or three-year-old.

3. The size of the horse should be in keeping with the size and weight of the rider. Very small children should have a small horse or pony, whereas a heavy man should have a horse of the weight-carrying type. An exceedingly tall man or woman also looks out of place if not mounted on a horse with considerable height.

4. Usually the novice will do best to start with a three-gaited horse and first master the three natural gaits before attempting to ride a horse executing the more complicated five gaits, should a five-gaited horse be desired.

5. Other conditions being equal, the breed and color of horse may be decided on the basis of preference.

6. When one wants a horse that is to be used for business purposes— an animal such as is desired by ranchers—the mount should be well suited to the type of work to be performed.

7. Before buying, take every possible precaution to avoid a horse that has undesirable traits or vices; question the owner, and observe the horse in its stall and when being ridden.

After the horse has been selected, it is important that he and the rider become acquainted with each other. Just as every automobile driver knows the major parts of a car—the steering wheel, tires, wheels, hood, fenders, windows, etc.—the horseman should be familiar with the important parts of a horse. This information may be secured by studying Figure 4-1 in Chapter 4.

CONTROL OF THE HORSE

The horse has whims and ideas of his own. Always, however, the rider should be the boss, with the mount promptly carrying out his wishes. With the experienced horseman, this relationship is clear-cut, for the rider is able to relay his feelings to the horse instantly and unmistakably.

A well-mannered horse may be said to be the combined result of desirable heredity, skillful training, and vigilant control. Once conception has taken place, it is too late to change the genetic make-up of the animal. However, the eventual training and control of the horse are dependent upon how well the horseman understands equine mental faculties as well as methods of utilizing these faculties so that the desired performance may be obtained.

Purebred horse breeding establishments have long been aware, consciously or unconsciously, of the equine mental faculties. As a result, most breeders have substituted gradual and early training programs for the so-called breaking of animals at three to five years of age. Even on some of the more progressive ranches, the cowboy and the bucking bronco are fast passing into permanent oblivion. The owners of the famous King Ranch in Texas report that they have discarded the former method of breaking three-year-olds in favor of starting training at three months of age. It has been their experience that the latter method has materially reduced injuries to both men and horses, has resulted in more really gentle mounts, and has cost less in time, labor, and money.

For complete control and a finished performance, the horse should have a proud and exalted opinion of himself; but at the same time he should subjugate those undesirable traits that make a beast of his size and strength so difficult to handle by a comparatively frail and small man. Complete control, therefore, is based on mental faculties rather than muscular force.

The faculties of the horse that must be understood and played upon to obtain skillful training and control at all times are summarized briefly in this chapter.

Memory

To a considerable degree, the horse's aptitude for training is due to his memory; for he remembers or recognizes the indications given him, the manner in which he responded, and the rewards or punishments that followed his actions. These facts must be taken into consideration both in training the young horse and in retaining control of the trained animal.

Discipline and reward must be administered very soon after the act (some competent horsemen say that it should be within three seconds) in order for the horse to associate and remember.

Confidence and Fear

In the wild state, the horse was his own protector; and his very survival was often dependent upon rapidity of escape. In a well-mannered horse, it is necessary that confidence in the rider replace fear. Thus, it is best to approach the horse from the front. He should be spoken to in a quiet, calm voice and should be patted by using comparatively slow movement of the hands to avoid exciting him. Above all, when one is approaching a horse, he should make certain that the animal knows of his presence. Startling a horse often causes accidents for which the animal is blameless.

During moments of fright, the good horseman utilizes the means by which the horse is calmed. However, when the horse is voluntarily and knowingly disobedient, the proper degree of punishment should be administered immediately.

Association of Ideas

Horses are creatures of habit; for example, when the grain bin door is heard to open, the horse regularly anticipates his feed. For this reason, the schooling of a horse should be handled by the same competent horseman, who allows the animal an opportunity to associate the various commands with the desired response. A well-trained horse may become confused and ill-mannered when poorly handled by several persons.

Willingness

A willing worker or performer is to be desired. Some animals submit to the horseman's subjugation with little trouble and hesitation, whereas others offer resistance to the point of being stubborn. Complete control over the mount at all times is achieved through the judicious employment of rewards and punishments.

Rewards

The two most common rewards given horses are a praising voice and a gentle stroking with the hand. Satisfying the horse's greediness for such things as a lump of sugar is also most effective, but this may make for great disappointment if the reward is not available at all times. To be effective, rewards must not be given promiscuously but only when deserved. It is also important that the same word always be used for the same thing and that the horseman means what he says.

Punishment

The two common types of equine punishment are the spur and the whip. Punishment should be administered only when the horseman is certain that the animal is being disobedient and not when the horse lacks sufficient training, has not understood some command, or has done something wrong because of the rider. When necessary, however, the punishment should be administered promptly, so that the animal understands why it is given; and it should be given with justice and with the horseman retaining a cool head at all times. Following punishment, the animal should be made to carry out the original command that he failed to follow, and then he should be properly rewarded.

TACK

Each horse should have his own saddle, bridle, halter, and lead shank. Then, the equipment can be adjusted to fit the particular horse.

Equipment should be selected so as to suit the intended purpose, as well as to fit both the horse and the rider. As in buying almost anything—food, a suit of clothes, and what not—you generally get what you pay for. In the long run, it is usually cheaper to buy superior quality tack. Then, by taking good care of it, one can derive satisfaction for many years.

The sections that follow give pertinent facts about some common tack items. Certainly, not all needed tack is listed. For example, a halter and lead shank are standard equipment—used to catch a horse in pasture or corral, to lead a horse from one place to another, and when grooming, saddling, or working around the horse.

Bits

The bit is the most important part of the bridle; in fact, the chief use of the bridle is to hold the bit in its place in the horse's mouth. There are more types of bits than of any other article of horse equipment. In this connection, it is interesting to note that the snaffle bit—which is still the most widely used of all varieties—was the first type to which historians make reference, having been developed by the early Greek horsemen. The bit provides communication between the hands of the rider or driver and the mouth of the horse.

Figures 16-2, 16-3, and 16-4 show the most common types of bits. It must be remembered, however, that there is hardly any limit to the number of variations in each of these kinds of bits.

The proper fit and adjustment of the bit is most essential, regardless of type. It should rest easily in the mouth, being sufficiently wide so as not to pinch the cheeks or cause wrinkles in the corners of the mouth. As a rule, curb-type bits rest lower in the mouth than the snaffle. All bits should be supplied with large rings or other devices to prevent them from passing through the mouth when either rein is drawn in turning.

The following additional points are pertinent to bits:

1. The snaffle bit is usually used when starting a horse in training.

2. The hunting (or egg butt) snaffle is used on hunters and jumpers.

3. The curb bit is a more severe bit, which may be used either alone or with the snaffle bit.

4. The Pelham bit is one bit, which is used with two reins and a curb chain. It is a combination of a snaffle and a curb bit and is used in park or pleasure riding and hunting.

5. The Weymouth bit along with a snaffle bit is known as a bit and bradoon.

6. Western bits are made similar to the curb bit, but they have longer shanks and are larger. They are usually used with a leather curb strap, although a leather curb strap with a small amount of chain in the middle is sometimes used.

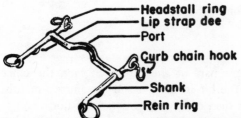

Weymouth Curb Bit: Used along with a snaffle bit in a Weymouth Bridle for 3- and 5-gaited horses.

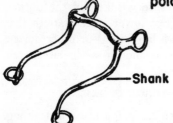

Pelham Curb Bit: — Used in a Pelham Bridle for hunters, polo ponies, and pleasure horses.

Walking Horse Bit: Frequently used on Walking Horses.

Snaffle Bit: The most widely used of all bits.

Dee Race Bit: Often used on Thoroughbred race horses.

Fig. 16-2. Five common types of English riding bits, and the parts of each. (Drawings by Steve Allured)

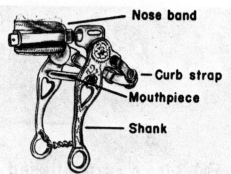

Hackamore Bit: Used on most cow
ponies.

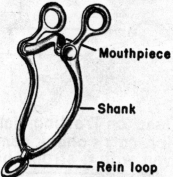

Roper Curved Cheek Bit: Used on many
roping horses.

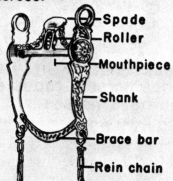

Spade Mouth Bit: Used on many
stock horses.

Fig. 16-3. Three common types of Western riding bits, and the parts of each. (Drawings
by Steve Allured)

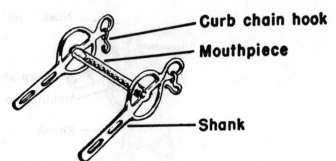

Liverpool Bit: A curb bit used on heavy harness horses

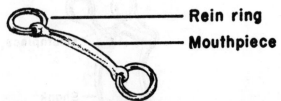

Bar Bit: Used on Trotting Harness Horses, which carry check reins and are driven with a strong hand

Half-cheek Snaffle Bit: Used on harness race horses, roadsters and fine harness horses

Fig. 16-4. Three common types of driving bits and the parts of each. (Drawings by Steve Allured)

Bridles and Hackamores

Light bridles and bits usually indicate competent horsemen and well-mannered horses. Bridles may be either single or double. A single bridle is equipped with one bit, whereas a double bridle is ordinarily equipped with both a snaffle bit and a curb bit, two headstalls, and two pairs of reins. Only one rein is used with Western bridles.

All bridles should be properly fitted, and the headstall should be located so that it neither slides back on the horse's neck nor pulls up against his ears. The cheek straps should be adjusted in length so that the bit rests easily in the mouth without drawing up the corners; and the throat latch should be buckled loosely enough to permit the hand, when held in a vertical position, to pass between it and the horse's throat.

Both the bosal hackamore and the hackamore bit bridle are used as a training device for Western horses and on horses with tender mouths. The bosal hackamore consists of an ordinary headstall which holds in place a braided rawhide or rope noseband knotted under the horse's jaw, and a pair of reins. It is an excellent device for controlling

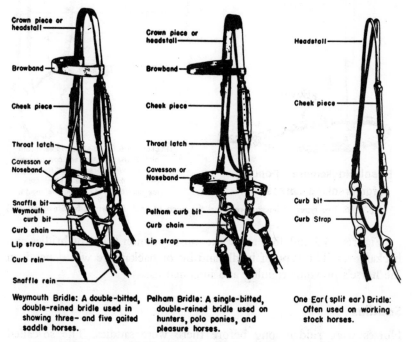

Weymouth Bridle: A double-bitted, double-reined bridle used in showing three- and five gaited saddle horses.

Pelham Bridle: A single-bitted, double-reined bridle used on hunters, polo ponies, and pleasure horses.

One Ear (split ear) Bridle: Often used on working stock horses.

Fig. 16-5. Three types of bridles, and the parts of each. (Drawings by Steve Allured)

and training a young horse without injuring its mouth. The hackamore is used extensively on the western ranges in the training of cow ponies, and it is used equally widely in the early training of polo ponies.

When properly adjusted, the hackamore should rest on the horse's nose, about four inches from the top of the nostrils (or at the base of the cheek bones of the horse's head). It should also permit the passage of two finger breadths between it and the branches of the jaw.

The hackamore bit bridle is a "fake" bit: it has the shanks on each side, but there is no mouthpiece.

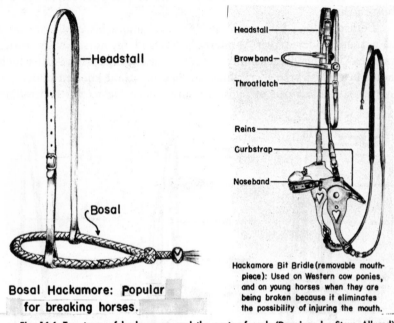

Bosal Hackamore: Popular for breaking horses.

Hackamore Bit Bridle (removable mouth-piece): Used on Western cow ponies, and on young horses when they are being broken because it eliminates the possibility of injuring the mouth.

Fig. 16-6. Two types of hackamores, and the parts of each (Drawings by Steve Allured)

Figures 16-5 and 16-6 show the most common types of bridles and hackamores. The type of bridle and bit or hackamore will depend on the horse's previous training and intended use.

Saddles

Horses were ridden long before there were saddles. The so-called "horse cloth" was first used about 800 B.C., but the use of saddles with trees did not exist until the fourth century A.D. Anne of Bohemia is credited with introducing the ladies' sidesaddle in the latter part of the fourteenth century.

Although considerable styling and individuality exist, the English saddle and the Western saddle are the two most common types.

THE ENGLISH SADDLE

The English saddle includes the flat types of saddles in which certain modifications are made specifically to adapt them for use in pleasure riding, training, racing, jumping, and polo. The English saddle is characterized by its relatively flat seat and its generally light construction. Its advocates claim that its use is a mark of distinction of the finished rider, as it permits the best in riding form, skill, and balance.

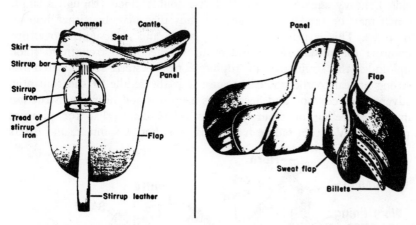

Fig. 16-7. An English saddle, and its parts. Left, upright position; right, underside. (Drawings by Steve Allured)

The following additional points are pertinent to the use of English saddles:

1. For show horses, use a white web or linen girth with the saddle.

2. Saddle blankets are usually not necessary.

3. For English pleasure riding or showing, select an English saddle; then use a double bit or Pelham bridle.

4. For hunting or jumping, use a forward seat English saddle, with a bridle having a hunting snaffle or Pelham bit.

THE WESTERN SADDLE

Western saddles were first developed and used by the Spaniards in Old Mexico. They constructed them with horns, and they liked them roomy, heavy, and ornate. Subsequently, American ranchers made some changes; they lightened them and made them less cumbersome, and they added the high pommel and swelled fork—better to provide extra leg grip should the horse buck or rear.

The Western saddle is the common saddle used by the cowboy. The essential features are: a steel, light metal, or wooden tree; a pommel varying in height and surmounted with a horn for roping; a comparatively deep seat; a cantle varying in height (the variation in the height of the pommel and cantle is determined by the uses to which the saddle is to be put and the personal preference of the rider); heavy square, or round, skirts; double cinch (though a single cinch may be used); and heavy stirrups that may be either hooded or open. This is primarily a work saddle and is designed to afford comfort for all-day riding and to provide enough strength to stand up under the strain of calf roping. The Western saddle often has strong appeal to the novice because it is the saddle of the romantic, adventurous cowboy and because its deep seat and heavy construction impart a feeling of security. Some riders claim that for pleasure riding, the Western saddle is too heavy, is hot in summer, and offers

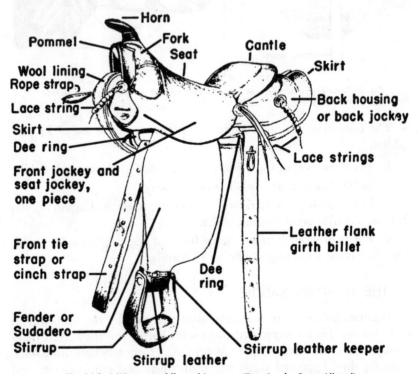

Fig. 16-8. A Western saddle and its parts. (Drawing by Steve Allured)

too much temptation to "pull leather" as a substitute for skill and balance. The average Western saddle weighs from 35 to 40 pounds.

Additional pertinent facts about Western saddles are:

1. They're used for Western riding of all kinds, both work and pleasure.

2. Western saddles are utilitarian. They're designed to provide all-day comfort, and the horn is a convenient and secure post around which the lariat can be tied or quickly wound when handling cattle.

3. The design of Western saddles—especially height of pommel and cantle—is determined by use and personal preference.

Westerners take pride in their saddles. To them, they're much more than something to throw over a horse's back, or to use in working cattle. They're symbolic of the development of the range, of trailing, and of the transition from the Texas longhorn to the prime bullock. Most makes and styles of Western saddles are accorded meaningful names, with such selections suggestive of their historical significance, their construction, and/or their use.

To reputable manufacturers and proud owners alike, the names of Western saddles are symbols of service, pledges of integrity, and assurances of courage, character, and wisdom.

Miscellaneous Equipment for Riders

It is beyond the scope of this discussion to describe or even to mention all of the many articles of horse equipment. An attempt will be made, however, to deal with the most generally used types, in addition to those already described.

SADDLE BLANKET (OR NUMNAH, PAD, OR CORONA)

With English saddles, saddle blankets are usually not necessary when the saddle is thoroughly cleaned after each ride, when the rider uses a balanced seat, and when the mount is properly groomed. When kept clean and when properly used, however, a blanket will usually prevent a sore back. For this reason, even with English saddles, many good horsemen always insist on the use of a saddle blanket.

A saddle blanket or corona is almost always used with Western saddles.

Felt, mohair, or pad blankets that are adapted to the various types of saddles may be secured. Many good horsemen even prefer a folded Navajo blanket, with a hair pad inside. The corona is a blanket cut to the shape of the saddle and has a large colorful roll around the edge that is quite showy for use with a stock saddle.

The saddle pad or blanket should be placed well forward on the horse's neck and then slid back into position so as to smooth down the hair. It should come to rest smoothly and in such manner that two and one-half to four inches of it will show in front of the saddle. After being used, the blanket or pad should be hung up to dry. It then should be brushed thoroughly to eliminate hair and dried sweat.

THE NOSEBAND

The noseband is a wide leather band which passes around the nose below the cheek bones. It is used to keep the mouth shut and the bit in position, as a means for attaching the standing martingale, or to enhance the appearance of the bridle. Heavy harness and most riding bridles are equipped with nosebands. The noseband should be adjusted so that it is about one and one-half inches below the cheek bone and loose enough so that two fingers may be placed under it.

MARTINGALES

Martingales are of two types: standing (or sometimes called a tie-down) and running (or ring). The standing martingale consists of a strap which extends from around the girth, between the forelegs, to the noseband and a light neck strap to keep the martingale from getting under the horse's feet when the head is lowered. When properly adjusted, it has the effect of preventing the elevation of the head beyond a certain level without cramping the horse. The standing martingale is most generally employed on saddle horses that rear and on polo ponies and stock horses that endanger their riders by throwing their heads up in response to a severe curb when pulled up sharply. On the other hand, some competent horsemen prefer to use the running martingale on horses that habitually rear. Such horsemen feel that the standing martingale sets the head too high.

The running martingale is not attached to the horse's head but terminates in two rings through which the reins pass. It is used for the same purpose as the standing martingale but permits more freedom of movement. Thus, it is better adapted to and more frequently used for jumping than the standing martingale.

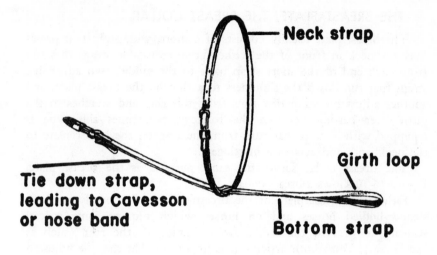

Neck strap

Girth loop

Tie down strap, leading to Cavesson or nose band

Bottom strap

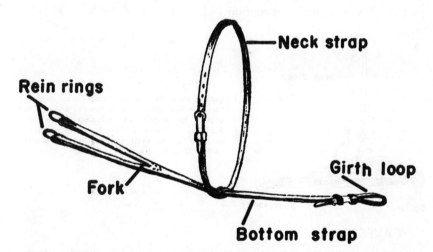

Neck strap

Rein rings

Girth loop

Fork

Bottom strap

Fig. 16-9. The two types of martingales: Upper, standing martingale, sometimes called a tiedown. It is sometimes used on saddle horses that rear and on polo ponies and stock horses that endanger their riders by throwing their heads up in response to a severe curb when pulled up sharply. Lower, a running martingale. It is used for the same purposes as the standing martingale, but permits more freedom of movement; thus it may be used on jumpers. (Drawings by Steve Allured)

Proper adjustment of the running martingale is obtained when, with the horse's head in a normal position, the snaffle reins stretched from the pommel form a straight line from bit to pommel.

THE BREAST PLATE; THE BREAST COLLAR

The breast plate usually consists of a short, wide strap that passes over the neck in front of the withers, two adjustable straps that run from each end of the short strap back to the saddle, two adjustable straps that run down the shoulders to a ring on the breast plate, and another adjustable strap that runs from this ring and attaches to the girth after passing between the forelegs. Sometimes this type is equipped with a strap that runs from the ring on the breast plate to the neckband, and acts as a martingale.

The breast collar serves the same purpose as the breast plate. Figure 16-10 shows a breast collar.

Either the breast plate or the breast collar is frequently used on slender-bodied horses and on horses which require some special security to prevent the saddle from slipping to the rear (such as racehorses). With both articles, it is important that they be adjusted as loosely as possible consistent with holding the saddle in place, with proper allowance made for motion and movement of the horse's neck.

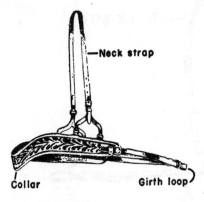

Fig. 16-10. The breast collar. It is frequently used on slender-bodied horses and on horses which require some special security to prevent the saddle from slipping to the rear (such as racehorses). The breast plate may be used for the same purposes as the breast collar. (Drawing by Steve Allured)

CAVESSON

The breaking or longeing cavesson consists of a heavy headstall, except that it has an additional strap known as the "jowl strap"—and a hinged, jointed, heavily padded, metal noseband with a ring at the top for the attachment of the longe. The cavesson (with the longe) is used for exercising, disciplining, and training horses.[2]

---

[2]Another type of cavesson is used on many bridles. It consists of a narrow strap around the nose which is held in place by another strap which goes over the head and behind the ears. The cavesson-type bridle was originally designed to prevent the horse from opening its mouth too wide when the reins are pulled, thereby getting away from the discipline of the bit.

LONGE (LUNGE)

The longe is a strong light strap (usually made of webbing or leather) about 30 feet long, one end of which is attached to the noseband of the cavesson.

LONGEING WHIP

A typical longeing whip has a stock about four feet long and a lash six to eight feet long. It is used when exercising and disciplining the horse in longeing.

SADDLING THE MOUNT

Regardless of the type of saddle—English or Western—it should be placed on the horse's back so that the girth will come about four inches to the rear of the point of the horse's elbow.

When first adjusted, the girth should be loose enough to admit a finger between it and the horse's belly. After tightening the saddle, it is always a good practice to "untrack" the horse—that is, to lead him ahead several paces before mounting. This procedure serves two purposes: First, if the horse is the kind that "blows up" so that he cannot be cinched snugly, the "untracking" will usually cause him to relax; and second, if a horse has any bad habits, he will often get them out of his system before the rider mounts.

After the horse has been ridden a few minutes, the girth should always be re-examined and tightened if necessary. The saddle should always be cinched tightly enough so that it will not turn when the horse is being mounted, but not so tight as to cause discomfort to the horse.

The length of stirrups will depend upon the type of riding. It may vary from very short on running horses to quite long on stock horses. The stirrup leather on English saddles should always be turned so that the flat side of the leather comes against the leg of the rider.

For correct posting, in English riding, the stirrup straps or stirrup leathers must be adjusted to the right length. If stirrups are too short, posting will be high and exaggerated. For English riding, the stirrups can be adjusted to the approximate correct length before mounting by making them about one inch shorter than the length of the rider's arm with fingers extended. When the rider is sitting in the saddle, with the legs extended downward and the feet out of the stirrups, the

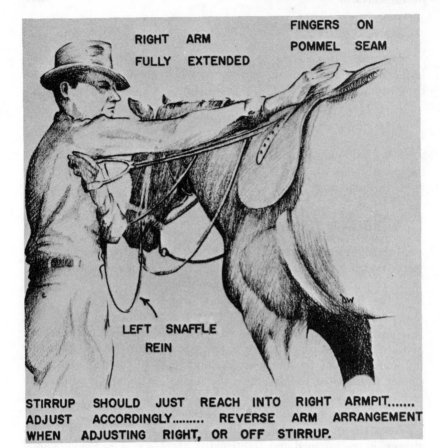

RIGHT ARM
FULLY EXTENDED

FINGERS ON
POMMEL SEAM

LEFT SNAFFLE
REIN

STIRRUP SHOULD JUST REACH INTO RIGHT ARMPIT.......
ADJUST ACCORDINGLY........ REVERSE ARM ARRANGEMENT
WHEN ADJUSTING RIGHT, OR OFF STIRRUP.

Fig. 16-11. Method of checking the stirrup straps of an English saddle for proper length.

bottom of the stirrup iron should touch just below the ankle bone. For Western riding, the length of stirrups may be considered as about right when there is approximately a three- inch clearance between the saddle tree and the crotch of the mounted rider standing in the stirrups.

CLOTHES FOR RIDERS

There is hardly any limit to the variety or cost of clothes that may be and are worn by riders. In general, however, riding attire, unlike street clothing, seldom changes in style. Moreover, riding togs are utilitarian. Peg top breeches, for example, are designed to give

Fig. 16-12. Proper riding attire. (Drawings by Ethel Gadberry)

Table 16-1

	Informal Park or School Riding, Morning or Afternoon Classes	Semi-formal, Afternoon or Evening Classes	Formal Evening	
			Five-gaited	Three-gaited
COAT:	Any conservative color, tweeds or checks.	Gabardine, wool gabardine, or dress worsted, or other men's-wear materials. Inverted pleats in back. Dark colors preferred. Summer—linen or tropical worsted.	One button, inverted pleats, black or midnight blue tuxedo style riding coat. Gentlemen usually wear a dark suit, instead of a tuxedo.	Black or midnight blue, tuxedo style. Soft pastel-colored coats can be worn. White coat in summer. Shawl collar with satin lapels. *Equitation Classes:* Must wear (1) dark tuxedo style with silk top hat in evening and (2) matched suit with derby in daytime.
JODHPURS OR BREECHES:	Jodhpurs of gabardine, whipcord, or cavalry twill in colors to match or in contrast to coat. Kentucky style—no flare at hip and with bell-bottoms.	Jodhpurs of same material as coat (riding habit). Kentucky style—bell-bottom, no flare at hip and no cuff.	Material and color to match coat, or black or midnight blue jods if pastel coat is worn.	Material and color to match coat (riding habit). Satin stripe down outside of jods.
VEST:	Optional. Light, solid color or tattersall check.	Solid color or tattersall check.	Solid colors or matching habit.	White pique or cummerbund (optional).
SHIRT:	Man's shirt, white or colored, broadcloth or oxford cloth.	Man's shirt in white or light color to match suit.	Man's shirt.	Formal style, white stiff front tuxedo. Shirt with wing collar and pleated front.
NECKWEAR:	Contrasting 4-in-hand tie, or bow tie.	Matching or contrasting color man's 4-in-hand tie.	4-in-hand tie, or bow tie.	Black, white, or midnight blue bow tie.
HAT:	Saddle derby to match jods or coat.	Saddle derby to match suit.	Saddle derby.	Silk top hat.

English Riding

CLOTHES FOR RIDERS[1]

Western Riding	Hunting and Jumping			
	Hunting (Informal)	Hunt Seat Equitation	Member of a Hunt (Formal)	Jumping
Tailored equitation suits may be worn (matching shirt and pants). Coats and jackets not usually worn, except in inclement weather.	Black oxford or tweed.	Black (or conservative color) oxford or tweed hunt coat.	Black hunt coat of melton or heavy twill. May wear: scarlet hunt livery; cutaway type; black coat of shadbelly. Collar: Same material and color as coat, unless rider has been invited to wear hunt-club colors in which case collar should conform to hunt livery. Buttons: Also to conform to hunt livery.	Any color of hunt coat in solid or checks. Jumping attire can be of any informal forward seat type.
Western cut pants of gabardine, cotton twill, cavalry twill, or wool; with chaps, shotgun chaps, or chinks. Conservative in color and well-tailored.	Brick, tan, buff, or canary breeches or jods with peg and cuff.	Buff, brick, or canary breeches.	Buff, brick, or canary with black coat. *Men:* white breeches with scarlet coat.	Breeches of a contrasting color to coat.
Leather or cloth (optional).	Hunting yellow or tattersal (optional).	Canary with black coat (optional).	Buff or yellow, or hunt colors if member.	Checkered or solid color.
Western type; color to match or contrast with western pants (solid or patterned fabric acceptable). It is trim fitting with long sleeves.	Stock shirt or ratcatcher.	Stock shirt.	White stock shirt.	Ratcatcher shirt with stock. Man's shirt.
Knotted kerchief; dogger type tie; choker; or silk scarf tied ascot style and tucked into open neck of shirt.	Choker, stock, or ratcatcher tie.	White stock or choker.	White stock, fastened with plain gold safety pin worn straight across stock.	4-in-hand tie, or stock.
Western hat; felt or straw.	Brown or black hunting derby; hunting cap if 18 years or under.	Hunting derby; hunting cap if 18 years or under.	Hunting silk hat; hat guard required with scarlet and shadbelly. Hunt caps for staff members and juniors. Derby with hat guard with black coat for adults.	Hunting derby, or hunt cap.

Table 16-1

	English Riding			
	Informal Park or School Riding, Morning or Afternoon Classes	Semi-formal, Afternoon or Evening Classes	Formal Evening	
			Five-gaited	Three-gaited
BOOTS:	Black or brown strap or elastic jodhpur boots.	Black or brown jodhpur boots.	Black jodhpur boots with tuxedo. Brown or black with matched suit.	Black leather or patent leather jodhpur boots.
GLOVES:	Leather gloves to blend with habit (optional).	Leather in a natural shade or to match suit (optional).	Leather to match habit.	Leather to match habit.
JEWELRY OR OTHER ACCESSO-RIES:	Cuff links, tie pin, belt. Spurs of unrowelled type, whip or crop (optional).	Tie clasp, cuff links, belt. Spurs and riding whip (optional).	Cuff links, tie pin; gaited riding whip and spurs (optional).	Formal shirt studs. Walk, trot stick (optional).

Other Occasions:
1. *Side Saddle Forward Seat for Hunting*—Hunting silk hat, hat guard required. Dark melton habit with matching skirt, black boots without tops. Spurs (optional). White or colored rain gloves, neckwear, coat collar, vest, sandwich case and flask same as member of a hunt.

[1]This table was reviewed by the following authorities: Mrs. Frances Reker, Owner and Riding Director, Frances Reker School of Horsemanship and Happy Horse Stables, Rockford, Minnesota; Miss Gloria Rawcliffe, equestrienne and the author's secretary, Clovis, California; and Professor Robert W.

ample seat room. Close fitting legs eliminate wrinkles that might cause chafing, and chamois leather lining inside the knees and calves prevents pinching of the muscles of the leg under the stirrup leathers and increases the firmness of the leg grip. Boots or jodhpurs protect the ankle from the stirrup iron; and high boots also protect the breeches from being snagged on objects along the trail, shield the trouser legs from the saddle straps and the horse's sides, and protect

(Continued)

Western Riding	Hunting and Jumping			
	Hunting (Informal)	Hunt Seat Equitation	Member of a Hunt (Formal)	Jumping
Western boots.	Black or brown boots, high or jods.	Black or brown hunt boots.	Regular hunting boots with tabs. Black calf. Black patent tops permissible for ladies; brown tops for men on staff.	Black or brown hunting boots.
Leather (optional).	Brown leather or rain gloves of string.	Optional.	Brown leather or rain gloves of white or yellow string.	Optional.
Hand carved belt and western belt buckle. Carry a rope or riata. If closed reins are used in Trail and Pleasure Horse Classes, hobbles must be carried. Spurs (optional).	String gloves under girth for rain. Stock or choker pin, belt, hunting crop, and spurs with straps to match boots.	Spurs of unrowelled type (optional). Crop or hat (optional). Stock pin worn straight across on stock tie or choker.	Rain gloves, sandwich case and flask. Regulation hunting whip. Spurs of heavy pattern with moderately short neck. Preferably without rowels. Worn high on heel. *Boot garter:* Plain black or black patent leather with patent leather boot tops. Brown with brown boot tops. White with white breeches.	Stock pin, belt, jumping bat, spurs optional.

2. *Side Saddle Show Seat*—Habit of dark blue, black, or oxford gray with matching or contrasting skirt. Black jodhpur boots. Bow tie or 4-in-hand. White shirt. Hard derby. White or pigskin gloves.
3. *Plantation Walking Horses*—Attire should be same as listed for 3- or 5-gaited. Ladies seldom wear hats; men can wear soft felt. (Tennessee Walking Horse)

Miller, Department of Animal Science, Montana State University, Bozeman, Montana.
For information on the subject of clothes for riders for specific show classes, see the current (issued yearly) *Rule Book* of the American Horse Shows Association.

the legs from rain and cold. For the most comfortable ride, breeches (either regulation or jodhpur type) should be made to order.

Appropriate clothes for riding for the most common occasions are listed in Table 16-1. The time of day, the type of riding horse, and the class in which shown determine the riding attire. In addition to selecting proper clothes, well-groomed and experienced riders place emphasis on fine tailoring, good materials, and proper fit. Also, when saddle horses are being ridden, gaudy colors, excess jewelry, and sequins are to be discouraged except in parade classes.

Western Boots

Western boots are more than a handsome trademark of the range. They're practical. The high heel is designed to give the wearer protection against losing his stirrups at critical moments; it prevents the foot from slipping through when pressure is applied for quick stops and turns. The top protects the ankles and calves of the legs against inclement weather, brush, insects, and snakes.

Modern Western boots possess two added features: namely, (1) comfort, and (2) adaptation for walking, so that the wearer can walk without it being a painful experience.

MOUNTING AND DISMOUNTING

Before mounting, two precautions should be taken: always check the cinch (or saddle girth) for tightness and the stirrup straps or leathers for length. A loose girth may let the saddle slip down on the horse's side or belly, especially when one is mounting and dismounting. When the girth is adjusted properly, one should be able to get only the first half of the fingers under it without considerable forcing.

When all precautions have been taken, the steps in mounting and dismounting a horse are as follows (see Figure 16-13):

1. Always mount from the left or "near" side of the horse. Stand beside the horse's left front leg and face diagonally toward the croup.[3] Then gather the reins in the left hand, adjusting them so that a gentle pressure (restraining but not backing the animal) is applied equally on each side of the horse's mouth, and place the left hand on or immediately in front of the horse's withers. Without letting go of the reins, open the fingers of your left hand and get a handful of the horse's mane; this will give you more stability and avoid jerking the horse's mouth.

---

[3] Another common method of mounting begins with facing the front of the horse while standing opposite the left stirrup. The method given in point 1 above is considered safer for the beginner, however; for if the horse should start to move as he is being mounted, the rider is automatically swung into the saddle and is not left behind. Also, the person mounting is out of the way of a horse that "cow kicks."

2. Turn the stirrup iron one-quarter turn toward you, steady the stirrup with the right hand and shove the left into it.

3. Hop off the right foot, swing around to face the horse, grasp the cantle (rear) of the saddle (in Western riding, the right hand is usually placed on the horn instead of the cantle) with the right hand, and spring upward until a standing position is reached, with the leg straight and facing the saddle and the left knee against the horse.

4. Lean on the left arm, shift the right hand from the cantle to the pommel (usually right-hand side of pommel) of saddle. Then, at the same time, swing the fully extended right leg slowly over the horse's back and croup, being careful not to kick him.

5. Ease down into the saddle; avoid punishing or frightening the horse by suddenly dropping the entire weight of the body into the saddle. Then shove the right foot into the right stirrup without looking down. Adjust both stirrups under the balls of the feet, and, simultaneously, gather the reins. Hold the reins as indicated in the section entitled "Holding the Reins."

6. Sit easily in the saddle, be alert and keep the head up, and allow the legs to hang comfortably with the heels well down and the toes turned out slightly. This position permits proper leg contact with the horse and a more secure seat.

7. Essentially, correct *dismounting* is just the reverse of mounting. In succession, the rider should carefully gather the reins in the left hand, place the left hand on the horse's withers and the right hand on the pommel of the saddle, stand up in the stirrups, kick the right foot free from the stirrup, transfer the weight to the left foot as the right leg is swung backward across the horse's back and croup, shift the right hand to the cantle of the saddle (or in Western riding, grasp the horn with the right hand), descend to the ground, and remove the left foot from the stirrup.

Another accepted way of dismounting from the English saddle consists in removing the left foot from the stirrup and sliding down with relaxed knees. The rider will never get hung in the stirrups when dismounting in this manner and, small children can get off a horse easily and without assistance.

From the above outline the novice should not gain the impression that in mounting and dismounting each step is so distinct and different as to be marked by intermittent pauses. Rather, when properly executed, mounting or dismounting is a series of rhythmic movements,

① Mount from left or "near" side, gather
reins in left hand, and place left hand
on or just in front of withers.

② Turn stirrup iron one-quarter turn, steady stirrup
with right hand and shove left foot into it.

③ Hop off the right foot, swing around to face the horse, grasp
the cantle (horn in western riding) with right hand, and
spring upward until standing position is reached.

④ Lean on left arm, shift right hand from cantle to
pommel (usually right-hand side of pommel) of
saddle; then swing extended right leg over
horse's back and croup.

and the entire operation is done so smoothly and gracefully that it
is difficult to discern where one stage ends and the next one begins.

HOLDING THE REINS

The rider may hold the reins either in the left hand alone or in
both hands. In Western riding, only one hand, usually the left, holds
the reins.

When holding the reins with both hands—as is usual in show-
ring riding and training—toss the "bight" (ends) of the reins to the

(5) Ease down into the saddle; then shove right foot into right stirrup without looking down.

(6) Sit easily, be alert and keep head up, and allow legs to hang comfortably with heels well down and toes turned out slightly.

(7) Dismounting - Gather reins in left hand, place left hand on horse's withers and right hand on pommel, stand up in the stirrups. Then proceed as instructed in point number 7 of the narrative.

Fig. 16-13. Diagrams showing the steps in mounting and dismounting a horse. (Drawing by artist Steve Allured, based on photos made especially for this book by Mrs. Fern P. Bittner, Instructor in Horsemanship, Lindenwood College, St. Charles, Mo.)

right (off) side of the horse's neck; in hunting and jumping, toss the bight to the left.

When holding the reins in one hand, the left for example—as in English style, cross country riding, or in Western riding—the bight should fall to the left side of the horse's neck and the right hand should be dropped loosely down the side or placed comfortably on the thigh of the right leg. The free hand should never be placed on the pommel of an English saddle or on the pommel or horn of a Western saddle.

Figures 16-14 and 16-15 illustrate better than words the correct methods of holding the reins.

Fig. 16-14. In Western reining, (1) only one hand can be used and hands cannot be changed, and (2) the hand is to be around the reins (as shown in the left and center drawings above). When using split reins, one finger between the reins is permitted (as shown in the right drawing above). (Drawings by Dennis Gadberry)

Methods of Holding the Reins English Style

DOUBLE - REIN BRIDLE

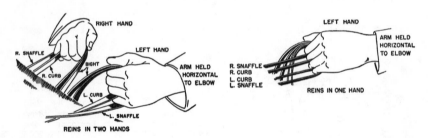

SINGLE - REIN BRIDLE

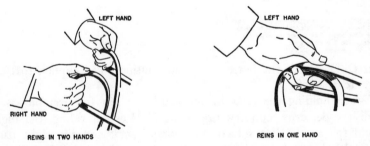

Fig. 16-15. Holding the reins English style: Top, double-rein bridle; bottom, single-rein bridle. (Courtesy, Washington State University)

In no case should the rein pressure be more vigorous than absolutely necessary, nor should the reins be used as a means of staying on the horse. A horse's mouth is tender, but it can be toughened by unnecessary roughness. Good hands appear to be in proper rhythm with the head of the horse. Beginners are likely to let the hands bob too much, thus jerking the horse's mouth unnecessarily and using the reins as a means of "hanging on" the horse. The desired "light hands" exist when a light feeling extends to the horse's mouth via the reins.

THE SEAT

As in any type of sport, correct riding must include rhythm and balance. The rider's movements must be in complete harmony with the horse's movements, for this assures greater security of the rider and freedom of action of the horse.

The balanced seat may be defined as that position of the mounted rider that requires the minimum of muscular effort to remain in the saddle and which interferes least with the horse's movements and equilibrium. In essence, it means that the rider must be "with the horse," rather than ahead of or behind him. When a balanced seat is maintained, the center of gravity of the rider is directly over the center of gravity of the horse. With the proper seat, the minimum use of the aids will be necessary to get immediate and correct response from the horse at any gait.

The balanced seat is obtained largely through shifting the point of balance of the upper body from the hips up; the knees, legs, ankles, and to a great extent the thighs remain in fixed position. Thus, the degree of forward inclination of the upper body will vary according to the speed and gait of the horse; but always the rider should remain in balance over his base of support. The eyes, chin, and chest are lifted, thus permitting clear vision ahead and normal posture of the back. It must also be remembered that the greater the speed and the inclination of the body forward, the shorter the stirrups. The jockey, therefore, rides his mount with very short stirrups and reins and a pronounced forward position. He rises out of his saddle and supports himself almost entirely with the stirrups, knees, and legs. In steeplechasing, the position of the rider is less extreme than in flat racing; for in this type of riding, it is necessary to combine speed with security.

From what has been said, it can be readily understood that there are different seats or positions for different styles of riding. Fashion,

Fig. 16-16. Correct show seat and riding attire for a three-gaited horse. (Drawing by Steve Allured; based on illustrations provided especially for this book by Mrs. Claud H. Drew, Columbia, Mo.)

Fig. 16-17. Correct show seat and riding attire for a five-gaited horse. (Drawing by Steve Allured; based on illustrations provided especially for this book by Mrs. Claud H. Drew, Columbia, Mo.)

particularly in the show-ring, also decrees that certain form be followed.

When riding a three- or five-gaited horse, at all gaits and either on the bridle path or in the show-ring, the rider assumes the show or park seat—sitting erect and well back in the saddle (leaving a space of at least a hand's breadth between the back of his jodhpurs and the cantle). The ball of the foot rests directly over the stirrup iron; knees are in; heels are lower than the toes; and the hands and reins are in such position that the horse will carry his head high and his neck arched. In this position, the body is easily erect and balanced on a base consisting of seat, thighs, knees, and stirrups; the chest is high and just forward of the true vertical; and the back is hollow, the waist relaxed, the head erect, and the shoulders square. Figures 16-16 through 16-18 show the correct seat and riding attire for a three-gaited horse, a five-gaited horse, and a Plantation Walking Horse, respectively.

Fig. 16-18. Correct show seat and riding attire at the running walk. (Drawing by Steve Allured; based on illustrations provided especially for this book by Mrs. Claud H. Drew, Columbia, Mo.)

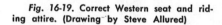

Fig. 16-19. Correct Western seat and riding attire. (Drawing by Steve Allured)

When using a stock saddle and riding Western style, the rider should sit straight, keep the legs fairly straight—or bent slightly forward at the knees—and rest the balls of the feet on the stirrup treads with the heels down. The left hand with the reins should be carried in a relaxed manner slightly above and ahead of the horn. The right hand should be placed on the thigh, or it may be dropped loosely down the side, or held about waist high without resting it on anything. In cutting horses or in barrel racing, the left hand may rest on the saddle horn. "Sitting" the saddle is required at all gaits. Neither posting the trot (jog) nor standing in the stirrups at the trot or gallop (lope) is accepted in Western style riding. Because speed and agility are frequently required of stock horses, a firm seat and superior balance are important. Figure 16-19 shows the correct western seat and riding attire.

In riding hunters (including cross country riding) and jumpers, the stirrups are shortened; the foot is shot home farther than when working at slower gaits (but with some portion of the ball of the foot still resting on the stirrup, and with the heel slightly down); the upper part of the rider's body is thrust forward, giving the "forward

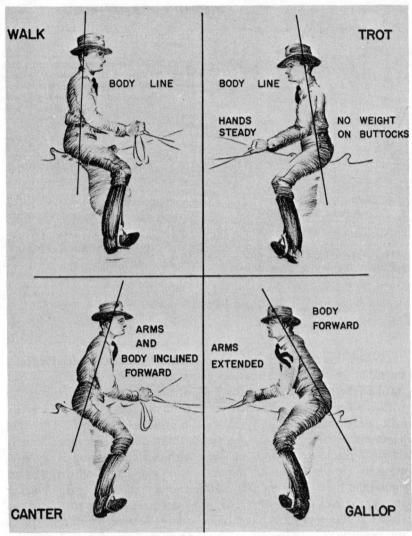

WALK

BODY   LINE

TROT

BODY   LINE

HANDS
STEADY

NO   WEIGHT
ON   BUTTOCKS

ARMS
AND
BODY INCLINED
FORWARD

BODY
FORWARD

ARMS
EXTENDED

CANTER

GALLOP

Fig. 16-20. The correct saddle position for hunting and jumping. Note the position for the walk, the trot, the canter, and the gallop.

seat"; and a comparatively loose rein is kept. The higher the jumps are, the shorter the stirrups should be and the more pronounced the forward inclination of the body. Figure 16-20 shows the correct saddle position for hunting and jumping.

Most polo players prefer to use medium-length stirrups, with feet shot home in the stirrups. This permits a good grip when turning at full speed. The stirrups are also sufficiently short to allow the player to stand up in the stirrup irons when making a long reach for the ball.

Each of these styles of riding differs in appearance, but the end result is the same—balanced riding. An accomplished horseman or horsewoman can and does change the seat to meet the style of riding.

PUTTING THE HORSE IN MOTION

After the rider is properly mounted, he is ready to put the horse in motion. This is accomplished by means of "the aids," which are really the only mutual language between the horse and rider.

The Natural Aids

The natural aids to retaining equilibrium and controlling the horse's movements are the legs, the hands and reins, the weight of the rider, and the voice. When necessary, these may be assisted by the artificial aids: spurs and crop. For a finished performance, all of the natural aids must be invoked in unison, and the artificial aids must be used sparingly if at all.

ACTION OF THE LEGS

The rider's legs are used primarily for the purposes of producing impulsion (forward movement) and increasing the gait. These results are obtained by a simple pressure on the horse by the inner calf muscles of the rider. Should this prove inadequate, the use of spurs or the whip may be resorted to. One of the rider's legs may be used with greater force than the other, thus displacing the horse's hind quarters laterally to prevent it from side stepping, to straighten it, or to change direction in a cramped space.

ACTION OF THE REINS

The reins are an intermediary between the rider and the mount; they afford direct contact between the hands and the horse's mouth. The reins regulate the impulsion—slowing, stopping, or backing the horse. The reins, acting through the mouth and the neck, are also used

to change direction of travel or to turn the horse to either the right
or the left.

ACTION OF THE WEIGHT

By shifting the position of his body from the hips up—a weight
of approximately one hundred pounds in the average person—the
rider can contribute materially to variations in the balance of the
horse. When moving, stopping, or turning, the rider may facilitate
and hasten the obedience of the mount by slightly displacing his
weight in the direction of desired movement.

The Artificial Aids

Ingenious man has devised many artificial aids which, when judiciously
used by an experienced horseman, may supplement effectively the
natural aids. In addition to the whip and spur, the following equipment may be listed under this category: longeing whip, link straps,
martingales, nosebands, various types of reins, and innumerable types
of bits.

Such artificial aids should be used sparingly—particularly the
spur and whip. Perhaps for the most part, they should be used only
when there has been disobedience to the natural aids.

Starting

In starting the horse, the rider should simultaneously invoke the use
of the natural aids. He should slightly tighten the reins to awake the
mount to attention, bring slight pressure with the inner calf muscles,
and incline the body forward. Finally, as a last resort, he may use judiciously one or more of the artificial aids.

Stopping

The rider stops the horse by pulling back on the reins in slow and repeated movements, by releasing the pressure the instant the animal
shows signs of obedience, and by repeating the action as often as
necessary to bring him to a dead stop. At the same time, the rider,
without standing up, puts his weight evenly into both stirrups and
leans slightly backward.

Turning

In turning, the rider must pull the rein on the side toward which it is desired that the horse shall go; at the same time he must slacken off the pressure on the opposite side. Simultaneously, more weight is shifted to the stirrup on the side of the turn. Adequate rein pressure should be applied, but it is not necessary to jerk or pull hard.

Executing the Gaits

After the rider has mastered the art of starting, stopping, and turning the mount, attention may be given to the gaits. The amateur had best use only the three natural gaits: the walk, trot, and canter. A description of these gaits, together with additional gaits and defects in the way of going, is found in Chapter 7. Knowledge of the different gaits should be mastered before one attempts to execute them.

THE WALK

Before trying the faster gaits, it is wise that the beginner first "learn to walk." The balanced seat and correct posture must be mastered. The back should be erect, but the waist should be supple. Often it is helpful to have the beginner walk the horse with the feet out of the stirrups while keeping the knee and hip joints relaxed, the shoulders square, the head back, the legs down, and the ankles relaxed.

THE TROT

Trotting is the roughest of all gaits to the beginner, but correct riding at this gait must be acquired. There are two ways of riding at the trot: the "close" or "cowboy seat," in which the rider remains firmly seated in the saddle at all times; and the "posting seat," in which the rider's body goes slightly up in the air in unison with the horse.

The beginner should not attempt to fast trot or to post until the balanced seat has been thoroughly mastered at the slow trot. Moreover, the slow trot (about six miles per hour) is not, as a rule, ridden by posting, nor do riders post when riding Western. The "posting seat" is used by most park-riding civilians and horse-show folks and by practically all cavalry services.

Posting the Trot

Posting may be described as the rising and descending of the rider with the rhythm of the trot. This action reduces the shock or jar of the trot for both horse and rider. Posting is accomplished by rising easily in the saddle in rhythm at one beat, of the two-beat trot, and settling back at the next beat. In posting, the rider inclines the upper part of the body slightly forward (while at the same time keeping the shoulders back, the chin up, and the legs under the body, with the heels down); supports himself by pressing the knees inward against the horse; and then permits his body to be impelled upward by the thrust of one of the hind legs (the left, for example). The rider remains up during the stride of the other hind leg (the right) and returns the seat nearly to the saddle only to be impelled upward again by the next thrust of the left hind leg. Sitting back in the saddle each time the right forefoot strikes the ground is known as posting on the right diagonal; whereas returning to the saddle when the left fore strikes the ground is known as posting on the left diagonal.

Some competent and experienced equitation instructors[4] report that they prefer to teach posting the correct diagonal as follows:

1. Watch the horse's shoulder and knee.

2. Rise in the saddle as the shoulder and knee of the outside foreleg come forward. The rider will then be posting to the outside foreleg or the one nearest the rail.

To change diagonals, the rider should learn to sit one or three or five beats of the trot—preferably one beat; to sit even beats puts the rider back where he was.

The rider should frequently alternate the diagonals used in posting as this makes for greater ease on the horse. When riding in a ring, the rider should post on the outside diagonal so that the work of the hind quarters will be equalized. For correct posting, the stirrups should be sufficiently short to permit the rider to carry most of the weight on the ball of the foot. Only a small portion of the weight should be carried on the inside of the thighs and knees. Correct posting is one of the most difficult phases of riding.

---

[4]This is the system used by Mrs. Claud H. Drew, Columbia, Mo., and Mrs. Fern P. Bittner, Lindenwood College, St. Charles, Mo.—noted equestriennes, instructors, and judges—who very kindly reviewed this book.

THE CANTER

The canter is a slow, restrained gallop. In the show-ring or on the bridle path, this gait is started from the walk rather than from the trot, although some horsemen—especially army personnel—recommend that the canter be demanded from the trot.

The horse is made to canter (1) by drawing his head up and his nose in with the reins, and with the nose held slightly to the opposite direction of the desired lead (thus, the nose should be slightly to the left for a right lead), (2) by shifting the weight of the rider slightly to the front and to the side of the desired lead, and (3) by applying the legs in such a manner as to urge the horse to go forward. When cantering, the rider should stay with the saddle and keep the knees and calves of the legs close to the horse. When cantering in a circular ring, the horse should "lead" or step out with the right forefoot when traveling to the right and with the left forefoot when traveling to the left. A well-trained animal should be capable of and willing to take either lead upon command. Moreover, to avoid tiring the animal, the lead should be shifted at intervals.

THE ADDITIONAL GAITS

In addition to the three natural gaits (walk, trot, and canter) five-gaited horses are expected to take one of the slow gaits—running walk, fox trot, or stepping pace (the stepping pace is the preferred slow gait in the show-ring)—and the rack. The amateur should not attempt to ride the added gaits until the three basic gaits have been mastered.

SOME RULES OF GOOD HORSEMANSHIP

Good riders observe the following rules:

1. Approach a horse from his left. Never walk or stand behind a horse unannounced; let him know that you are there by speaking to and placing your hand on him. Otherwise, you may get kicked.

2. Pet a horse by first placing your hand on his shoulder or neck. Do not dab at the end of his nose.

3. Grasp the reins close to the bit on the left side when leading a horse.

4. Walk the horse to and from the stable; this prevents him from running home and from refusing to leave the stable.

5. See that the saddle blanket, numnah, pad, or corona is clean and free of dried sweat, hair, caked dirt, or any rough places—any of which will cause a sore back.

6. Check the saddle and bridle (or hackamore) before mounting. The saddle should fit and be placed just back of the withers; it should not bear down on or rub the withers, nor should it be placed too far back. The girth should be fastened snugly and should not be too close to the forelegs. Be sure that the bridle (or hackamore) fits comfortably and that the curb chain or strap is flat in the chin groove and fastened correctly.

7. Mount and dismount from the left side. Make the horse stand until the rider is properly seated in the saddle or has dismounted.

8. Assume the correct seat for the style of riding intended.

9. Retain the proper tension on the reins; avoid either tight or dangling reins.

10. Keep the hands and voice quiet when handling your horse. Avoid "clacking" to the horse, loud laughing or screaming (never scream—no matter how excited or frightened you may be; it will only make matters worse), and slapping him with the ends of the reins; such things are unnecessary and in poor taste.

11. Warm up the horse gradually; walk him first, then jog him slowly.

12. Keep to the right side of the road except when passing, and never allow your horse to wander all over the road. Give right-of-way courteously.

13. Walk the horse across bridges, through underpasses, and over pavements and slippery roads.

14. Slow down when making a sharp turn.

15. Walk the horse when going up or down hill; running may injure his legs and wind. Do not race horses; when so handled, they form bad habits and may get out of control.

16. Keep the horse moving when a car passes. If you stop, he may act up or back into the passing vehicle.

17. Anticipate such distractions as cars, stones, paper, trees, bridges, noises, dogs, children, etc.; in other words, think ahead of your horse.

18. Vary the gaits; and do not force the horse to take a rapid gait—canter, rack, or trot—for more than a half mile at a time without allowing a breathing spell in the interim.

19. Keep the horse under control at all times. If you are riding a runaway horse, try to stop him by sawing the bit back and forth in

his mouth so as to break (a) his hold on the bit and (b) his stride; if in an open space, pull one rein hard enough to force him to circle.

20. Practice firmness with the horse and make him obey your wishes; he will have more respect for you. At the same time, love and understand him and he will reward you with the finest friendship and the grandest sport.

21. Never lose your temper and jerk a horse; a bad-tempered person never makes for a good-tempered horse.

22. Lean forward and loosen the reins if a horse rears. If you lean back and pull, the horse may fall over backwards.

23. Pull up the reins of a bucking horse; keep his head up.

24. Loosen the reins and urge the horse forward with your legs if he starts backing. Don't hold the reins too tightly when the horse is standing still.

25. Bring the horse in cool; walk him at the end of the ride.

26. Do not allow the horse to gorge on water when he is hot; water a warm horse slowly—just a few swallows at a time.

27. Do not turn the horse loose at the stall entrance. Walk into the stall with him, turn him around, so that he is facing the door, then depart. In a tie stall, make certain that the horse is tied securely with proper length rope.

28. Groom the horse thoroughly after each ride.

29. Wash the bit off carefully before it is hung in the tack room; remove hair and sweat from the saddle and girth before putting them on the rack; and wash all leather equipment with saddle soap at frequent intervals, thereby preserving the leather and keeping it pliable.

In addition to observing the above rules, good riders show consideration for other riders by observing the following additional practices—whether on the bridle path or on the trail, in the show-ring, or under other circumstances:

1. Keep abreast (about five feet apart), or keep a full horse's length behind other mounts, to prevent kicking.

2. Never dash up to another horse or group of horses at a gallop; to do so invites injury to yourself and the horses.

3. Never rush past riders who are proceeding at a slower gait; this may startle both horses and riders and cause an accident. Instead, approach slowly and pass cautiously on the left side.

4. Wait quietly when one person has to dismount, as when closing a gate. Do not run off and leave that person.

5. Never race after a mounted runaway horse—to do so will only

make him run faster; instead, if possible, another rider should circle and come up in front of him. In case a rider is thrown, stop the other horses and keep quiet; generally the loose horse will return to the group where he may be caught.

6. Do not trespass on private property.

7. Leave gates the way you found them; otherwise, livestock may get out.

HORSE-DRAWN VEHICLES

Prior to the advent of improved roads and automobiles, the horse was used to draw vehicles, most of which originally evolved to meet practical needs, following which they were embellished to meet in-

Table 16-2

APPROPRIATE HORSE-DRAWN VEHICLES

Use	Breed	Appropriate Vehicle	Comments
Racing	Standardbred Shetland	Sulky; a light vehicle with bicycle wheels. **Sulky** 	The pneumatic tire racing sulky was first introduced in 1892.
Roadster: Horses	Standardbred, pre-dominately; al-though other breeds may be used.	Cart or bike; buggy or road wagon. 	The sport of showing roadsters originated in the horse and bug-gy era, to satisfy the desire to own an attractive horse that possessed the necessary speed to pass any of his rivals. In the show-ring, roadsters may be shown hitched (1) to sulky or (2) to buggy or road wagon; the latter may be singly or in pairs. Roadster vehicles must be at-tractive and light, but strong. Roadster horses are also shown under saddle.
Ponies		Same as above.	

(Continued)

Table 16-2 (Continued)

Use	Breed	Appropriate Vehicle	Comments
Hackney (or heavy harness horses): Horses Ponies		Viceroy, miniature side rail buggy of type used for fine harness horses, or gig. Tandem Hackneys may be shown with either a two- or four-wheeled vehicle; a gig or viceroy.	The heavy leather used on these animals was first decreed by fashion in England, where it stemmed from the idea that to drive handsomely one had to drive heavily. In this country, heavy harness horses are reminiscent of the Gay Nineties, when bob-tailed hackneys hitched to high seated rigs made a dashing picture as they pranced down the avenue. Vehicles for hackneys must be of heavy construction, elegant design, and devoid of shiny parts (the latter tends to blind spectators).
Fine Harness: Horses Ponies	American Saddle Horses, predominately; although other breeds are so used.	Preferably a small side rail buggy with four wire wheels, but without a top. Same as above.	A fine harness horse is exactly what the name implies—a fine horse presented in fine harness. The entire ensemble is elegant and represents the ultimate in grace and charm.
Pleasure Driving	Any Breed	Any two-wheeled or four-wheeled vehicle. 	
Breaking or Training Cart	Any Breed	Two-wheeled training cart. 	When training green horses, two-wheeled training carts should be used, because (1) they are strong and (2) they will not tip over easily.

dividual tastes. There was the dignified family *Carriage* with a fringe on top; the *Buckboard* with its jump seat—the pick-up truck of grand-father's time; the *Governess Cart,* with its door at the rear and two seats facing each other; the high two-wheeled *Dog Cart,* for trans-porting hounds to the hunt; the high seated *Rig* of the society matron;

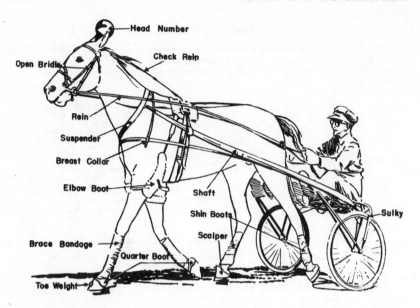

Fig. 16-21. Trotter's harness and rigging. (Courtesy, The United States Trotting Association)

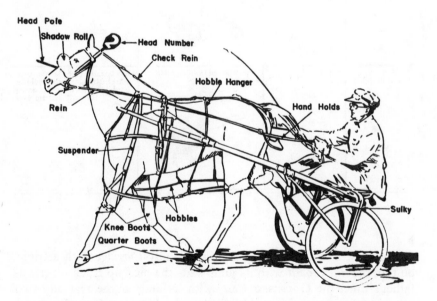

Fig. 16-22. Pacer's harness and rigging. (Courtesy, The United States Trotting Association)

the old fashioned top *Buggy* of the country doctor; and the *Roadster* of the young gallant. Even hitches evolved for practical reasons. Tandem driving, for example, was originated by the hunting men of Old England. Wishing to spare their hunting mount as they traveled to and from the meet, these ingenious huntsmen devised the method of driving him ahead; where he trotted between slack traces, while the horse to the rear did all of the work.

It is noteworthy, therefore, that most horse vehicles of today are of historical significance; indeed, they are reminiscent of the horse and buggy era.

Harness and Rigging for Trotters and Pacers

It is not within the scope of this book to cover all types and parts of harness. But some conception of the subject may be obtained by studying Figures 16-21 and 16-22, showing the standard harness and rigging used on trotters and pacers.

HOW TO CLEAN AND CARE FOR TACK

As used herein, tack, gear, and equipment embrace all articles used on, or attached to, riding and driving horses.

Good tack, gear, and equipment are expensive; hence, they merit good care. If properly cared for, they will last for years.

Ideally, each article should be cleaned thoroughly every time it is used on the horse. However, the owner and/or caretaker of pleasure horses may not be able to devote this amount of time. For the busy person, therefore, it is recommended that the vital parts be cleaned following each use—that the bottom of the saddle and the inside of the bridle be cleaned, that the bit be washed, and that the pad or blanket (if used) be brushed after drying out and before re-using. Then a thorough cleaning should be administered to all tack and equipment once each week.

The tack, gear, and equipment used on race and show horses, where maximum performance is all-important, should be thoroughly cleaned after each usage.

The general principles presented in the accompanying discussion also apply to the equipment used on race or show horses, with the following changes:

Do not use soap (or cream) on leather boots used on horses; it tends to deteriorate the stitching and catch a film of dirt. Instead, brush (preferably with a circular brush) to eliminate the sweat, dirt, and grime; wipe dry with a cloth; rub in petroleum jelly or liquid preservative; and, before using, dust with talcum powder or corn starch, either of which will absorb moisture and smooth out minor rough or chafing spots.

Why Clean

Good tack is expensive. Proper cleaning will do the following:

1. Extend the life of leather and metal.
2. Impart softness and pliability to leather.
3. Make for comfort to the horse. It will lessen saddle and harness sores from the use of dirty, crusted, and stiff leather; and avoid irritation and infection from a rusty, moldy, and dirty bit.
4. Assure that minor tack defects will be noticed and repaired promptly, before they become serious.
5. Protect the user, by minimizing the breaking of a rein or line, girth, girth straps, stirrup leathers, or other vital parts.
6. Impart pride and pleasure in the ownership and use of equipment. Your equipment, your horse, and you will look smart and feel smart.

Cleaning Equipment

The following items of cleaning equipment are commonly used:

1. A saddle rack on which to rest the saddle when it's being cleaned. Preferably, the rack should be designed so that it will also hold the saddle upside down, to facilitate cleaning the underside as well as the top.
2. A bridle rack, peg, or hook on which to hang the bridle for cleaning.
3. A harness rack for cleaning (if you have harness).
4. A bucket for warm water.
5. Three sponges, preferably (although one sponge will suffice if rinsed properly):
   a. One for washing—for cleaning off sweat, dirt, mud, etc.
   b. The second for applying leather preservative or glycerine soap.

    c. The third for occasional application of neatsfoot or other similar oil.
6. A chamois cloth for drying off leather.
7. Cheese cloth (about a yard) for applying metal polish.
8. A flannel rag for polishing metal.

Cleaning Materials

The usual cleaning materials are:
1. Saddle soap, or a bar of castile soap, for cleaning.
2. A leather preservative, or bar of glycerine soap, for finishing.
3. Neatsfoot oil.
4. Metal polish.
5. Petroleum jelly.

Order of Cleaning

To assure that all tack and all parts are cleaned (that none is overlooked), it is important that some logical, practical, and regular order be followed, automatically and routinely. Any order that accomplishes this purpose will be satisfactory.

The following is suggested for articles used in riding, and is perhaps most common:
1. Clean the saddle:
    a. Remove and clean girth.
    b. Clean underside of saddle.
    c. Get topside of saddle.
    d. Clean nearside (left).
    e. Clean offside (right).
2. Clean the bridle.
3. Clean the martingale, etc. if used.
4. If a saddle pad or blanket is used, brush it after it has dried.
A similar procedure should be used for articles used in driving.

How to Do It

Once a week, wash with saddle soap or with castile soap as described and apply light neatsfoot oil or other leather dressing to all leather parts. Avoid excess oil, which will darken new leather and soil clothing.

Fig. 16-23. Cleaning the saddle. (Courtesy, Western Horseman, Colorado Springs, Colo.)

THE SADDLE

1. Remove girth; clean as described under point 3 below.
2. Turn saddle upside down.
3. Wash panel (that part of saddle in contact with horse's back) and gullet (underside center). With sponge wetted in warm water and wrung out, apply saddle soap to leather, and rub to work up a stiff lather to remove sweat and dirt before it hardens. The amount of dirt will determine how much soap, water, and elbow grease are necessary.
4. Wash rest of saddle in same manner, following the order given under "Order of Cleaning."
5. Dry entire saddle with chamois.
6. Take second sponge, dampen slightly, and apply leather preservative or glycerine soap without suds to all parts of saddle, following the order given.

THE BRIDLE

Wash the bit in warm water.

On the leather part, follow exactly the same procedure given for the saddle; wash thoroughly with warm water and saddle soap or castile soap, dry with chamois, and apply either preservative or glycerine soap with slightly damp sponge.

Using cheese cloth, apply metal polish to all metal parts; then polish with flannel. If the bridle is not to be used for a time, clean and dry the bit, and apply a light coat of petroleum jelly, to prevent pitting or rusting.

THE HARNESS

Follow the same procedure as given for saddle and bridle.

BLANKETS AND PADS

Hang up or spread out to dry; then brush off hair and dried sweat.

VEHICLES

Carts, sulkys, buckboards, and viceroys should be kept clean at all times. If vehicles are to be used in the show-ring, they should be washed a few hours ahead. Then apply metal polish to chrome, and wipe enamel wood finish with soft, dry flannel. Upholstering should be brushed, vacuumed, or washed—according to the material.

After Cleaning

After cleaning, tack should be handled as follows:

1. Store in a cool, dry place.
2. Hang the bridle on its rack, neatly and so that all parts drape naturally without bending.
3. Place the saddle on its rack.
4. Hang the harness on a rack.
5. Cover the saddle, bridle, and harness.
6. Protect vehicles from the weather, and use dust covers.

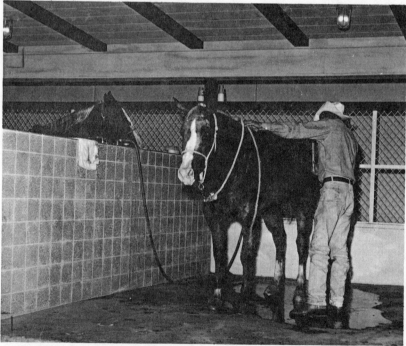

Fig. 16-24. Wash stall in Rex Cauble's Cutter Bill Championship Arena, Denton, Texas, where horses may be washed after a workout. When washing, use lukewarm water and a mild soap, rinse thoroughly with cool water, then keep the horse out of drafts while rubbing him dry with a clean cloth. Except for the mane and tail, it is usually not advisable to wash a horse within two weeks of a show because washing removes the natural oil. (Courtesy, Roy Davis, Editor, *Quarter Horse Journal*)

Table 16-3

GROOMING EQUIPMENT AND HOW TO USE IT

Article	What It Is: How to Use It	Used for	Grooming Procedure: How to Do It
Hoof Pick		To clean out the feet.	To assure that the horse will be groomed thoroughly and that no body parts will be missed, follow a definite order. This may differ according to individual preference, but the following procedure is most common: 1. *Clean out the feet.*—Use the hoof pick. Work from the heel toward the toe. Clean thoroughly the depressions between the frog and the bars. Inspect for thrush and loose shoes.
Curry Comb (Rubber or metal)	Use gently and in small circles, rather than with pressure and in long strokes. Do not use the metal curry comb below the knees or hocks, about the head, or over bony predominences. Nor should it be used on horses that have been clipped recently, or that have a thin coat of hair.	To groom horses that have long thick coats. To remove caked mud. To loosen matted scurf and dirt in the hair. To clean the brush.	2. *Groom the body.*—Hold the curry comb in the right hand and the brush in the left hand, and proceed as follows: a. Start with the left side. b. Follow this order: the neck, breast, withers, shoulders, foreleg down to the knee, back, side, belly, croup, and hind legs down to the hock. Then brush from the knee and hock down toward the hoofs. At frequent intervals, clean the dust and hair from the brush with the curry comb, and knock the curry comb against your heel or the back of the brush to free it from dirt. Curry gently, but brush vigorously. Brush the hair in the direction of its natural lie. Brush with care in the regions of the flanks, between the fore and hind legs, at the point of the elbows, and in the fetlocks. After grooming the left side, transfer the brush to the right hand and the curry comb to the left hand; then groom the right side in the same order as described above.
Body Brush	The body brush is the principal tool used for grooming.	To brush the entire body.	
Dandy Brush	The dandy brush is made of stiff fiber usually about 2 inches in length.	To remove light dirt from the skin. To brush the mane & tail.	3. *Brush the head; comb and brush the mane and tail.*—Use the body brush on the head. Groom the mane and tail as follows: a. Brush downward, using either the body brush or the dandy brush. b. Clean the tail by: (1) Brushing upward, a few strands of hair at a time; or by (2) Picking or separating out a few hairs at a time by hand. (3) Occasionally, washing with warm water and soap.
Mane & Tail Comb	Use as directed in last column.	To comb out matted mane and tail.	
Sweat Scraper		To remove excess perspriation from heated, wet, and sweating animals.	
Grooming Cloth	The grooming cloth can be made from old toweling or blankets. It should be about 18 to 24 inches square.	To remove dirt and dust from the coat. To wipe out the eyes, ears, nostrils, lips, & dock. To give the coat a final sheen or polish. To dry or ruffle the coat before brushing.	4. *Wipe with the grooming cloth.*—Use the grooming cloth to: a. Wipe about the ears, face, eyes, nostril, lips, sheath, and dock, and b. Give a final polish to the coat. 5. *Check the grooming.*—Pass the fingertips against the natural lie of the hair. If the coat and skin are not clean, the fingers will be dirtied and gray lines will show on the coat where the fingers passed. Also inspect the ears, face, eyes, nostrils, lip, sheath, and dock. 6. *Wash and disinfect grooming equipment.*—Wash with soap and warm water often enough to keep clean. Disinfect as necessary as precaution against the spread of diseases.

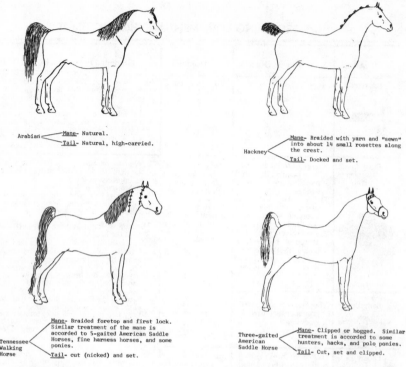

Fig. 16-25. "Hair cuts" and "hair do's" common to breeds and uses of horses. (Drawings by Dennis Gadberry)

GROOMING

Proper grooming is necessary to (1) make and keep the horse attractive, and (2) maintain good health and condition. Grooming cleans the hair, keeps the skin functioning naturally, lessens skin diseases and parasites, and improves the condition and fitness of the muscles.

Wild horses groomed themselves by rolling and taking dust baths.

How to Groom a Horse

Grooming should be rapid and thorough, but not so rough or severe as to cause irritation, either to the horse's skin or temper.

Horses that are stabled or in small corrals should be groomed thoroughly at least once daily. Those that are worked or exercised should be groomed both before leaving the stable and immediately upon their

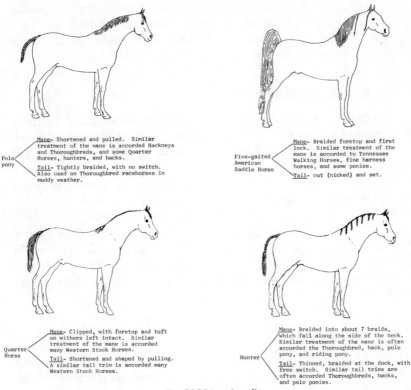

Polo pony

Mane- Shortened and pulled. Similar treatment of the mane is accorded Hackneys and Thoroughbreds, and some Quarter Horses, hunters, and hacks.

Tail- Tightly braided, with no switch. Also used on Thoroughbred racehorses in muddy weather.

Five-gaited American Saddle Horse

Mane- Braided foretop and first lock. Similar treatment of the mane is accorded to Tennessee Walking Horses, fine harness horses, and some ponies.

Tail- cut (nicked) and set.

Quarter Horse

Mane- Clipped, with foretop and tuft on withers left intact. Similar treatment of the mane is accorded many Western Stock Horses.

Tail- Shortened and shaped by pulling. A similar tail trim is accorded many Western Stock Horses.

Hunter

Mane- Braided into about 7 braids, which fall along the side of the neck. Similar treatment of the mane is often accorded the Thoroughbred, hack, polo pony, and riding pony.

Tail- Thinned, braided at the dock, with free switch. Similar tail trims are often accorded Thoroughbreds, hacks, and polo ponies.

Fig. 16-25 (continued)

return. Heated, wet, or sweating animals should be handled as follows:

1. Remove the equipment as fast as possible; wipe it off, and put it away.

2. Remove excess perspiration with a sweat scraper; then rub briskly with a grooming or drying cloth to dry the coat partially.

3. Blanket and walk the horse until cool.

4. Allow a couple of swallows of water every few minutes while cooling out.

The needed articles of grooming equipment, and instructions on how to use them, are given in Table 16-3.

In addition to the routine grooming, horses should be sharpened up by shearing or clipping at such intervals as necessary.

Custom decrees certain breed differences in "hair cuts" and "hair do's." These are illustrated in Figure 16-25.

Clipping and shearing may be done as follows:

1. *Protect inside of ears.*—Place a wad of cotton in the ears, to cut down on noise from clippers and prevent hair from falling into ears.

2. *Clip long hairs.*—Remove long hairs from about the head, the inside of the ears, on the jaw, and around the fetlocks.

SHOWING HORSES

There is no higher artistic accomplishment than that of breeding and showing a champion horse—an animal representing an ideal which has been produced through intelligent breeding and then trained and fitted to the height of perfection. Those who achieve such distinction are not artists whose materials are the colors, the brush, and the canvas of the painter; nor artists whose tools are the clay and the marble of the sculptor—but artists whose materials are the "green pastures and the still waters" that have inspired musicians to capture their beauty in pastoral symphonies, and painters to reproduce their splendor in landscape designs; artists whose materials are the living flesh and blood of animals molded to perfection through heredity and environment.

Showing at Halter[5]

Many horsemen lack knowledge of the correct showing technique for breeding classes, even though they may be quite professional in exhibiting in performance classes.

The guiding principles adhered to by most successful horsemen when showing at halter are:

1. Train the horse early.
2. Groom the horse thoroughly.
3. Dress neatly for the occasion.
4. Enter the ring promptly and in tandem order when the class is called; and line up at the location requested by the ringmaster or the judge, or, if directed, continue to move around the ring in tandem order.
5. Stand the horse squarely on all four feet, and with the forefeet on higher ground than the hind feet. The standing position of the

---

[5]Breeding classes are shown "in hand," which means that they are exhibited at the halter preferably, or when wearing a bridle. The halter should be clean, properly adjusted, and fitted with a fresh looking leather or rope lead. If the horse is shown when wearing a bridle, the exhibitor should avoid jerking on the reins so vigorously that injury will be inflicted on the mouth.

horse should vary according to the breed; for example, Arabians are not stretched, whereas American Saddlers are stood with their front legs straight under them and their hind legs back slightly. Other breeds are generally stood in a slightly stretched position; somewhat intermediate between these two examples.

When standing and facing the horse, hold the lead strap or rope in the left hand 10 to 12 inches from the halter ring and in such manner as to encourage a head-up position.

6. Unless the judge requests otherwise, when called upon the horse should first be shown at the walk and then at the trot. To move the horse, proceed as follows:

a. Either (1) reduce the length of the lead strap or rope by a series of "figure 8" folds or by coils, held in the right hand, or (2) hold the upper part of the lead strap or rope in the right hand and the lower end (or "figure 8" folded or coiled end) in the left hand, and lead from the left side of the horse. If the horse is well-mannered, give him two to three feet of lead so that he can keep his head, neck, and body in a straight line as he moves forward. But keep the lead taut so that there is continuous contact between the exhibitor and horse. Do not look back.

b. Smartly and briskly move the horse forward in a straight line for 50 to 100 feet (as directed), with the head up.

c. Turn to the right; that is, turn the horse away from the exhibitor and walk around the horse (if the horse is turned to the left, he is more apt to step on the exhibitor). Make the turn in as small a space as practical, and as effortless as possible. Old-time draft horsemen, who had no peers in showing to halter, made the horse pivot around the showman.

When showing at the trot, bring the horse to a walk and ease slightly to the left before turning.

d. Show some knee action (by the exhibitor) when exhibiting the horse, without overdoing the matter.

e. Trail with a whip if permitted and/or desired.[6] If it is done, the "trailer" should follow at a proper distance, keep the animal moving in a straight line, avoid getting between the judge and the horse, and always cross over in front of the horse at the turn.

---

[6] Most light horses are given early schooling by trailing with the whip, but custom decrees showing them without this aid.

7. After (a) walking down (about 50 feet) and walking back, and (b) trotting down (about 100 feet) and trotting back, set the horse up with reasonable promptness in front of the judge.[7] Then, after the judge has given a quick inspection, move to the location in the line indicated by the ringmaster or judge (observing the points mentioned in item 5).

8. Keep the horse posed at all times; keep one eye on the judge and the other on the horse.

9. When the judge signals the exhibitor to change positions, back the horse, or, if there is room, turn him to the rear of the line, and approach the new position from behind.

10. Avoid letting the horse kick when in close proximity to other horses.

11. Keep calm, confident, and collected. Remember that the nervous showman creates an unfavorable impression.

12. Work in close partnership with the animal.

13. Be courteous and respect the rights of other exhibitors.

14. Do not stand between the judge and the horse.

15. Be a good sport; win without bragging and lose without squealing.

Showing in Performance Classes

The performance classes for horses are so many and varied that it is not practical to describe them in a book of this type. Instead, the reader is referred to the official Rule Book of the American Horse Shows Association and to the rules printed in the programs of local horse shows.

Selected References

Title of Publication	Author(s)	Publisher
Leg at Each Corner, A	Norman Thelwell	E. P. Dutton & Company, New York, N.Y., 1966.
Horsemanship	M. E. Ensminger	Ext. Bul. 536, Washington State University, Pullman, Wash.

---

[7] In order to save time, the judge may ask that the horses be walked down and trotted back. Such procedure is very proper.

Title of Publication	Author(s)	Publisher
Horsemanship	Mrs. A. W. Jasper	Boy Scouts of America, New Brunswick, N. J., 1958.
Horsemanship	J. M. Kays	4-H Circ. 109, University of Missouri, Columbia, Mo., 1952.
Horsemanship and Horsemastership	Volume I Parts one and two	The Cavalry School, Fort Riley, Kans., 1945.
Horsemanship and Horsemastership	Volume III Part five	The Cavalry School, Fort Riley, Kans., 1945.
Horsemanship and Horsemastership	Edited by Gordon Wright	Doubleday & Company, Inc., Garden City, N. Y., 1962.
Horses and Horsemanship 4-H Horse Program	Federal and State Extension Services	National 4-H Service Committee, Inc., Chicago, Ill., 1965.
Horse Science Handbook, Volume 3	Edited by M. E. Ensminger	Agriservices Foundation, 3699 East Sierra Avenue, Clovis, Calif.
Horse Shows	A. N. Phillips	The Interstate Printers & Publishers, Inc., Danville, Ill., 1956.
"How to Ride a Horse"	*Sports Illustrated* Magazine	May 18 and May 25, 1959.
"Riding Clothes"	*Life* Magazine	May 5, 1947.
Rulebook (Published annually)		The American Horse Shows Association, 40 East 54th St., New York, N. Y.

17

In this chapter . . .

17

Management

GOOD HORSEMEN practice good management. To be sure, horse management practices vary from area to area, according to the size of the enterprise—whether one horse or several are involved—and between horsemen. In a general sort of way, however, the principles of good management are the same under all conditions.

SOME MANAGEMENT PRACTICES

Without attempting to cover all management practices, some facts relative to, and methods of accomplishing, common horse management practices follow.

Marking or Identifying Horses

The method of marking or identifying animals varies according to the class of animals and the objectives sought. Thus, some methods of marking are well adapted to one class of animals but not to another; ear notches, for example, are commonly used for identifying swine, but should not be used for horses. On the western range, marking by branding is primarily a method of establishing ownership.

With a purebred herd of horses, marking is a means of ascertaining ancestry or pedigree. This is particularly important where one person only knows the individuals in a given herd, and, suddenly and without warning, that person is no longer available. Under such circumstances, many a valuable registered horse has been sold as a grade, simply because positive identity could not be established.

In racehorses, an infallible means of identification is necessary in order to prevent "ringers." *A ringer is a horse that is passed off under false identity, with the idea of entering him in a race below his class where he is almost certain to win.* In the early 1920's, the most common camouflage for a ringer was a coat of paint—hence the terms "dark horse" and "horse of another color." Formerly, the ringer's nemesis was rain; today, it is the lip-tattoo system, which must accompany horses of most breeds to every major racing meet.

One of the duties of a steward, through his horse identification assistant, is that of assuring that each starter in a race is actually the horse named in the entry. This is necessary because only a relatively small percentage of the more prominent racehorses are fondly recognized on sight by the public; the vast majority of racehorses are known only by names and past performances.

The Thoroughbred Racing Protective Bureau (TRPB), Inc., Chrysler Building, New York, perfected a lip tattoo so that the member tracks of the Thoroughbred Racing Association (TRA) are able to guarantee to the public the identity of each and every horse running at their tracks. The system consists of tattoo branding, with forgery-proof dies, The Jockey Club serial number (the registry number) under the upper lip of the horse, with a prefix letter added to denote the age of the horse (see Fig. 17-1). The process is both simple and

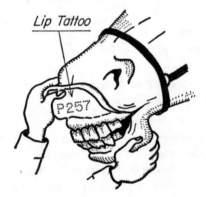

Lip Tattoo

Fig. 17-1. A drawing showing the lip tattoo under the upper lip of a horse. The prefix letter denotes the age of the horse, and the numbers denote The Jockey Club registry number. (Drawing by R. F. Johnson)

painless. It is applied by expert crews of the TRPB to two-year-olds as they come to each TRA track.

Pinkerton's National Detective Agency, The Jockey Club, and others have also developed a method of identifying horses which corresponds to the human system of fingerprinting employed by the FBI and police departments throughout the world. A horse can be identified by its "chestnuts" or "night-eyes"; these consist of a horny growth on

Fig. 17-2. Universal Horse Identification System, showing (1) code card and (2) horse "chestnut." (Courtesy, Pinkerton's National Detective Agency, Inc.)

each of the four legs.[1] Studies reveal (1) that no two chestnuts are exactly alike, and (2) that from the yearling stage on, these chestnuts retain their distinctive sizes and shapes. The chestnuts are photographed, and then classified according to (1) size, and (2) distinctive pattern. In comparison with the lip-tattoo system, it is necessary that a more highly trained person record and use the chestnut system of identification.

The ink and tattoo equipment used by the Thoroughbred Protective Bureau is not available to the public; and "fingerprinting" horse chestnuts is both costly and complex. Also, except as a means of establishing herd ownership on range horses (where all animals in a specific herd are given the owner's registered brand), hot-iron hide brands are seldom used as a means of marking or identifying horses because they tend to damage the appearance of the animal and decrease its saleability.

---

[1]Chestnuts occur on the inside of each front leg above the knee and on the back legs below the hock. In rare instances, a horse lacks a chestnut on one or both hind limbs.

However, the following two methods of individual identification are available for use by horse owners:

1. *The lip tattoo.*—Lip tattoo equipment and ink similar to that used by the Thoroughbred Racing Protective Bureau is manufactured and sold commercially.[2] The manufacturer's step-by-step instructions relative to the use of the Wilmot Tattoo Gun read as follows:

a. After the digits are placed in the head of the tattoo gun, place the gun head with the digits in a dish of antiseptic (such as Zephiran chloride, available at any drug store).

b. Roll and hold upper lip back with fingers; do not place anything back of lip.

c. Wipe upper lip clean with cotton saturated with rubbing alcohol.

d. Shake gun to dry off excess antiseptic.

e. Apply tattoo gun, making sure gun and digits are square with lip. Hold gun rigidly and with sufficient pressure to withstand recoil action of gun.

f. Apply ink and rub into perforations with thumb. Use more ink if bleeding persists. Leave any excess ink on lip.

2. *Cold branding.*—This new and promising method, developed by Dr. Keith Farrell, DVM, U. S. Department of Agriculture staff member stationed at Washington State University, makes use of a super-chilled (by dry ice or liquid nitrogen) copper branding "iron" which is applied to a closely clipped surface, to produce either (a) no hair or "bald brands" on white areas or on white animals, or (b) white hair brands on colored animals. Experimentally, Dr. Farrell has studied a wide range of brand sizes and animals, from very tiny figures on suckling mice to very large figures on game animals. But, to date, most of the trials have been with cattle. It is conjectured that horses may be cold branded under the mane, with brands one to two inches high. Horsemen who have need for some method of individually marking or indentifying horses would do well to follow cold branding experimental studies with care, for the technique appears to be very promising.

Care of the Feet[3]

The value of a horse lies chiefly in its ability to move; hence, good feet

---

[2]The Wilmot Tattoo Gun (patent applied for), along with digits 0-9 ($\frac{3}{8}$" size) and black tattoo ink, may be obtained from Stone Mfg. & Supply Company, 1212 Kansas Avenue, Kansas City, Mo.

[3]This section was authoritatively reviewed by Mr. Don Canfield, the Horse Science School farrier-instructor.

and legs are necessary. The important points in the care of a horse's feet are to keep them clean, prevent them from drying out, trim them so they retain proper shape and length, and shoe them correctly when shoes are needed.

Each day, the feet of horses that are shod, stabled, or used should be cleaned and inspected for loose shoes and thrush.

Thrush is a disease of the foot, caused by a necrotic fungus, and characterized by a pungent odor. It causes a deterioration of tissues in the cleft of the frog or in the junction between the frog and bars. This disease produces lameness and, if not treated, can be serious.

HORSESHOEING

Horseshoeing is a time-honored profession. In the Golden Age of the horse, which extended from the Gay Nineties to the mechanization of American agriculture, every school boy knew and respected the village blacksmith who plied his trade "under the spreading chestnut tree."

It is not necessary that horse owners and managers be expert farriers. Yet, they should be knowledgeable relative to (1) anatomy and nomenclature of the foot (see Figures 3-4 and Table 3-1, Chapter 3), (2) what constitutes proper stance and motion, and how to correct some common faults through trimming, (3) the basic horseshoeing tools and how to use them, (4) how to recognize good and faulty shoeing, (5) kinds of shoes, and (6) treatment of dry hoofs.

Proper Stance; Correcting Common Faults

Before trimming the feet or shoeing a horse, it is important to know what constitutes both proper and faulty conformation. This is pictured in Chapter 4, Figures 4-15 and 4-16.

Figure 17-3 shows the proper posture of the hoof and incorrect postures caused by hoofs grown too long either in toe or heel. The slope is considered normal when the toe of the hoof and the pastern have the same direction. This angle should be kept always in mind and changed only as a corrective measure. If it should become necessary to correct uneven wear of the hoof, the correction should be made gradually over a period of several trimmings.

Prior to the trimming of the feet, the horse should be inspected while standing squarely on a level area—preferably a hard surface. Then it should be seen in action, both at the walk and the trot.

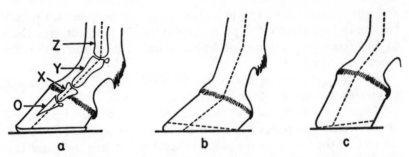

Fig. 17-3. (a) Properly trimmed hoof with normal foot axis: O—coffin bone; X—short
pastern bone; Y—long pastern bone; Z—cannon bone. (b) Toe too long, which breaks the
foot axis backward. Horizontal dotted line shows how hoof should be trimmed to restore
normal posture. (c) Heel too long, which breaks the foot axis forward. Horizontal dotted
line shows how trimming will restore the correct posture.

The hoofs should be trimmed every month or six weeks, whether
the animal is shod or not. If shoes are left on too long, the hoofs grow
out of proportion. This may throw the horse off balance and place
extra stress upon the tendons. Hence, the hoofs should always be kept
at the proper length and the correct posture. They should be trimmed
near the level of the sole; otherwise they will split off if the horse
remains unshod. The frog should be trimmed carefully, with only
ragged edges removed that allow the filth to accumulate in the crevices,
and the sole should be trimmed sparingly, if at all. The wall of the
hoof should never be rasped.

Table 17-1 shows the common faults and how to correct them
through proper trimming.

Horseshoeing Tools, and How to Use Them

Horses are shod to protect the foot from breaking and wearing away
faster than the growth of the horn. Also, shoes may be used to change
gaits and action, to correct faulty hoof structure or growth, and to
protect the hoof itself from such conditions as corns, contraction, or
cracks. When properly done, shoes should interfere as little as possible
with the physiological functions of the different structures of the foot
or with the gaits of the horse.

Just as do-it-yourself wood workers, mechanics, and what not
usually have a shop and some tools, so the horseman should have certain
basic horseshoeing tools, and know how to use them. Table 17-2 may
be used as a guide in selecting tools.

Table 17-1

COMMON FOOT FAULTS, AND HOW TO CORRECT THEM

Fault	How It Looks	How to Trim
Splayfoot	Front toes turned out, heels turned in.	Trim the outer half of the foot.
Pigeon-toed	Front toes turned in, heels turned out—the opposite of splayfoot.	Trim the inner half of foot more heavily; leave the outer half relatively long.
Quarter crack	Vertical crack on side of hoof.	Keep the hoof moist, shorten the toes, and use a corrective shoe.
Cocked ankles	Standing bent forward on fetlocks—most frequently the hind ones.	Lower the heels to correct. However, raising the heels makes for more immediate horse comfort.
Contracted heels	Close at the heels.	Lower the heels and allow the frog to carry more of the weight, which tends to spread the heels apart.

How to Recognize Good and Faulty Shoeing

The following check list may be used as a means by which to evaluate a shoeing job, whether plied by yourself or a professional farrier:

1. *As Viewed from the Front.—*

Yes No

☐ ☐ Are the front feet the same size, the toes the same length, and the heels the same height?

☐ ☐ Is the foot in balance in relation to the leg?

☐ ☐ Is the foot directly under the leg, is the axis of the foot in prolongation to the axis of the upper leg bones, and is the weight of the body equally distributed over the foot structure?

2. *As Viewed from the Side.—*

Yes No

☐ ☐ Does the axis of the foot coincide with the axis of the pastern?

☐ ☐ Does the slope of the wall from the coronet to the lower border parallel the slope of the pastern?

☐ ☐ Has the lower outer border of the wall been rasped?

Table 17-2

HORESHOEING TOOLS AND THEIR USE

Tools	Use
Anvil	As a block to shape shoes, and as the farrier's work bench.
Forge	To heat steel or shoes in preparation for shaping them for the horse being shod.
Vise	To finish shoes, and to hold metal.
Knife	To remove dirt and trim excess frog and sole from the foot. The hook on the end is used to trim the frog and clean the crevice between the bar and frog.
Nippers or Parers	To trim the wall of the hoof and other parts that are too hard for the knife. There is hardly any limit to the sizes and descriptions of these items; some are one-sided, others are two-sided.
Hoof Level	To determine the angle of the hoof relative to the ground surface.
Clinch Cutter	To cut clinches prior to pulling shoes.
Rasp	To level the foot after trimming; one side is coarse, and the other side fine.
Driving Hammer	To drive nails into hoof.
Hardy	As a wedge in the anvil hole, in cutting steel of the desired length and in cutting off shoes.
Hammers	To shape shoes. Various kinds of hammers may be used.
Tongs	To hold hot metal.
Nails	Assorted sizes of nails are available for different types of horseshoes.
Apron	To protect the horseshoer from sparks, from cuts that might otherwise be inflicted by slips of the knife or rasp, and from possible nail injury of nervous horses.

☐ ☐ Does the conformation of the foot and the type of shoe used warrant the amount of rasping done?

3. *As the Height and Strength of Nailing Are Inspected Closely.—*

Yes No

☐ ☐ Do the nails come out of the wall at the proper height and in sound horn?

☐ ☐ Are the nails driven to a greater height in the wall than necessary?

☐ ☐ Is the size of the nail used best suited for the size and condition of the foot and the weight of the shoe?

☐ ☐ Are the clinches of sufficient thickness where the nail comes out of the wall to insure strength?

☐ ☐ Are the clinches smooth and not projecting above the surface of the wall?

4. *As the Outline and Size of the Shoe Are Scrutinized.—*

Yes No

☐ ☐ Is the toe of the shoe fitted with sufficient fullness to give lateral support to the foot at the moment of breaking over and leaving the ground?

☐ ☐ Are the branches of the shoe from the bend of the quarter to the heel fitted fuller than the outline of the wall to provide for expansion of the foot and normal growth of horn between shoeing periods?

☐ ☐ Are the heels of the shoe of sufficient length and width to cover the buttresses?

☐ ☐ Are the heels finished without sharp edges?

☐ ☐ Does the shoe rest evenly on the bearing surface of the hoof, covering the lower border of the wall, white line, and buttresses?

☐ ☐ Is the shoe concaved so that it does not rest upon the horny sole?

☐ ☐ Are the nail heads properly seated?

☐ ☐ Is the shoe the correct size for the foot?

☐ ☐ Will the weight of the shoe provide reasonable wear and protection to the foot?

☐ ☐ Have the ragged particles of the horny frog been removed?

Kinds of Shoes

A number of factors should be considered when selecting the shoes for a given horse; among them:

1. *The proper size.*—The shoe should fit the foot, rather than any attempt being made to trim the hoof to fit the shoe.

2. *Front vs. hind shoes.*—Front shoes are more nearly circular and wider at the heels than hind shoes.

3. *The individual horse.*—His weight, the shape and texture of his hoof, and the set of his legs should be considered.

4. *The use to which the horse is put, and the kind of ground.*—A plain shoe or a rim shoe is satisfactory for most horses used for pleasure, cutting, roping, barrel racing, polo, and jumping; whereas racing plates, to aid in gripping the track, are needed on running horses. Also, there are many corrective shoes, a few of which are listed in Table 17-3.

Shoes may be either hand-made or ready-made (factory-made). The latter are becoming increasingly popular because they (1) require a minimum of work, and (2) are ideal for the do-it-yourselfer. Both steel and aluminum shoes are available. Fig. 17-4 shows four common types of horseshoes.

Table 17-3
SOME CORRECTIVE SHOES, AND THEIR USE

Kind of Corrective Shoe	Purpose or Use
The bar shoe	To apply pressure to the frog of the foot, or to relieve pressure on any part of it.
The rocker toe shoe	For use on horses that stumble, that forge, or that have ringbone or sidebone.
The squared toe shoe with trailer	For cow-hocked horses.
The lateral extension toed shoe	For horses that either toe out or toe in.

TREATMENT OF DRY HOOFS

Hoofs may become dry and brittle; sometimes they split and produce lameness. The frog loses its elasticity and is no longer effective as a shock absorber. If the dryness is prolonged, the frogs shrink in size and the heels contract.

Dry hoofs usually can be prevented by using one or more of the following treatments: Packing them with a specially prepared formulation, applying a good hoof dressing, keeping the ground wet around the watering tank, and/or attaching wet burlap sacks around them.

A ready-made shoe is suited for most riding and driving horses.

Ready-Made Shoe

A self-cleaning rim shoe is suited for horses used for riding, cutting, roping, barrel racing, polo, and jumping.

Rim Shoe

A hot shoe is one that must be heated and shaped prior to being used.

Hot Shoe

A racing plate meets the exacting needs of race horses—it is light in weight, and it grips the track.

Racing Plate

Fig. 17-4. Common types of horseshoes.

CARE OF THE FOAL'S FEET

Foals may become unsound of limb when the wear and tear is not equally distributed due to an unshapely hoof. On the other hand, faulty limbs may be helped or even corrected by regular and persistent trimming. Such practice also tends to educate the foal and to make shoeing easier at maturity. If the foal is run on pasture, trimming of the feet may be necessary long before weaning time. A good practice is to check the feet regularly every month or six weeks and if necessary to trim a small amount each time, rather than too much at any one time. Tendons should not receive undue strain by careless trimming of the feet. Usually, only the outer rim should be trimmed, though sometimes it is necessary to cut down the heel or frog or to shorten the toes. The necessary trimming may be done with the rasp, farrier's knife, and nippers (using the rasp for the most part).

Before the feet are trimmed, the foal should be inspected first while standing squarely on a hard surface. Then it should be seen in action, both at the walk and the trot.

Early Training of the Foal

Foals are gentle, and their education should begin early in life. In all too many cases the idea has prevailed that so-called "breaking" begins only at the time the young horse is placed in use. Not only will early training of the foal be easier, but it will result in a better-trained and more serviceable horse. In training the young foal, give only one lesson at a time, making certain that each lesson is mastered in order.

TRAINING THE FOAL TO LEAD AND STAND

At ten days to two weeks of age, a well-fitted halter should first be placed on the foal. After the foal has become accustomed to the halter for one to two days, the next lesson should be that of tying it securely in the stall and alongside the mare (never allow the foal to get loose as it will try to repeat what it has once accomplished). Also, make certain that it does not get tangled up in the rope or otherwise encounter injury. This tying up should last from thirty minutes to an hour's time each day for two or three days, and the foal should be carefully groomed and handled while in this position. After each leg is rubbed, the foot should be handled frequently so that there will be no struggling or fright as the feet are picked up. Following this, the foal should be led about, first in company with the mare, and after a few days it should be led alone. Leading should be practiced at both the walk and the trot. When stopped, the foal should assume a standing position squarely on all four legs and with the head up—in show position. While all this education is being given, the usual commands for stopping and going should first be given and then promptly executed. In training the foal, the horseman should, at all times, exercise great patience, gentleness, and firmness.

Most Kentucky Thoroughbred breeders simply lead the young foal from the stall to the paddock, and back, with the mare—thus teaching it to lead in a very natural and casual way.

Weaning the Foal

Weaning of the foal is more a matter of preparation than of absolute separation from the dam. The simplicity with which it is accomplished depends very largely upon the thoroughness of the preparation.

AGE OF WEANING

Foals are usually weaned at four to six months of age, depending on conditions. When either the foal or the mare is not doing well, when the mare is being given heavy work, or when the dam has been re-bred on the ninth day after foaling, it may be advisable to wean the foal at a comparatively early age. On the other hand, when both the mare and the foal seem to be doing well, when the mare is idle, when breeding has been delayed following foaling, or when it is desirable to develop the foal to the maximum, the weaning may very well be delayed until six months of age.

If by means of the creep or a separate grain box, the foal has become accustomed to the consumption of considerable grain and hay (about ¾ pound of grain per each 100 pounds live weight daily), weaning will result in very little disturbance or setback. Likewise, if the ration of the dam has been decreased (lessened by one-half) a few days before the separation, usually her udder will dry up with no difficulty.

SEPARATION OF MARE AND FOAL

When all preliminary precautions and preparations for weaning have been made, the separation should be accomplished. This should be complete and final with no opportunity for the foal to see, hear, or smell its dam again. Otherwise, all which has been gained up to this time will be lost, and it will be necessary to begin all over again. Perhaps

Fig. 17-5. A good method for training the foal to lead. Note that the rope is looped around the quarters, with one end tied in a knot on top of the back and the other end run through the nose band of the halter. When both the lead rope and the rope around the quarters are pulled simultaneously, most foals respond very readily. (Drawing by R. F. Johnson)

the best arrangement is to shut the foal in the stall to which it has been accustomed and to move the mare away to new quarters, making certain that all obstructions have first been removed so that there is no possibility of injury to the foal while it is fretting over the separation.

After the weanlings have remained in the stable for a day or two and have quieted down, they should be turned out on pasture. Where a group of weanlings is involved, undue running and possible injury hazard may be minimized in this transition by the following procedure: First turn two or three of the least desirable animals out and let them tire themselves out, and then turn the rest of the weanlings out and they will do very little running.

With a great number of foals, it is advisable to separate the sexes, and even to place some of the more timid ones to themselves. In all cases, it is best not to run the foals with older horses.

DRYING-UP THE MARE

Some successful horsemen use the following procedure in drying-up mares:

1. Rub an oil preparation (such as camphorated oil or a mixture of lard and spirits of camphor) on the bag, and take the mare from the foal and place her on less lush pasture or grass hay.

2. Examine the udder and place oil on it at intervals, but do not milk it out for five to seven days. It will fill up and get tight, *but do not milk it out.* At the end of five to seven days, when the bag is soft and flabby, milk out what little secretion remains (perhaps not more than a half a cup).

Castration

Regardless of age or time, the operation is best performed by an experienced veterinarian. A colt may be castrated when only a few days old, but most horsemen prefer to delay the operation until the animal is about one year of age. Although there is less real danger to the animal and much less setback with early altering, the practice results in imperfect development of the fore parts. On the other hand, leaving the colt entire for a time will result in more muscular, bold features and better carriage of the fore parts. Therefore, weather and management conditions permitting, the time of altering should be determined by the development of the individual animal. Thus, underdeveloped colts may be left entire six months or even a year longer than overdeveloped ones. Breeders of Thoroughbred horses usually prefer to have the horses first race as an entire.

There is less danger of infection if colts are castrated in the spring of the year soon after they are turned out on a clean pasture. Naturally, this should be done sufficiently early so as to avoid hot weather and fly time.

Breaking (Training)

The good horseman who has followed a program of training and educating the foal from the time it was a few days old has already eliminated the word "breaking." To him the saddling and/or harnessing of the young horse is merely another step in the training program, which is done with apparent ease and satisfaction.

A good age and time for harnessing and working the horse is during the winter as a rising two-year-old. At this season there is usually sufficient leisure time and the work is not of a rushing nature.

Exercise

Regular exercise is essential to strong, sound feet and legs and to health.

Fig. 17-6. Correct method of longeing a horse, with a longeing cavesson and long web tape longe line in use. (Drawing by R. F. Johnson)

Except during times of inclement weather and when being worked heavily, horses should be out in the open where they can romp and play on natural footing as much as possible. For this purpose, pastures are ideal, especially for young animals.

Where exercise on pastures is not feasible, mature animals should be exercised for an hour daily under saddle or hitched to a cart.

When handled carefully, the broodmare should be exercised within a day or two of foaling. Above all, when not receiving forced exercise or on idle days, she should not be confined to a stable or a small, dry lot.

Frequently, in light horses, bad feet exclude exercise on roads, and faulty tendons exclude exercise under saddle. Under such conditions, one may have to depend upon (1) exercise taken voluntarily in a large paddock, (2) longeing or exercising on a thirty- to forty-foot rope, or (3) leading.

Transporting Horses

Horses are transported via trailer, van, truck, rail, boat, and plane. Regardless of the method, the objectives are: To move them safely, with the maximum of comfort, and as economically as possible. To this end, selection of the equipment is the first requisite. But equipment alone, no matter how good, will not suffice.

The trip must be preceded by proper preparation, including conditioning of horses; and horses must receive proper care, including smooth movement en route.

Most horses are transported in trailers which have the distinct advantage of door-to-door transportation.

The accompanying discussion presents, in summary form, pertinent points relative to transporting horses, with special emphasis on motor and rail transportation. The same principles also apply to boat and plane shipments.

1. *Get horses used to being loaded early in life.*—Early training is a most important part of transporting horses. Thus, where it is expected that horses will be subjected to transportation later in life, it is most important that they be accustomed to transportation as youngsters before they get too big and strong—perhaps by vanning them when it is necessary to move them from one part of the farm to another.

2. *Provide health certificate, and statement of ownership.*—A health certificate, signed by a licensed veterinarian, is required for most interstate shipments. Some states also require a mallein test for glanders.

Foreign shipments must be accompanied by a health certificate, approved by a government veterinarian—a requisite which takes several days.

Experienced horsemen recognize that sick horses should not be transported—for the protection of other horses as well as for their own safety, and that horses in poor condition ship poorly.

Branded horses must be accompanied by a brand certificate, and all horses should be accompanied by a statement of ownership.

3. *Schedule properly.*—Schedule the transportation so that animals will arrive in ample time. Thus, show, sale, and race animals should arrive a few days early.

4. *Have the horses relaxed.*—Like people, horses ship best if relaxed, and are not overtired prior to loading out.

5. *Clean and disinfect public conveyance.*—Before using, thoroughly clean and disinfect (live steam is excellent for this purpose) any type of public conveyance. This is important from a disease prevention standpoint. Also, remove nails or other projections and injury hazards.

6. *Bed properly.*—The floor should first be bedded with a base of dry sand so that the animals will not slip, and then covered with long, clean, bright straw, or with sawdust or shavings. Also, work the bedding over at frequent intervals while in transit and remove contaminated portions, in order to avoid ammonia and heat.

7. *Allow for air space without drafts.*—A requisite for successful shipping is that provision be made for plenty of fresh air, without drafts.

8. *Have a competent caretaker accompany horses.*—Valuable horses should not be entrusted to the care of an inexperienced person. Instead, engage the services of a competent caretaker, an experienced shipper. Competent help will cost more money, but such services are always a good investment.

9. *Use rope shanks, except on stallions, and tie with a slip knot.* —Where animals are tied, use a five-eighths inch cotton rope shank, five feet long, with a big swivel snap at the end. Chain shanks are too noisy.

Always tie with a slip knot, because it can be easily and quickly released in case of an emergency. With rail shipments, especially, it is important that horses not be tied too short, so they can get their heads down and blow the cinders and other foreign matter out of their noses.

10. *Feed lightly.*—The grain allowance should be limited to a half feed before loading out and for the first feed after reaching the destination. In-transit horses should be given all the good quality hay that they will eat—preferably some alfalfa, so as to keep the bowels open—but no concentrate.

Commercial hay nets or homemade burlap containers may be used to hold the hay while in transit; but do not place them too high.

11. *Water liberally.*—When transporting horses, give them clean, fresh water at frequent intervals—all they will drink, unless it is extremely hot and there is danger of gorging. Beginning about a week before moving horses, it is a good idea to add a tiny bit of molasses to each pail of water, then continue this practice while in transit, thereby avoiding any flavor or taste change in the water.

12. *Pad the stalls.*—Most experienced shippers favor padding the stalls to lessen injury, especially where a valuable animal is involved. Thus, either coconut matting or a sack of straw properly placed may save the hocks from injury.

13. *Check the ramp.*—Before loading or unloading horses on a ramp to which you are not accustomed, check the ramp for soundness; nothing is more disturbing than to have a horse go through a rotten board. Also, protect the sides of a ramp if necessary; baled straw may be used for this purpose.

In trucking or vanning, use a ditch or bank if a ramp is not available, but get it as nearly level to the vehicle as possible.

14. *Take a box of tools and supplies along.*—The following tools and supplies should be taken along in a suitable box, especially with rail and van shipments: Pinch bar, hammer, hatchet, saw, nails, pliers, flashlight, extra halters and shanks, a twitch, a canvas slapper or a short piece of hose, a pair of gloves, a fork and broom, a fire extinguisher, and colic and shipping fever medicine provided by the local veterinarian.

15. *Give attention to shoes, blankets, and bandages.*—Never allow horses to wear calked shoes during shipment. They may wear smooth shoes, but even these should be removed from the hind feet if two or more animals are turned loose in a box car. Whenever possible, ship horses barefoot.

In cool weather, horses may be blanketed—provided an attendant is present to take over if the horse gets entangled.

The legs of racehorses in training should be bandaged, in order to keep the ankles from getting scuffed up or the tendons bruised. With breeding stock, except valuable stallions and young stock, this is not necessary. When bandages are used, they should be re-set often.

16. *Easy does it.*—In loading and unloading horses, always be patient, and never lose your temper. Always try a bit of kindness first. To reassure the horse, pat it and speak to it, and play with its shank. If this fails, it may be desirable on occasion to resort to one of the following :

> a. *The twitch.*—Sometimes the use of the twitch at the right time is desirable, especially if the horse is tossing its head about.
>
> b. *The canvas slapper.*—When a horse must be disciplined, a canvas slapper or a short rubber hose can be used effectively; these articles make a lot of noise without inflicting much hurt.
>
> c. *A bucket of water.*—If a horse gets very excited and is about to break out, dash a bucket of water in its face; usually it will back off and think.
>
> d. *A tranquilizer.*—A nervous, excitable horse may be calmed by use of a tranquilizer, which had best be administered by a veterinarian.
>
> e. *The use of the tail.*—If the horse won't move or is kicking, grab hold of its tail and push it up over the horse's back. In this position, the horse can't kick and can be pushed along.

17. *Keep together horses that are used to each other.*—Biting, kicking, and/or fretting is alleviated or lessened by stabling together, or in close proximity to each other, those horses that are used to working, pasturing, or stabling together when home.

18. *Control insects.*—In season, flies and other insects may molest in-transit animals. When necessary, therefore, use a reliable insecticide, according to directions, in order to control insects.

VAN, TRAILER, AND TRUCK SHIPMENTS

Vans, trailers, and trucks have the distinct advantage of door-to-door transportation; that is, loading from in front of one stable and unloading in front of another.

The van or van-like trailer is a common and satisfactory method of transportation where three to eight horses are involved. There is hardly any limit to the kinds of vans, ranging from rather simple to very palatial pieces of equipment.

The trailer is usually a one- or two-horse unit, which is drawn behind a car or truck. Generally speaking, this method of transpor-

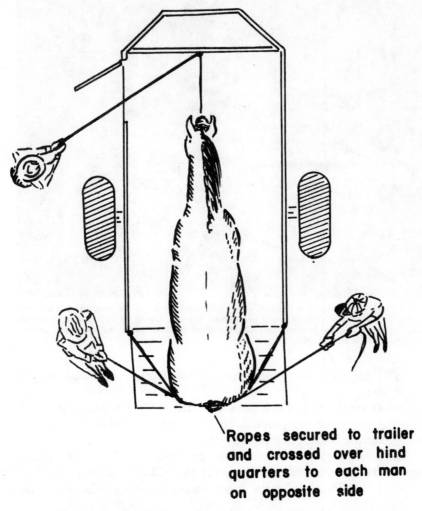

Ropes secured to trailer
and crossed over hind
quarters to each man
on opposite side

Fig. 17-7. Easy does it! This shows an easy way in which to load a "green" horse in a truck or trailer. (Drawing by R. F. Johnson)

tation is best adapted to short distances—less than 500 miles. Horses are trailered to shows, races, endurance rides, breeding establishments, to new owners, from one work area to another on the range; in fact, it may well be said that today's horses are well traveled.

Most experienced horse shippers frown upon shipping horses in an open truck.

Fig. 17-8. Interior of a loaded horse van. Vans vary all the way from one-horse trucks to the palatial sizes of the larger stables. The van should be equipped with special matting made for the purpose, thus assuring good footing. As in rail shipments, proper ventilation is important. (Courtesy, USDA)

The requisites for good motor transportation, regardless of the type, are:

1. *Good footing.*—Such as is afforded by (a) a heavy coconut matting made for the purpose, or (b) sand covered with straw or other suitable bedding material.

2. *Steady, careful driving.*—As distinguished from fast, jerky, and/or reckless driving—which makes for added stress and tiring. If weather conditions make the roads hazardous, the horses should be unloaded.

3. *Nurse stops.*—Nurse stops should be made at not to exceed three-hour intervals where mares and foals are involved.

4. *Proper ventilation.*—There should be plenty of fresh air without drafts.

RAIL SHIPMENTS

Experienced shippers, who have used various methods of transportation, are generally agreed that horses ship more comfortably by

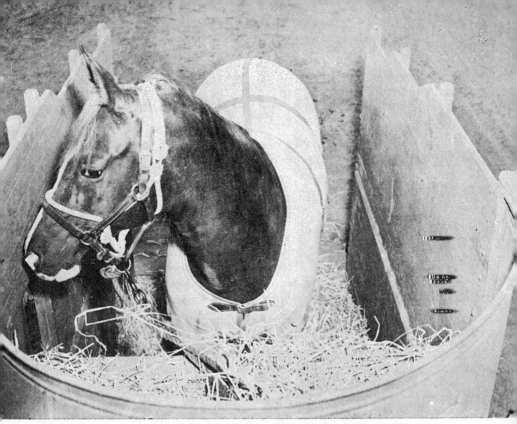

Fig. 17-9. Front view of a horse in a trailer, showing animal properly blanketed, double tied, and with hay in the manger. Trailers are a very popular means of transporting one or two horses. (Courtesy, USDA)

Fig. 17-10. Horse van of Gem State Stables, Thoroughbreds, Tipton, California. (Courtesy, Harry W. and Velma V. Morrison, owners)

rail than by any other way, despite the decline in freight shipments.

Rail shipments may be either by freight or express. Some instructions specific to rail shipments follow:

1. *Do not overload a car.*—Except for young stock, most experienced horse shippers insist on separate stabling for valuable, mature horses that are being shipped via either freight or express.

Where stabled—preferably two abreast—a 36-foot box car (freight) will accommodate 12 head, without crowding. Where not stabled, a 36-foot box car will accommodate 22 mature light horses. With the latter arrangement, the horses should be loaded crosswise of the car with heads and tails alternating, and they should not be tied in the car. In fact, the halter rope should be removed entirely from each horse as it is placed in the car.

Special horse cars, commonly called Palace Cars because of their luxurious fixtures, can be obtained for either express or freight, from either the railroad companies or the Arms-Yaeger Car Co. The latter company rents stock cars to the express or railroad companies. The standard 48-foot Palace Car is equipped with 18 stalls, but different sized cars and accommodations are available.

2. *Obtain less-carload freight rates when eligible.*—Frequently, horsemen desire to ship one or a few head of animals by freight, at the less-carload rates (L.C.L.). On L.C.L. shipments, the charge is for a minimum of 3,000 pounds for the first horse and 1,500 pounds for each additional horse. In order to make sure that the less-carload rates apply instead of the substantially higher carload rate, the following procedure should be observed:

a. Order the car in writing, and specify that less-carload shipment is involved.

b. Place the following notation on the livestock contract: "Exclusive use of the car is not requested; shipment is less-carload."

3. *In some cases, use wooden cars.*—Unless steel cars are well insulated and properly ventilated, a wooden car should be used.

4. *Construct proper stalls.*—If stalls are used, build them (a) strong enough to endure a quick train stop without pitching the horses on their heads, (b) so that the horses will be stabled two

Fig. 17-11. Three horses properly quartered and tied in a box car. Where speed is important, animals should be shipped via American Express; otherwise freight is entirely satisfactory and much less expensive. (Courtesy, USDA)

abreast (sometimes three abreast, if they are small) and in the direction of travel.[4]

5. *Place stallions in the end of a car.*—When stallions are loaded in a mixed car, place them in one end, and, if necessary, hang a blanket in front of them.

6. *Ship weanlings loose.*—Most experienced shippers prefer to ship weanlings loose, with three to four head in a box stall.

7. *Provide panel doors and water facilities in railroad car.*—The side doors of a box car should be left open and the openings protected with slatted panels. Ventilation without drafts is very necessary; and cold is preferred over warm temperatures.

8. *Cut off the heat when expressing.*—When shipping horses via

---

[4]Good horsemen disagree on whether animals should face toward or away from the direction of travel. Some feel that horses, like people, are less likely to get car sick if they face in the direction of travel. Others prefer to stable so that the horses face away from the direction of travel, because, so they argue, they get less cinders and dust in their nostrils.

express, get the heat cut off underneath the car. Remember that horses can stand more cold than heat.

9. *Bill rail shipments as instructed.*—Rail shipments should be billed with care; thus when animals are to be raced or shown, bill them out to the track or exposition, respectively, in keeping with the instructions given.

10. *Insure.*—The carrier's regular liability via rail is as follows: (a) by freight, $150 per horse; (b) by express, $200 per horse. Additional transportation insurance can be obtained at rates quoted by insurance companies.

11. *Observe the 28-hour law.*—Horses shipped in carload lots must be unloaded at the end of each 28-hour period and fed, watered, and rested; although this may be extended to 36 hours if the written consent of the shipper is obtained.

12. *Obtain a free pass for the caretaker(s).*—One male adult caretaker is allowed a free pass with each stock or box car of horses shipped via freight, but up to six caretakers may accompany a Palace Car, either by freight or by express.

13. *Do not express in a crate if you can avoid it.*—Horses can be expressed in a crate. However, little of this is done at the present time, because (a) crates are expensive, (b) the crate must be dismantled and moved to another car in Chicago, in East to West shipments, and (c) baggage cars are generally too hot for the well-being of horses in the wintertime.

14. *Know and observe the regulations relative to show cars.*—There are certain railroad regulations which apply to all animals which are transported to exhibitions. These are:

a. *Obtain one-half rail fare.*—Usually show animals can be transported by rail at one-half fare provided the following regulations are observed:

(1) *They are returned to point of origin.*—Within thirty days after the close of the exposition or fair, they are returned to the point of origin via the same line or lines as the initial movement, and

(2) *The bill of lading is accompanied by proper certification.*—The bill of lading must be accompanied by a certification of the fair secretary or manager stating that the animals were exhibited and have not changed ownership.

Also, half rates may be obtained when transporting a car of show animals to more than one exposition, but the procedure is somewhat complicated. Briefly, it involves the following:

(1) *Proper waybilling.*—Waybilling at the regular tariff rate to each point of exhibition, with the rate on the inbound charges later reduced to one-half upon complying with point (2) of the preceding section, and

(2) *Proper billing from last show.*—Finally, when loading out from the last show for return to the point of origin, the shipment is billed at one-half the tariff rates, provided that point (2) of the preceding section is complied with in regard to the last show of the circuit.

All half rates, as indicated above, will apply only when the carrier's liability is limited to $150 per horse (or pony, burro, donkey, mule, jack, or jenny).

b. *Hold show car for reuse.*—If the show car is to be reused, it should be locked, unless all materials and equipment are removed.

In addition to the information contained herein, it is desirable always to consult the local railroad agent, railroad livestock agent, or local railroad freight traffic office before making a shipment of horses via rail.

BOAT AND PLANE SHIPMENTS

Boat and plane shipments are a specialty, the details of which had best be left in the hands of an experienced person or agency, such as an importing or exporting company. At the present time, such shipments are largely confined to valuable registered horses and polo ponies, and, for the most part, transatlantic movements, although some valuable horses are now being flown across the nation.

Bedding Horses

A soft, comfortable bed will insure proper rest and make for a cleaner animal and easier grooming. But bedding has the following added values from the standpoint of manure:

1. It soaks up the urine, which contains about one-half the total plant food of manure.

2. It makes manure easier to handle.

3. It absorbs plant nutrients, fixing both ammonia and potash in

Fig. 17-12. An Appaloosa loaded in a jet cargoliner, ready for flight. With this arrangement, loading in the stall is accomplished on the ground. The stall containing the horse is
then lifted into the airplane door by fork lift and maneuvered into position and tied down
by the loading crew. (Courtesy, Western Horseman)

relatively insoluble forms that protect them against losses by leaching.
This characteristic of bedding is especially important in peat moss,
but of little significance with sawdust and shavings.

KIND AND AMOUNT OF BEDDING

The kind of bedding material selected should be determined primarily by (1) availability and price, (2) absorptive capacity, (3)
cleanness (this excludes dirt or dust which might cause odors or
stain horses), (4) ease of handling, (5) ease of cleanup and disposal,
(6) non-irritability from dust or components causing allergies, (7)
texture or size, and (8) fertility value or plant nutrient content. In
addition, a desirable bedding should not be excessively coarse, and
should remain well in place and not be too readily kicked aside.

Table 17-4 lists some common bedding materials and gives the
average water absorptive capacity of each. Cereal straw and wood
shavings are the favorite bedding materials for horses.

Naturally, the availability and price per ton of various bedding
materials vary from area to area, and from year to year. Thus, in
the New England states shavings and sawdust are available, whereas

other forms of bedding are scarce, and straws are more plentiful in
the Central and Western states.

Table 17-4 shows that bedding materials differ considerably in
their relative capacities to absorb liquid.

Table 17-4

WATER ABSORPTION OF BEDDING MATERIALS

Material	Lbs. of Water Absorbed per Cwt. of Air-Dry Bedding	Material	Lbs. of Water Absorbed per Cwt. of Air-Dry Bedding
Barley straw	210	Sand	25
Cocoa shells	270	Sawdust (top quality pine)	250
Corn stover (shredded)	250	(run-of-the-mill hardwood)	150
Corncobs (crushed or ground)	210	Sugar cane bagasse	220
Cottonseed hulls	250	Tree bark (dry, fine)	250
Flax straw	260	(from tanneries)	400
Hay (mature, chopped)	300	Vermiculite[1]	350
Leaves (broadleaf)	200	Wheat straw (long)	220
(pine needles)	100	(chopped)	295
Oat hulls	200	Wood chips (top quality pine)	300
Oat straw (long)	280	(run-of-the-mill hardwood)	150
(chopped)	375	Wood shavings (top quality pine)	200
Peanut hulls	250	(run-of-the-mill hardwood)	150
Peat moss	1,000		
Rye straw	210		

[1]This is a mica-like mineral mined chiefly in South Carolina and Montana.

Other facts of importance, relative to certain bedding materials
and bedding uses, are:

1. *Wood products (sawdust, shavings, tree bark, chips, etc.).*—
The suspicion that wood products will hurt the land is rather widespread but unfounded. It is true that shavings and sawdust decompose
slowly, but this process can be expedited by the addition of nitrogen
fertilizers. Also, when plowed under, they increase soil acidity, but
the change is both small and temporary.

Softwood (on a weight basis) is about twice as absorptive as hardwood, and green wood has only 50 percent the absorptive capacity
of dried wood.

2. *Cut straw.*—Cut straw will absorb more liquid than long straw;
cut oats or wheat straw will take up about 25 percent more water
than long straw from comparable material. But there are disadvantages
to chopping; chopped straws may be dusty.

From the standpoint of the value of plant food nutrients per ton of air dry material, peat moss is the most valuable bedding and wood products the least valuable.

The minimum desirable amount of bedding to use is the amount necessary to absorb completely the liquids in manure. For 24-hour confinement, the minimum daily bedding requirements of horses, based on uncut wheat or oats straw, is 10 to 15 pounds. With other bedding materials, these quantities will vary according to their respective absorptive capacities (see Table 17-4). Also, more than minimum quantities of bedding may be desirable where cleanliness and comfort of the horse are important.

In most areas, bedding materials are becoming scarcer and higher in price, primarily because (1) geneticists are breeding plants with shorter straws and stalks, (2) there are more competitive and numerous uses for some of the materials, and (3) the current trend toward more confinement rearing of livestock requires more bedding.

Horsemen may reduce bedding needs and costs as follows:

1. *Chop bedding.*—Chopped straw, waste hay, fodder, or cobs will go further and do a better job of keeping horses dry than long materials.

2. *Ventilate quarters properly.*—Proper ventilation lowers the humidity and keeps the bedding dry.

3. *Provide exercise area.*—Where possible and practical, provide for exercise in well-drained, dry pastures or corrals, without confining horses to stalls more than necessary.

Stable Management

The following stable management practices are recommended:

1. Remove the top layer of clay floors yearly; replace with fresh clay, and level and tamp. Also, keep the stable floor higher than the surrounding area, thereby making for dryness.

2. Keep stalls well lighted.

3. Use properly constructed hay racks to lessen waste and contamination of hay, with the possible exception of maternity stalls.

4. Scrub concentrate containers at such intervals as necessary, and after feeding a wet mash.

5. Work over bedding daily, removing excrement and wet, stained or soiled material, and provide fresh bedding.

6. Practice rigid stable sanitation to prevent fecal contamination of feed and water.

7. Lead foals when taking them from the stall to the paddock and back, as a way in which to further their training.

8. Restrict the ration when horses are idle, and provide either a wet bran mash the evening before an idle day or turn idle horses to pasture.

9. Provide proper ventilation at all times—by means of open doors, windows that open inwardly from the top, or stall partitions slatted at the top.

10. Keep stables in repair at all times, so as to lessen injury hazards.

MANURE

The term *manure refers to a mixture of animal excrements (consisting of undigested feeds plus certain body wastes) and bedding.*

The rise in light horse numbers, along with the shift of much of the horse population from the nation's farms and ranches to stables and small enclosures in surburban areas, has made for manure disposal problems.

From the standpoint of soils and crops, barnyard manure contains the following valuable ingredients:

1. *Organic matter.*—It supplies valuable organic matter which cannot be secured in chemical fertilizers. Organic matter—which constitutes 3 to 6 percent, by weight, of most soils—improves soil tilth, increases water-holding capacity, lessens water and wind erosion, improves aeration and has a beneficial effect on soil microorganisms and plants. It is the "lifeblood" of the land.

2. *Plant food.*—It supplies plant food or fertility—especially nitrogen, phosphorus, and potassium. In addition to these three nutrients, manure contains organic matter, calcium, and trace elements such as boron, manganese, copper, and zinc. A ton of well-preserved horse manure, free of bedding, contains plant food nutrients equal to about 100 pounds of 13-2-12 fertilizer (see Table 17-5). Thus, spreading manure at the rate of 8 tons per acre supplies the same amounts of nutrients as 800 pounds of a 13-2-12 commercial fertilizer.

Amount, Composition, and Value of Manure Produced

The quantity, composition, and value of manure produced vary according to species, weight, kind and amount of feed, and kind and amount of bedding. The author's computations are on a fresh manure (exclusive of bedding) basis. Table 17-5 presents data by species per

Table 17-5

QUANTITY, COMPOSITION, AND VALUE OF FRESH MANURE (FREE OF BEDDING) EXCRETED BY 1,000 POUNDS LIVE WEIGHT OF VARIOUS KINDS OF FARM ANIMALS

Animal	Tons Excreted/ year/1000 Lbs. Live Weight[1]	Composition and Value of Manure on a Tonnage Basis[2].						
		Excre- ment	Lbs./ Ton[3]	Water	N	P[4]	K[4]	Value/ Ton[5]
Horses and foals	8	Liquid Solid Total	400 1600 2000	(%) 60	(lbs.) 13.8	(lbs.) 2.0	(lbs.) 12.0	($) 2.76
Sheep	6	Liquid Solid Total	660 1340 2000	65	28.0	4.2	20.0	5.36
Cow	12	Liquid Solid Total	600 1400 2000	79	11.2	2.0	10.0	2.32
Steer (finishing cattle)	8.5	Liquid Solid Total	600 1400 2000	80	14.0	4.0	9.0	2.98
Swine	16	Liquid Solid Total	800 1200 2000	75	10.0	2.8	7.6	2.19
Chicken	4.5	Total	2000	54	31.2	8.0	7.0	5.68

[1]*Manure Is Worth Money—It Deserves Good Care.* University of Illinois Circ. 595, 1953, p. 4.

[2]Last 5 columns on the right from: *Farm Manures,* University of Kentucky Circ. 593, 1964, p. 5, Table 2.

[3]From: Reference Material for 1951 Saddle and Sirloin Essay Contest, p. 43, compiled by M. E. Ensminger, data from *Fertilizers and Crop Production,* by Van Slyke, published by Orange Judd Publishing Co.

[4]Phosphorus (P) can be converted to P_2O_5 by multiplying the figure given above by 2.29, and potassium (K) can be converted to K_2O by multiplying by 1.2.

[5]Calculated on the assumption that nitrogen (N) retails at 12¢, phosphorus (P) at 19¢, and potassium (K) at 6¢ per pound in commercial fertilizers.

1,000 pounds live weight, whereas Table 17-6 gives yearly tonnage and value.

The data in Table 17-5 and Fig. 17-13 are based on animals confined to stalls the year around. Actually, the manure recovered and available to spread where desired is considerably less than indicated because (1) animals are kept on pasture and along roads and lanes much of the year, where the manure is dropped, and (2) losses in weight often run as high as 60 percent when manure is exposed to the weather for a considerable time.

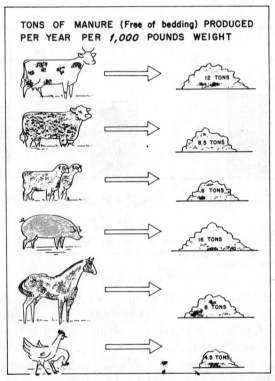

Fig. 17-13. On the average, each class of stall-confined animals produces per year per 1,000 pounds weight the tonnages shown above. (Drawing by R. F. Johnson)

About 75 percent of the nitrogen, 80 percent of the phosphorus, and 85 percent of the potassium contained in animal feeds are returned as manure. In addition, about 40 percent of the organic matter in feeds is excreted as manure. As a rule of thumb, it is commonly estimated that 80 percent of the total nutrients in feeds are excreted by animals as manure.

The urine makes up 20 percent of the total weight of the excrement of horses and 40 percent of that of hogs; these figures represent the two extremes in farm animals. Yet the urine, or liquid manure, contains nearly 50 percent of the nitrogen, 6 percent of the phosphorus and 60 percent of the potassium of average manure; roughly one-half of the total plant food of manure (see Figure 17-14). Also, it is note-worthy that the nutrients in liquid manure are more readily available to plants than the nutrients in the solid excrement. These are the reasons why it is important to conserve the urine.

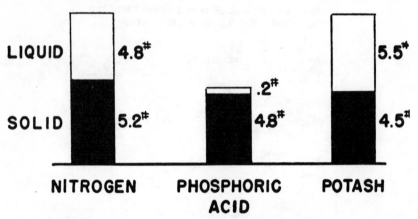

Fig. 17-14. Distribution of plant nutrients between liquid and solid portions of a ton of average farm manure. As noted, the urine contains about half the fertility value of manure. (Drawing by Steve Allured)

The actual monetary value of manure can and should be based on (1) increased crop yields, and (2) equivalent cost of a like amount of commercial fertilizer. Numerous experiments and practical observa-tions have shown the measurable monetary value of manure in in-creased crop yields. Tables 17-5 and 17-6 give the equivalent cost of a like amount of commercial fertilizer.

Currently, we are producing manure (exclusive of bedding) at the rate of 1.8 billion tons annually (see Table 17-6). That is sufficient manure to add nearly one ton each year to every acre of the total land area (1.9 billion acres) of the United States.

Based on equivalent fertilizer prices (see Table 17-5 right hand column), and livestock numbers (Table 17-6), the yearly manure crop

Table 17-6

TONNAGE AND VALUE OF MANURE (EXCLUSIVE OF BEDDING) EXCRETED IN 1967 BY U.S. LIVESTOCK

Class of Livestock	Produced by Animals Maintained Throughout Year[1]	Produced by Animals That Died During Year[2]	Produced by Animals Slaughtered During Year[3]	Total by Class of Livestock	Total Value of Manure[4]
	(tons)	(tons)	(tons)	(tons)	($)
Horses.............	53,400,000	—	—	53,400,000	147,384,000.00
Cattle (beef and dairy) .	1,077,248,700	446,913	cattle 192,032,258 calves 7,862,024	1,277,589,895	2,964,008,556.40
Sheep...........	16,591,500	37,650	3,949,392	20,578,542	205,785.42
Swine...........	217,052,000	1,264,392	160,834,912	379,151,304	830,341,355.76
Chickens.........	95,523,750	2,653,344	2,392,902	154,632,258	878,311,225.44
Turkeys..........	7,216,110		46,846,152		
Totals...	1,467,032,060	4,402,299	413,917,640	1,885,351,999	4,820,250,923.02

[1]Basis January 1, 1968, animal numbers.
[2]Computed basis ½ year.
[3]Computed basis ½ year. Average slaughter weights used.
[4]Computed on the basis of the value/ton given in the right hand column of Table 17-5.

is worth 4.8 billion dollars. That is potential annual income of $1,518 for each of the nation's 3.1 million farms.

Of course, the value of manure cannot be measured alone in terms of increased crop yields and equivalent cost of a like amount of commercial fertilizer. It has additional value for the organic matter which it contains, which almost all soils need, and which farmers and ranchers cannot buy in a sack or tank.

Also, it is noteworthy that, due to the slower availability of its nitrogen and to its contribution to the soil humus, manure produces rather lasting benefits which may continue for many years. Approximately one-half of the plant nutrients in manure are available to and effective upon the crops in the immediate cycle of the rotation to which the application is made. Of the unused remainder, about one-half, in turn, is taken up by the crops in the second cycle of the rotation; one-half of the remainder in the third cycle, etc. Likewise, the continuous use of manure through several rounds of a rotation builds up a back-log which brings additional benefits, and a measurable climb in yield levels.

Horsemen sometimes fail to recognize the value of this barnyard crop because (1) it is produced whether or not it is wanted, and (2) it is available without cost.

Modern Ways of Handling Manure

Modern handling of manure involves maximum automation and a minimum loss of nutrients. Among the methods being used are: scrapers; power loaders; conveyors; industrial-type vacuums; slotted floors with the manure stored underneath or emptying into irrigation systems; storage vats; spreaders (including those designed to handle liquids alone or liquids and solids together); dehydration; and lagoons. Actually, there is no one best manure management system for all situations; rather, it is a matter of designing and using that system which will be most practical for a particular set of conditions.

Both small and large horse establishments face the problem of what to do with horse manure, once it is removed from the stable. Because the feces of horses are the primary source of infection of internal parasites, fresh horse manure should never be spread on pastures grazed by horses. The following alternatives for disposing of horse manure exist:

1. Spread fresh manure on those fields that will be plowed and cropped, where there is sufficient land and this is feasible.

2. Contract with a nearby mushroom or vegetable grower, on a mutually satisfactory basis.

3. Store the manure in a suitable tightly constructed pit for at least a two-week interval prior to spreading, allowing the spontaneously generated heat to destroy the parasites.

4. Compost it in an area which will neither pollute a stream nor be offensive to the neighbors; then spread it on the land.

Objectionable Features of Manure

Despite the recognized value of horse manure, it does possess the following objectionable features:

1. *It may propagate insects.*—Unless precautions are taken, often manure is the preferred breeding place for flies and other insects. It is noteworthy, however, that comparitively few house flies are reared in horse manure.

2. *It may spread diseases and parasites.*—Where animals are allowed to come in contact with their own excrement, there is always danger of infections from diseases and parasites.

3. *It may produce undesirable odors.*—Where manure is stored improperly, there may be a nuisance from odors.

4. *It may scatter weed seeds.*—Even when fermented, manure usually contains a certain quantity of viable weed seeds which may be scattered over the land.

MANAGEMENT OF SUB-HUMID, HUMID, AND IRRIGATED PASTURES

Many good pastures have been established only to be lost through careless management. Good pasture management in the sub-humid, humid, and irrigated areas involves the following practices:

1. *Controlled grazing.*—Nothing contributes more to good pasture management than controlled grazing. At its best, it embraces the following:

a. *Protection of first year seedings.*—First year seedings should be grazed lightly or not at all in order that they may get a good start in life. Where practical, instead of grazing, it is preferable to mow a new first year seeding about three inches above the ground and to utilize it as hay or silage, provided there is sufficient growth to justify this procedure.

Fig. 17-15. Standardbred mares and foals on pasture at Walnut Hall Farm, Lexington, Kentucky—the oldest Standardbred nursery in the United States, which was founded before the turn of the century.

Good horsemen, good pastures, and good horses go hand in hand. (Courtesy, Public Relations Director, the U. S. Trotting Association, Columbus, Ohio)

b. *Rotation or alternate grazing.*—Rotation or alternate grazing is accomplished by dividing a pasture into fields (usually two to four) of approximately equal size, so that one field can be grazed while the others are allowed to make new growth. This results in increased pasture yields, more uniform grazing, and higher quality forage.

Generally speaking, rotation or alternate grazing is (1) more practical and profitable on rotation and supplemental pastures than on permanent pastures, and (2) more beneficial where parasite infestations are heavy than where little or no parasitic problems are involved.

c. *Shifting the location of salt, shade, and water.*—Where portable salt containers are used, more uniform grazing and scattering of the droppings may be obtained simply by the practice of shifting the location of the salt to the less grazed areas of the pasture. Where possible and practical, the shade and the water should be shifted likewise.

d. *Deferred spring grazing.*—Allow six to eight inches of growth before turning horses out to pasture in the spring, thus giving grass a needed start. Anyway, the early spring growth of pastures is high in moisture and washy.

e. *Avoiding close late fall grazing.*—Pastures that are grazed closely late in the fall start late in the spring. With most pastures, three to five inches of growth should be left for winter cover.

f. *Avoiding overgrazing.*—Never graze more closely than two to three inches during the pasture season. Continued close grazing reduces the yield, weakens the plants, allows weeds to invade, and increases soil erosion. The use of temporary and supplemental pastures, may "spell off" regular pastures through seasons of drought and other pasture shortages and thus alleviate overgrazing.

g. *Avoiding undergrazing.*—Undergrazing seeded pastures should also be avoided, because (1) mature forage is unpalatable and of low nutritive value, (2) tall-growing grasses may drive out such low-growing plants as white clover due to shading, and (3) weeds, brush, and coarse grasses are more apt to gain a foothold when the pasture is grazed insufficiently. It is a

Fig. 17-16. Clipping to control weeds and brush increases yields and improves the quality of pastures. (Drawing by R. F. Johnson)

good rule, therefore, to graze the pasture fairly close at least once each year.

2. *Clipping pastures and controlling weeds.*—Pastures should be clipped at such intervals as necessary to control weeds (and brush) and to get rid of uneaten clumps and other unpalatable coarse growth left after incomplete grazing. Pastures that are grazed continuously may be clipped at or just preceding the usual haymaking time; rotated pastures may be clipped at the close of the grazing period. Weeds and brush may also be controlled by chemicals, by burning, etc.

3. *Topdressing.*—Like animals, for best results grasses and legumes must be fed properly throughout a lifetime. It is not sufficient that they be fertilized (and limed if necessary) at or prior to seeding time. In addition, in most areas it is desirable and profitable to topdress pastures with fertilizer annually, and, at less frequent intervals, with reinforced manure and lime (lime to maintain a pH of about 6.5). Such treatments should be based on soil tests, and are usually applied in the spring or fall.

Fig. 17-17. In most areas, it is desirable and profitable to topdress pastures with fertilizer annually, and at less frequent intervals with reinforced manure and lime. (Drawing by R. F. Johnson)

4. *Scattering droppings.*—The droppings should be scattered three or four times each year and at the end of each grazing season in order to prevent animals from leaving ungrazed clumps and to help them fertilize a larger area. This can best be done by the use of a brush harrow or chain harrow.

5. *Grazing by more than one class of animals.*—Grazing by two or more classes of animals makes for more uniform pasture utilization and fewer weeds and parasites, provided the area is not overstocked.

Different kinds of livestock have different habits of grazing; they show preference for different plants and graze to different heights.

6. *Irrigating where practical and feasible.*—Where irrigation is practical and feasible, it alleviates the necessity of depending on the weather.

7. *Supplementing to provide needed nutrients.*—Although the horse ration should be as economical as possible, condition and results in show, sale, and use are the primary objectives, even at somewhat added expense. Generally, this calls for supplemental feeding on pasture—for providing added energy, protein, minerals, and vitamins.

Fig. 17-18. A chain harrow is ideal for scattering droppings; controlling parasites; seeding, maintaining, or renovating pastures; and/or maintaining a show-ring or track. (Courtesy, Pegus Company, Inc., 3699 East Sierra Avenue, Clovis, Calif. 93612)

Extending the Grazing Season

In the South and in Hawaii, year-round grazing is a reality on many a successful farm. By careful planning and by selecting the proper combination of crops, other areas can approach this desired goal.

In addition to lengthening the grazing season through the selection

Table 17-7

POINTERS ON CARING FOR HORSE PASTURES AND RECREATIONAL AREAS

For	When	How to Do It	Comments
Pasture Maintenance	Spring and Fall. Spring and Fall, plus three to four times during grazing season	Use a chain harrow to: 1. Tear out the old, dead material. 2. Stimulate growth through gentle cultivating action. 3. Prevent a sod-bound condition. 4. Increase moisture penetration. Also use a chain harrow to scatter animal droppings 5. Help control parasites. 6. Fertilize a larger area. 7. Prevent animals from leaving ungrazed clumps.	Good horsemen, good pastures, and good horses go hand in hand. Yet, altogether too many horse pastures are merely gymnasiums or exercising grounds. This need not be so. Through improved pasture maintenance, you can: 1. Produce higher yields of nutritious forage. 2. Extend the grazing season from early in the spring to late in the fall. 3. Provide a fairly uniform supply of feed throughout the entire season.
Pasture Renovation	Spring or Fall.	Use a chain harrow to work the fertilizer and seed into the soil, and yet destroy a minimum of the existing sod.	Run-down pastures can be brought back into production without plowing and reseeding.
Preparing Pasture Seedbed	Spring or Fall.	Use a chain harrow to: 1. Level 2. Smooth down 3. Pack	When properly prepared, a seed-bed should be so firm that you barely leave a footprint when you walk across it. The firmer the better, from the standpoint of moisture conservation and small seeds.
Racetracks; Show-Rings	Whenever the track or ring becomes bedded. Just before the race or show; and between races or show events.	Set a chain harrow for maximum or light penetration, depending on the condition of the track or ring. Use a chain harrow as a drag mat to smooth and fill holes.	Good racetracks and show-rings must be firm, yet resilient. Because it's flexible, a chain harrow can be pulled at good speed, as is necessary between races or show events, and yet do an excellent job of smoothing and filling holes.
Bridle Paths; Farm Lanes; Dirt Roads	Whenever they become rough or uneven.	Use a chain harrow at maximum penetration to put in shape; then turn over to level and fill up holes.	

of species, earlier spring pastures can be secured by avoiding grazing too late in the fall and by the application of a nitrogen fertilizer in the fall or early spring. Nitrogen fertilizers will often stimulate the growth of grass so that it will be ready for grazing ten days to two weeks earlier than unfertilized areas.

Pointers on Caring for Horse Pastures and Recreational Areas

There is a paucity of information on the care of horse pastures, turfs, and recreational areas. Few college courses even mention them, and precious little authoritative literature has been published on the subject.

Table 17-7 tells how successful operators maintain, renovate, and seed horse pastures, and how they care for racetracks, show-rings, bridle paths, and other like areas. These areas can no longer be taken for granted. They're big and important—and they'll get bigger. Hence, they merit the combined best recommendations of scientists and practical operators.

Selected References

Title of Publication	Author(s)	Publisher
Elements of Farrier Science	D. M. Canfield	Enderes Tool Co., Inc., Albert Lea, Minn., 1966.
Horsemanship and Horsemastership	Vol. II Part Three	The Cavalry School, Fort Riley, Kans., 1946.
Horse Science Handbook, Volume 3	Edited by M. E. Ensminger	Agriservices Foundation, 3699 East Sierra Avenue, Clovis, Calif., 1966.
Horseshoeing	A. Lungwitz, translated by John W. Adams	Oregon State University Press, Corvallis, Ore., 1966.
Selecting, Fitting and Showing Horses	J. E. Nordby H. E. Lattig	The Interstate Printers & Publishers, Inc., Danville, Ill., 1963.
Stockman's Handbook	December 1956 1957 and 1958	Stockmen's Short Course, Washington State University, Pullman, Wash.
Stud Manager's Handbook	November—1951, 1952, 1953, 1954, 1958, and 1962	Stud Manager's Course, Box 1520, Lexington, Ky.
Stud Manager's Handbook	December, 1961	Washington State University, Pullman, Wash.

18

In this chapter . . .

18

Business Aspects of Horse Production

IN THE PRESENT ERA, many horse enterprises are owned and operated as businesses, with a profit motive—just as other stockmen have cattle, sheep, or swine enterprises. These horsemen must treat their operations as businesses and become more sophisticated; otherwise, they won't be in business very long. Other horsemen keep horses as a hobby—for much the same reason that some folks play golf, hunt, fish, or go boating. When kept for the latter purpose, their cost should be looked upon much like that of any other hobby or an evening's entertainment; that is, decide in advance how much you can afford to spend, then stop when that amount has been spent.

There was a time when horsemen-hobbyists operated much like most fishermen and hunters, who do not wish to be reminded of the cost per pound of their catch or quarry. The guiding philosophy of these hobbyists is very similar to that of the story attributed to J. Pierpont Morgan, who once admonished an inquiring friend that, "If you have to ask what it costs to maintain a yacht, you can't afford it." But this attitude among horsemen-hobbyists has changed, primarily because of (1) inheritance taxes making it increasingly difficult to pass wealth from one generation to the next, and (2) closer scrutiny of tax write-offs. Also, even when horses are kept primarily for the fun of it, most owners derive more pleasure therefrom when the operation pays, or nearly pays, its way—it's a matter of pride and a challenge. For these reasons, more and more folks who keep horses primarily for pleasure, like those who keep horses for profit, are interested in improving the business aspects of their enterprises.

705

CAPITAL

Horsemen who are in business to make a profit should never invest money, either their own or borrowed, unless they are reasonably certain that it will make money. Capital will be needed for land, buildings, machinery and equipment, horses, feed, supplies, labor, and miscellaneous items.

Whether establishing or enlarging a horse enterprise, the most common question, a two-pronged one, is—how much money will it take, and how much will it make? This information is needed by both horsemen and lenders. Unfortunately, a simple answer cannot be given. However, the following guides will be helpful:

1. *Land, buildings, machinery and equipment, and horse and labor costs.*—Generally speaking, it is not too difficult to arrive at these costs.

The horseman can easily determine the prevailing price of land in the area under consideration, either by inquiring of local land owners or reputable realtors. Where new buildings must be constructed, local architects can quote approximate costs on a square foot basis. Likewise, dealers can give prices on major items of machinery and equipment.

Horse prices vary widely, by breed and age, and according to quality. Nevertheless, auction or private treaty sales, or a knowledgeable horseman, will aid one in establishing the prevailing price for the breed, age, and quality desired. Also, going wages can usually be determined rather easily for a particular area.

2. *Feed, tack, and drug costs.*—Where no pasture whatsoever is available, a 1,000-pound horse will consume about 30 pounds of feed (hay and grain) daily, or about 5½ tons per year. Where an all-pelleted ration is used, 20 percent less feed will suffice, primarily because there is practically no wastage; hence, the allowance of a 1,000-pound horse on an all-pelleted ration may be computed on the basis of 25 pounds per day, or 4½ tons per year.

Based on a study made by the author, on the average and for the United States as a whole, it appears that the annual expenditure for feed, tack, and drugs is as follows:

Feed:

Commercial feed....................	$ 52.80	
Farm-grown hay and grain[1].........	211.20	
Pasture[1]	96.00	
Total feed		$360.00
Tack		300.00
Drugs		75.00
		$735.00

Certainly, feed, tack, and drug costs will vary widely, some being more and other less than the above figures.

3. *Size of horse enterprise.*—Generally speaking, larger horse enterprises contribute to increased profits for the following reasons:

a. They result in fewer hours of labor per horse.

b. They are more apt to be used to capacity. For example, if for an establishment producing 20 foals per year the depreciation, interest, repairs, insurance, and taxes cost $12,000 annually, that's $600 per foal. If the same facilities were used to produce 40 foals per year, the cost would be lessened to $300 per foal. This shows how increased numbers can reduce the building and equipment cost per foal.

Guidelines Relative to Facility and Equipment Costs

Overinvestment is a mistake. Some horsemen invest more in land and buildings than reasonably can be expected to make a satisfactory return; others invest too much in feed mills and equipment. Sometimes operators of small establishments fail to recognize that it may cost half as much to mechanize for 10 horses as it does for 60.

In order to lessen the hazard of overinvestment, guidelines are useful. Here are two:

Guideline No. 1.—The break-even point on how much you can afford to invest in equipment to replace hired labor can be arrived at by the following formula:

---

[1]Where hay, grain, and/or pasture are home-produced, their estimated sale value should be used as a basis of arriving at feed costs of the horse enterprise.

Annual saving in hired
$$\frac{\text{labor from new equipment}}{\text{(divide by) .15}} = \text{amount you can afford to invest.}$$

Example:

If hired labor costs $3,600 per year, this becomes—

$$\frac{\$3,600}{.15} = \$24,000, \text{ the break-even point on new equipment.}$$

Since labor costs are going up faster than machinery and equipment costs, it may be good business to exceed this limitation under some circumstances. Nevertheless, the break-even point, $24,000 in this case, is probably the maximum expenditure that can be economically justified at the time.

Guideline No. 2.—Assuming an annual cost plus operation of power machinery and equipment equal to 20 percent of new cost, the break-even point to justify replacement of one hired man is as follows:

If annual cost of one hired man is[2]	The break-even point on new investment is
$2,500 (20%) × 5	$12,500
3,500 (20%) × 5	17,500
4,500 (20%) × 5	22,500

Example:

Assume that the new cost of added equipment comes to $1,500, that the annual cost is 20 percent of this amount, and that the new equipment would save one hour of labor per day for six months of the year. Here's how to figure the value of labor to justify an expenditure of $1,500 for this item:

$1,500 (new cost) × 20% = $300
300 (annual ownership use cost) ÷ 180 hrs. (labor saved) =
$1.67 per hour.

So, if labor costs less than $1.67 per hour, you probably shouldn't buy the new item.

CREDIT IN THE HORSE BUSINESS

Total farm assets are estimated at $273 billion, while the total farm

---

[2]This is assuming that the productivity of men at different salaries is the same, which may or may not be the case.

debt is about $40 billion. This means that, in the aggregate, farmers have nearly an 85 percent equity in their business, and 15 percent borrowed capital. Perhaps they have been too conservative, for it is estimated that one-fourth to one-third of American farmers could profit from the use of more credit in their operations.

Credit is an integral part of today's horse business. Wise use of it can be profitable, but unwise use of it can be disastrous. Accordingly, horsemen should know more about it. They need to know something about the lending agencies available to them, the types of credit, how to go about obtaining a loan, and methods of computing interest.

The common lending sources of farm credit are: commercial banks, production credit associations, Federal land banks, individuals and other private lenders, life insurance companies, merchants and dealers, and the Farm Home Administration.[3]

Data are not available to show the amount of money borrowed by horsemen. However, it is known that farmers and ranchers borrow over $6 billion a year (which is about one-sixth of the credit which they will use) from the farm credit system - - - which includes the Federal land banks, Federal intermediate credit banks, production credit associations, and banks for cooperatives. Also, it is reported that on January 1, 1964, commercial banks held 85 percent of the reported non-real-estate loans to farmers in California, production credit associations held 12 percent, and all other sources had only 3 percent.[4] Grain companies, feed companies, and various other suppliers are also important sources of credit to horsemen.

Types of Credit

Following are the three general types of agricultural credit to consider, based on length of life and type of collateral needed:

1. *Short-term or production credit.*—This is for up to one year. It is used for purchase of feed and operating expenses.

2. *Intermediate credit.*—This type of credit may be for one to seven years. It is used for the purchase of breeding stock, machinery, equipment, and semipermanent investments. Repayment is made from the profits over several production periods.

---

[3]Information relative to each of these credit sources is given in *The Stockman's Handbook*, 4th ed., Sec. XVII.

[4]*Cattle Feeding in California*, Bank of America, Economic Research Department, Feb. 1965, p. 29.

3. *Long-term credit.*—This type of credit is used for land and major farm building, and for physical plant construction. Repayment is made over several years, from profits.

Credit Factors Considered and Evaluated by Lenders

Potential money borrowers sometimes make their first big mistake by going in "cold" to see a lender—without adequate facts and figures—, with the result that they already have two strikes against them regarding their getting the loan.

When considering and reviewing horse loan requests, the lender tries to arrive at the repayment ability of the potential borrower. Likewise, the borrower has no reason to obtain money unless it will make money.

Lenders need certain basic information in order to evaluate the soundness of a loan request. To this end, the following information should be submitted:

1. *Analysis and feasibility study.*—Lenders are impressed with a borrower who has a written down feasibility study, showing where he is now, where he's going, and how he expects to get there. In addition to spelling out the goals, this report should give assurance of the necessary management skills to achieve them. Such an analysis of the present and projection into the future is imperative in big operations.

2. *The applicant, farm, and financial statement.*—It is the borrower's obligation, and in his best interest, to present the following information to the lender:

   a. *The applicant:*

     (1) Name of applicant and wife; age of applicant.

     (2) Number of children (minors, legal age).

     (3) Partners in business, if any.

     (4) Years in area.

     (5) References.

   b. *The farm:*

     (1) Owner or tenant.

     (2) Location; legal description and county, and direction and distance from nearest town.

     (3) Type of enterprise: breeding, racing, riding stable, etc.

   c. *Financial statement:* This document indicates the borrower's financial record and current financial position, his potential ahead, and his liability to others. The borrower should always have sufficient slack to absorb reasonable losses due to such unforeseen happenstances as storms, droughts, diseases, and poor markets, thereby permitting the lender to stay with him in adversity and to give him a chance to recoup his losses in the future. The financial statement should include the following:

(1) Current assets:
    (a) Horses and other animals.
    (b) Feed.
    (c) Machinery.
    (d) Cash—There should be reasonable cash reserves, to cut interest costs, and to provide a cushion against emergencies.
    (e) Bonds or other investments.
    (f) Cash value of life insurance.

(2) Fixed assets:
    (a) Real property, with estimated value.
    (b) Farm property.
    (c) City property.
    (d) Long term contracts.

(3) Current liabilities:
    (a) Mortgages.
    (b) Contracts.
    (c) Open account—to whom owed.
    (d) Co-signer or guarantor on notes.
    (e) Any taxes due.
    (f) Current portion of real estate indebtedness due.

(4) Fixed liabilities—amount and nature of real estate debt:
    (a) Date due.
    (b) Interest rate.
    (c) To whom payable.
    (d) Contract or mortgage.

3. *Other factors.*—Shrewd lenders usually ferret out many things, among them:

a. *The potential borrower.*—Most lenders will tell the potential borrower that he is the most important part of the loan.
Lenders consider his:
    (1) Character.
    (2) Honesty and integrity.
    (3) Experience and ability.

(4) Moral and credit rating.

(5) Age and health.

(6) Family cooperation.

(7) Continuity, or line of succession.

Lenders are quick to sense the "high-liver"—the fellow who lives beyond his income; the poor manager—the kind who would have made it except for hard luck, and to whom the hard luck happened many times; and the dishonest, lazy, and incompetent.

In recognition of the importance of the man back of the loan, "key man" insurance on the owner or manager should be considered by both the lender and the borrower.

b. *Production records.*—This refers to a good set of records showing efficiency of production. On a horse breeding establishment, for example, such records should show prices of horses sold, percent foal crop, filly replacement program, depreciation schedule, average crop yield, and other pertinent information. Lenders will increasingly insist on good records.

c. *Progress with previous loans.*—Has the borrower paid back previous loans plus interest? Has he reduced the amount of the loan, thereby giving evidence of progress?

d. *Profit and loss (P & L).*—This serves as a valuable guide to the potential ahead. Preferably, this should cover the previous three years. Also, most lenders prefer that this be on an accrual basis (even if the horseman is on a cash basis in reporting to the Internal Revenue Service).

e. *Physical plant.*—

(1) Is it an economic unit?

(2) Does it have adequate water, and is it well balanced in feed and horses?

(3) Is there adequate diversification?

(4) Is the right kind of horse enterprise being conducted?

(5) Are the right crops and varieties grown; and are approved methods of tillage and fertilizer practices being followed?

(6) Is the farmstead neat and well kept?

f. *Collateral (or security).*—

(1) Adequate to cover loan, with margin.

(2) Quality of security:

(a) Grade and age of horses.

(b) Type and condition of machinery.

(c) If grain storage is involved, adequacy of protection from moisture and rodents.

(d) Government participation.

(3) Identification of security:

(a) Tattoo or brands on horses.

(b) Serial numbers on machinery.

4. *The loan request.*—Horsemen are in competition for money from urban businessmen. Hence, it is important that their request for a loan be well presented and supported. The potential borrower should tell the purpose of the loan, how much money is needed, when it's needed, the soundness of the venture, and the repayment schedule.

Credit Factors Considered by Borrowers

Credit is a two-way street; it must be good for both the borrower and the lender. If a borrower is the right kind of person and on a sound basis, more than one lender will want his business. Thus, it is usually well that a borrower shop around a bit; that he be familiar with several sources of credit and what they have to offer. There are basic differences in length and type of loan, repayment schedules, services provided with the loan, interest rate, and the ability and willingness of lenders to stick by the borrower in emergencies and times of adversity. Thus, interest rates and willingness to loan are only two of the several factors to consider. Also, if at all possible, all borrowing should be done from one source; a one-source lender will know more about the borrower's operations and be in a better position to help him.

Helpful Hints for Building and Maintaining a Good Credit Rating

Horsemen who wish to build up and maintain good credit are admonished to do the following:

1. *Keep credit in one place, or in few places.*—Generally, lenders frown upon "split financing." Shop around for a creditor (a) who is able, willing, and interested in extending the kind and amount of credit needed, and (b) who will lend at a reasonable rate of interest; then stay with him.

2. *Get the right kind of credit.*—Don't use short-term credit to finance long-term improvements or other capital investments.

3. *Be frank with the lender.*—Be completely open and aboveboard.

Mutual confidence and esteem should prevail between borrower and lender.

4. *Keep complete and accurate records.*—Complete and accurate records should be kept by enterprises. By knowing the cost of doing business, decision-making can be on a sound basis.

5. *Keep annual inventory.*—Take an annual inventory for the purpose of showing progress made during the year.

6. *Repay loans when due.*—Borrowers should work out a repayment schedule on each loan, then meet payments when due. Sale proceeds should be promptly applied on loans.

7. *Plan ahead.*—Analyze the next year's operation and project ahead.

Calculating Interest

The total cost of using credit varies according to (1) rate of and method of computing interest, and (2) length of time the loan is needed. There are four commonly used methods of calculating interest, namely:

1. *Flat rate of interest (or simple interest) methods.*—In which a specified rate of interest is paid on the original amount of the loan. For example, if $1,000 is borrowed for 12 months at 6 percent interest, the total interest will be $60.

2. *Added-on interest method.*—In which the interest is added to the principal at the time the loan is made. Thus, if the loan is repaid in 12 equal monthly installments, the true interest rate will be approximately 12 percent, because the interest is charged on the total original amount of the loan and does not decrease with each successive payment.

3. *Unpaid balance method.*—In which interest is paid only on the amount which has not been repaid. Thus, if $1,000 is borrowed for 12 months at 6 percent interest, but half the original loan is repaid at the end of six months, six months' interest would be saved on $500. Hence, the interest on this $500 would be 3 percent, whereas the interest on the remaining $500 not repaid until the end of the 12 months would be 6 percent. Thus, the total interest cost would be $45.

4. *Discount method.*—In which the lender discounts the loan in advance. For example, with a $1,000 loan for 12 months at 6 percent the borrower actually has only $940 to use—rather than $1,000. Hence, the true interest rate on $950 would be 6.4 percent. If the borrower must have $1,000, the lender may write the loan for an amount large

enough to discount the interest and yet provide $1,000 to the borrower.

Table 18-1 shows the true interest rate of a $1,000 loan, with the interest computed by each of the above methods.

Table 18-1

TRUE INTEREST RATES ON A $1,000 LOAN,
BY FOUR METHODS OF COMPUTING

Method of Computing Interest	Principal (12 mo.)	Interest @6%	Total to Repay	True Interest Rate
1. Flat rate of interest: paid in one sum at end of loan period	$1,000	$60	$1,060	6%
2. Added-on interest: principal repaid in equal monthly installments..........................	$1,000	$60	$1,060	12%
3. Unpaid balance: $500 paid in 6 mos., $500 at end of 12 mos.	$1,000	$45	$1,045	6%
4. Discount.............................	$1,000	$60	940	6.4%

BUDGETS IN THE HORSE BUSINESS

A budget is a projection of records and accounts and a plan for organizing and operating ahead for a specific period of time. A short-time budget is usually for one year, whereas a long-time budget is for a period of years. The principal value of a budget is that it provides a working plan through which the operation can be coordinated. Changes in prices, droughts, and other factors make adjustments necessary. But these adjustments are more simply and wisely made if there is a written budget to use as a reference.

How to Set Up a Budget

It's unimportant whether a printed form (of which there are many good ones) is used or one made up on an ordinary ruled 8½" x 11" sheet placed sidewise. The important things are that (1) a budget is kept, (2) it be on a monthly basis, and (3) the operator be "comfortable" with whatever form or system is to be used.

An important part of any budget, or any system of accounting, is that there shall be a listing, or chart, of classifications or categories under which the owner wants the transactions accumulated. In a horse operation that both breeds and races, there may be 150 or more such classifications. From the standpoint of facilitating record keeping, each classification is usually given a number for identification purposes. Then the farm bookkeeper, or the farm manager, codes or classifies each transaction into the proper category.

No budget is perfect. But it should be as good an estimate as can be made—despite the fact that it will be affected by such things as droughts, diseases, markets, and many other unpredictables.

A simple, easily kept, and adequate budget can be evolved by using forms such as those shown in Tables 18-2, 18-3, and 18-4.

The Annual Cash Expense Budget should show the monthly breakdown of various recurring items—everything except the initial loan and capital improvements. It includes labor, feed, supplies, fertilizer, taxes, interest, utilities, etc.

The Annual Cash Income Budget is just what the name implies— an estimated cash income by months.

The Annual Cash Expense and Income Budget is a cash flow chart obtained from the first two forms. It's a money "flow" summary by months. From this, it can be ascertained when money will need to be borrowed, how much will be needed, and the length of the loan along with a repayment schedule. It makes it possible to avoid tying up capital unnecessarily, and to avoid unnecessary interest.

How to Figure Net Income

Table 18-4 shows a gross income statement. There are other expenses that must be taken care of before net profit is determined, namely:

1. *Depreciation on buildings and equipment.*—It is suggested that the "useful life" of horse buildings and equipment be as follows, with depreciation accordingly:

Buildings—25 years.

Machinery and equipment—10 years.

Sometimes a higher depreciation, or amortization, is desirable because it produces tax savings and is protection against obsolescence due to scientific and technological developments.

2. *Interest on owner's money invested in farm and equipment.*— This should be computed at the going rate in the area, say 8 percent.

Here's an example of how these work:

Let's assume that on a given horse establishment there was a

Table 18-2

ANNUAL CASH EXPENSE BUDGET

For _____
(date)

_____
(name of farm)

Item	Total	Jan.	Feb.	Mar.	Apr.	May	June	July	Aug.	Sept.	Oct.	Nov.	Dec.
Labor hired													
Feed purchased													
Stud fees													
Gas, fuel, grease													
Taxes													
Insurance													
Interest													
Utilities													
etc.													
Total													

Table 18-3

ANNUAL CASH INCOME BUDGET

For _____
(date)

_____
(name of farm)

Item	Total	Jan.	Feb.	Mar.	Apr.	May	June	July	Aug.	Sept.	Oct.	Nov.	Dec.
30 yearlings													
30 stud fees, @ $500 each													
490 bu. wheat													
etc.													
Total													

Table 18-4

ANNUAL CASH EXPENSE AND INCOME BUDGET (Cash Flow Chart)

For _____
(date)

_____
(name of farm)

Item	Total	Jan.	Feb.	Mar.	Apr.	May	June	July	Aug.	Sept.	Oct.	Nov.	Dec.
Gross income	25,670					1,000	1,000	etc.					
Gross expense	13,910					575	2,405	etc.					
Difference	11,760					425	1,405	etc.					
Surplus (+) or Deficit (-)	+					+	-						

gross income of $100,000 and a gross expense of $60,000, or a surplus of $40,000. Let's further assume that there are $40,000 worth
of machinery, $30,000 worth of buildings, and $175,000 of the
owner's money invested in farm and equipment. Here is the result:

Gross profit $40,000
Depreciation—
   Machinery: $40,000 @ 10% = $ 4,000
   Buildings: $30,000 @ 4% =   1,200
                                  $ 5,200
   Interest: $175,000 @ 8% = 14,000
                     Total.........   19,200
Return to labor and management.............$20,800

Some people prefer to measure management by return on invested
capital, and not wages. This approach may be accomplished by paying
management wages first, then figuring return on investment.

Enterprise Accounts

When one has a diversified horse enterprise—for example when producing yearlings for sale, having a racing or showing stable, standing stallions for public service, and growing corn—enterprise accounts should
be kept; in this case four different accounts for four different enterprises. The reasons for keeping enterprise accounts are:

1. It makes it possible to determine which enterprises have been
most profitable, and which least profitable.

2. It makes it possible to compare a given enterprise with compet-
ing enterprises of like kind, from the standpoint of ascertaining comparative performance.

3. It makes it possible to determine the profitableness of an enterprise at the margin (the last unit of production). This will give an
indication as to whether to increase the size of a certain enterprise at
the expense of an alternative existing enterprise when both enterprises
are profitable in total.

ANALYZING A HORSE BUSINESS; IS IT PROFITABLE?

Most people are in business to make money—and horsemen are
people. In some areas, particularly near cities and where the population

is dense, land values may appreciate so as to be a very considerable profit factor. Also, a tax angle may be important. But neither of these should be counted upon. The horse operation should make a reasonable return on the investment; otherwise, the owner should not consider it a business.

The owner or manager of a horse establishment needs to analyze his business—to determine how well he's doing. With big operations, it's no longer possible to base such an analysis on the bank balance statement at the end of the year. In the first place, once a year is not frequent enough, for it is possible to go broke, without really knowing it, in that period of time. Secondly, a balance statement gives no basis for analyzing an operation—for ferreting out its strengths and weaknesses. In large horse enterprises, it is strongly recommended that progress be charted by means of monthly or quarterly closings of financial records.

Also, a horseman must not only compete with other horsemen down the road, but he must compete with himself—with his record last year and the year before. He must work ceaselessly at making progress and lowering costs of production.

To analyze a horse business, three things are essential: (1) good records, (2) enterprise accounts—that is, with such categories as boarding horses, racing stable, breaking and training yearlings, etc., and (3) profit indicators.

Through enterprise accounts, the owner or farm manager can get answers to such questions as the following:

1. How much does it cost me to board horses of different ages each month during the year?

2. How much is it costing to run a racing stable (or show stable)?

3. What is the actual cost of breaking and training a yearling?

4. Are grooms producing at or below standard rates of performance?

5. Is it profitable for me to produce crops along with my breeding operation?

6. Should I let out my crop land on a cash rental or share-cropping arrangement, or should we do the farming ourselves?

7. Should I produce or buy hay?

Profit indicators are a gauge for measuring the primary factors contributing to profit. In order for a horseman to determine how well he's doing, he must be able to compare his own operation with something else, for example: (1) his own historical five-year average, (2) the average for the U.S. or for his particular area, or (3) the top 5 percent. The author favors the latter, for high goals have a tendency to spur superior achievement.

Admittedly, profit indicators are not perfect, simply because no two horse enterprises are the same. Nationally, there are wide area differences in climate, feeds, land costs, salaries and wages, and other factors. Nevertheless, indicators as such serve as a valuable yardstick. Through them, it is possible to measure how well a given operation is doing—to ascertain if it is out of line in any one category, and, if so, the extent to which it is out of line.

After a few years of operation, it is desirable that a horse operator evolve his own yardstick and profit indicators, based on his own historical records and averages. Even with these, there will be year-to-year fluctuations due to seasonal differences, horse and feed price changes, disease outbreaks, changes in managers, wars and inflation, and other happenstances.

COMPUTERS IN THE HORSE BUSINESS

Accurate and up-to-the-minute records and controls have taken on increasing importance in all agriculture, including the horse business, as the investment required to engage therein has risen. Today's successful horsemen must have, and use, as complete records as any other business. Also, records must be kept current.

Big and complex enterprises have outgrown hand record keeping. It's too time consuming, with the result that it doesn't allow management enough time for planning and decision making. Additionally, it does not permit an all-at-once consideration of the complex interrelationships which affect the economic success of the business. This has prompted a new computer technique known as linear programming.

Linear programming is similar to budgeting, in that it compares several plans simultaneously and chooses from among them the one likely to yield the highest returns. It is a way in which to analyze a great mass of data and consider many alternatives. It is not a managerial genie, nor will it replace decision-making managers. However, it is a modern and effective tool in the present age, when just a few dollars per head or per acre can spell the difference between profit and loss.

There is hardly any limit to what computers can do if fed the proper information. Among the difficult questions that they can answer for a specific operation are:

1. *How is the entire operation doing so far?* It is preferable to obtain quarterly or monthly progress reports, often making it possible to spot trouble before it's too late.

2. *What enterprises are making money; which ones are freeloading or losing?* By keeping records by enterprises—breeding horses, racing stable, wheat, corn, etc.—it is possible to determine strengths and weaknesses, then either to rectify the situation or shift labor and capital to a more profitable operation. Through "enterprise analysis," some operators have discovered that one part of the business may earn $5, or more, per hour for labor and management, whereas another may earn only $1 per hour, and still another may lose money.

3. *Is each enterprise yielding maximum returns?* By having profit or performance indicators in each enterprise, it is possible to compare these (1) with the historical average of the same establishment, or (2) with the same indicators of other operations.

4. *How does this operation stack up with its competition?* Without revealing names, the computing center (local, state, area, or national) can determine how a given operation compares with others—either the average, or the top (say 5 percent).

5. *How can you plan ahead?* By using projected prices and costs, computers can show what moves to make for the future—they can be a powerful planning tool. They can be used in determining when to plant, when to schedule farm machine use, etc.

6. *How can income taxes be cut to the legal minimum?* By keeping accurate record of expenses and figuring depreciations accurately, computers make for a saving in income taxes on most establishments.

7. *What is the least-cost ration formulation and the best buy in ingredients?* Many large horse breeding establishments, and most commercial feed companies, now use computers for ration formulation and as a buying and selling aid of feed ingredients. An electronic computer can't do a thing that a good mathematician can't, but it can do it a lot faster and check all possible combinations. It alleviates the endless calculations and hours common to hand calculations. For example, it is estimated that there may be as many as 500 practical solutions when as many as six quality specifications and 10 feedstuffs are considered. For these reasons, the use of computers in horse ration formulation and in the buying and selling of feed ingredients will increase.

For providing answers to these questions, and many more, computer accounting costs an average of 1 percent of the gross income.

There are three requisites for linear programming a horse establishment, namely:

1. Access to a computer.
2. Computer know-how, so as to set the program up properly and be able to analyze and interpret the results.
3. Good records.

The pioneering computer services available to farmers were operated by universities, trade associations, and government; most of them were on an experimental basis. Subsequently, others have entered the field, including commercial data processing firms, banks, machinery companies, feed and fertilizer companies, and farm suppliers. They are using it as a "service sell," as a replacement for the days of "hard sell."

Programmed farming is here to stay, and it will increase in the horse business.

Computers in Horse Breeding Operations

In the past, the biggest deterrent to adequate records on a horse breeding establishment has been the voluminous and time-consuming record keeping involved. Keeping records as such does not change what an animal will transmit, but records must be used to locate and propagate the genetically superior animals if genetic improvement is to be accomplished.

Performance testing has been covered elsewhere in this book (see Chapter 12); thus, repetition at this point is unnecessary.

In addition to their use in performance testing, computerized records can be used for breeding record purposes—as a means of keeping management up-to-date and as an alert on problems to be solved or work to be done. Each animal must be individually identified. Reports can be obtained at such intervals as desired, usually monthly or every two weeks. Also, the owner can keep as complete or as few records as desired. Here are several of the records that can be kept by computer:

1. Pedigrees.
2. Records of animals that need attention, such as:
   a. Animals four months old that are unregistered.
   b. Animals ready for inspection or scoring.
   c. Mares that have been bred two consecutive times.
   d. Mares that have not conceived two months after foaling.

    e. Mares due to foal in 30 days.

    f. Foals seven months of age that haven't been weaned.

    g. Animals that have not received their seasonal vaccinations; for example, that have not been vaccinated against sleeping sickness by May 1.

    h. Animals that have not been treated for parasites at the scheduled time.

3. A running or cumulative inventory of the herd, by sex; including foals dropped, foals due, and purchases and sales—in number of animals and dollars.

4. The depreciation of purchased animals according to the accounting method of choice.

MANAGEMENT

According to Webster, *management is "the act, art, or manner of managing, or handling, controlling, directing, etc."*

Three major ingredients are essential to success in the horse business: (1) good horses, (2) a sound feed and care program, and (3) good management.

Management gives point and purpose to everything else. The skill of the manager materially affects how well horses are bought and sold, the health of the animals, the results of the rations, the stresses of the horses, the growth rate of young stock, the performance of labor, the public relations of the establishment, and even the expression of the genetic potential of the horses. Indeed, a manager must wear many hats—and he must wear each of them well.

The bigger and the more complicated the horse operation, the more competent the management required. This point merits emphasis because, currently, (1) bigness is a sign of the times, and (2) the most common method of attempting to "bail out" of an unprofitable horse venture is to increase its size. Although it's easier to achieve efficiency of equipment, labor, purchases, and marketing in big operations, bigness alone will not make for greater efficiency as some owners have discovered to their sorrow, and others will experience. Management is still the key to success. When in financial trouble, owners should have no illusions on this point.

In manufacturing and commerce, the importance and scarcity of top managers are generally recognized and reflected in the salaries paid to persons in such positions. Unfortunately, agriculture as a whole has lagged; and altogether too many owners still subscribe to the philosophy that the way to make money out of the horse business is to hire a manager cheap, with the result that they usually get what they pay for—a "cheap manager."

Traits of a Good Manager

There are established bases for evaluating many articles of trade, including hay and grain. They are graded according to well-defined standards. Additionally, we chemically analyze feeds and conduct feeding trials. But no such standard or system of evaluation has evolved for managers, despite their acknowledged importance.

The author has prepared the Manager Check List given in Table 18-5, which (1) employers may find useful when selecting or evaluat-

Table 18-5

MANAGER CHECK LIST

☐ CHARACTER
Has absolute sincerity, honesty, integrity, and loyalty; is ethical.

☐ INDUSTRY
Has enthusiasm, initiative, and aggressiveness; is willing to work, work, work.

☐ ABILITY
Has horse know-how and experience, business acumen—including ability systematically to arrive at the financial aspects and convert this information into sound and timely management decisions, knowledge of how to automate and cut costs, common sense, and growth potential; is organized.

☐ PLANS
Sets goals; prepares organization chart and job description; plans work and works plans.

☐ ANALYZES
Identifies the problem, determines pros and cons, then comes to a decision.

☐ COURAGE
Has the courage to accept responsibility, to innovate, and to keep on keeping on.

☐ PROMPTNESS AND DEPENDABILITY
Is a self-starter; has "T.N.T.," which means that he does it "today, not tomorrow."

☐ LEADERSHIP
Stimulates subordinates and delegates responsibility.

☐ PERSONALITY
Is cheerful; not a complainer.

ing a manager, and (2) managers may apply to themselves for self-improvement purposes. No attempt has been made to assign a percentage score to each trait, because this will vary among horse establishments. Rather, it is hoped that this check list will serve as a useful guide (1) to the traits of a good manager, and (2) to what the boss wants.

Organization Chart and Job Description

It is important that every worker know to whom he is responsible and for what he is responsible; and the bigger and the more complex the operation, the more important this becomes. This should be written down in an organization chart and a job description.

Here's how they look (see next page for job descriptions):

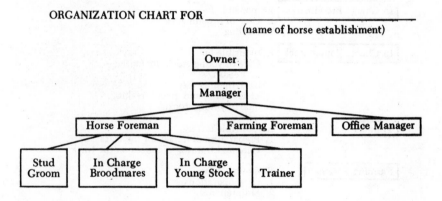

ORGANIZATION CHART FOR _____
(name of horse establishment)

Incentive Basis for the Help

Big horse establishments must rely on hired labor, all or in part. Good help—the kind that everyone wants—is hard to come by; it's scarce, in strong demand, and difficult to keep. And the farm-horse manpower situation is going to become more difficult in the years ahead. There is need, therefore, for some system that will (1) give a big assist in getting and holding top-flight help and (2) cut costs and boost profits. An incentive basis that makes hired help partners in profit is the answer.

Many manufacturers have long had an incentive basis. Executives are frequently accorded stock option privileges, through which they prosper as the business prospers. Common laborers may receive bonuses based on piecework or quotas (number of units, pounds produced).

JOB DESCRIPTIONS ON_____
(name of horse establishment)

Owner	Responsible for: 1. Making policy decisions. 2. Borrowing capital. (List other.)
Manager	Responsible for: 1. Supervising all staff. 2. Preparing proposed long-time plan. 3. Budgets.
Horse Foreman	Responsible for: 1. All horse operations. 2. Directing his staff.
Stud Groom	Responsible for: 1. Care of stallions. 2. Teasing and breeding mares. 3. Breeding records.
In Charge Broodmares	Responsible for: 1. Care of broodmares. 2. Foaling.

In Charge Young Stock	Responsible for:
	1. Care of young stock, including—
	  a. Feeding.
	  b. Trimming feet.
	  c. Gentling and green breaking.
	2. Sale of young stock.

Trainer	Responsible for: 1. Preparation of horses for the track. 2. Care and training of horses on the track.
Farming Foreman	Responsible for: 1. Crop operations. 2. Maintenance.
Office Manager	Responsible for: 1. Records. 2. Budgets.

Also, most factory workers get overtime pay and have group insurance and a retirement plan. A few industries have a true profit-sharing arrangement based on net profit as such, a specified percentage of which is divided among employees. No two systems are alike. Yet, each is designed to pay more for labor, provided labor improves production and efficiency. In this way, both owners and laborers benefit from better performance.

Family-owned and family-operated horse enterprises have a built-in incentive basis; there is pride of ownership, and all members of the family are fully cognizant that they prosper as the business prospers.

Also, there is an incentive basis in racehorses; both trainers and jockeys share in winnings. However, few horse breeding establihments or riding stables have evolved with an incentive basis for the help. They should give serious consideration to doing so.

Sometimes employers erroneously conclude that providing an incentive basis means that they are giving up a portion of their normal net. For a brief period of time, this may be true. But with the right kind of help, and over a period of time, it will make money for both owners and employees.

Many different incentive plans can be, and are, used. There is no best one for all operations. The various plans given in Table 18-6 are intended as guides only.

The incentive basis chosen should be tailored to fit the specific operation, with consideration given to kind and size of operation, extent of owner's supervision, present and projected productivity levels, mechanization, and other factors.

HOW MUCH INCENTIVE PAY?

After (1) reaching a decision to go on an incentive basis, and (2) deciding on the kind of incentive, it is necessary to arrive at how much the incentive should be. Here are some guidelines that may be helpful in determining this:

1. Pay the going base, or guaranteed, salary; then add the incentive pay above this.

2. Determine the total stipend (the base salary plus incentive) to which you are willing to go.

3. Before making any offers, always check the plan on paper to see (a) how it would have worked out in past years based on your records, and (b) how it will work out as you achieve the future projected production.

REQUISITES OF AN INCENTIVE BASIS

Owners who have not previously had experience with an incentive basis are admonished not to start with any plan until they are sure of both their plan and their help. Also, it is well to start with a simple plan; then a change can be made to a more inclusive and sophisticated plan after experience is acquired.

Table 18-6

INCENTIVE PLANS FOR HORSE ESTABLISHMENTS

Types of Incentives	Pertinent Provisions of Some Known Incentive Systems in Use	Advantages	Disadvantages	Comments
Bonuses	A flat, arbitrary bonus; at Christmas time, year-end, or quarterly or other intervals. A tenure bonus such as: (1) 5% to 10% of the base wage or 2 to 4 weeks' additional salary paid at Christmas time or year-end, (2) 2 to 4 weeks vacation with pay, depending on length and quality of service, or (3) $3.00 to $20.00 per week set aside and to be paid if employee stays on the job a specified time.	It's simple and direct.	Not very effective in increasing production and profits.	
Equity-building plan	Employee is allowed to own a certain number of horses. These are usually fed without charge.	It imparts pride of ownership to the employee.	The hazard that the owner may feel employee accords his own animals preferential treatment; suspicioned if not proved.	
Production sharing	$50 for every mare conceiving above 75%. $100 for every live foal born (foal standing and nursing) above 60%, based on mares bred.	It's an effective way to achieve higher conception and foal crop.	Net returns may suffer. If a high performance level already exists, further gains or improvements may be hard to come by.	

(Continued)

Table 18-6 (Continued)

Types of Incentives	Pertinent Provisions of Some Known Incentive Systems in Use	Advantages	Disadvantages	Comments
Profit sharing:		It's an effective way to get hired help to cut costs.		There must be prior agreement on what constitutes gross or net receipts, as the case may be, and how it is figured.
1. Percent of gross income in cash.	1% to 2% of the gross, with each employee sharing on a prorata of salary basis.	It's a good plan for a hustler.	Percent of gross does not impart cost of production consciousness. Controversy may arise (1) over accounting procedure; e.g., from the standpoint of the owner a fast tax write-off may be desirable on new equipment, but this reduces the net shared with the worker; and (2) because some owners are prone to overbuild and overequip, thereby decreasing net.	Generally, a working owner should accord himself a salary as part of the operating expense of the business, just as he allows salaries to other help. Then, all operating costs, including interest on the owner's money, should be deducted as expenses. Books should not be opened up to all employees. Access to books should be limited to supervisory personnel and the bookkeeper. Most laborers do not understand accounting principles; hence, opening up the books to them may lead to gossip, suspicion, and distrust.
2. Percent of net income in cash.	10% to 20% of the net after deducting all costs, with each employee sharing on a prorata of salary basis.		There may not be any net some years.	

(Continued)

Table 18-6 (Continued)

Types of Incentives	Pertinent Provisions of Some Known Incentive Systems in Use	Advantages	Disadvantages	Comments
3. Percent of net income as investment in the business.	Giving employees an investment (stock) in the future growth and expansion of the business in an amount equal to 20% of the yearly net profit, with each employee sharing on a prorata basis of salary basis.	Employees stand to profit if the business grows and prospers.		
4. Percent of net income placed in trust account.	A certain percent (say 20%) of the net earnings placed in a trust account, and (1) divided among the employees on a prorata of salary basis, and (2) paid to employees upon retirement or completion of a specified number of years' service.	Provides for retirement income and encourages continuity of service. There is a considerable saving in income tax paid.	Some employees do not wish to wait so long for their added compensation.	
Production sharing and prevailing price	Table 18-7 gives a proposed incentive basis for a breeding establishment that derives most of its income from the sale of yearlings. Table 18-8 gives a proposed incentive basis for a riding stable.	It embraces the best features of both production and profit sharing, without the major disadvantages of each. It (1) encourages high productivity and likely profits, (2) is tied in with prevailing prices, (3) does not necessitate opening the books, and (4) is flexible —it can be split between	It is a bit more complicated than some other plans, and it requires more complete records.	When properly done, and all factors considered, this is the most satisfactory incentive basis for a horse establishment selling yearlings or operating a riding stable. Also, it can be adapted to any other type of horse enterprise.

(Continued)

Table 18-6 (Continued)

Types of Incentives	Pertinent Provisions of Some Known Incentive Systems in Use	Advantages	Disadvantages	Comments
		owner and employee on any basis desired, and the production part can be adapted to a sliding scale or escalator arrangement.		
Using a score card (rating)	The score is the basis for bonus, salary raise, and other considerations. The score method involves the preparation of a score card listing desired traits and performance, with a numerical value assigned to each according to its relative importance (see Figure 18-1).	This method works well in an office in which the personnel are carefully selected.		

Regardless of the incentive plan adopted for a specific operation, it should encompass the following essential features:

1. Good owner (or manager) and good workers. No incentive basis can overcome a poor manager. He must be a good supervisor and fair to his help. Also, on big establishments, he must prepare a written-down organization chart and job description so the help knows (a) to whom they are responsible, and (b) what their responsibilities are. Likewise, no incentive basis can spur employees who are not able, interested, and/or willing. This necessitates that employees must be selected with special care where they will be on an incentive basis. Hence, the three—good owner (manager), good employees, and good incentive—go hand in hand.

2. It must be fair to both employer and employees.

3. It must be based on and make for mutual trust and esteem.

4. It must compensate for extra performance, rather than substitute for a reasonable base salary and other considerations (house, utilities, and certain provisions).

5. It must be as simple, direct, and easily understood as possible.

6. It should compensate all members of the team, from top to bottom.

7. It must be put in writing, so that there will be no misunderstanding.

8. It is preferable, although not essential, that workers receive incentive payments (a) at frequent intervals, rather than annually, and (b) immediately after accomplishing the extra performance.

9. It should give the hired help a certain amount of responsibility, from the wise exercise of which they will benefit through the incentive arrangement.

10. It must be backed up by good records; otherwise, there is nothing on which to base incentive payments.

11. It should be a two-way street. If employees are compensated for superior performance, they should be penalized (or, under most circumstances, fired) for poor performance. It serves no useful purpose to reward the unwilling, the incompetent, and the stupid. No overtime pay should be given to an employee who must work longer because of slowness or correcting mistakes of his own making. Likewise, if the

reasonable break-even point on an operation is not reached because of obvious neglect (for example, not being on the job at foaling time), the employee(s) should be penalized (or fired).

INDIRECT INCENTIVES

Normally, we think of incentives as monetary in nature—as direct payments or bonuses for extra production or efficiency. However, there are other ways of encouraging employees to do a better job. The latter are known as indirect incentives. Among them are: (1) good wages; (2) good labor relations; (3) an adequate house plus such privileges as the use of the farm truck or car, payment of the electric bill, use of a swimming pool, hunting and fishing, and the furnishing of meat, milk, and eggs; (4) good buildings and equipment; (5) vacation time with pay, time off, sick leave; (6) group health; (7) security; (8) the opportunity for self-improvement that can accrue from working for a top man; (9) the right to invest in the business; (10) an all-expense-paid trip to a short course, show, or convention; and (11) a year-end bonus for staying all year. Such indirect incentives will be accorded to the help of more and more establishments, especially the big ones.

INCENTIVE BASIS FOR A
HORSE BREEDING ESTABLISHMENT

On horse breeding establishments there is need for some system which will encourage caretakers to (1) get a high conception rate; (2) be good nursemaids to newborn foals, though it may mean the loss of sleep; and (3) develop and sell surplus animals advantageously.

From the standpoint of the owner of a horse breeding establishment, production expenses remain practically unchanged regardless of the efficiency of the operation. Thus, the investment in land, buildings and equipment, stallion and broodmares, feed, and labor differs very little with a change (up or down) in the percent foal crop; and income above the break-even point is largely net profit. Yet, it must be remembered that owners take all the risks; hence, they should benefit most from profits.

On a horse breeding establishment, the author recommends that profits beyond the break-even point (after deducting all expenses, including the salary of the owner) be split on an 80:20 basis. This means that every dollar made above a certain level is split, with the owner taking 80 cents and the employees getting 20 cents. Also, there is merit in an escalator arrangement, with the split changed to 70:30, for example, when a certain plateau of efficiency is reached. Moreover, that which goes to the employees should be divided on the basis of their respective contributions, all the way down the line; for example, 25 percent of it might go to the manager, 25 percent might be divided among the foremen, and 50 percent of it divided among the rest of the help; or that which goes to the employees may be divided on a prorata of salary basis.

Gross income in horse breeding operations is determined primarily by (1) percent conception on mares bred, (2) percent foal crop, and (3) prices on horses sold. The first two factors can easily be determined. Usually, enough horses are sold to establish prices or values; otherwise, the going price can be used.

The incentive basis proposed in Table 18-7 for horse breeding operations is simple, direct, and easily applied. As noted, it is based on the number and price of yearlings sold.

Break-Even Point

Whenever possible, the break-even point on a horse establishment—the dollars gross necessary in order to break even—should be arrived at from actual records accumulated by the specific horse establishment, preferably over a period of years. Perhaps, too, break-even points should be moving averages, based on 5 to 10 years, with older years dropped out and more recent years added from time to time, thereby reflecting improvements in efficiency due primarily to changing technology, rather than to the efforts of the caretakers.

With a new horse operation, on which there are no historical records from which to arrive at a break-even point, it is recommended that the figures of other similar operations be used at the outset. These can be revised as actual records on the specific enterprise become available. It is important, however, that the new operation start on an incentive basis, even though the break-even point must be arbitrarily assumed at the time.

Table 18-7

A PROPOSED INCENTIVE BASIS FOR A BREEDER WHO SELLS YEARLINGS

Yearling Crop Sold Based on 100 Mares Bred to Produce	Price of Yearlings	How It Works
(no. of yearlings sold)	($)	On this particular establishment, 100 mares are bred annually, and each year 15 top fillies are retained as herd replacements. Over and above this, the break-even point is 50 yearlings marketed annually. Thus, if 100 mares were bred in 1968, to break even there would have to be 65 yearlings in 1969, out of which 15 would be kept and 50 marketed.
30	200	
35	300	
40	400	
45	500	
50 → (break even)	600	Moreover, the historical records of this establishment show that $600/head is the break-even point, provided 50 yearlings are sold—or a total gross of $30,000.
55	700	The sale of each yearling in excess of 50 head involves only $300 expense, primarily for added feed.
60	800	Thus, if 60 yearlings are marketed at an average of $1,000, that's a gross of $60,000. The break-even point is $30,000 (50 yearlings @ $600) plus the added cost of
65	900	$3,000 to produce 10 more yearlings (10 X $300), or a total of $33,000. Hence, the net is $27,000. With an escalator arrangement, there might be an 80:20 split
70	1,000	on a net up to $27,000; a 70:30 split of a net from $27,000 to $40,000; and a 65:35 split of a net in excess of $40,000.
75	1,100	It is recommended that division among employees be on a prorata of salary basis.
80	1,200	

INCENTIVE BASIS FOR A RIDING STABLE

An incentive basis for riding stable help is needed for motivation purposes, just as it is in racing or breeding horses. It is the most effective way in which to lessen absenteeism; make for superior training, teaching, and public relations; and improve housekeeping.

A proposed incentive basis for a riding stable is shown in Table 18-8. For this incentive basis to work at its best, the organization should have each Instructor-Trainer under the supervision of the Director of Riding Stable, and responsible for a specific unit of 40 to 80 horses. This includes serving as a working foreman in their care, and handling all the instruction and training therewith.

This unit-responsibility-and-care arrangement is patterned after Grosbois in France, and Newmarket in England, where it has been highly successful for many years. It will require that the facilities be developed with the unit type of operation in mind. But it has the very great virtue of making each Instructor-Trainer responsible for the success of his (or her) division—horses, facilities, keep of premises, and instruction—thereby minimizing supervision and avoiding "passing the buck." In addition, each Instructor-Trainer is responsible for such assignments as delegated by the Director, including record keeping.

In the operation of a riding stable, where teaching equitation and training horses are the two primary sources of income, there is need for Instructors-Trainers who are able to (1) keep their stables filled with horses in training, and (2) keep their classes filled with students; for, here again, the overhead cost is little different between well-filled and empty classrooms and stables. The incentive basis proposed in Table 18-8 will accomplish these objectives.

THE SCORE CARD INCENTIVE BASIS

As the name implies, the score card method involves the preparation of a score card. In the score card, each major desired trait and performance is given a numerical value according to its relative importance.

The score card which the author uses in evaluating the staff members in his office is herewith presented as Figure 18-1.

Table 18-8

A PROPOSED INCENTIVE BASIS FOR EACH INSTRUCTOR-TRAINER IN A RIDING STABLE

Yearly Gross from Boarding-Training Horses (@ $160/mo., $1,920/yr.)	Yearly Gross from Conducting Riding Classes (@$5/student/2-hr. lesson)	How It Works
(no. horses; $ gross/yr.)	(students, class days; gross)	Each Instructor-Trainer is responsible for his own unit. He receives a basic salary of $450/mo. plus living quarters.
2 horses; $3,840/yr.	One class of 6 students/day; 300 days/yr. instruction = $9,000 gross.	To cover all expenses—the Instructor-Trainer's salary, grooms, horses, facilities, equipment, feed, insurance, and overhead, requires 3 horses being boarded-trained and one class of 12 students receiving 300 days instruction, or a total gross of $23,760 ($5,760 + $18,000). That's the break-even point.
3 horses; $5,760/yr. ← (break-even)	One class of 12 students/day; 300 days/yr. instruction = $18,000 gross.	With 5 horses boarded-trained and two classes instead of one, the gross would be increased to $45,600. The added expense to generate $45,600 instead of $23,760 is small—only $1,200 more for keeping two horses. Hence, the net on the $45,600 is: $45,600—($23,760 + $1,200), or $20,640.
5 horses; $9,600/yr.	Two classes of 12 students/day; 300 days/yr. instruction = $36,000 gross.	With an 80:20 division, $16,512 would go to the owner, and $4,128 would be distributed among the employees. Or, if desired, the split could be on an escalator arrangement, with the employees getting a higher percentage as the net increases. Whatever the division, it is suggested that it be divided among them on a prorata of salary basis.

PERSONAL SCORE CARD

	Pts. or %	1969 June 30	1969 Dec. 31	1970 June 30	1970 Dec. 31	1971 June 30	1971 Dec. 31
For_____							
USE: This score card is applied by Dr. and Mrs. Ensminger to each staff member every six months, then the results are discussed with each person in a private conference.							
PURPOSE: To provide staff with an evaluation which they may use as a basis for self-improvement, and to recognize and reward superior performance.							
CHARACTER: Absolute sincerity, honesty, integrity, loyalty; ethical.....	10						
INDUSTRY: Works hard; has enthusiasm, initiative, and aggressiveness; a desire to get the job done, and a willingness to let the boss worry about raises; not afraid of long hours when necessary, not a clock watcher........	15						
ABILITY AND PERFORMANCE: Skilled and competent in area of work; is neat and accurate; turns out adequate work; has know-how, clarity, common sense, good judgment, and maturity; is organized; shows growth potential and self-improvement; not a know-it-all; accepts responsibility, masters the job assignments without being told "what to do next"; plans work, organizes, and keeps on top; efficient and cuts costs; recognizes that the "boss" must make decisions and give directions..........	40						
INTEREST: Genuine interest in work —not just pay-day and five o'clock....	10						
COURAGE: To innovate—to try the new, and to keep on keeping on.......	5						
PROMPTNESS AND DEPENDABILITY: A self-starter, does it today and not tomorrow...................	10						
PERSONALITY AND APPEARANCE: Cheerful; not a complainer; a member of the team.................	10						
	100						

Fig. 18-1. Score card and incentive basis in use in the author's office.

Considerations According to Score

Based on the average of two scores per year (Figure 18-1), the following considerations are accorded by the author to his office staff:

1. *Christmas Bonus.*

Score	Grade	Employee Should:	Christmas Bonus[5]
59 or under	Poor	Improve, work longer hours, and/or look for a job elsewhere	None
60-74	Fair	Improve and work longer hours	None
75-79	Good	Keep Improving	$ 50
80-84	Good	Keep Improving	$100
85-89	Good+	Keep Improving	$150
90-94	Excellent	Keep Improving	$200
95-100	Superior	Keep on keeping on	$250

2. *Health insurance; extra vacation time.*—Full-time employees on appointment (not on hourly basis) exceeding (and maintaining) a minimum score of 75 after 6 months' service or 80 after 2 years' service, will be accorded the following added considerations:

After Years' Service	Consideration
½ year (6 mos.)	Health insurance[6] for employee (not family), with employer and employee each paying 50% of premiums. (Employer will terminate health insurance upon termination of employment of employee.)
2 years	Health insurance for employee (not family), with employer paying premiums. (Employer will terminate health insurance upon termination of employment of employee.)
3 years	Added work day of paid vacation.[7]
4 years	Added work day of paid vacation.
5 years	Added work day of paid vacation.
6 years	Added work day of paid vacation.
7 years	Added work day of paid vacation.

3. *Merit increases.*—Salary increases will be on a merit basis only, and determined by (a) average annual score of the employee, (b) how well the businesses are doing, and (c) going wages of the area for the particular assignment. Whatever salary increase is accorded will be on a January 1 basis only, following the second six months' review.

---

[5]Based on full-time employees and 12 months' prior service; regular half-time employees are accorded half these amounts. Those not on the job 12 months are accorded consideration on a proportion to 12 months' basis.

[6]Health insurance is not accorded employees who already have such protection via the spouse.

[7]Thus, at the end of seven (7) years, employees meeting the stipulated score requisite will have health insurance and three weeks (15 work days) vacation with pay.

STALLION BREEDING CONTRACTS

Stallion breeding contracts should always be in writing; and the higher the stud fee, the more important it is that good business methods prevail. Neither "gentlemen's agreements" nor barn door records will suffice.

From a legal standpoint, a stallion breeding contract is binding to the parties whose signatures are affixed thereto. Thus, it is important that the contract be carefully read and fully understood before signing.

Following is a sample stallion breeding contract.[8]

STALLION SERVICE CONTRACT

(To be executed in duplicate for each mare; one copy to be retained by each party.)

This Contract for the breeding season of———————made and entered into
                                                        (year)

by and between

_____ , _____
        (owner of stallion)   (address)
hereinafter designated Stallion Owner, and

_____ , _____
        (owner of mare)   (address)
hereinafter designated Mare Owner.

This contract covers_____

The stallion, _____ ,whose service fee is $_____;
                    (name of stallion)

        $_____of which is paid with this contract, and the balance of
        $_____will be paid before the mare leaves_____
                                                            (name of farm or ranch)

and

The mare, _____ , Reg. No._____ , by_____
                                                                    (sire)

        out of_____ , age_____ , color_____.
                (dam)

The Mare Owner agrees that—

Upon arrival, the mare will (a) be halter-broken, (b) have the hind shoes removed, and (c) be accompanied by a health certificate signed by a veterinarian, certifying that she is healthy and in sound breeding condition.

Stallion Owner will not be responsible for accident, disease, or death to the mare, or to her foal (if she has a foal).

Stallion Owner may, at his discretion, have his veterinarian (a) check

---

[8] Sample prepared by the author of this book.

and treat the mare for breeding condition or diseases, and (b) treat her for parasites if needed; with the expenses of such services charged to Mare Owner's account and paid when the mare leaves the farm or ranch.

He will pay the following board on his mare at the time the mare leaves the farm or ranch: Feed and facilities $_____/day.

Should the mare prove barren, or should the foal die at birth, he will send notice of same, signed by a licensed veterinarian, within five days of such barren determination or death.

Should he fail to deliver the above mare to Stallion Owner's premises on or before_____, Stallion Owner shall be under no
           (date)
further obligation with respect to any matter herein set forth.

This contract shall not be assigned or transferred. In the event the mare is sold, any remaining unpaid fee shall immediately become due and payable and no refund shall be due anyone under any circumstances.

The Stallion Owner agrees that—

He will provide suitable facilities for the mare and feed and care for her in a good and husbandlike manner.

Mare owner will not be responsible for any disease, accident, or injury to Stallion Owner's horses.

A live foal is guaranteed—meaning a foal that can stand up alone and nurse.

The Stallion Owner and Mare Owner mutually agree that—

This contract is not valid unless completed in full.

Should the above-named stallion die or become unfit for service, or should the above-named mare die or become unfit to breed, this contract shall become null and void and money paid as part of this contract shall be refunded to Mare Owner.

Should the mare prove barren, or should the foal die at birth, with certification of same provided to Stallion Owner within the time specified, Stallion Owner has the option either to (a) rebreed the mare the following year, or (b) refund the $_____ portion of the breeding fee, thereby cancelling this entire contract.

The mare will not receive more than _____ covers during the breed-
                           (no.)
ing season; and she will not be bred before_____19____
                                (date)

                    or after_____19____
                                (date)

_____   _____   _____
(date)   (signature; Mare Owner or Rep.)   (address)

_____   _____   _____
(date)   (signature; Stallion Owner or Rep.)   (address)

In addition to the provisions made in the sample stallion breeding contract presented here, and most other similar contracts, the author suggests that the following matters be covered in the stallion breeding contract:

1. *Facts about the mare.*—There should be record of the mare's temperament; thereby lessening danger to her, to the stallion, and to the personnel. Also, historical information should be included about the mare's breeding record and peculiarities, and her health—preferably with the health record provided by the veterinarian who has looked after her.

2. *Some management understandings.*—The parties to the contract should reach an understanding relative to the mare's veterinary care, parasite control, seasonal injections, foot trimming, etc., and then put it in writing.

3. *An incentive basis.*—Generally, stallion owners guarantee a live foal, which means that the foal must stand and nurse; otherwise, the stud fee is either refunded or not collected, according to the stipulations. Of course, it is in the best interests of both parties that a strong, healthy foal be born. One well-known Quarter Horse establishment reports that their records reveal that of all mares settled during a particular three-year period, 19 percent of them subsequently either resorbed or aborted feti, or the foal or mare died. Further, their investigation of these situations showed that the vast majority of these losses could have been averted by better care and management. They found many things wrong—ranging from racing mares in foal to turning them to pastures where there was insufficient feed. To alleviate many, if not most, of these losses—losses that accrue after the mare has been examined and pronounced safe in foal, then taken away from the stallion owner's premises—the author suggests that an incentive basis be incorporated in the stallion breeding contract. For example, the stallion owner might agree to reduce the stud fee (1) by 10, 15, or 20 percent (state which), provided a live foal is born; or (2) by 25 to 33⅓ percent provided the mare owner's veterinarian certifies that the mare is safe in foal 30 days after being removed from the place where bred, with payment made at that time and based on conception rather than on birth of a live foal.

SYNDICATED HORSES

Reduced to simple terms, a syndicated horse is one that is owned by several people. Most commonly, it's a stallion; although an expensive yearling or broodmare is sometimes syndicated. Also, any number of people can form a syndicate. However, there is a tendency to use the term "partnership" where two to four owners are involved, and to confine the word "syndicate" to a larger group of owners.

Each member of the syndicate owns a certain number of "shares," depending on how much he purchased or contributed. It's much like a stock market investor, who may own one or several shares in General Electric, IBM, or some other company. Sometimes one person may own as much as a half-interest in a horse. Occasionally, half-shares are sold.

Generally speaking, the number of shares in a stallion is limited to the number of mares that may reasonably be bred to him in one season —usually 30 to 35, with Thoroughbred stallions.

Why and How Owners Syndicate

The owner of a stallion that has raced successfully usually has the opportunity to choose between: (1) continuing as sole owner of the horse, and standing him for service privately or publicly, or (2) syndicating him. In recent years, more and more owners of top stallions have elected to syndicate. The most common reasons for so doing are:

1. The stallion owner does not have a breeding farm or an extensive band of broodmares.

2. The owner believes that the stallion under consideration may not nick well with many of his mares; or perhaps the stallion is closely related to the mares.

3. The owner has need for immediate income. Moreover, the profit, according to a Tax Court ruling, is subject to the frequently advantageous capital-gains treatment on income tax. By contrast, if sole ownership is retained, considerable promotional and advertising expenses will be involved for approximately three years—until the stallion's get make their debut on the tracks; and, in the meantime, practically no income can be expected until about a year from entering stud, at which time the usual "live foal" guarantee is met. Until this condition is fulfilled, any stud fees that are collected are generally held in escrow, as protection if they should have to be returned.

4. Syndicating spreads the risk, should the stallion get injured or die, or prove unsuccessful as a sire.

The owner may arrange the syndication himself, usually with competent legal advice; or, if preferred, the syndication can be turned over to a professional manager, who will generally take a free share as his organization fee.

The following pointers are pertinent to successful syndication of stallions:

1. *Check fertility.*—Before syndicating, it is a good idea to check the fertility by test-mating to a cold-blooded (draft) mare. Of course, if the stallion is still racing, and has not been retired to stud, this is impossible.

2. *Establish stud fee.*—A common rule of thumb is that each syndicate share is worth four times the stud fee. Hence, if it is decided that the stallion under consideration will command a $5,000 stud fee, each share would be worth $20,000. If 30 shares are involved, the horse would have a value of $600,000 for syndication purposes.

3. *Determine time of Payment.*—In most cases, payment is due upon the signing of the syndicate contract, although some contracts (a) allow 30, 60, or 90 days, or (b) provide that the price of a share may be paid on the installment plan over a two- or three-year period.

4. *Put it in writing.*—Syndication agreements should be clear, detailed, and in writing. In addition to identifying the horse, the agreement should state (a) the shareholder's proportionate interest (say 1/32); (b) the breeding rights of a shareholder (for example, the right to breed one mare per season to the horse, so long as he is in good health and able to breed); (c) the method of distributing services by lot, should it be necessary to limit the number of mares bred during any given season; (d) the method of disposing of, and the price to charge for, any extra services (over and above one per share, for example) during a given season; (e) the place where the horse shall stand, or how such determination will be made (usually by majority vote of the shareholders); and (f) how other policy matters not covered in the agreement will be determined (usually by majority vote).

Generally, such routine matters as the feed, care, and health of the stallion, and the scheduling of mares are left to the discretion of the syndicate manager, at a stated fee per month, with each shareholder billed proportionate to his number of shares. The manager also handles the promotion and advertising, insurance, and unusual veterinary expenses, as stipulated by the syndicate, with the costs prorated among its members.

Normally, a shareholder can barter his breeding service to another stallion. However, he cannot sell his share without prior approval of the manager and giving the other shareholders the right to buy it at the price offered; and, normally, this same stipulation applies to the sale of a service during any season.

Also, provision is usually made for sale of the horse should the majority of the shareholders so desire, with them also determining, at the time of sale, the price and whether sale shall be at private treaty or auction. Further, the contract usually provides for "pensioning," or otherwise disposing of, a sire should he become sterile or be overtaken by old age before dying.

In short, a syndicate agreement, like any good legal contract, attempts to spell out every foreseeable contingency that may arise during the stud's career, and to arrange for majority vote of the shareholders to settle any unforeseen contingencies.

The Nashua Syndicate Agreement, used by Mr. Leslie B. Combs II, Spendthrift Farm, Lexington, Kentucky, who has probably contributed more than any other person to stallion syndication, follows. It is also noteworthy that, when Mr. Combs syndicated Nashua, he sold all but one share of a total of 32, each at $39,100 (for a total of $1,251,200), over the telephone in one afternoon; and the only reason that the one share was not sold until the next morning was that he couldn't reach one of his regular clients on the telephone the previous afternoon.

Sample Syndicate Agreement

The syndicate agreement used when the noted Thoroughbred stallion, Nashua, was syndicated follows.[9]

~~~~~~

NASHUA SYNDICATE AGREEMENT

THIS AGREEMENT, made as of December 15, 1955, between the several persons whose names and addresses are set out in the Schedule hereto attached as the original Subscribers, and being referred to collectively as "the Shareholders."

WITNESSETH:

WHEREAS, Leslie Combs II, Spendthrift Farm, Ironworks Pike, Lexing-

(continued)

---

[9]This agreement was provided through the courtesy of Mr. Leslie B. Combs II and published by Agriservices Foundation in *Stud Manager's Handbook*, Vol. 1, beginning on p. 45.

ton, Kentucky, has purchased the thoroughbred horse NASHUA (B. c., 1952), by *NASRULLAH-SEGULA, by JOHNSTOWN from the Estate of William Woodward, Jr. and has formed a Syndicate to acquire the ownership thereof upon the following terms and conditions:

1. The ownership of NASHUA shall be divided into thirty-two (32) shares, and the purchasers of said thirty-two (32) shares have paid the total purchase price of One Million, Two Hundred and Fifty-One Thousand, Two Hundred Dollars, ($1,251,200.00), or the sum of Thirty-Nine Thousand, One Hundred Dollars ($39,100.00) per share.

2. Each of the thirty-two (32) shares shall be on an equal basis with the others and shall be indivisible, and only a full share shall have any of the rights hereunder; provided, however, that there is expressly reserved, and the within sale is made subject to one (1) free nomination to NASHUA each year during his life for each of the following named persons, their heirs and assigns: John W. Hanes, 460 Park Avenue, New York City, C. J. Devine, 48 Wall Street, New York City, and Leslie Combs II, Spendthrift Farm, Lexington, Kentucky.

3. NASHUA shall be returned to training as soon as practicable and shall race under the personal management and supervision of a Committee consisting of John W. Hanes, C. J. Devine, and Leslie Combs II, as agents for the shareholders. The Committee shall have full charge of and complete control over the future racing career of NASHUA, including but not limited to (a) the employment of a trainer, (b) the selection of tracks at which he will be trained and raced, (c) the races to which he will be nominated and in which he will be actually started, (d) the selection and employment of a jockey or jockeys, (e) the name and colors under which he will be raced, and (f) how long NASHUA shall race and when he shall be retired from racing, and the actions, decisions and judgments of the Committee with respect to any and all of the foregoing matters shall be final, conclusive and binding upon all of the Shareholders and shall not give rise to any liability upon the Committee or the individual members thereof so long as they act in good faith.

All expenses incurred by the Committee in training and racing NASHUA shall be paid by the Shareholders in proportion to the number of shares owned by each of them, and the earnings of NASHUA shall likewise be divided amongst the Shareholders proportionately. The Committee shall furnish each Shareholder periodically with a statement showing the expenses and earnings.

The Committee is authorized to execute such leases or other instruments as may be required under the rules of The Jockey Club and/or the various Racing Commissions and other governmental bodies having jurisdiction of the premises to qualify NASHUA to race.

If a member of the Committee should die, resign or be unable to serve for any reason, then the remaining members of the Committee shall select his successor from amongst the Shareholders.

4. Upon retirement to the stud, NASHUA shall stand and shall be kept and maintained at Spendthrift Farm, Ironworks Pike, in Fayette County, Kentucky, under the sole personal management and supervision of Leslie

Combs II, and he shall be entitled to charge and receive the prevailing rates for stallion keep. Leslie Combs II shall have complete charge of advertising the stallion and shall have the authority to select a veterinarian. Owners of shares shall pay all charges, costs and expenses incurred in connection with said stallion in the proportion that their respective shares bear to the whole number of shares.

5. Each Shareholder in each breeding season shall be entitled to one (1) free nomination to said stallion for each share owned by him, subject to the payment of his share of the Syndicate expenses and the provisions of Paragraph 6; provided, however, that in NASHUA's first full season in the stud he shall be limited to a book of twenty-five (25) mares, and the owners of the thirty-two (32) nominations shall be determined by lot at a drawing to be held at such time and place as the aforesaid Committee may determine, and notice of which shall be sent by registered mail or by telegram to each Shareholder at least five (5) days prior thereto. Each share and each free nomination shall be regarded as if it were the subject of separate ownership and shall be on an equal basis, the one with the other.

Thereafter, if the veterinarian attending said stallion and the Syndicate Manager, Leslie Combs II, shall certify that in their opinion NASHUA's book may be increased without injury to him, then additional yearly nominations may be sold by the Syndicate Manager at the regular stud fee and the yearly proceeds thereof shall be divided among the Shareholders in proportion to the number of shares owned by each.

Each mare bred to NASHUA must be in sound breeding condition and free from infection or disease, and no mare shall be covered more than six (6) times in any breeding season.

6. If Leslie Combs II, with the advice and approval of the veterinarian, shall determine that NASHUA shall be bred to less than thirty-five (35) mares in any stud season, then the Shareholders and those persons holding the three (3) free nominations in each year (as provided in Paragraph 2 herein) who collectively shall be entitled to such reduced number of nominations shall be determined by lot, and any Shareholder or holder of said free nominations who has suffered by reason of the drawing of lots in any season shall not be submitted to the risk of drawing in any subsequent season unless and until all other Shareholders and holders of said free nominations, have suffered as the result thereof; and for the purpose of this clause each share and free nomination shall be regarded as if it were the subject of separate ownership and shall be on an equal basis, the one with the other. Notice of the decision to reduce NASHUA's book to less than thirty-five (35) nominations and of the time and place of the drawing shall be sent by the Syndicate Manager to each Shareholder and holder of a free nomination by registered mail or by telegram at least five (5) days prior to said drawing.

7. Leslie Combs II shall employ the usual care customarily employed in Fayette County, Kentucky, in the management of NASHUA, but shall not be responsible for any injury, disease or death of said stallion, nor for any injury, disease or death of any mare resulting from breeding or attempted breeding to said stallion.

(continued)

8. Leslie Combs II shall have and is hereby granted the right and option to purchase any share or shares which any owner desires to sell, and such owner shall first offer the same to Leslie Combs II with the price requested for the same. If Leslie Combs II is unwilling to pay the price requested by the owner, then such owner may secure a written offer elsewhere for such share or shares, and if the owner is willing to accept such written offer he shall present the same to Leslie Combs II, who shall have the right to purchase, within forty-eight hours thereafter, such share or shares for the price so offered in writing and which the owner was willing to accept. In the event Leslie Combs II fails to purchase such share or shares within the time specified, then such owner may accept such written offer. This option shall apply in the same manner and under the same conditions to such share or shares in the new ownership. This option shall apply to and have priority over any hypothecation, distraint or other alienation of said share or shares or any interest therein, and any and all transfers of any share or shares are expressly subject to said option.

9. All notices required hereunder shall be effective and binding if sent by prepaid registered mail, telegram, cable, or delivered in person to the address of the respective Shareholders set out in the Schedule attached or such address as shall hereafter be designated in writing to the Syndicate Manager.

10. The Shareholders accept delivery of NASHUA without examination as to his fertility and breeding soundness, as no veterinary examination with reference thereto has been made or will be made prior to his retirement from racing.

11. The undersigned hereby subscribes for_____shares in the Syndicate for the total sum of $_____, payable in cash upon the execution of this Agreement, and in consideration thereof Leslie Combs II has sold and conveyed_____Shares to undersigned, subject to all of the terms and conditions herein.

This Agreement may be executed in several counterparts, and when executed by the Shareholders the several counterparts shall constitute the agreement between the parties as if all signatures were appended to one original instrument.

WITNESS the hand of the undersigned as of the day and date first above written.

_____

Name

_____

_____

Address

Approved:

_____

Syndicate Manager

HORSEMEN AND INCOME TAXES[10]

General tax information applicable to all livestock is fully covered in the section entitled "Tax Management and Reporting on the Livestock Farm" of *The Stockman's Handbook*, a book by the same author and the same publisher as this book. Hence, the reader is referred thereto. In the discussion that follows, the author has directed his efforts specifically to horsemen, so that they will be aware of the tax implications involved, and so that they may take steps to avoid certain pitfalls. Also, horsemen are admonished to consult a competent tax advisor before embarking upon any sizeable horse operation.

Cash vs. Accrual Method

There are two standard methods of reporting, the Cash Basis and the Accrual Basis. Most horsemen use the Cash Basis, in which income is reported when it is actually received and expenses are recorded when actually paid. It does not include the value of products sold or services performed for which payment was not actually available during the taxable year. In addition to being simple and easy, the Cash Basis has the advantage of allowing the horseman partially to control his income for tax purposes by timing year-end payment of expenses.

From a management standpoint, however, the Accrual Basis is preferred because it more nearly reflects the income of a particular period. Under it, income is accounted for when it is earned and expenses are recorded when incurred rather than when paid. Also, the Accrual Basis necessitates that complete annual inventories be kept, with taxes paid on increases of inventory, and deductions made for any decreases in inventory.

On large horse establishments, it is recommended that both record systems be used—the Cash Basis for tax purposes, and the Accrual Basis for management purposes. A competent accountant can set up such a system with the same set of records simply by adding a few memo accounts that are removed at the end of the year when closing the books for tax purposes.

Hobby or Business

The first real hazard, and one which should be avoided like the plague

---

[10]This section was authoritatively reviewed by Messrs. Stephen H. Hart and Don D. Etter, Attorneys, Denver, Colo.

unless it really applies, is that participation in the horse business—whether in breeding, racing, training, and/or showing—may be regarded by the Internal Revenue Service (IRS), as indulgence in a hobby or diversion rather than a true business venture, with the result that any losses accruing therefrom are disallowed in their entirety. This should cause no concern to those who derive their entire living from the horse business or to those successful horsemen who normally operate at a profit. Rather, it is the person of independent means, or one who is profitably engaged in another enterprise or other enterprises, who is likely to be challenged when he or she has an unbroken string of loss years accruing from breeding, racing, and/or showing operations. Also, IRS does not automatically take cognizance of the fact that breeding programs designed to develop a new breed of horses, or even to build up a herd, take many years. It is essential, therefore, that the horseman establish a profit-making motive and a reasonable chance of achieving this aim. Then, he must conduct his operations in a business-like manner throughout, and refrain from anything that may cause his actions even to be suspicioned as pursuit of a hobby rather than the conducting of a business.

In breeding, racing, training, and/or showing horses, a fine line often separates a hobby from a business. Moreover, a hobby sometimes turns out to be a profitable venture to the point that the taxpayer may turn it into a business. In any event, once the question is raised, the burden of proof—whether the horse enterprise shall be classed as a hobby or a business by IRS and the court—is with the taxpayer. In various cases, the courts have noted the following factors as indicative that the enterprise is a business rather than a hobby:

1. That the taxpayer is able to show that serious study went into the initial planning and long-range development of the horse enterprise (breeding, racing, training, and/or showing); for example, that a recognized and qualified consultant was employed to make a feasibility study, following which he was retained to guide the proposed program.

2. That the farm or stable is being directed by an able manager, whose credentials give evidence of both technical training and business ability.

3. That the taxpayer is giving personal attention to all phases of the operation and exhibiting good and sound business judgment. That there has been a practical, common-sense approach—that the enterprise has been run like a business, rather than like a plaything.

4. That the farm, ranch, or stable is located in an area adapted to the type of horse enterprise being conducted.

5. That the facilities are functional in design, rather than like a "country estate." For example, it's difficult to justify a situation where the principal improvements to a horse farm consist of a swimming pool, tennis court, and guest house.

6. That good and complete records are available, showing all transactions. Although good records as such will not establish the enterprise as a business, the absence of such records may constitute adverse evidence.

7. That there is ample evidence that a profitable breeding and marketing program takes several years. Horse breeding may be likened to (a) the beginning orchardist who plants young trees, then cultivates, sprays, waters, prunes, and replaces for a number of years before he harvests the first crop; or (b) the producer of a timber crop, where it takes up to 25 years to get into production. It doesn't seem unreasonable, therefore, that it should require 8 to 12 years in which to get a horse breeding establishment on a profitable basis, for in that period of time, only 2 to 3 generations of horses can be produced.

8. That the enterprise is of such magnitude that it can conceivably make a profit, considering all the circumstances of the particular situation.

9. That the advertising and promotion programs have been sound, and in keeping with those followed by other similar businesses that have been successful.

10. That there has been proper and rigid culling of horses.

11. That the taxpayer has exhibited evidence of keeping abreast of the latest developments in the horse field through such things as attending recognized short courses, acquiring a technical library in the field, and subscribing to related periodicals—all of which indicate the intent of the taxpayer to conduct a sound business enterprise.

It is emphasized that the matter of INTENT is paramount. Generally speaking, taxpayers who meet, to a reasonable degree, these 11 points can, if necessary, prove to the courts their "intent to show a profit from a business venture."

Proof of INTENT is especially difficult if (1) the taxpayer is wealthy and over a period of years has sustained heavy losses sufficient to put an average horseman out of business, or (2) there is some interest connected with the horse enterprise of greater importance in the taxpayer's scheme of life than making a profit. Indeed, these two points tend to indicate an expensive hobby, rather than a business.

The Fifth Year Loss Rule (Section 270)

Frequently, horsemen are confused by the limitations of deductions provided by Section 270 of the Internal Revenue Code, which can cause loss deductions over a five-year period to be disallowed despite the fact that the taxpayer's operation has been established as a business and the profit motive is not in question.

As a business, losses are deductible provided they do not exceed $50,000 per year for each of five consecutive years. Five heavy loss years can happen in operations that are well managed; for example, as a result of (1) stallions' proving unsuccessful as sires, because of which their progeny neither win nor sell well for a period of years, or (2) an outbreak of abortion, or some other disease, resulting in few foals during a period of years. If some such situation arises, and losses for each of five consecutive years exceed the gross income by $50,000, the taxpayer's net income is recomputed for each of the years in question, and, on the recomputation, deductions attributable to the business are allowable only to the extent of $50,000 plus gross income.

In considering Section 270, it is particularly noteworthy that the taxpayer is not required to show a profit in the fifth year. He could, for example, lose $50,000 to $150,000 annually for four consecutive years, but lose only $49,000 in the fifth year, and avoid the application of this section altogether. Thus, forward planning is essential when it appears that a taxpayer may be headed into fifth year trouble. To keep fifth year losses under $50,000, he may have to sell more of his horses than planned, curtail or cease his racing or showing activities, refrain from projected purchases, or, since Section 270 applies only to individuals, even incorporate his business.

Of course, where such circumstances as the above exist, the IRS agent may try to get fifth year losses over $50,000. To this end, he may attempt to change depreciation rates, or shift deductions or income between years; or he may even try to find additional deductions that should have been claimed. Good accounting records become extremely important in such cases.

Appraisal, Salvage, and Depreciation

In 1962, the Treasury issued "useful life" guidelines. If these are followed, the taxpayer will not be challenged. They are:

Buildings .... 25 years
Machinery and equipment .... 10 years
Breeding and work horses .... 10 years

Definitions of "appraisal, salvage, and depreciation" as applied to horses follow:

Appraisal refers to the act of establishing the worth of the horse.

Salvage refers to the remaining value, if any, of an animal after it has served its intended purpose—for example, at the end of usefulness as a breeding animal, or at the end of a racing or showing career.

Depreciation refers to the amortization or write-off of the cost of a horse over the period of its useful life.

In each of the above, the horseman, or the specialist to whom such matters are entrusted, should apply rates which he can justify.

Generally speaking a knowledgeable horseman can arrive at an acceptable appraisal on a horse or horses by using other current sales of similar animals as a basis to estimate value. Of course, purchase price as such establishes value for depreciation purposes.

Breeding animals have no appreciable salvage value at the end of their reproductive life. On the other hand, the salvage value of a race-horse that is retired to stud is a matter of opinion.

Depreciation figures on horses are difficult to come by, and they vary according to source, use, and breed. Unfortunately, no adequate scientific study of the actual average useful life of horses for racing, showing, and breeding purposes has been undertaken. Moreover, the Internal Revenue Service has not stipulated any depreciation rates other than suggesting that horses used for breeding or work purposes should have a 10-year life.

The accounting firm of Owens, Potter and Hisle, Lexington, Kentucky, which specializes in accounting for horse establishments, has developed Table 18-9 as a depreciation guide of the useful lives of race and breeding horses.

The author suggests that the depreciation schedule on show horses be the same as those given for racehorses in Table 18-9.

Table 18-9

HORSE DEPRECIATION GUIDE[1]

Age When Acquired	Years of Useful Life Remaining		
	Racehorses	Broodmares	Stallions
1	6		
2	5		
3	4		
4	3	10	10
5	3	9	9
6	2	9	9
7	2	8	8
8	2	7	7
9		7	7
10		6	6
11		5	5
12		5	5
13		5	5
14		4	4
15		4	4
16		4	4
17		3	3
18		3	3
19		2	2
20		2	2
21		2	2

[1]From: *The Blood-Horse*, Dec. 2, 1967, p. 3747, with the permission of Mr. John C. Owens and Mr. Rex B. Potter, of the firm of Owens, Potter and Hisle, Lexington, Ky.

Horsemen have claimed and been allowed rates widely at variance with the figures given in Table 18-9. For example, some owners claim depreciation on yearlings from date of acquisition, whereas others date it from the time they are placed in training; but such practices might prove difficult to defend in a well-fought tax case. If the return is filed in a district where there are few horsemen, the examiner may fail to challenge the method simply because he is unfamiliar with the peculiarities of the industry. Inconsistent practices are likely to continue unless the horse industry itself takes initiative and accumulates factual studies, made by an independent agency, which horsemen can present. Without doubt, the results of such a research study would more than justify the cost.

Any one of the following three methods may be used in computing depreciation of horses:

1. *The straight line method,* in which annual depreciation on the

horse is determined by dividing its purchase price when acquired, less its estimated salvage value, if any, by the total number of years of useful life remaining (see Table 18-9). For example, according to Table 18-9, a racehorse acquired at age three has an expected useful race life of four years. Hence, a depreciation of 25 percent would be taken each year under the straight line method.

The following example will serve to illustrate how the straight line method works:

Example: A mare costing $8,000 was purchased at age four, at which age she also dropped her first foal. For purposes of computing depreciation, it is estimated that she has 10 more years of useful life remaining (Table 18-9). Further, it is estimated that her salvage value at the end of this period (at age 14) will be $100. How much depreciation may be taken each year by the straight line method?

Answer: $8,000 — $100 = $7,900, the depreciation which may be taken over a 10-year period; hence—

100 ÷ 10 = 10%, annual percentage write off

$7,900 × 10% = $790, annual dollars write off.

2. *The declining balance method*, in which the largest depreciation is taken during the early years of life, and a gradually smaller allowance is taken in later years. The amount of depreciation taken each year is subtracted before figuring the next year's depreciation, so that the same depreciation rate is applied to a smaller or declining balance each year. The maximum rate under this method may not exceed twice the rate that would be used under the straight line method. For example, if *new* tangible property has an estimated useful life of five years remaining, the depreciation rate under the straight line method is 20 percent; but under the declining balance system, depreciation may be figured at any rate that does not exceed 40 percent.

Horses that are purchased are usually considered *"used property,"* and, therefore, limited to 150 percent of the straight line rate. Salvage value is not deducted before figuring depreciation under this method, but depreciation must stop when the unrecovered cost is reduced to salvage value.

3. *The sum of the years-digit method*, in which a different fraction is applied each year to the basis of the property less its estimated salvage value. The denominator, or bottom of the fraction, which remains constant, is the total of the numbers representing the years of useful

life of the horse. For example, if the useful life is five years, the denominator is 15 (1 plus 2, plus 3, plus 4, plus 5, equals 15). The numerator, or top of the fraction, is the number of years of life remaining at the beginning of the year for which the computation is made. For the first year of an estimated five year life, the numerator would be 5, the second year 4, etc. Thus, for a horse with a useful life of five years, the fraction to be applied to the cost minus salvage to figure depreciation for the first year is 5/15; the fraction for the second year is 4/15, etc.

In addition to the three methods of depreciation given above, there's Section 179, "bonus" depreciation. This permits the taxpayer to write off 20 percent of the cost, or portion of the cost, of a purchased horse during the first taxable year for which a depreciation deduction is allowable, provided (1) the horse has an estimated useful life of at least six years, (2) the horse was acquired from an unrelated person, and (3) the maximum write-off is $2,000 for the year, or $4,000 on a joint return. This "bonus" depreciation applies to both new and used property; hence, young broodmares, young stallions, and purchased yearlings put into training will so qualify.

Before a horseman adopts any method of depreciation, competent tax assistance should be sought. Many factors must be considered. For example, sometimes the use of the declining balance method, or some other accelerated method, may produce such large depreciation deductions that the five-year loss problem (Section 270) may be encountered.

Capital Gain

Since capital gain is not taxed nearly so heavily as ordinary income, it is wise to report the maximum income thereunder. For most horsemen, the tax rate on capital gain is based on only one-half of the gain reported. Even for those in the highest tax bracket, the tax on capital gain cannot, according to law, exceed 25 percent of the profit realized.

Actually, horses are seldom capital assets as such. Instead, they may be "Section 1231 Assets" that also qualify for capital gain treatment; a special group on which the deduction of the entire loss against ordinary income is permitted, if loss is sustained, and losses are not limited to the $1,000 per year as are capital losses.

Generally speaking a six-month retention of racehorses is the minimum for purposes of taking capital gain, while one year is the minimum on breeding stock. Disposal of broodmares and stallions that have been held by the taxpayer for some time and used regularly for breeding is not normally questioned. A protest is much more likely in the case of a horse that has not in fact been used for either breeding or racing.

If the taxpayer is primarily a market breeder disposing of his annual crop of weanlings or yearlings, it is normally considered that these animals were held primarily for sale to customers in the ordinary course of the owner's trade or business. Therefore, the gains are taxed as ordinary income and are not subject to the favorable capital gain treatment.

If the taxpayer is primarily a racing man who retains most of the horses he raises, disposing only of the unsuitable ones, there is opportunity to claim and support capital gain treatment. Likewise, the taxpayer who does not maintain any broodmares, but purchases all his stock and then races and disposes of them, may justify capital gain treatment. Also, horses lost in a claiming race are considered as being sold; hence, they are subject to capital gain treatment.

The common argument advanced by an IRS agent in denying capital gain treatment is that the taxpayer held the particular animal primarily for sale. To bolster his conclusion, he may cite the sale of similar animals that year, or in previous years; or the advertising, entry, and/or cataloging of the animal prior to sale. Unfortunately for the taxpayer, an IRS agent may jump to an unsupported conclusion based merely on the fact of sale.

Of course, not all cases are clear-cut. Some lie within a gray area, rather than being clearly either ordinary income or capital gain treatment. For example, circumstances may cause a change in plans. A horseman who is in the business of breeding and selling yearlings may decide to keep and race one of them. After training the horse and starting it in two races as a two-year-old, the owner decides to sell it. If the sale of this animal is considered as a racehorse, it qualifies for the capital gain treatment. On the other hand, if the horse is considered property normally held for sale to customers, the profit will be taxed as ordinary income. In such cases, the *Intent* of the owner becomes most important. To establish the latter, the owner should put it in writing. At the time the decision was reached to retain and race this horse, he should write a memo to his bookkeeper or to his files, giving the date that the animal was placed in training and the reasons for racing instead of selling as a yearling.

Also, it is noteworthy that horses, and other livestock, were excepted from a 1962 recapture provision. Thus, a horseman can purchase breeding stock (broodmares and stallions), apply one of the accelerated depreciation methods, and still realize capital gains upon sale, provided the animals are held for the required period. This means that a horseman who is in the 70 percent tax bracket can deduct the depreciation from his income at the 70 percent rate; then when he recaptures it upon sale the gain is taxable at only 25 percent.

Some Disturbing Horse Tax Developments

Among some recent tax developments of concern to horsemen are the following:

1. *Denial of deduction of training expense of yearlings.*—Previously, many taxpayers treated all such expenses as deductions against ordinary income. However, some revenue agents are now requiring that they be capitalized as part of the cost of each horse and be recovered via depreciation over its useful life.

2. *Denial of deduction of breeding fees as ordinary expense in the year paid.*—Some agents have attempted to require the capitalization of breeding fees, rather than permit them to be treated as deductions against ordinary income, as has been done in the past.

3. *The status of unborn foals.*—There is disagreement as to whether income subsequently derived from an unborn foal should be treated as ordinary income or capital gain.

In the Event of a Court Case

In the event of a court case, it is usually advisable that the taxpayer appear in person and testify, rather than expect that his attorney and accountant handle the matter entirely. This is especially important from the standpoint of establishing intent, for no one knows the original intent better than the owner. Additionally, it is usually advisable that the testimony of recognized experts in the field be used to substantiate the fact that there was, or is, a reasonable expectation of making a profit. However, whether or not the taxpayer and/or experts testify in a particular case should be left to the decision of the lawyer, for nothing is worse for the taxpayer than not giving the lawyer free rein to develop the case.

INSURANCE

Few horsemen examine closely or understand the insurance coverage that they buy, either on their horses or in the area of liability. Thus, to the end that they may be more knowledgeable on this subject, sections on horse insurance and liability follow.

Horse Insurance[11]

The ownership of a fine horse constitutes a risk, which means that there is a chance of financial loss. Unless the owner is in such strong financial position that he alone can assume this risk, the animal should be insured.

Several good companies write horse insurance: and, in general, the policies and rates do not differ greatly.

Generally, the pertinent provisions of horse insurance, and the things for which the owner should look, are:

1. *Coverage and annual rate.*—The annual rate for insurance generally ranges from 1½ to 6 percent, depending on the risk involved and the type of coverage. Thus, one prominent livestock insurance company uses the following bases:

a. An annual rate of 1½ to 2 percent to cover fire, lightning, windstorm, and transportation losses only.

b. An annual rate of 4 percent on studs and 4½ percent on mares used for breeding purposes but not for racing.

c. An annual rate of 4½ to 5 percent on horses used for flat races, with an added charge of 1½ percent on horses raced in claiming races (additional charges are also made on steeplechasers).

d. Coverage for castration of colts and tail setting, when performed by a licensed veterinarian, may be added to the policy, usually at a charge of 1 percent for the former and ½ percent for the latter.

e. Air and ocean transportation protection may be added at quoted rates.

2. *Age limits.*—Generally horses may be insured at the regular rate from 30 days of age up to 12 to 15 years of age, although some companies lower the age limits for animals used for certain purposes.

---

[11]This section was accorded the authoritative review of Mr. Frank Harding, Harding & Harding Livestock Insurance, 125 South Third St., Geneva, Ill.

Also, some companies will not insure mares against foaling hazards if they are eight years old or over and have not previously foaled.

3. *Requisites for insurance.*—In order to obtain insurance, the following information is generally required: Identification (markings and/or tattoo) of animal, age, individual valuation, and a statement of health from the local veterinarian.

It is recommended that the person desiring or having insurance confer with his local insurance agent, read the policy with care, and change the provisions of the policy at such intervals as required or when special circumstances arise.

Liability

Most horsemen are in such financial position that they are vulnerable to damage suits. Moreover, the number of damage suits arising each year is increasing at an almost alarming rate, and astronomical damages are being claimed. Studies reveal that about 95 percent of the court cases involving injury result in damages being awarded.

Several types of liability insurance offer a safeguard against liability suits brought as a result of injury suffered by another person or damage to their property.

Comprehensive personal liability insurance protects an operator who is sued for alleged damages suffered from an accident involving his property or family. The kinds of situations from which a claim might arise are quite broad, including injuries caused by animals, equipment, or personal acts.

Both workmen's compensation insurance and employer's liability insurance protect operators against claims or court awards resulting from injury to hired help. Workmen's compensation usually costs slightly more than straight employer's liability insurance, but it carries more benefits to the worker. An injured employee must prove negligence by his employer before the company will pay a claim under employer's liability insurance, whereas workmen's compensation benefits are established by state law and settlements are made by the insurance company without regard to who was negligent in causing the injury. Conditions governing participation in workmen's compensation insurance vary among the states.

ESTATE PLANNING

Human nature being what it is, most horsemen shy away from suggestions that someone help plan the disposition of their property and other assets. Also, many of them have a long-standing distrust of lawyers, legal terms, and trusts, and, to them, the subject of taxes seldom makes for pleasant conversation.

If no plans are made, estate taxes and settlement costs often run considerably higher than if proper estate planning is done and a will is made to carry out these plans. Today, the horse business is big business; many horsemen have well over $100,000 invested in land, horses, and equipment. Thus, it is not a satisfying thought to one who has worked hard to build and maintain a good horse establishment during his lifetime to feel that his heirs will have to sell the facilities and horses to raise enough cash to pay Federal Estate and Inheritance Taxes. By using a good estate planning service, a horseman can generally save thousands of dollars for his family in estate and inheritance taxes and in estate settlement costs. For assistance, horsemen should go to an estate planning specialist—an individual or company specializing in this work, or to the trust department of a commercial bank.

Inheritance and Partnerships

Nothing pleases parents more than seeing their children succeed; and, generally speaking, having them take over the home establishment makes for the ultimate in parental pride and satisfaction. Moreover, such an arrangement can provide a fine financial start in life for the young man who desires to carry on—provided, while the parents are still living, advantage is taken of the very considerable savings in Federal inheritance taxes, as provided by law.

Regulations permit parents to make (1) one specific gift of $60,000 tax free, and (2) an annual tax-free gift, repeated for a number of years, of $6,000; and these gifts may be in the form of interest in the livestock operation. Thus, in the first year, it is possible to transfer a maximum interest of $66,000 in the horse establishment to an heir without entailing the payment of any Federal inheritance tax. It is necessary, however, to file a gift tax return.

Frequently, even where it is the full intent and desire of the parents and the children that the latter continue with the horse establishment, the gift tax provision is not considered. Then, upon death of the parents, the heir(s) may be required to raise such a large amount of cash to pay the inheritance taxes that a part or all of the operation may have to be liquidated.

A sound logical step in this transfer is a partnership contract between the parents and their heir(s) recorded with the Clerk of Court in the county in which the farm is located. Appropriate counsel should be consulted in the preparation and recording of this agreement. Where the partnership contract is between a father and the heir, a provision should be included permitting the heir to purchase the father's share of the partnership for a fixed amount. The amount stipulated will then go into the father's estate. This will provide for proper and uninterrupted operation of the horse establishments, because, upon the father's death, the partnership is legally terminated.

Selected References

Title of Publication	Author(s)	Publisher
Farmer's Handbook, The	John M. White	University of Okla. Press, Norman, Okla., 1948.
Farm Management	Robert R. Hudelson	The Macmillan Company, New York, N.Y., 1939.
Farm Management Economics	Earl O. Heady Harold R. Jensen	Prentice-Hall, Inc., Englewood Cliffs, N.J., 1955.
Stockman's Handbook, The	M. E. Ensminger	The Interstate Printers & Publishers, Inc., Danville, Ill., 1970.

19

Glossary of Horse Terms

A MARK OF DISTINCTION of a good horseman is that he "speaks the language"—he uses the correct terms and knows what they mean. Even though horse terms are used glibly by people in the horse and pony business, often they are baffling to the newcomer.

Many terms that are defined or explained elsewhere in this book are not repeated in this chapter. Thus, if a particular term is not listed herein, the reader should look in the Index or in the particular chapter and section where it is discussed.

A

Across the board: A combination pari-mutuel (race) ticket on a horse is known as "across the board," meaning that you collect something if your horse runs first, second, or third.

Action: Movement of the feet and legs—should be straight and true.

Aficionado: Ardent follower, supporter, or enthusiast; a fan.

Age: The age of horses is computed from the first of January.

Aged horse: Correctly speaking, a horse eight years of age or over; but the term is often used to indicate a horse that is smooth-mouthed—that is, twelve years of age or older. Since one year of a horse's life corresponds to approximately three of a man's, it follows that at age seven a horse "comes of age," or attains maturity.

Aids: The legs, hands, weight, and voice, as used in controlling a horse.

Alter: To castrate a horse; to geld.

Anatomy: The science of the structure of the animal body and the relation of its parts.

Appointments: Equipment and clothing used in showing.

Arab: Used interchangeably with Arabian; hence, a breed of horses.

Asterisk: Used in front of a horse's name, an asterisk (*) indicates "imported." Used in front of a jockey's name, it indicates that he is an apprentice rider.

Astringent: A drug, such as tannic acid, alum, and zinc oxide or sulphate, that causes contraction of tissues.

At the end of the halter: Sold with no guarantee except title.

B

Back: The command to move backward.

Balanced seat: That position of the mounted rider that requires the minimum of muscular effort to remain in the saddle and which interferes least with the horse's movements and equilibrium.

Balk: Refuse to go.

Banged: Hair of the tail cut off in a straight line.

Bangtail: Slang term for a racehorse, as in the old days running horses usually had banged tails, often banged close to the dock, or docked and banged. Also, a wild horse.

Barefoot: Unshod.

Barren: A mare that is not in foal.

Bars: May refer either to the bars of the mouth, or of the hoof.

Base narrow: Standing with front or rear feet close together, yet standing with legs vertical.

Base wide: Standing with front or rear feet wide apart, yet with legs vertical.

Bean-shooter: A horse that throws its front feet violently forward at the trot, with little flexion, "landing" about 12 inches above the ground. A very undesirable trait.

Beefy hocks: Thick, meaty hocks, lacking in quality.

Big hitch: A "heavy hitch" of draft horses in fours, sixes, eights, or even more.

Bight of the reins: The part of the reins passing between thumb and fingers and out the top of the hand.

Bishoping: The practice of artificially altering the teeth of older horses in an attempt to make them sell as young horses.

Blinker: An attachment to the bridle or hood, designed to restrict the vision of the horse from the sides and rear and to focus the vision forward.

Blister: An irritant applied as a treatment for unsoundness and blemishes.

Blood-horse: A pedigreed horse. To most horsemen, the term is synonymous with the Thoroughbred breed.

Bloom: Hair that is clean and of a healthy texture.

Blow: To blow wind after strenuous exercise.

Blow out: To walk or exercise a horse either to loosen its muscles for further exercise, or to prevent chilling and stiffening after a hard workout.

Blue eye: An unsound eye with a blue appearance; the sight may or may not be entirely gone.

Bolting: Eating too rapidly. Animals that do this are said to be bolting their feed. Also, an animal's breaking out of control or trying to run away.

Bone: The measurement of the circumference around the cannon bone about halfway between the knee and fetlock joints. Eight inches of bone is average for the Thoroughbred. "Flat bone" indicates that the cannon and the back tendon are parallel, with the tendon clean-cut and standing well away from the cannon bone. The word "flat" refers to the appearance of the cannon, which is wide and flat when viewed from the side although narrow from the front, and does not mean that the bone itself is flat.

Boots: Protective covering for the legs or feet, generally used when exercising. Some types of boots are used for balance and perfection in gait.

Bosal: The braided rawhide or rope noseband of a bosal hackamore. The bosal is knotted under the horse's jaw.

Bowlegged: Wide at the knees, close at the feet.

Brace bandages: Resilient bandages on the legs of horses worn in some cases in an effort to support lame legs, and worn in other cases to protect a horse from cutting and skinning its legs while racing.

Brand: A mark used as means of identification.

Break: To teach a young horse to obey commands, and accept direction and control.

Breaking: A horse's leaving its gait and "breaking" into a gallop. A trotter or pacer must remain on gait in a race. If it makes a break, the driver must immediately pull it back to its gait.

Breeder: Owner of the dam at the time of service who was responsible for the selection of the sire to which she was mated.

Breeding: An attempt to regulate the progeny through intensive selection of the parents.

Breedy: Smart and trim about the head and front part of body.

Breezing: A race workout in which a horse is running at a controlled speed.

Brittle hoofs: Hoofs that are abnormally dry and fragile.

Broke: Tamed and trained to a particular function, as halter-broke. Also, to leave or alter gait; e.g., the trotter broke stride.

Broken crest: A heavy neck which breaks over and falls to one side.

Broken-knees: Knees with scars on them, indicating that the horse has fallen. Often scars are an indication that the horse is awkward and inclined to stumble.

Broodmare: A mare kept for breeding or reproductive purpose.

Broomtail: A wild and untrained western range horse of inferior quality.

Brothers (or *Sisters*):

  Full brothers: By the same sire and out of the same dam.

  Half brothers: Out of the same dam, by different sires. This is one of the most frequently misused terms. Horses by the same sire and out of different dams are referred to as "by the same sire," or else the name of the sire is used, as "by Man o' War." This distinction is for a definite purpose, for only a few horses can be half brothers (or half sisters) to a famous horse, but hundreds can be by the same sire. This restricted definition tends to give a little of the credit to good broodmares instead of leaving the meaning ambiguous.

  Brothers in blood: By the same sire out of full sisters; or by full brothers out of the same dam, or any combination of exactly the same blood.

  Three-quarter brothers: For example, horses having the same dam and whose sires have identical sires but different dams.

  Seven-eighths brothers: The progeny of a horse and his son produced by the same mare, or similar combinations of lineage.

Brush: To force a horse to top speed over a short distance.

Brushing: Striking the fetlock with the other hoof, which results in just roughing the hair fetlock, or in an actual injury.

Bucking: Springing with a quick leap, arching the back, and descending with the forelegs rigid and the head held as low as possible.

Buck-kneed: Standing with the knees too far forward.

Bug boy: An apprentice jockey.

Bull pen: Auction ring.

C

Calf-kneed: Standing back on knees; opposite from buck-kneed.

Calico-pinto: A multicolored or spotted pony.

Calk: Grips on the heels and the outside of the front shoes of horses, designed to give the horse better footing and prevent slipping.

Calking: Injury to the coronary band by the shoe of the horse. Usually incurred by horses whose shoes have calks, or by horses that are "rough-shod," as for ice.

Capped elbow: An enlargement of the elbow, usually caused by contact with the shoe when the horse is lying down.

Capriole: An intricate movement performed by the Lipizzan horses in the Spanish Riding School in Vienna. It is considered the ultimate of all high-school and classical training. The horse leaps into the air, and, while in the air, kicks out with the hind feet. The Capriole also, like so many other forms of high-school work, belongs to the Medieval methods of combat, in which, by means of such jumps by the horse, the surrounded rider could rid himself of adversaries, and the enemy, by the horse's kicking out with the hind legs, was prevented from getting within striking distance with sword and lance.

Cast: Refers to a horse's falling or lying down close to a wall or fence so that it cannot get up without assistance.

Cat-hammed: Having long, relatively thin thighs and legs.

Cavesson: Head stall with a nose band (often quite large) used for exercising and training horses.

Champing: A term that describes the horse's playing with the bit. Its development is encouraged in bitting a young horse by using a bit with "keys" attached to the mouthpiece, which tends to make the

(Continued)

saliva flow and keep the mouth moist—an aid in producing a "soft" mouth.

Check: Short for checkrein.

Checkrein: A strap coupling the bit of a bridle to the harness back band to keep the head up and in position.

Cheek: A cheek strap, a part of the bridle.

Chestnut: The horny growth on the inside of the horses's legs, above the knees and below the hocks.

Chukker: A seven-and-one-half-minute period in a polo game. (From the Hindu language, meaning "a circle.")

Cinch: Girth of a Western saddle.

Claiming race: A race in which all the horses are entered at stated prices and may be claimed (purchased) by any other owner of a starter in the race. In effect, all horses in a claiming race are offered for sale.

Clean: A term indicating that there are no blemishes or unsoundnesses on the legs.

Clicking: Striking the forefoot with the toe of the hind foot on the same side. Also known as forging.

Cluck: To move the tongue in such a way as to produce clucks. The command to go, proceed; the signal to increase speed.

Coarse: Lacking in quality—shown in texture of hair, hairy fetlocks, all-over lack of refinement, common head; flat and shelly feet, and gummy legs.

Cob: A close-knit horse, heavy-boned, short-coupled and muscular, but with quality, and not so heavy or coarse as to be a draft animal. A cob is usually small, standing under 15 hands.

Cobby: Close-coupled, stoutly built. Like a cob.

Cock horse: An extra horse used with English stage coaches, ridden behind the coach in ordinary going, but hitched before the team for added draft when coming to steep hills or heavy going. The cock horse was usually of a flashy color.

Cold-backed: Describes a horse that humps his back and does not settle down until the saddle has been on a few minutes. Some "cold-backed" horses will merely tuck their tails and arch their backs when first mounted, but others will take a few crow hops until warmed up.

Cold-blood: A horse of draft horse breeding.

Cold-jawed: Tough-mouthed.

Collected: In good form when in action.

Colt: A young stallion under three years of age; in Thoroughbreds, the age is extended to include four-year-olds.

Combination horse: One used for saddle and driving.

Condition: The state of health.

Conformation: Body shape or form.

Congenital: Acquired during development in the uterus and not through heredity.

Cool out: To cause a horse to move about quietly after heavy exercise.

Coon footed: Having long low pasterns and shallow heels.

Corn: Injury to the sensitive laminae of the sole, frog, bars, or posterior quarters of the hoof.

Coupling: The section between the point of the hip and the last rib. A short-coupled horse is considered to be an easy keeper, while a long-coupled horse is said to "take a bale of hay a day." The width of four fingers is considered to constitute a short coupling.

Cow hocks, cow-hocked: Standing with the joints of the hocks bent inward, with the toes pointing outward.

Crab bit: Bit with prongs extending at the horse's nose. Purpose is to tip the horse's head up and help prevent him from ducking his head, bowing his neck, and pulling hard on the rein.

Crest: The top part of the neck. This is very well developed in stallions.

Cribber: Animal which bites or sets the teeth against something and "sucks" wind.

Crop: A riding whip with a short, straight stock and a loop.

Crop-eared: Refers to an animal which has had the tips of its ears either cut off or frozen off.

Crossbred: Produced by a sire and dam of differing breeds.

Crow hops: Mild or playful bucking motions.

Crupper: A leather strap with a padded semicircular loop. The loop end goes under the tail and the strap end is affixed at the center of the back band of a harness or the cantle of a saddle to prevent the saddle from slipping over the withers.

Cryptorchid: A stallion with one or both testicles retained in the abdomen.

Curb: An enlargement at the rear of the leg and below the point of the hock. Also, a bit mouthpiece, designed to bring pressure to bear on the horse's bars.

Curry: Cleaning (grooming) with curry comb, dandy brush, body brush, sponge, rub rag, hoof pick, etc.

Cut-out: The cutting out of certain animals in a herd.

Cutting horse: A cow horse used in cutting cattle from the herd.

D

Daisy-cutter: A horse that seems to skin the surface of the ground at the trot. Such horses are often predisposed to stumbling.

Dam: The female parent of a horse.

Dapple: Small spots, patches, or dots contrasting in color or shade with the background, such as dapple-gray.

Dash: Race decided in a single trial.

Dead heat: A racing term referring to two or more contestants that arrive simultaneously at the finish line.

Dental star: A marking on the incisor teeth of horses, used in judging their age. It first appears on the lower central and intermediate incisors when the horse is about eight years of age.

Diagonal: Refers to the forefoot's moving in unison with its opposite hindfoot at the trot. If it is the left forefoot, it is called the left diagonal.

Dish-faced: A term used if the face is concave below the eyes, and, especially in Arabians, if the profile shows a definite depression below the level of the eyes. This term is also applied to some horses and many ponies that have flat or concave foreheads with prominent temples, but this type is the absolute opposite to the "dish" of the Arab, which has a prominent forehead.

Dishing: Carrying the foot forward in a lateral arc in a trot, but advancing the knee in a straight line.

Distaff side: The female side, as in a pedigree.

Dock: The solid portion of the tail.

Docked: A tail in which part of the dock has been removed.

Docking and setting: Removing part of the dock of the tail, cutting the tendons, and "setting" the tail to make the horse carry it high.

Double-gaited: A term applied to a horse that can both trot and pace with good speed.

Drafty: Having the characteristics of a draft horse. Heavy and lacking in quality.

Drag hunt: A hunt staged on horseback with hounds following a laid trail, made by dragging a bag containing anise seed or litter from a fox's den.

Dressage: The guiding of a horse through natural maneuvers without emphasis on the use of reins, hands, and feet.

Dutchman's team: It is customary to hitch the smaller horse of a team on the left side. When a careless horseman hitches his larger horse on the near side, he is said to be driving a "Dutchman's team."

Dwelling: A discernible hesitation of the foot in stride, common in high-going horses.

E

Ear down: To restrain an animal by biting or twisting its ear.

Eastern: Applied to horses of Arab, Barb, or similar breeding.

Entire: An ungelded male.

Equestrian: One who rides horseback.

Equestrienne: A female equestrian.

Equine: A horse. Correctly speaking, the term includes all the members of the family *Equidae*—horses, zebras, and asses.

Equitation: The act or art of riding horseback.

Ergot: The horny growth at the back of the fetlock joint; the spurs of a horse's hoofs.

Estrus: The estrus period is commonly called "heat."

Ewe neck: A neck like that of a sheep, with a dip between the poll and the withers. Also termed a "turkey neck" and "upside-down neck."

F

Family: The lineage of an animal as traced through either the males or females, depending upon the breed.

Farrier: A horseshoer.

Far side: The right side of a horse.

Favor: To favor one leg; to limp slightly.

Feather in eye: A mark across the eyeball, not touching the pupil; often caused by an injury, it may be a blemish or some other defect.

Feral: Describes a wild horse—one that has escaped from domestication and become wild, as contrasted to one originating in the wild.

Fetlock joint: The connection between the cannon and the pastern bones.

Fetus: The unborn animal as it develops in the uterus.

Filly: A young female horse under three years of age; in Thoroughbreds, it includes four-year-olds.

Film patrol: The practice of recording a race on film.

Firing: Applying a hot iron or needle to a blemish or unsoundness as a treatment.

First lock: The first lock of the mane on or in back of the poll (when the poll is clipped). The first lock is sometimes braided with a ribbon, as is the foretop.

Flat bone: (See *"Bone."*)

Flat foot: A foot the angle of which is less than 45°, or one in which the sole is not concave, or one with a low, weak heel.

Flat race: A race without jumps.

Flat-sided: Lacking spring in ribs.

Flaxen: A light colored mane or tail.

Flea-bitten: Describes a white horse covered with small, brown marks, or any "mangy-looking" animal.

Floating: Filing off the sharp edges of a horse's teeth.

Foal: A young, unweaned horse of either sex.

Foaling: Giving birth to a foal.

Follicle: A bubblelike structure on the ovary which contains an egg.

Foot-lock or *feather:* Long hair which grows back of the fetlock.

Forage: Vegetable material in a fresh, dried, or ensiled state which is fed to livestock (pasture, hay, silage).

Forehand: The "front" of the horse, including head, neck, shoulders, and forelegs—in other words, that portion of the horse in front of the center of gravity.

Foretop, forelock: The lock of hair falling forward over the face.

Forging: (See *Clicking.*)

Form: The past performance of a racehorse; often a table giving details relating to a horse's past performance.

Four-in-hand: A hitch of four horses, consisting of two pairs, with one pair in front of the other.

Fox hunt: A hunt with hounds, staged on horseback, after a live fox. The fox may have been released from captivity or tracked and flushed out of hiding by the hounds.

Frog: A triangular-shaped, elasticlike formation in the sole of the horse's foot.

Full brothers (or *sisters*): Horses having the same sire and the same dam.

Furlong: A racing distance of one-eighth mile.

Futurity: A race in which the animals entered were nominated before birth.

G

Gamete: A mature sex cell (sperm or egg).

Gear: The equipment and accessories used in harness driving (except the vehicle) and in polo playing (except the bridles and saddles). (See *Tack.*)

Gee: The teamster's term signaling a turn to the right.

Geld: To cut or castrate a male horse.

Gelding: A male horse that was castrated before reaching maturity.

Genotype selection: Selection of breeding stock not necessarily from the best appearing animals but from the best breeding animals, according to genetic make-up.

Germ plasm: Germ cells and their precursors, bearers of hereditary characters.

Get: Progeny or offspring.

Get-up: The command to go; proceed; move forward. When repeated, it means to increase speed. "Giddap," slang.

Girth: The strap or webbing that holds the saddle or backband in place.

Girth-place: The place for the girth, as the name implies, it is marked by a depression in the underline just in back of the front legs.

Glass-eyed: The term applied to an eye that is devoid of pigment.

Good mouth: Said of an animal 6 to 10 years of age.

Goose-rumped: An animal having a short, steep croup that narrows at the point of the buttocks.

Grade: An animal of unknown ancestry. If it shows some specific breed characteristics, it may be suffixed with the name of that breed; e.g., grade Shetland.

Grain: Harvested cereals or other edible seeds, including oats, corn, milo, barley, etc.

Grease: A low grade infection affecting the hair follicles and skin at the base of the fetlock joint.

Green broke: A term applied to a horse that has been hitched or ridden only one or two times.

Groom: A person who tends and cares for horses; an attendant, horseman, hostler, swipe (not preferred).

Gummy-legged: Having legs in which the tendons lack definition, or do not stand out clearly.

Gymkhana: A program of games on horseback.

H

Hack: A horse used for riding at an ordinary gait over roads, trails, etc.

Half-bred: When capitalized, this denotes a horse sired by a Thoroughbred and registered in the Half-Bred Stud Book.

Halter puller: A horse that pulls back on the halter rope.

Hammer-head: A coarse-headed animal.

Hamstrung: Disabled by an injury to the tendon above the hock.

Hand: A 4-inch unit of measurement.

Hand-canter: A semiextended canter, midway between a promenade canter and a gallop.

Handicap: A race in which chances of winning are equalized by assigned weights; heaviest weights are given to the best horses, and lightest weights to the poorest.

Hard-mouthed: Term used when the membrane of the bars of the mouth where the bit rests have become toughened and the nerves deadened because of the continued pressure of the bit.

Hat-rack: An emaciated animal.

Haute école: "High school," the highest form of specialized training of the riding horse.

Haw: The teamster's term signaling a turn to the left.

Hay belly: Having a distended barrel due to the excessive feeding of bulky rations, such as hay, straw or grass. Also called "grass belly."

Heat: One trip in a race that will be decided by winning two or more trials.

Heredity: Characteristics transmitted to offspring from parents and other ancestors.

Herring-gutted: Lacking depth of flank, which is also termed "single-gutted."

Heterozygous: Having unlike genes which can be present for any of the characteristics such as coat color, size, etc.

Hidebound: Having the hide tight over the body.

High School: The highest form of specialized training of riding horses.

Hippology: The study of the horse.

Hitch: To fasten a horse; e.g., when hitched to a rail. Also, a connection between a vehicle and a horse. Also, a defect in gait noted in the hind legs, which seem to skip at the trot.

Hitching: Having a shorter stride in one hind leg than in the other. Also, fastening a horse to an object or vehicle.

Hobbles: Straps which encircle the pasterns or fetlock joints on the front legs of the horse and are connected with a short strap or chain, to prevent it from roaming too far when turned out to graze. Another type of hobble is used on the hind legs (often around the hocks) of a mare in breeding, to prevent her from kicking the stallion.

Hogged mane: A hogged mane is one that has been clipped short.

Homozygous: Having like genes in a horse which can be present for any of the characteristics of the animal such as coat color, size, etc.

Homozygous dominant: A dominant character that produces only one kind of gamete.

Homozygous recessive: A recessive character that produces two kinds of gametes; one carries the dominant gene, while the other carries the recessive gene.

Honda: A ring of rope, rawhide, or metal on a lasso through which the loop slides.

Hopples: The term applied to hobbles (leather or plastic straps with semicircular loops) used in harness racing, which are placed on the gaskin and forearm, connecting the fore and hind legs of the same side in pacers, and running diagonally in trotters, connecting the diagonal fore and hind legs. Such hopples, which were invented by a railroad conductor named John Browning in 1885, are used to keep a horse on gait; i.e., to prevent trotters from pacing and pacers from trotting.

Hormone: A body-regulating chemical secreted by a gland into the blood stream.

Horse: In the restricted sense this applies to an entire, not a gelding or mare.

Horsemanship: The art of riding horseback.

Hot-blooded: Of Eastern or Oriental blood.

Hot-walker: One employed to cool out horses.

Hunt: Pursuit of game. As used by horsemen, the term usually implies a hunt on horseback with hounds.

Hybrids: Crosses of species, not breeds. The mule is a hybrid, cross between the horse family and the ass family.

I

Import: To bring horses from another country.

Importing: In registering horses from another country in the registry's stud book of their breeds, the certificates of registration issued bear the abbreviation Imp. and the country of export; e.g., Imp. Hydroplane (Eng.). When a name, such as Hydroplane has been previously granted to a horse foaled (born) in this country, a symbol is added; e.g., Imp. Hydroplane II (Eng.) Imported is also denoted by an asterisk in front of the name; e.g., *Hydroplane II (Eng.).

Indian broke: Horses trained to allow mounting from the off side.

Indian pony: A pinto.

In-hand: Refers to horses shown in halter classes.

J

Jack: A bone spavin.

Jerk line: A single rein, originally used in western U.S. It was fastened to the brake handle and ran through the driver's hand to the bit of the lead animal.

Jockey Club: Probably the most exclusive club in America, limited to 50 members. The Jockey Club is custodian of the American Stud Book, registry of Thoroughbred horses.

Jockey stick: A stick fastened to the hame of the near horse and the bit of the off horse for use in driving with a single rein to prevent crowding.

Jog cart: A cart longer and heavier than a racing sulky, used in warm-up miles because it's more comfortable for the driver than a sulky.

Jogging: A slow warm-up exercise of several miles with the horse going the wrong way of the track.

Jughead: A stupid horse. Also one with a large, ugly head.

K

Kick: Movement by a horse of the back or front leg, or legs, with intent to hit a person or other object.

Knee-sprung: (See *Buck-kneed.*)

L

Lead: The leading foot (leg) of a horse under saddle. When cantering circularly, the foot to the inner arc of the circle—clockwise, a right foot lead; and counter clockwise, a left foot lead.

Lead line: A chain, rope, or strap, or combination thereof, used for leading a horse.

Leaders: The head team in a four- , six- , or eight-pony hitch.

Left lead: Left front foot and left rear foot lead on the canter.

Legs out of the same hole: Very narrow-fronted. Such horses usually stand basewide; i.e., the feet stand wider apart than the distance across the legs at the chest.

Levade: An exercise of the *haute école,* especially as performed in the Spanish Riding School at Vienna. In the Levade the horse is in a half rearing position, with the forelegs well bent and the hind legs in a crouching position.

Lineback: An animal having a stripe of distinctive color along the spine.

Lines, reins: A leather strap, webbing, or rope attached to the bit or bits for control and direction. In driving, lines are sometimes called reins. In riding, reins are never called lines.

Long-coupled: Too much space between the last rib and the point of the hip.

Lope: The western adaptation of a very slow canter. It is a smooth, slow gait in which the head is carried low.

Lop-neck, fallen-neck, or *broken-crest:* A heavy neck that breaks over or falls to one side.

Lugger: A horse that pulls at the bit.

Lugging and pulling: Some horses pull on the reins, "lug" on one rein, or bear out or in with the driver, making it hard to drive them and to rate the mile at an even clip.

Lunge (also *Longe*)*:* The act of exercising a horse on the end of a long rope, usually in a circle.

M

Maiden: A mare that has never been bred. Also, on the race track, it refers to a horse (stallion, mare, or gelding) that has not won a race on a recognized track. In the show ring, it refers to a horse that has not won a first ribbon in a recognized show in the division in which it is showing.

Mane: Long hair on the top of the neck.

Manners: A way of behaving.

Mare: A mature female four years or older; in Thoroughbreds, five years or older.

Mascot: A companion for a horse. The most common mascots are ponies, goats, dogs, cats, and chickens.

Matron: A mare that has produced a foal.

Mixed-gaited: Said of a horse that will not adhere to any one true gait at a time.

Moon-blindness, moon-eye: Periodic ophthalmia, an eye disease.

Morning glory: A horse that works out in record time in the morning but that does not live up to its promise in an actual race.

Mottled: Marked with spots of different colors: dappled, spotted.

Mounting: The act of getting on a horse.

Mouthing: Determining the approximate age of a horse by examining the teeth.

Mudder: A horse that runs well on a track that is wet, sloppy, or heavy.

Mustang: Native horse of the Western Plains.

Mutation: A sudden variation which is later passed on through inheritance and which results from changes in a gene or genes.

Mutton-withered: Being low in the withers, with heavy shoulder muscling.

Muzzle: The lower end of the nose which includes the nostrils, lips, and chin.

N

Near side: The left side of a horse.

Neck rein: To guide or direct a horse by pressure of the rein on the neck.

Neigh: The loud, prolonged call of a horse.

O

Off side: The right side of a horse.

Open bridle: Bridle without blinds or blinkers covering the eyes. Some bridles are rigged with blinds that shut off vision to the rear and side and a few horses are raced with goggles or "peekaboo" blinds.

Open-hocked: Wide apart at the hocks with the feet close together.

Oriental: (See *Eastern.*)

Orloff trotter: A breed of horses originating in the USSR in the eighteenth century, principally through the interest of Count Alexis Gregory Orloff Chesminski. Used in the Soviet Union for light work, pleasure driving and riding, exhibition at fairs in various forms of competition including dressage, and extensively in harness racing.

Outlaw: A horse that cannot be broken.

Ova: The female reproductive cell.

Ovary: The female organ that produces eggs. There are two ovaries.

Over-reach: The hitting of the forefoot with the hind foot.

Overshot jaw: The upper jaw protruding beyond the lower jaw. Same as "parrot mouth."

Ovulation: The time when the follicle bursts and the egg is released.

Ovum: Scientific name for egg.

P

Pair: Two horses hitched abreast. Also, used in reference to two horses ridden side by side, together as in pair classes.

Pari-mutuels: Machine-controlled pool betting, invented in France in 1865, by a perfume-shop proprietor named Pierre Oller.

Parrot mouth: (See *Overshot jaw.*)

Passage: A movement of the *haute école.* This is a slow, cadenced, rather high trot with a fairly long period of suspension, giving the impression that the horse is on springs, or "trotting on air." Also a term for diagonal movement of the horse while facing straight forward, at the walk or trot.

Pastern: That part of the leg between the fetlock joint and the coronary band of the hoof.

Pedigree: A record of the ancestry of an animal.

Pedigree breeding: Selection on the combined bases of the merits of the individual and the average merits of its ancestry.

Piaffe: A dressage movement in which the horse does a cadenced trot in place, without moving from the spot. It is the foundation of all high school movements.

Piebald: Refers to black-and-white coat color.

Pigeon-toed: Pointing toes inward and heels outward.

Pig-eyed: Having small, narrow, squinty eyes, set back in the head; also, having thick eyelids.

Pinto: A multicolored, spotted horse.

Pirouette: A dressage exercise in which the horse holds its forelegs more or less in place while it moves its hindquarters around them.

Pivot: A movement in dressage in which the horse pivots around its hindquarters, holding one hindleg more or less in place and side-stepping with the other hindfoot.

Place: To finish second in a race.

Placenta: The membrane by which the fetus is attached to the uterus. Nutrients from the mother pass into the placenta and then through the navel cord to the fetus. When the animal is born, the placenta is expelled. It is commonly called the "afterbirth."

Plug: A horse of common breeding and poor conformation.

Point: The team in back of the leaders in an eight-horse hitch.

Points: Black coloration from the knees and hocks down, as in most bays and browns, and in some buckskins, roans, and greys.

Polo pony: A "pony" used for polo. Polo ponies of today are mostly of Thoroughbred breeding. They must be fast, and tough and courageous enough to stand the bumping, riding-off, and the many quick stops and turns.

Pop-eyed: Refers to a horse whose eyes are generally more prominent or bulge out a little more than normal; also to a horse that is "spooky" or attempts to see everything that goes on.

Post: The starting point of a race.

Post position: Refers to race starting position. Beginning with position No. 1 nearest the rail, horses line up at the starting gate according to number.

Posting: The rising and descending of the rider with the rhythm of the trot.

Pounding: A "heavy foot" contact with the ground, common in high-going horses.

Prepotency: Refers to breeding power, as measured by the degree in which parent likeness is transmitted to offspring.

Produce: Offspring.

Progenitor: One that originates or precedes.

Progeny: Refers to offspring or descendants of one or both parents.

Puffs: Wind galls, bog spavins, or thoroughpins.

Pulled tail: A tail thinned by hairs being pulled.

Purebred: An animal descended from a line of ancestors of the same breed but not necessarily registered. This should not be confused with "Thoroughbred," a breed of horse.

Purse: Race prize money to which the owners of horses in the race do not contribute.

Q

Quality: Refinement, as shown in a neat and well-chiselled head, fine texture of hair with little or no fetlock, clean bone, good texture of hoof, etc.

R

Random: Three horses hitched in single file, usually to a dogcart.

Rangy: Elongated, lean, muscular, of slight build.

Rat tail: A tail with a short hair coat.

Rattlers: Rattlers (wooden, rubber, or plastic balls) or links of light chain fastened about the pasterns of high-going harness and saddle horses and ponies. Weighted boots are also used to enhance action.

Reata: Spanish for lariat.

Recessive: A characteristic which appears only when both members of a pair of genes are alike.

Reins: (See Lines.)

Remuda: A collection of riding horses at a roundup from which are chosen those used for the day. A relay of mounts.

Ribbed-up: Said of a horse on which the back ribs are well arched and incline well backwards, bringing the ends closer to the point of the hip and making the horse shorter in coupling.

Ridgeling: A horse with at least one testicle in the abdomen. A ridgeling is difficult to geld, and often retains the characteristic of a stallion.

Right lead: Right front foot and right rear lead on the canter.

Ringer: A horse passed off under false identity, with the idea of entering it in a race below its class where it is almost certain to win.

(Continued)

With today's lip tattoo system of identification, ringers are a thing of the past.

Roach backed: Arched-backed, razorbacked.

Roached mane: A mane that has been cut short and tapered so that it stands upright. It is not so short as a clipped mane.

Roarer: A wind-broken animal that makes a loud noise in drawing air into the lungs.

Rollers, rattlers: Wooden balls on a cord, encircling a horse's pastern to give the horse more action.

Roman-nosed: Refers to a horse having a profile that is convex from poll to muzzle.

Rubdown: A rubbing of the body with a rough towel, usually given after exercise to promote circulation and remove fatigue.

S

Saliva test: The testing of saliva for the presence of drugs or narcotics.

Schooling: Training and developing natural characteristics in a pony.

Scoring: Preliminary warming up of horses before the start. The horses are turned near the starting point and hustled away as they will be in the race.

Scotch collar: Housing over the collar of draft show harness.

Scraper: A metal or wooden, slightly concave, tool shaped like a hook at the upper end and used with one hand for scraping sweat and liquid from the body. Also, a thin metal strip with handles affixed at either end, used with both hands for scraping sweat and liquid from the body.

Scrotum: The sac-like pouch that suspends the testicles outside the male animal.

Scrub: A low-grade animal.

Self-colored: A term applied to the mane and tail when they are the same color as the body coat.

Sell at halter: To sell with no guarantee except the title.

Semen: Sperm mixed with fluids from the accessory glands.

Serviceably sound: Said of a horse that has nothing wrong that will materially impair its value for the intended use.

Set-tail: A tail in which the cords have been cut or "nicked" and the tail put in a set.

Sex cells: The egg and the sperm, which unite to create life. They transmit genetic characteristics from the parents to the offspring.

Shadbelly: (See *Herring-gutted.*)

Shoe-boil: (See *Capped elbow.*)

Short-coupled: Describes a horse having a short distance (usually not more than four fingers' width) between the last rib and the point of the hip.

Show: Finishing third in a race.

Sickle-hocked: Very crooked in the hind leg, usually light of bone, and cut in under the hock. Such a conformation is predisposed to curbiness.

Sire: The male parent.

Sisters: (See *Brothers.*)

Skewbald: Refers to coat color other than black—such as bay, brown, or chestnut—combined with white.

Slab-sided: Flat-ribbed.

Sloping shoulders: Shoulders properly angulated and laid back.

Smoky eye: A whitish-clouded eye. (See *Wall eye.*)

Smooth: Unshod, "barefoot."

Smooth coat: Short, hard, close-fitting coat of hair.

Smooth-mouthed: No cups in the teeth. Indicates a horse is 12 years of age or older.

Snorter: An excitable horse.

Soft: Easily fatigued.

Solid color: Having no white markings.

Sound: Said of a horse free from injury, flaw, mutilation, or decay; also one that is guaranteed free from blemishes and unsoundness.

Speck in eye: A spot in the eye, but not covering the pupil. It may or may not impair the vision. (See *Feather in eye.*)

Sperm, sperm cell: Male sex cell produced in the testicles.

Spooky: Nervous.

Sprinter: A horse who performs best at distances of a mile or under.

Stag: A male horse that was castrated after reaching maturity.

Stake races: A stake, short for sweepstake, is just what the name implies. Each owner puts up an equal amount of money (nominating fees, fees for keeping them eligible, and starting fees) and the winner takes all. Also, the track usually puts up added money. Actually, few stake races are run on a winner-take-all basis; rather, the money is divided between the first four horses.

Stall: Space or compartment in which an animal is placed or confined. It may be a straight stall with the animal tied at the front end

(Continued)

(a tie-stall) or a compartment with the animal loose inside (a box-stall).

Stallion: A male horse four years old or over; in Thoroughbreds, five years old or over.

Standing halter: Similar to a martingale, it is a strap that runs from the girth to a tight halter on the horse's head. It helps keep the horse from throwing its head up and going into a break.

Star gazer: A horse that holds its head high in an awkward position.

Steeplechaser: A horse used in cross-country racing with jumps.

Sterile: A term used to designate a stallion that is infertile.

Stock horse: In the West this term designates a cow horse. In other localities it can also mean a stallion used at stud.

Straight shoulder: Said of shoulder lacking sufficient angulation.

Stride: The distance covered by one foot when in motion. Greyhound, holder of the world's trotting record at 1:55¼, had a stride of more than 27 feet.

Stud: A male horse (stallion) kept for breeding. Also, an establishment or farm where animals are kept for breeding.

Substance: A combination of good bone, muscularity, and width and depth of body.

Suckling: A foal that is not weaned.

Sulky or *bike:* Light racing rig with bicycle-type wheels used in harness races. The sulkies weigh from 29 to 37 pounds, and usually have hardwood shafts, although aluminum and steel sulkies have been introduced recently.

Surcingle: A belt, band, or girth passing over a saddle or over anything on a horse's back to bind the saddle fast.

Swan neck: A long, slim, swanlike neck.

Swaybacked: Having a decided dip in the back. Also termed "easy-backed" and "saddle-backed."

Swing team: The middle team in a six-horse hitch, or the team in front of the wheelers in an eight-horse hitch.

T

Tack: Equipment used in riding and driving horses, such as saddles, bridles, etc.

Tack room: Place for storage of bridles, saddles, other equipment and accessories used in horseback riding. Also a display room for pictures, prizes, ribbons, trophies, and the like.

Tail (*banged* or *thinned*): A tail is banged if the hair is cut off in a straight line below the dock; it is thinned if it is shortened; and it is thinned and tapered if the hairs are pulled and broken.

Tail female: The female, or bottom line of a pedigree.

Tail male: The sire line, or top line in a pedigree.

Tail-set: A crupper-like contrivance, with a shaped section for the tail, which brings the tail high so that it can be doubled and tied down, to give it an "arch" and extremely high carriage; but a tail so set must first be "nicked" to give such results. The set is worn most of the time while the horse is in the stable, and until a short time before the horse is to be shown. Horses with "set" tails are usually "gingered" before entering the ring, in order to assure high tail carriage while being shown.

Tandem: Said of two horses, one hitched in front of the other.

Tapadera: A long, decorative covering over the stirrup used in parade classes.

Teaser: A horse, usually a stallion or a ridgeling, used to test the response of a mare prior to breeding, or used to determine if a mare is in heat and ready to breed.

Temperament: Refers to the horse's suitability for the job it is to perform.

Testicle: A male gland which produces sperm. There are two testicles.

Thong: The lash of the whip.

Thrifty condition: Healthy, active, vigorous.

Tie: To attach or fasten by use of a halter and a shank.

Toe weight: A metal weight (knob) fitted to a spur previously placed on the front hoof to induce a change or balance in motion. Used extensively in the training and racing of harness horses.

Tongue-loller: A horse whose tongue hangs out.

Totalisator: The mechanical "brains" of the pari-mutuel system.

Tote board: The indicator board of the totalisator on which is flashed all pari-mutuel information before or after a race.

Tout: A low-order con man who peddles tips, betting systems, etc. to the unwary racegoer.

Traces: The parts of a harness which run from the collar to the single-tree.

Trappy action: A short, quick stride.

Troika: The word "troika" is a Russian word meaning trio or three. A troika hitch is a three-horse combination team hitched to a vehicle; e.g., a carriage, wagon, sleigh, or sled. The carriage is the vehicle of common use and it is known as a charaban. It is a light four-wheeled two-passenger vehicle with an elevated seat for the driver.

Tucked-up: Having the belly under the loin. Refers also to a small-waisted horse. Differs from "herring-gutted" and similar conditions, in that a horse may be "tucked-up" temporarily due to hard work, lack of water, lack of bulk in the diet, etc. Also, called "gaunted-up" or "ganted-up."

Twitch: A rope run through the end of a stick, used on the horse's upper lip; it is tightened by twisting in order to attract the horse's attention so it will stand still.

Type: Type may be defined as an ideal or standard of perfection combining all the characteristics that contribute to the animal's usefulness for a specific purpose.

U

Underpinning: The legs and feet of the horse.

Unicorn: An unusual three-horse hitch with two horses hitched as a pair and a third hitched in front of the pair.

V

Veterinarian: One who treats diseases or afflictions of animals medically and surgically; a practitioner of veterinary medicine or surgery.

Viceroy: A lightweight, cut-under, wire-wheeled show vehicle with curved dash, used for some heavy harness classes, and especially for Hackney Ponies, Shetlands, and Harness Show Ponies.

W

Wall-eye: Also termed glass, blue, china, or crockery eye; refers to lack of color in a horse's eye.

Warm-up, warming up: The process or routine of graduated exercise until the horse is properly conditioned for a strenuous effort.

Weanling: A weaned foal.

Wheelers: The team on the pole or tongue, hitched directly in front of a rig or wagon in a four or more horse hitch.

Whip: An instrument or device of wood, bone, plastic, leather, fiberglass, metal, or combination thereof with a loop or cracker of leather or cord at the upper end; used for disciplining or goading an animal. Sometimes a required accessory when exhibiting (driving), as in a horse show. Also, one who handles a whip expertly, one who drives a horse in harness other than racing, or one who "whips in" or manages the hounds of a hunt club.

White line: The union between the sole and the wall of the foot.

Whoa: The command to stop; stand. When repeated softly, means to slow down, but may also mean attention.

Winding, log-walking, or *walking the rope:* A type of paddling in which the striding leg is carried in a twisting motion about and in front of the supporting leg.

Windy, or *wind-broken:* Said of an animal that whistles or roars when exerted.

Wrangling: Rounding up range horses.

Y

Yearling: A horse between one and two years of age.

APPENDIX

In the appendix . . .

$$I$$

Energy Terms and
Feed Composition[1]

IN CHART FORM, Figure I-1 shows the conventional energy system. Apparent digestible energy (DE), metabolizable energy (ME), and net energy (NE) are usually calculated by the conventional system.

Figure I-2 shows where the various energy fractions originate. Since some of the fecal energy is of metabolic origin and some of the urinary energy is of endogenous origin, the scheme shown in Fig. I-2"A" has been modified to give Figure I-2"B" which gives true digestible energy (TDE), true metabolizable energy (TME), and true net energy (TNE). Since the metabolic energy and endogenous energy are part of the net energy requirements under this scheme, these items are shown as part of the maintenance energy.

ENERGY TERMS

A part of the confusion and disagreement over the calorie system stems from a lack of understanding of terms, and from the coining of numerous "pet" names. For this reason, under the heading, "Glossary of Energy Terms" the author has elected to present the terms, and brief definitions of each, after the monumental work of Harris.[2] Additionally, use of the calorie system necessitates a working knowledge of the metric system (see Appendix Section III).

---

[1] The author gratefully acknowledges the authoritative help of Dr. Lorin E. Harris, Utah State University, in the preparation of this section.

[2] *Biological Energy Interrelationships and Glossary of Energy Terms.* National Academy of Sciences, NRC, Pub. No. 1411, by Lorin E. Harris.

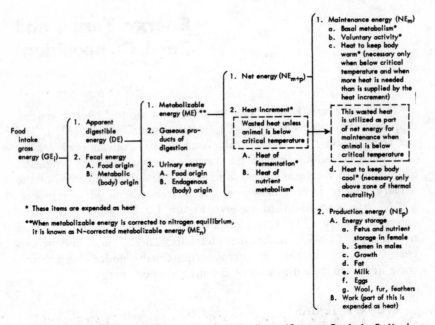

Fig. I-1. The utilization of energy, conventional scheme. (Courtesy Dr. Lorin E. Harris, Utah State University)

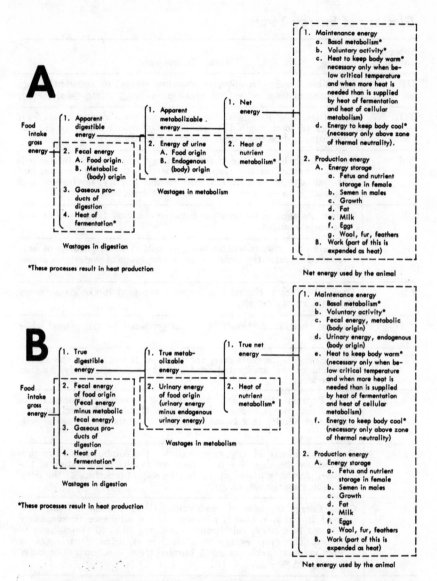

A

Food intake gross energy

1. Apparent digestible energy
2. Fecal energy
   A. Food origin.
   B. Metabolic (body) origin
3. Gaseous products of digestion
4. Heat of fermentation*

Wastages in digestion

1. Apparent metabolizable energy
2. Energy of urine
   A. Food origin
   B. Endogenous (body) origin

Wastages in metabolism

1. Net energy
2. Heat of nutrient metabolism*

1. Maintenance energy
   a. Basal metabolism*
   b. Voluntary activity*
   c. Heat to keep body warm* necessary only when below critical temperature and when more heat is needed than is supplied by heat of fermentation and heat of cellular metabolism)
   d. Energy to keep body cool* (necessary only above zone of thermal neutrality).
2. Production energy
   A. Energy storage
      a. Fetus and nutrient storage in female
      b. Semen in males
      c. Growth
      d. Fat
      e. Milk
      f. Eggs
      g. Wool, fur, feathers
   B. Work (part of this is expended as heat)

Net energy used by the animal

*These processes result in heat production

B

Food intake gross energy

1. True digestible energy
2. Fecal energy of food origin (Fecal energy minus metabolic fecal energy)
3. Gaseous products of digestion
4. Heat of fermentation*

Wastages in digestion

1. True metabolizable energy
2. Urinary energy of food origin (urinary energy minus endogenous urinary energy)

Wastages in metabolism

1. True net energy
2. Heat of nutrient metabolism*

1. Maintenance energy
   a. Basal metabolism*
   b. Voluntary activity*
   c. Fecal energy, metabolic (body origin)
   d. Urinary energy, endogenous (body origin)
   e. Heat to keep body warm* (necessary only when below critical temperature and when more heat is needed than is supplied by heat of fermentation and heat of cellular metabolism)
   f. Energy to keep body cool* (necessary only above zone of thermal neutrality)
2. Production energy
   A. Energy storage
      a. Fetus and nutrient storage in female
      b. Semen in males
      c. Growth
      d. Fat
      e. Milk
      f. Eggs
      g. Wool, fur, feathers
   B. Work (part of this is expended as heat)

Net energy used by the animal

*These processes result in heat production

Fig. I-2. The utilization of energy (scheme to show where various portions originate). Since some of the fecal energy is of metabolic origin and some of the urinary energy is of endogenous origin, the scheme shown in Figure I-2"A" has been modified to give Figure I-2"B". Since the metabolic energy and endogenous energy are part of the net energy requirements under this scheme, these items are shown as part of the maintenance energy. (Courtesy, Dr. Lorin E. Harris, Utah State University)

Glossary of Energy Terms

Abbreviation	Term—Definition
DE	Digestible Energy (or apparent absorbed energy, or apparent energy of digested food) is the food intake gross energy minus fecal energy.
TDE	True Digestible Energy is the food intake gross energy minus fecal energy of food origin (FE minus FE_m) minus energy in gaseous products of digestion minus heat of fermentation.
BM	Basal Metabolism is the chemical change which occurs in the cells of an animal in the fasting and resting state when it uses just enough energy to maintain vital cellular activity, respiration, and circulation as measured by the basal metabolic rate.
CB	Carbon Balance is the relation between the food intake carbon and the carbon output.
cal	A calorie (cal, always written with a small c) is the amount of heat required to raise the temperature of one gram of water one degree centigrade.
EB	Energy Balance is the relation between the food intake gross energy and the energy output.
FHP	Fasting Heat Production is the heat produced by the animal while fasting.
FE	Fecal Energy is the gross energy of the feces. It consists of the energy content of the undigested food and the metabolic (body) fraction of the feces.
FE_m	Fecal Energy, Metabolic, is the amount of energy contained in the metabolic (body) fraction of feces (i.e., abraded intestinal mucosa, digestive fluids) that is not obtained from unabsorbed ration residues.
GPD	Gaseous Products of Digestion includes the combustible gases produced in the digestive tract incident to the fermentation of the ration. Methane makes up by far the major proportion of the combustible gases produced.
GE	Gross Energy (or heat of combustion) is the amount of heat, measured in calories, that is released when a substance is completely oxidized in a bomb calorimeter containing 25 to 30 atmospheres of oxygen. The gross energy of a feed, feces, urine, tissue, eggs, or other material is determined by burning them in a bomb calorimeter (see Fig. 13-5).
GE_i	Gross Energy Intake is the gross energy of the food consumed.
HF	Heat of Fermentation is the heat produced in the digestive tract as a result of microbial action.
HI	Heat Increment is the increase in heat production following consumption of feed when the animal is in a thermo-neutral environment.

(Continued next page)

Glossary (Continued)

Abbreviation	Term—Definition
HBC	**Heat to Keep Body Cool** is the extra energy expended by the animal when the temperature of the environment is above the animal's zone of thermal neutrality.
HBW	**Heat to Keep Body Warm** is the additional heat needed to keep the animal's body warm when the temperature of the environment is below the critical temperature.
HNM	**Heat of Nutrient Metabolism** is the heat produced as a result of the utilization of absorbed nutrients.
HP	**Heat Production (Total)** of an animal consuming food in a thermo-neutral environment is composed of the heat increment (heat of fermentation plus heat of nutrient metabolism) plus heat used for maintenance (basal metabolism plus voluntary activity). It can be estimated by three procedures; namely, (1) by measuring the quantity of oxygen an animal consumes (open circuit method), (2) by measuring directly the amount of heat produced by the animal (direct method), and (3) by the comparative slaughter technique. For the latter, two comparable animals are slaughtered, one at the beginning of the test period and the other at the end of the test period, and the energy content of each is determined. Then, the difference between these two values represents the amount of energy gained. The total heat production and energy utilization of a lactating animal are illustrated in Figure 1-3.
kcal	**A kilocalorie** is 1,000 small calories.
Mcal	**A Megacalorie,** or a therm, is equivalent to 1,000 kilocalories or 1,000,000 calories.
$W^{0.75}$	**Metabolic Body Size** is defined as the weight of the animal raised to the three-fourths power.
ME	**Metabolizable Energy** is the food intake gross energy minus fecal energy, minus urinary energy, minus energy in the gaseous products of digestion.
TME	**True Metabolizable Energy** is the food intake gross energy minus fecal energy of food origin (FE minus FE_m), minus energy in gaseous products of digestion, minus heat of fermentation energy, minus urinary energy of food origin (UE minus UE_e).
ME_n	**N-Corrected Metabolizable Energy** is the food intake gross energy minus fecal energy, minus energy in the gaseous products of digestion, minus urinary energy; the total is then corrected for nitrogen retained or lost from the body.
TME_n	**N-Corrected True Metabolizable Energy** is the food intake gross energy minus fecal energy of food origin (FE minus FE_m), minus energy in gaseous products of digestion, minus heat of fermentation energy, minus urinary energy of food origin (UE minus UE_e); the total is then corrected for nitrogen retained or lost from the body.

(Continued next page)

Glossary (Continued)

Abbreviation	Term—Definition
NE or NE $_{m+p}$	Net Energy is the difference between metabolizable energy and heat increment and includes the amount of energy used either for maintenance only or for maintenance plus production.
NE $_m$	Net Energy for Maintenance is the fraction of net energy expended to keep the animal in energy equilibrium.
NE $_p$	Net Energy for Production is the fraction of net energy required in addition to that needed for maintenance that is used for work or for tissue gain (growth and/or fat production) or for the synthesis of a fetus, milk, eggs, wool, fur or feathers.
NE $_{egg}$	Net Energy for Egg Production.
NE $_{fat}$	Net Energy for Fat Production.
NE $_{fur}$	Net Energy for Fur Production.
NE $_{growth}$	Net Energy for Growth.
NE $_{milk}$	Net Energy for Milk Production.
NE $_{preg.}$	Net Energy for Pregnancy.
NE $_{wool}$	Net Energy for Wool Production.
NE $_{work}$	Net Energy for Work.
	Note: These abbreviations could be used in feed composition tables or where more than one kind of production is being discussed.
TNE	True Net Energy is the intake gross energy minus the fecal energy of food origin (FE—FE$_m$) minus energy in gaseous products, minus heat of fermentation energy, minus urinary energy or direct food origin (UE—UE$_e$), minus heat of nutrient metabolism.
TNE $_m$	True Net Energy for Maintenance is the sum of the energy required for basal metabolism, voluntary activity, metabolic fecal energy (body origin), and endogenous urinary energy (body origin).
NB	Nitrogen Balance is the nitrogen in the food intake (NI) minus the nitrogen in the feces (FN), minus nitrogen in the urine (UN).
NCR	Nutrient to Calorie Ratio. There is acceptable evidence that the energy needs of animals and their requirements of the several nutrients are quantitatively correlated. This does not necessarily mean a direct cause-and-effect relation, but it does mean that there is an optimum balance between them. For those nutrients that are needed to metabolize energy, it is logical to consider that the amount of energy metabolized "determines" their requirements. Hence, it is logical to express nutrients in weight per unit of energy needed.

(Continued next page)

Glossary (Continued)

Abbreviation	Term—Definition
NCR (Continued)	For example, it is suggested that the protein to calorie ratio should be expressed as grams of protein per 1000 kcal metabolizable energy (g protein/1000 kcal ME). If the ME is corrected for nitrogen retained or lost from the body, then the abbreviation should be g protein/1000 kcal ME_n. This same dimension may easily be extended to other nutrients as g calcium/1000 kcal or mg riboflavin/ 1000 kcal, etc.
PFV	**Physiological Fuel Values** expressed in calories, are units used in the United States to measure food energy in human nutrition. It is similar to metabolizable energy.
UE	**Urinary Energy** is the gross energy of the urine.
UE_e	**Urinary Energy, Endogenous** is the amount of energy contained in the endogenous (body) fraction of the total urine.
VA	**Energy of Voluntary Activity** is the amount of energy needed by an animal to provide the energy required in getting up, standing, moving about to obtain food, grazing, drinking, lying down, etc.

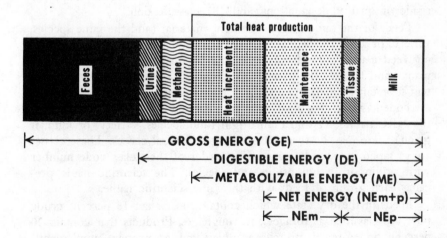

Fig. I-3. The total heat production and energy utilization of a lactating animal, adapted from data of W. P. Flatt. (Courtesy, Dr. Lorin E. Harris, Utah State University)

FEED COMPOSITION

Nutrient compositions of feedstuffs are necessary for intelligent ration preparation, animal health, and feed efficiency. Table I-1 contains the most commonly used feeds for horses. It was adapted for this book by Dr. Lorin E. Harris, and it is being reproduced through the courtesy of the National Research Council, National Academy of Sciences.

It contains data, if available, for proximate composition, gross energy (GE), mineral, vitamin, and amino acid contents of feeds. Where available, apparent digestible protein, apparent digestible energy (DE), metabolizable energy (ME), and total digestible nutrients (TDN) are listed.

NRC Nomenclature

The nomenclature of the feeds under which the analytical data are shown is based on the National Research Council (NRC) scheme.[3] It is designed to give (to the extent that the information is available or applicable) a qualitative description of the product as to its: (1) origin or parent material, (2) species, variety, or kind, (3) the part actually eaten, (4) the process(es) and treatment(s) to which it has been subjected, (5) the stage of maturity, (6) cutting or crop, (7) grade or quality designations, and (8) classification.

Feeds of the same origin or parent material (and the same species, variety, or kind, if designated) have been subgrouped into the following feed classes: (1) dry forages and roughages, (2) pasture, range plants, and forages fed green, (3) silages, (4) energy feeds, (5) protein supplements, (6) minerals, (7) vitamins, and (8) additives. Classes are coded as indicated above and are included in parentheses following the NRC names. Within each origin (and species, variety, or kind, if given) there may be feeds that belong to several classes. These classes are grouped in ascending numerical order of their class code number with origin or within origin and species. The scientific name precedes each group of feeds with the same scientific name.

Feeds in the dry state which contain more than 18 percent crude fiber are classified as forages and roughages. Products that contain 20 percent or more of protein are classified as protein supplements.

---

[3] Harris, Lorin E., Symposium on feeds and meats terminology. III. A system for naming and describing feedstuffs, energy terminology, and the use of such information in calculating diets. J. Animal Sci. 22:535-547. 1963.

Products with less than 20 percent protein are classified as energy feeds. (These guidelines are approximate and there is some overlapping.) The feeds have been classified in this way because each class has certain properties that are considered in balancing a ration. Fruits, nuts, and roots, have been classified as energy feeds because most of the by-product feeds from these subclasses furnish, primarily, energy to the animal.

To reduce the names to minimum printing or punch-card space requirement, a system of abbreviations has been devised covering many of the terms involved in the eight components of the name. These are listed in this section under the heading, "Feed Term Abbreviations."

The system of naming is illustrated as follows:

COMPONENTS

1. Origin ....Clover
2. Variety ....red
3. Part eaten ....aerial pt
4. Process ....s-c
5. Maturity ....pre-blm
6. Cutting ....cut 1
7. Grade ....leafy
8. Classification ....(1)

The NRC name is written out in linear form with the components of the name separated by commas and without other punctuation. Commas are not included within the eight components so that the reader may readily recognize the entire component. The name would appear as:

Clover, red, aerial pt, s-c, pre-blm, cut 1, leafy, (1)

This example would be read:

Clover, red, aerial part, sun-cured, pre-bloom, first cutting, leafy. It is a dry roughage.

The Association of American Feed Control Officials (AAFCO) names, Canada Feeds Act (CFA) names and other common names appear after the NRC names. Cross references (where necessary) have been included so the NRC name may be readily located.

Although care has been taken to include cross references, it is suggested that the entire list of feeds under a given origin be checked so that a feed is not missed.

An example of a feed which has different names is as follows:

COMPONENTS

1. Origin ....Barley
3. Part ....flour by-prod mil-rn
8. Classification ....(4)

Other names:
    Barley mill by-product (AAFCO)
    Barley mixed feed (CFA)

Each feed has been given a six-digit reference number, the first of which indicates the feed classification. For the above example the Names and Feed reference number would appear as follows:

Barley, flour by-prod mil-rn, (4)
    Barley mill by-product (AAFCO)
    Barley mixed feed (CFA)
Ref no 4-00-523

The analytical data are expressed in the metric system (with the exception of the bushel weights of the cereal grains) and are on an "as fed" as well as a "dry" basis. The NRC reference feed number may be used as an identification on electronic computers for linear programming.

It has not been possible to obtain apparent digestible energy (DE) and metabolizable energy (ME) values for all feedstuffs. In some of these cases, values have been estimated using the following formulae:

$$DE\ (kcal/kg) = \frac{TDN\%}{100} \times 4409.2$$
$$ME\ (kcal/kg)\ for\ horses = DE\ (kcal) \times 0.82$$

Where energy data were lacking for individual feeds, cattle data were used.

The International Standards for vitamin A activity based on vitamin A and beta-carotene are as follows: One International Unit (IU) of vitamin A = one USP unit = vitamin A activity of 0.300 mcg of crystalline vitamin A alcohol, corresponding to 0.344 mcg of vitamin A acetate or 0.550 mcg of vitamin A palmitate. Beta-carotene is the standard for pro-vitamin A. One International Unit of vitamin A activity is equivalent to 0.6 mcg of beta-carotene or 1 mg of beta-carotene = 1667 IU of vitamin A. International Standards for vitamin A are based on the utilization by the rat of vitamin A and/or beta-carotene.

The vitamin A equivalent for carotene was calculated by assuming that 0.6 mcg of beta-carotene = one IU of vitamin A.

Because the various species do not convert carotene to vitamin A in the same ratio as rats, it is suggested that the following conversion rate be used:

CONVERSION OF BETA-CAROTENE TO VITAMIN A FOR DIFFERENT SPECIES[1]

Species	Conversion mg beta-carotene to IU vitamin A		IU vitamin A activity (calculated from carotene)
	(mg)	(IU)	(%)
Standard	1 =	1,667	100.
Horses			
Growth	1 =	555	33.3
Pregnancy	1 =	333	20.0
Sheep	1 =	400-500	24.0-30.0
Swine	1 =	500	30.0
Beef cattle	1 =	400	24.0
Dairy cattle	1 =	400	24.0
Poultry	1 =	1,667	100.
Rat	1 =	1,667	100.
Man	1 =	556	33.0

[1]W. M. Beeson, 1965. Relative potencies of vitamin A and carotene for animals. *Federation Proc.* 24:924-926.

Individual feed samples may vary widely from indicated averages because of influencing factors as crop, variety, harvesting and storage conditions, and climate and soil pertinent to the locality where the feed was produced. Therefore, the values given should be used with judgment, often in conjunction with more specific information on hand about the feed.

FEED TERM ABBREVIATIONS

Abbreviation	Feed Term
AAFCO	Association of American Feed Control Officials
by-prod	by-product
Ca	calcium
Can	Canadian
c-bolt	coarse bolted
CFA	Canada Feeds Act
chop	chopped
c-sift	coarse sifted
comm	commercial
cond	condensed
CW	Canadian Western
dehy	dehydrated
dig	digestibility, digestible
distil	distillation, distillers
dry-mil	dry milled
dry-rend	dry rendered
equiv	equivalent
F	fluorine
fbr	fiber
f-grnd	fine ground
fm	foreign material (including seeds other than the principal product or grain)
f-scr	fine screened
f-sift	fine sifted
g	gram
gr	grade
grnd	ground
hydro	hydrolyzed
ICU	International Chick Unit
insol	insoluble
IU	International Units
kcal	kilocalories
kg	kilogram
mech-extd	mechanically extracted, expeller extracted, hydraulic extracted, or old process
mcg	microgram
mg	milligram
mil-rn	mill run
mn	minimum
mx	maximum
N	nitrogen
No	Northern
P	phosphorus
precip	precipitated
proc	processed, processing
prot	protein
pt	part(s)
res	residue
s-c	sun-cured
shred	shredded
skim	skimmed
sol	solubles
solv-extd	solvent extracted
US	United States
w	with
wet-rend	wet rendered
wo	without
wt	weight

Formulas for Adjusting Moisture Content

The majority of feed composition tables are on an "as fed" basis, while most of the National Research Council nutrient requirement tables are on an "approximate 90 percent dry matter" basis. Also, feeds contain varying amounts of dry matter. Hence, it would be much simpler if both feed composition and nutrient requirement tables were on a dry basis.

The significance of water content of feeds becomes obvious in the following examples. When using Total Digestible Nutrients (TDN) as a measure of energy value, some of the high-moisture tubers show almost the same feeding value per unit of their dry matter content as the cereal grains:

Feed	Water	Dry Matter	Energy Value (TDN)	
			As Fed	Dry Matter Basis
			%	
Corn, grain 10	90	80		90
Barley, grain 10	90	77		85
Melons, whole 94	6	5		80
Potatoes, tuber 79	21	18		85
Apples, fruit 82	18	13		74

As shown, dry matter becomes a common denominator for the comparison for feeds, particularly as to energy value; but this applies to other nutrients, also.

The following formulas may be used for adjusting moisture contents:

From Dry to as Fed

To be used in converting the amounts of ingredients of a dry diet to a wet diet having a given percent of dry matter.

Formula 1

$$\text{Parts of ingredient in wet diet} = \frac{\% \text{ ingredient in dry diet} \times \% \text{ dry matter wanted in diet}}{\% \text{ dry matter in ingredient}}$$

Total the parts and add enough water to make 100 parts (or 100 percent).

From Wet to Dry

To be used in calculating the amount of an ingredient that should be contained in a dry diet if the amount required in a wet diet having a given percent of dry matter is known.

Formula 2

$$\text{\% of ingredient in wet diet} = \frac{\text{\% ingredient in wet diet}}{\text{\% dry matter wanted in diet}} \times \text{\% dry matter in ingredient}$$

From Wet to Dry

To be used if the diet is on an as-fed basis and it is desired to change the amounts of the ingredients to a dry basis.

Formula 3

$$\text{Parts on wet basis} = \text{\% ingredient in wet diet} \times \text{\% dry matter of ingredient}$$

Perform this calculation for each ingredient; then add the products and divide each product by the sum of the products.

From Wet to Dry

To be used if the diet is on an as-fed basis and it is desired to compare the nutrient content of the diet with dry-basis requirements.

Formula 4

$$\text{\% nutrient in dry diet[4] (total)} = \frac{\text{\% nutrient in wet diet (total)}}{\text{\% dry matter in diet (total)}}$$

Composition of Some Common Horse Feeds

Refer to Table I-1, which follows.

---

[4] The term "dry diet" means a diet calculated on a dry (moisture-free) basis; "as fed" means a diet calculated to contain the amount of dry matter as it is fed to the animal.

TABLE I-1 — COMPOSITION OF SOME COMMON HORSE FEEDS[a]

ALFALFA. Medicago sativa

Alfalfa, aerial pt, dehy grnd, mn 17 prot, (1)

Ref no 1-00-023

Feed name or analyses		As fed	Dry
		Mean	Mean
Dry matter	%	93.0	100.0
Ash	%	9.0	9.7
Crude fiber	%	24.3	26.1
Ether extract	%	3.0	3.2
N-free extract	%	38.9	41.8
Protein (N x 6.25)	%	17.9	19.2
Horses	dig prot %	14.0	15.0
Energy			
Horses	DE kcal/kg	2543.	2734.
Horses	ME kcal/kg	2085.	2242.
Horses	TDN %	58.	62.
Calcium	%	1.33	1.43
Chlorine	%	.46	.49
Iron	%	.046	.049
Magnesium	%	.29	.31
Continued			

Feed name or analyses		As fed	Dry
		Mean	Mean
Phosphorus	%	.24	.26
Potassium	%	2.49	2.68
Sodium	%	.09	.10
Cobalt	mg/kg	.360	.390
Copper	mg/kg	9.9	10.6
Iodine	mg/kg	.150	.161
Manganese	mg/kg	29.0	31.2
Selenium	mg/kg	.600	.645
Zinc	mg/kg	16.0	17.2
Carotene	mg/kg	161.2	173.3
Choline	mg/kg	1518.	1632.
Folic acid	mg/kg	2.10	2.26
Niacin	mg/kg	45.8	49.2
Pantothenic acid	mg/kg	30.0	32.2
Riboflavin	mg/kg	12.3	13.2
Thiamine	mg/kg	3.5	3.8
a-tocopherol	mg/kg	128.0	137.6
Vitamin B6	mg/kg	6.30	6.77
Vitamin K	mg/kg	8.70	9.35
Vitamin A equiv	IU/g	268.7	288.9
Alanine	%	.90	.97
Arginine	%	.70	.75
Aspartic acid	%	1.90	2.04
Continued			

Feed name or analyses		As fed	Dry
		Mean	Mean
Glutamic acid	%	1.70	1.83
Glycine	%	.90	.97
Histidine	%	.40	.43
Isoleucine	%	.70	.75
Leucine	%	1.30	1.40
Lysine	%	.80	.86
Methionine	%	.20	.22
Phenylalanine	%	.80	.86
Proline	%	.90	.97
Serine	%	.70	.75
Threonine	%	.80	.86
Tryptophan	%	.40	.43
Tyrosine	%	.50	.54
Valine	%	.90	.97

Alfalfa, aerial pt, dehy grnd, mn 20 prot, (1)

Ref no 1-00-024

		As fed	Dry
Dry matter	%	93.1	100.0
Ash	%	10.3	11.1
Crude fiber	%	20.2	21.7
Continued			

(1) dry forages and roughages
(2) pasture, range plants, and forages fed green
(3) silages
(4) energy feeds
(5) protein supplements
(6) minerals
(7) vitamins
(8) additives

[a]Data and feed names were arranged for this book by Dr. Lorin E. Harris, Utah State University.

TABLE I-1 – COMPOSITION OF SOME COMMON HORSE FEEDS (Continued)

Feed name or analyses		Mean As fed	Dry
Ether extract	%	3.6	3.9
N-free extract	%	38.4	41.2
Protein (N x 6.25)	%	20.6	22.1
Horses	dig prot %	16.0	17.2
Energy			
Horses	DE kcal/kg	2545.	2734.
Horses	ME kcal/kg	2087.	2242.
Horses	TDN %	58.	62.
Calcium	%	1.52	1.63
Chlorine	%	.58	.62
Iron	%	.040	.043
Magnesium	%	.35	.38
Phosphorus	%	.27	.29
Potassium	%	2.52	2.71
Sodium	%	.86	.92
Cobalt	mg/kg	.320	.344
Copper	mg/kg	10.6	11.4
Iodine	mg/kg	.140	.150
Manganese	mg/kg	34.0	36.5
Selenium	mg/kg	.500	.537
Zinc	mg/kg	18.0	19.3
Carotene	mg/kg	216.4	232.4
Choline	mg/kg	1618.	1738.
Folic acid	mg/kg	2.67	2.87
Niacin	mg/kg	54.7	58.7
Pantothenic acid	mg/kg	32.8	35.2
Riboflavin	mg/kg	15.5	16.6
Thiamine	mg/kg	3.9	4.2
a-tocopherol	mg/kg	147.0	157.9
Vitamin B6	mg/kg	7.90	8.48
Vitamin K	mg/kg	14.70	15.79

Continued

Feed name or analyses		Mean As fed	Dry
Vitamin A equiv	IU/g	360.7	387.4
Alanine	%	1.10	1.18
Arginine	%	.90	.97
Aspartic acid	%	2.10	2.26
Glutamic acid	%	2.10	2.26
Glycine	%	1.00	1.07
Histidine	%	.40	.43
Isoleucine	%	.80	.86
Leucine	%	1.50	1.61
Lysine	%	.90	.97
Methionine	%	.30	.32
Phenylalanine	%	1.10	1.18
Proline	%	1.00	1.07
Serine	%	.90	.97
Threonine	%	.90	.97
Tryptophan	%	.50	.54
Tyrosine	%	.70	.75
Valine	%	.10	.11

Alfalfa, hay, s-c, immature, (1)

Ref no 1-00-050

		As fed	Dry
Dry matter	%	89.1	100.0
Ash	%	8.6	9.7
Crude fiber	%	23.4	26.3
Ether extract	%	2.4	2.7
N-free extract	%	35.5	39.8
Protein (N x 6.25)	%	19.1	21.5
Horses	dig prot %	13.4	15.0

Continued

Feed name or analyses		Mean As fed	Dry
Energy			
Horses	DE kcal/kg	2239.	2513.
Horses	ME kcal/kg	1836.	2061.
Horses	TDN %	51.	57.
Calcium	%	1.89	2.12
Chlorine	%	.30	.34
Iron	%	.020	.020
Magnesium	%	.23	.26
Phosphorus	%	.27	.30
Potassium	%	2.01	2.26
Sodium	%	.20	.22
Sulfur	%	.56	.63
Manganese	mg/kg	34.4	38.6
Carotene	mg/kg	446.6	501.2
Vitamin A equiv	IU/g	744.5	835.5

Alfalfa, hay, s-c, pre-blm, (1)

Ref no 1-00-054

		As fed	Dry
Dry matter	%	84.5	100.0
Ash	%	6.0	7.1
Crude fiber	%	24.1	28.5
Ether extract	%	2.7	3.2
N-free extract	%	35.3	41.8
Protein (N x 6.25)	%	16.4	19.4
Horses	dig prot %	9.9	11.7

Continued

Feed name or analyses		Mean	
		As fed	Dry
Energy			
Horses	DE kcal/kg	2347.	2778.
Horses	ME kcal/kg	1925.	2278.
Horses	TDN %	53.	63.
Calcium	%	1.06	1.25
Phosphorus	%	.19	.23

Alfalfa, hay, s-c, early blm, (1)

Ref no 1-00-059

		As fed	Dry
Dry matter	%	90.0	100.0
Ash	%	8.5	9.4
Crude fiber	%	26.8	29.8
Ether extract	%	2.0	2.2
N-free extract	%	36.2	40.2
Protein (N x 6.25)	%	16.6	18.4
Horses	dig prot %	11.4	12.7
Cellulose	%	1.8	2.0
Lignin	%	.8	.9
Energy	GE kcal/kg	4050.	4500.
Horses	DE kcal/kg	2262.	2513.
Horses	ME kcal/kg	1855.	2061.
Horses	TDN %	51.	57.
Calcium	%	1.12	1.25
Chlorine	%	.34	.38

Continued

(1) dry forages and roughages
(2) pasture, range plants, and forages fed green

7

Feed name or analyses		Mean	
		As fed	Dry
Iron	%	.020	.020
Magnesium	%	.27	.30
Phosphorus	%	.21	.23
Potassium	%	1.87	2.08
Sodium	%	.14	.15
Sulfur	%	.27	.30
Cobalt	mg/kg	.080	.090
Copper	mg/kg	12.1	13.4
Manganese	mg/kg	28.4	31.5
Carotene	mg/kg	114.5	127.2
Vitamin A equiv	IU/g	190.9	212.0

Alfalfa, hay, s-c, mid-blm, (1)

Ref no 1-00-063

		As fed	Dry
Dry matter	%	89.2	100.0
Ash	%	7.6	8.5
Crude fiber	%	27.6	30.9
Ether extract	%	1.8	2.0
N-free extract	%	37.0	41.5
Protein (N x 6.25)	%	15.2	17.1
Horses	dig prot %	10.8	12.1
Cellulose	%	2.4	2.7
Lignin	%	.7	.8

Continued

(3) silages
(4) energy feeds
(5) protein supplements

8

Feed name or analyses		Mean	
		As fed	Dry
Energy			
Horses	DE kcal/kg	2281.	2557.
Horses	ME kcal/kg	1870.	2097.
Horses	TDN %	52.	58.
Calcium	%	1.20	1.35
Iron	%	.010	.010
Magnesium	%	.31	.35
Phosphorus	%	.20	.22
Potassium	%	1.30	1.46
Copper	mg/kg	13.7	15.4
Manganese	mg/kg	14.7	16.5
Carotene	mg/kg	29.7	33.3
Vitamin A equiv	IU/g	49.5	55.5

Alfalfa, hay, s-c, full blm, (1)

Ref no 1-00-068

		As fed	Dry
Dry matter	%	87.7	100.0
Ash	%	7.8	8.9
Crude fiber	%	29.7	33.9
Ether extract	%	1.6	1.8
N-free extract	%	34.6	39.5
Protein (N x 6.25)	%	14.0	15.9
Horses	dig prot %	10.0	11.4

Continued

(6) minerals
(7) vitamins
(8) additives

9

TABLE I-1 – COMPOSITION OF SOME COMMON HORSE FEEDS (Continued)

Feed name or analyses		As fed (Mean)	Dry (Mean)
Energy			
Horses	DE kcal/kg	2204.	2513.
Horses	ME kcal/kg	1807.	2061.
Horses	TDN %	50.	57.
Calcium	%	1.13	1.28
Iron	%	.010	.020
Magnesium	%	.31	.35
Phosphorus	%	.18	.20
Potassium	%	.48	.55
Copper	mg/kg	11.8	13.4
Manganese	mg/kg	29.6	33.7
Carotene	mg/kg	32.4	37.0
Vitamin A equiv	IU/g	54.0	61.7

Alfalfa, hay, s-c, mature, (1)

Ref no 1-00-071

Feed name or analyses		As fed (Mean)	Dry (Mean)
Dry matter	%	91.2	100.0
Ash	%	7.1	7.8
Crude fiber	%	34.2	37.5
Ether extract	%	1.5	1.7
N-free extract	%	35.9	39.4
Protein (N x 6.25)	%	12.4	13.6
Horses	dig prot %	8.7	9.5
Energy			
Horses	DE kcal/kg	2212.	2425.
Horses	ME kcal/kg	1813.	1988.
Horses	TDN %	50.	55.

Alfalfa, leaves, dehy grnd, (1)
Alfalfa leaf meal, dehydrated (AAFCO)

Ref no 1-00-137

Feed name or analyses		As fed (Mean)	Dry (Mean)
Dry matter	%	92.2	100.0
Ash	%	11.0	11.9
Crude fiber	%	19.6	21.3
Ether extract	%	3.0	3.2
N-free extract	%	38.0	41.2
Protein (N x 6.25)	%	20.6	22.4
Horses	dig prot %	15.3	16.6
Energy			
Horses	DE kcal/kg	2276.	2469.
Horses	ME kcal/kg	1866.	2024.
Horses	TDN %	52.	56.
Calcium	%	1.64	1.78
Chlorine	%	.31	.34
Iron	%	.036	.039
Phosphorus	%	.23	.25
Potassium	%	2.07	2.25
Cobalt	mg/kg	.199	.216
Copper	mg/kg	10.6	11.5
Manganese	mg/kg	36.8	39.9
Carotene	mg/kg	149.0	161.6
Niacin	mg/kg	32.9	35.7
Pantothenic acid	mg/kg		
Riboflavin	mg/kg	18.1	19.6
Thiamine	mg/kg	5.5	6.0
Vitamin D₂	IU/g	.4	.4

Alfalfa, aerial pt, fresh, (2)

Ref no 2-00-196

Feed name or analyses		As fed (Mean)	Dry (Mean)
Dry matter	%	27.2	100.0
Ash	%	2.4	9.0
Crude fiber	%	7.4	27.4
Ether extract	%	.8	3.0
N-free extract	%	11.2	41.3
Protein (N x 6.25)	%	5.2	19.3
Horses	dig prot %	4.1	15.0
Energy			
Horses	DE kcal/kg	732.	2690.
Horses	ME kcal/kg	600.	2206.
Horses	TDN %	16.	61.
Calcium	%	.47	1.72
Chlorine	%	.13	.47
Iron	%	.010	.030
Magnesium	%	.07	.27
Phosphorus	%	.08	.31
Potassium	%	.55	2.03
Sodium	%	.05	.20
Sulfur	%	.11	.39
Cobalt	mg/kg	.020	.090
Copper	mg/kg	2.7	9.9
Manganese	mg/kg	13.7	50.5
Zinc	mg/kg	4.8	17.6
Carotene	mg/kg	54.1	198.9
Vitamin A equiv	IU/g	90.2	331.6
Vitamin D₂	IU/g		.2

ALFALFA–BROME, SMOOTH. Medicago sativa, Bromus inermis

Alfalfa-brome, smooth, aerial pt, fresh, early blm, (2)

Ref no 2-00-261

Feed name or analyses		Mean	
		As fed	Dry
Dry matter	%	21.6	100.0
Ash	%	2.1	9.8
Crude fiber	%	5.5	25.3
Ether extract	%	.8	3.6
N-free extract	%	9.0	41.7
Protein (N x 6.25)	%	4.2	19.6
Horses	dig prot %	3.1	14.4
Energy			
Horses	DE kcal/kg	590.	2734.
Horses	ME kcal/kg	484.	2242.
Horses	TDN %	13.	62.
Calcium	%	.33	1.52
Magnesium	%	.08	.35
Phosphorus	%	.08	.37
Potassium	%	.84	3.87

ALFALFA-ORCHARDGRASS. Medicago sativa, Dactylis glomerata

Alfalfa-orchardgrass, aerial pt, ensiled, mn 50 dry matter, (3)

Ref no 3-08-143

Feed name or analyses		Mean	
		As fed	Dry
Dry matter	%	61.0	100.0
Ash	%	6.2	10.1
Crude fiber	%	18.6	30.5
Ether extract	%	2.6	4.3
N-free extract	%	23.7	38.9
Protein (N x 6.25)	%	9.9	16.2
Horses	dig prot %	5.7	9.4
Energy			
Horses	DE kcal/kg	1452.	2381.
Horses	ME kcal/kg	1190.	1952.
Horses	TDN %	33.	54.

ANIMAL. Scientific name not used

Animal, bone, cooked dehy grnd, mn 10 P, (6)
Feeding bone meal (CFA)

Ref no 6-00-397

Feed name or analyses		Mean	
		As fed	Dry
Dry matter	%	94.5	100.0
Ether extract	%	9.6	10.2
Protein (N x 6.25)	%	17.8	18.8
Calcium	%	25.82	27.32
Phosphorus	%	12.35	13.07
Fluorine	mg/kg	2000.00	2116.40

Animal, bone, steamed dehy grnd, (6)
Bone meal, steamed (AAFCO)

Ref no 6-00-400

		As fed	Dry
Dry matter	%	95.0	100.0
Ash	%	71.8	75.6
Crude fiber	%	2.0	2.1
Ether extract	%	3.2	3.4
Protein (N x 6.25)	%	12.1	12.7
Horses	dig prot %	8.2	8.6

Continued

(1) dry forages and roughages
(2) pasture, range plants, and forages fed green

(3) silages
(4) energy feeds
(5) protein supplements

(6) minerals
(7) vitamins
(8) additives

13

14

15

TABLE I-1 – COMPOSITION OF SOME COMMON HORSE FEEDS (Continued)

Feed name or analyses		As fed	Dry
Energy			
Horses	DE kcal/kg	670.	705.
Horses	ME kcal/kg	549.	578.
Horses	TDN %	15.	16.
Calcium	%	28.98	30.51
Iron	%	.084	.088
Magnesium	%	.64	.67
Phosphorus	%	13.59	14.31
Sodium	%	.46	.48
Cobalt	mg/kg	.100	.100
Copper	mg/kg	16.3	17.2
Manganese	mg/kg	30.4	32.0
Zinc	mg/kg	424.6	447.1
Niacin	mg/kg	4.2	4.4
Pantothenic acid	mg/kg	2.4	2.5
Riboflavin	mg/kg	.9	.9
Thiamine	mg/kg	.4	.4

Continued

Animal, bone charcoal, retort-charred grnd, (6)
Bone black (CFA)
Bone char (CFA)
Spent bone black

Ref no 6-00-403

		As fed	Dry
Dry matter	%	90.0	100.0
Protein (N x 6.25)	%	8.5	9.4
Calcium	%	27.10	30.11
Magnesium	%	.53	.59
Phosphorus	%	12.73	14.14

Continued

16

Feed name or analyses		As fed	Dry
Potassium	%	.14	.16
Arginine	%	1.80	2.00
Histidine	%	.20	.22
Isoleucine	%	.60	.67
Leucine	%	.80	.89
Lysine	%	1.00	1.11
Methionine	%	.20	.22
Phenylalanine	%	.50	.56
Threonine	%	.50	.56
Valine	%	.70	.78

Animal, bone phosphate, precip dehy, mn 17 P, (6)
Bone phosphate (AAFCO)

Ref no 6-00-406

		As fed	Dry
Dry matter	%	99.0	100.0
Ash	%	86.4	87.3
Ether extract	%	.3	.3
Protein (N x 6.25)	%	.4	.4
Calcium	%	28.00	28.28
Phosphorus	%	11.20	11.31

17

Feed name or analyses		As fed	Dry
BARLEY. Hordeum vulgare			
Barley, grain, (4)			
Ref no 4-00-530			
Dry matter	%	89.0	100.0
Ash	%	2.4	2.7
Crude fiber	%	5.0	5.6
Ether extract	%	1.9	2.1
N-free extract	%	68.2	76.6
Protein (N x 6.25)	%	11.6	13.0
Horses	dig prot %	8.7	9.8
Energy	GE kcal/kg	4084.	4589.
Horses	DE kcal/kg	3257.	3660.
Horses	ME kcal/kg	2671.	3001.
Horses	TDN %	74.	83.
Calcium	%	.08	.09
Iron	%	.005	.006
Magnesium	%	.12	.14
Phosphorus	%	.42	.47
Potassium	%	.56	.63
Sodium	%	.02	.02
Cobalt	mg/kg	.100	.100
Copper	mg/kg	7.6	8.6
Manganese	mg/kg	16.3	18.3
Zinc	mg/kg	15.3	17.2
Biotin	mg/kg	.20	.20
Choline	mg/kg	1030.	1157.
Folic acid	mg/kg	.50	.60

Continued

18

Feed name or analyses		Mean	
		As fed	Dry
Niacin	mg/kg	57.4	64.5
Pantothenic acid	mg/kg	6.5	7.3
Riboflavin	mg/kg	2.0	2.2
Thiamine	mg/kg	5.1	5.7
a-tocopherol	mg/kg	6.1	6.8
Vitamin B_6	mg/kg	2.90	3.30
Arginine	%	.53	.60
Cystine	%	.18	.20
Glycine	%	.36	.40
Histidine	%	.27	.30
Isoleucine	%	.53	.60
Leucine	%	.80	.90
Lysine	%	.53	.60
Methionine	%	.18	.20
Phenylalanine	%	.62	.70
Threonine	%	.36	.40
Tryptophan	%	.18	.20
Tyrosine	%	.36	.40
Valine	%	.62	.70

Barley, grain, Pacific coast, (4)

Ref no 4-07-939

		As fed	Dry
Dry matter	%	89.0	100.0
Ash	%	2.3	2.6

Continued

Feed name or analyses		Mean	
		As fed	Dry
Crude fiber	%	6.2	7.0
Ether extract	%	2.2	2.5
N-free extract	%	68.5	77.0
Protein (N x 6.25)	%	9.7	10.9
Horses	dig prot %	7.3	8.2
Energy			
Horses	DE kcal/kg	3218.	3616.
Horses	ME kcal/kg	2639.	2965.
Horses	TDN %	73.	82.
Calcium	%	.06	.07
Phosphorus	%	.40	.45
Choline	mg/kg	937.	1054.
Niacin	mg/kg	44.1	49.6
Pantothenic acid	mg/kg	7.3	8.2
Riboflavin	mg/kg	1.3	1.5
Thiamine	mg/kg	4.0	4.5

BEET, SUGAR. Beta saccharifera

Beet, sugar, molasses, mn 48 invert sugar min 79.5 degrees brix, (4)

Beet molasses (AAFCO)

Molasses (CFA)

Ref no 4-00-668

Feed name or analyses		Mean	
		As fed	Dry
Dry matter	%	77.0	100.0
Ash	%	8.2	10.6
Ether extract	%	.2	.3
N-free extract	%	61.9	80.4
Protein (N x 6.25)	%	6.7	8.7
Horses	dig prot %	3.8	5.0
Energy			
Horses	DE kcal/kg	3021.	3924.
Horses	ME kcal/kg	2478.	3218.
Horses	TDN %	68.	89.
Calcium	%	.16	.21
Iron	%	.010	.010
Magnesium	%	.23	.30
Phosphorus	%	.03	.04
Potassium	%	4.77	6.20
Sodium	%	1.17	1.52
Cobalt	mg/kg	.400	.500

Continued

(1) dry forages and roughages
(2) pasture, range plants, and forages fed green
(3) silages
(4) energy feeds
(5) protein supplements
(6) minerals
(7) vitamins
(8) additives

19   20   21

TABLE I-1 – COMPOSITION OF SOME COMMON HORSE FEEDS (Continued)

Feed name or analyses		As fed	Dry (Mean)
Copper	mg/kg	17.6	22.9
Manganese	mg/kg	4.6	6.0
Niacin	mg/kg	42.2	54.8
Pantothenic acid	mg/kg	4.6	6.0
Riboflavin	mg/kg	2.4	3.1

Beet, sugar, pulp, dehy, (4)
Dried beet pulp (AAFCO)
Dried beet pulp (CFA)

Ref no 4-00-669

		As fed	Dry
Dry matter	%	91.0	100.0
Ash	%	3.6	3.9
Crude fiber	%	19.0	20.9
Ether extract	%	.6	.7
N-free extract	%	58.7	64.5
Protein (N x 6.25)	%	9.1	10.0
Lignin	%	8.0	8.8
Horses	dig prot %	6.3	6.9
Energy			
Energy	GE kcal/kg	3837.	4217.
Horses	DE kcal/kg	2889.	3175.
Horses	ME kcal/kg	2370.	2604.
Horses	TDN %	76.	83.
Calcium	%	.68	.75
Iron	%	.030	.033
Magnesium	%	.27	.30
Phosphorus	%	.10	.11
Potassium	%	.21	.23
Cobalt	mg/kg	.100	.100

Continued

22

Feed name or analyses		As fed	Dry (Mean)
Copper	mg/kg	12.5	13.7
Manganese	mg/kg	35.0	38.5
Zinc	mg/kg	.7	.8
Choline	mg/kg	829.	912.
Niacin	mg/kg	16.3	17.9
Pantothenic acid	mg/kg	1.5	1.6
Riboflavin	mg/kg	.7	.8
Thiamine	mg/kg	.4	.4
Vitamin D₃	ICU/g	1.0	1.0
Arginine	%	.30	.33
Histidine	%	.20	.22
Isoleucine	%	.30	.33
Leucine	%	.60	.66
Lysine	%	.60	.66
Phenylalanine	%	.30	.33
Threonine	%	.40	.44
Tryptophan	%	.10	.11
Tyrosine	%	.40	.44
Valine	%	.40	.44

Beet, sugar, pulp w molasses, dehy, (4)

Ref no 4-00-672

		As fed	Dry
Dry matter	%	92.0	100.0
Ash	%	5.7	6.2
Crude fiber	%	16.0	17.4
Ether extract	%	.5	.5
N-free extract	%	60.7	66.0

Continued

23

Feed name or analyses		As fed (Mean)	Dry
Protein (N x 6.25)	%	9.1	9.9
Horses	dig prot %	6.0	6.5
Energy			
Horses	DE kcal/kg	3002.	3263.
Horses	ME kcal/kg	2462.	2676.
Horses	TDN %	68.	74.
Calcium	%	.56	.61
Magnesium	%	.13	.14
Phosphorus	%	.08	.11
Potassium	%	1.64	1.78

BERMUDAGRASS. Cynodon dactylon

Bermudagrass, hay, s-c, (1)

Ref no 1-00-703

		As fed	Dry
Dry matter	%	91.1	100.0
Ash	%	6.1	6.7
Crude fiber	%	27.0	29.6
Ether extract	%	1.8	2.0
N-free extract	%	48.1	52.8
Protein (N x 6.25)	%	8.1	8.9
Horses	dig prot %	4.4	4.8
Energy			
Horses	DE kcal/kg	1727.	1896.
Horses	ME kcal/kg	1417.	1555.
Horses	TDN %	39.	43.
Calcium	%	.42	.46

Continued

24

Feed name or analyses		Mean	
		As fed	Dry
Magnesium	%	.19	.21
Phosphorus	%	.24	.27
Potassium	%	1.56	1.72
Copper	mg/kg	9.0	9.9
Manganese	mg/kg	83.9	92.6
Carotene	mg/kg	224.8	248.1
Vitamin A equiv	IU/g	374.7	413.6

Bone - see Animal

Bone black - see Animal, bone charcoal

Bone char - see Animal, bone charcoal

Bone charcoal - see Animal

Bone phosphate - see Animal, bone phosphate

Bran - see Wheat

Feed name or analyses		Mean	
		As fed	Dry
Magnesium	%	.16	.17
Phosphorus	%	.16	.18

Birdsfoot trefoil - see Trefoil, birdsfoot

BLUEGRASS. Poa spp

Bluegrass, hay, s-c, (1)

Ref no 1-00-744

		As fed	Dry
Dry matter	%	90.6	100.0
Ash	%	7.3	8.1
Crude fiber	%	27.4	30.3
Ether extract	%	2.7	3.0
N-free extract	%	42.6	47.0
Protein (N x 6.25)	%	10.5	11.6
Horses	dig prot %	6.3	7.0
Energy			
Horses	DE kcal/kg	2517.	2778.
Horses	ME kcal/kg	2064.	2278.
Horses	TDN %	57.	63.
Calcium	%	.35	.39
Iron	%	.020	.030

Continued

Feed name or analyses		Mean	
		As fed	Dry
Iron	%	.026	.029
Magnesium	%	.15	.17
Phosphorus	%	.18	.20
Potassium	%	1.34	1.47
Iodine	mg/kg	.105	.115
Carotene	mg/kg	117.2	128.7

BERMUDAGRASS, COASTAL. Cynodon dactylon

Bermudagrass, coastal, hay, s-c, (1)

Ref no 1-00-716

		As fed	Dry
Ash	%	4.7	5.1
Dry matter	%	91.5	100.0
Crude fiber	%	27.9	30.5
Ether extract	%	2.0	2.2
N-free extract	%	48.2	52.7
Protein (N x 6.25)	%	8.7	9.5
Horses	dig prot %	4.7	5.1
Energy			
Horses	DE kcal/kg	1775.	1940.
Horses	ME kcal/kg	1456.	1591.
Horses	TDN %	40.	44.
Calcium	%	.42	.46

Continued

(1) dry forages and roughages
(2) pasture, range plants, and forages fed green
25

(3) silages
(4) energy feeds
(5) protein supplements
26

(6) minerals
(7) vitamins
(8) additives
27

TABLE I-1 – COMPOSITION OF SOME COMMON HORSE FEEDS (Continued)

Brewers dried grains - see Grains

Brewers dried yeast - see Yeast, brewers

BROME. Bromus spp

Brome, hay, s-c, (1)

Ref no 1-00-890

Feed name or analyses		Mean	
		As fed	Dry
Dry matter	%	89.7	100.0
Ash	%	7.7	8.6
Crude fiber	%	28.7	32.0
Ether extract	%	2.3	2.6
N-free extract	%	40.4	45.0
Protein (N x 6.25)	%	10.6	11.8
Horses	dig prot %	4.5	5.0
Energy			
Horses	DE kcal/kg	1740.	1940.
Horses	ME kcal/kg	1427.	1591.
Horses	TDN %	39.	44.

28

Brome, aerial pt, fresh, early blm, (2)

Ref no 2-00-893

Feed name or analyses		Mean	
		As fed	Dry
Dry matter	%	30.0	100.0
Ash	%	2.4	8.1
Crude fiber	%	8.5	28.3
Ether extract	%	1.1	3.7
N-free extract	%	13.8	46.0
Protein (N x 6.25)	%	4.2	13.9
Horses	dig prot %	2.9	9.7
Energy			
Horses	DE kcal/kg	899.	2998.
Horses	ME kcal/kg	737.	2458.
Horses	TDN %	20.	68.
Calcium	%	.12	.41
Magnesium	%	.03	.11
Phosphorus	%	.12	.39
Potassium	%	.80	2.67
Carotene	mg/kg	55.2	183.9
Vitamin A equiv	IU/g	92.0	306.6

29

CALCIUM PHOSPHATE, DIBASIC

Calcium phosphate, dibasic, comm, (6)
Dicalcium phosphate (AAFCO)

Ref no 6-01-080

Feed name or analyses		Mean	
		As fed	Dry
Dry matter	%	96.0	100.0
Calcium	%	22.20	23.13
Phosphorus	%	17.90	18.65
Fluorine	mg/kg	768.00	800.00

CARROT. Daucus spp

Carrot, roots, fresh, (4)

Ref no 4-01-145

Feed name or analyses		Mean	
		As fed	Dry
Dry matter	%	11.9	100.0
Ash	%	1.2	10.1
Crude fiber	%	1.1	9.2
Ether extract	%	.2	1.6
N-free extract	%	8.2	69.0
Protein (N x 6.25)	%	1.2	10.1
Horses	dig prot %	.6	5.0

Continued

30

Feed name or analyses		Mean	
		As fed	Dry
Energy			
Horses	DE kcal/kg	430.	3616.
Horses	ME kcal/kg	353.	2965.
Horses	TDN %	10.	82.
Calcium	%	.05	.42
Chlorine	%	.06	.50
Iron	%	.002	.017
Magnesium	%	.02	.17
Phosphorus	%	.04	.34
Potassium	%	.25	2.10
Sodium	%	.19	1.60
Sulfur	%	.02	.17
Copper	mg/kg	1.3	10.9
Manganese	mg/kg	3.7	31.1
Carotene	mg/kg	106.0	890.8
Niacin	mg/kg	14.8	124.4
Pantothenic acid	mg/kg	2.0	16.8
Riboflavin	mg/kg	.7	5.9
Thiamine	mg/kg	.7	5.9

Feed name or analyses		Mean	
		As fed	Dry
CATTLE. Bos spp			
Cattle, milk, dehy, feed gr mx 8 moisture mn 26 fat, (5)			
Dried whole milk (AAFCO)			
Milk, whole, dried			
Ref no 5-01-167			
Dry matter	%	93.7	100.0
Ash	%	5.4	5.8
Crude fiber	%	.2	.2
Ether extract	%	26.4	28.2
N-free extract	%	36.4	38.9
Protein (N x 6.25)	%	25.2	26.9
Horses	dig prot %	24.4	26.0
Energy			
Horses	DE kcal/kg	5795.0	6184.
Horses	ME kcal/kg	4752.	5071.
Horses	TDN %	108.	115.
Calcium	%	.89	.95
Chlorine	%	1.45	1.55
Iron	%	.017	.018
Phosphorus	%	.68	.72
Potassium	%	1.01	1.08
Sodium	%	.36	.38

Continued

Feed name or analyses		Mean	
		As fed	Dry
Manganese	mg/kg	.4	.4
Biotin	mg/kg	.37	.39
Carotene	mg/kg	7.0	7.5
Niacin	mg/kg	8.4	9.0
Pantothenic acid	mg/kg	22.7	24.2
Riboflavin	mg/kg	19.6	20.9
Thiamine	mg/kg	3.7	3.9
Vitamin B_6	mg/kg	4.63	4.94
Vitamin A equiv	IU/g	11.7	12.5
Vitamin D_2	IU/g	.3	.3
Arginine	%	.90	.96
Histidine	%	.70	.75
Isoleucine	%	1.30	1.39
Leucine	%	2.50	2.67
Lysine	%	2.20	2.35
Methionine	%	.60	.64
Phenylalanine	%	1.30	1.39
Threonine	%	1.00	1.07
Tryptophan	%	.40	.43
Tyrosine	%	1.30	1.39
Valine	%	1.70	1.81

(1) dry forages and roughages
(2) pasture, range plants, and forages fed green
31

(3) silages
(4) energy feeds
(5) protein supplements
32

(6) minerals
(7) vitamins
(8) additives
33

TABLE I-1 — COMPOSITION OF SOME COMMON HORSE FEEDS (Continued)

Cattle, milk, fresh, (5)
Milk, cattle, fresh

Ref no 5-01-168

Feed name or analyses		Mean As fed	Dry
Dry matter	%	12.0	100.0
Ash	%	.8	6.7
Ether extract	%	3.7	30.8
N-free extract	%	4.4	36.7
Protein (N x 6.25)	%	3.1	25.8
Horses	dig prot %	3.0	24.8
Energy			
Horses	DE kcal/kg	688.	5732.
Horses	ME kcal/kg	564.	4700.
Horses	TDN %	16.	130.
Choline	mg/kg	876.	7296.
Niacin	mg/kg	1.8	15.0
Pantothenic acid	mg/kg	8.1	67.5
Riboflavin	mg/kg	1.8	15.0
Thiamine	mg/kg	0.4	3.3
Arginine	%	.10	.83
Histidine	%	.10	.83
Isoleucine	%	.20	1.67
Leucine	%	.30	2.50
Lysine	%	.30	2.50
Methionine	%	.10	.83
Phenylalanine	%	.10	.83
Threonine	%	.10	.83
Tyrosine	%	.20	1.67
Valine	%	.20	1.67

34

Cattle, milk, skim centrifugal, (5)

Ref no 5-01-170

Feed name or analyses		Mean As fed	Dry
Dry matter	%	9.6	100.0
Ash	%	.6	6.1
Crude fiber	%	.0	.0
Ether extract	%	.1	1.5
N-free extract	%	6.1	63.9
Protein (N x 6.25)	%	2.7	28.5
Horses	dig prot %	2.6	27.4
Energy			
Horses	DE kcal/kg	394.	4100.
Horses	ME kcal/kg	323.	3362.
Horses	TDN %	9.	93.
Calcium	%	.12	1.26
Iron	%	.002	.017
Phosphorus	%	.10	1.03
Potassium	%	.10	1.01
Sulfur	%	.03	.32
Cobalt	mg/kg	.010	.110
Copper	mg/kg	.1	.9
Manganese	mg/kg	.	.4
Niacin	mg/kg	1.1	11.5
Pantothenic acid	mg/kg	3.5	36.8
Riboflavin	mg/kg	2.0	20.7
Thiamine	mg/kg	.4	4.6
Arginine	%	1.20	12.50
Histidine	%	.90	9.38
Isoleucine	%	2.30	23.96

Continued

35

Feed name or analyses		Mean As fed	Dry
Leucine	%	3.30	34.38
Lysine	%	2.80	29.17
Phenylalanine	%	1.50	15.62
Serine	%	1.60	16.67
Threonine	%	1.40	14.58

Cattle, milk, skim dehy, mx 8 moisture, (5)
Dried skimmed milk, feed grade (AAFCO)
Milk, skimmed, dried

Ref no 5-01-175

Feed name or analyses		Mean As fed	Dry
Dry matter	%	94.0	100.0
Ash	%	7.6	8.1
Crude fiber	%	.2	.2
Ether extract	%	.9	1.0
N-free extract	%	51.8	55.1
Protein (N x 6.25)	%	33.5	35.6
Horses	dig prot %	30.1	22.0
Energy			
Horses	GE kcal/kg	3456.	3677.
Horses	DE kcal/kg	3563.	3791.
Horses	ME kcal/kg	2922.	3109.
Horses	TDN %	81.	86.
Calcium	%	1.26	1.34
Iron	%	.005	.005
Magnesium	%	.11	.12
Phosphorus	%	1.03	1.10
Potassium	%	1.67	1.78
Cobalt	mg/kg	.110	.117
Copper	mg/kg	11.5	12.2

Continued

36

Feed name or analyses		Mean As fed	Dry
Manganese	mg/kg	2.2	2.3
Biotin	mg/kg	.33	.35
Choline	mg/kg	1426.	1517.
Folic acid	mg/kg	.62	.66
Niacin	mg/kg	11.5	12.2
Pantothenic acid	mg/kg	33.7	35.8
Riboflavin	mg/kg	20.1	21.4
Thiamine	mg/kg	3.5	3.7
a-tocopherol	mg/kg	9.2	9.8
Vitamin B6	mg/kg	3.97	4.22
Vitamin B12	mcg/kg	41.9	44.6
Vitamin D2	IU/g	.4	.4
Arginine	%	1.20	1.28
Cystine	%	.50	.53
Glutamic acid	%	6.80	7.24
Glycine	%	.20	.21
Histidine	%	.90	.96
Isoleucine	%	2.30	2.45
Leucine	%	3.30	3.51
Lysine	%	2.80	2.98
Methionine	%	.80	.85
Phenylalanine	%	1.50	1.60
Threonine	%	1.40	1.49
Tryptophan	%	.40	.42
Tyrosine	%	1.30	1.38
Valine	%	2.20	2.34

(1) dry forages and roughages
(2) pasture, range plants, and forages fed green
37

Cattle, whey, dehy, mn 65 lactose, (4)
Dried whey (AAFCO)
Whey, dried

Ref no 4-01-182

Feed name or analyses		Mean As fed	Dry
Dry matter	%	94.0	100.0
Ash	%	9.7	10.3
Ether extract	%	.8	.9
N-free extract	%	69.6	74.1
Protein (N x 6.25)	%	13.8	14.7
Horses	dig prot %	11.8	12.6
Energy			
Horses	DE kcal/kg	3695.	3930.
Horses	ME kcal/kg	3030.	3223.
Horses	TDN %	69.	73.
Calcium	%	.87	.93
Iron	%	.016	.017
Magnesium	%	.13	.14
Phosphorus	%	.79	.84
Cobalt	mg/kg	.094	.100
Copper	mg/kg	43.1	45.9
Manganese	mg/kg	4.6	4.9
Biotin	mg/kg	.40	.40
Choline	mg/kg	20.	21.
Folic acid	mg/kg	.90	1.00
Continued			

(3) silages
(4) energy feeds
(5) protein supplements
38

Feed name or analyses		Mean As fed	Dry
Niacin	mg/kg	11.2	11.9
Pantothenic acid	mg/kg	47.7	50.8
Riboflavin	mg/kg	29.9	31.8
Thiamine	mg/kg	3.7	3.9
Arginine	%	.40	.43
Cystine	%	.30	.32
Histidine	%	.20	.21
Isoleucine	%	.90	.96
Leucine	%	1.40	1.49
Lysine	%	1.10	1.17
Methionine	%	.20	.21
Phenylalanine	%	.40	.43
Threonine	%	.80	.85
Tryptophan	%	.20	.21
Tyrosine	%	.30	.32
Valine	%	.70	.74

CLOVER, ALSIKE. Trifolium hybridum

Clover, alsike, hay, s-c, (1)

Ref no 1-01-313

		As fed	Dry
Dry matter	%	87.9	100.0
Ash	%	7.6	8.7
			Continued

(6) minerals
(7) vitamins
(8) additives
39

TABLE I-1 – COMPOSITION OF SOME COMMON HORSE FEEDS (Continued)

Feed name or analyses		Mean As fed	Dry
Crude fiber	%	25.8	29.4
Ether extract	%	2.5	2.9
N-free extract	%	38.9	44.3
Protein (N x 6.25)	%	12.9	14.7
Horses dig prot	%	8.2	9.3
Energy	GE kcal/kg	3890.	4425.
Horses	DE kcal/kg	2326.	2646.
Horses	ME kcal/kg	1907.	2170.
Horses	TDN %	53.	60.
Calcium	%	1.15	1.31
Chlorine	%	.69	.78
Iron	%	.020	.030
Magnesium	%	.40	.45
Phosphorus	%	.22	.25
Potassium	%	1.50	1.70
Sodium	%	.40	.46
Sulfur	%	.18	.21
Copper	mg/kg	5.3	6.0
Manganese	mg/kg	60.7	69.0
Carotene	mg/kg	164.4	187.0
Vitamin A equiv	IU/g	274.0	311.7

CLOVER, CRIMSON. Trifolium incarnatum.

Clover, crimson, hay, s-c, (1)

Ref no 1-01-328

Dry matter	%	87.4	100.0
Ash	%	8.3	9.4

Continued

40

Feed name or analyses		Mean As fed	Dry
Crude fiber	%	28.1	32.2
Ether extract	%	2.0	2.3
N-free extract	%	34.2	39.2
Protein (N x 6.25)	%	14.8	16.9
Horses dig prot	%	10.3	11.8
Energy			
Horses	DE kcal/kg	2313.	2646.
Horses	ME kcal/kg	1896.	2170.
Horses	TDN %	52.	60.
Calcium	%	1.24	1.42
Chlorine	%	.55	.63
Iron	%	.060	.070
Magnesium	%	.24	.27
Phosphorus	%	.16	.18
Potassium	%	1.35	1.54
Sodium	%	.34	.39
Sulfur	%	.24	.28
Manganese	mg/kg	149.7	171.3

CLOVER, LADINO. Trifolium repens

Clover, ladino, hay, s-c, (1)

Ref no 1-01-378

Dry matter	%	91.2	100.0
Ash	%	8.7	9.5
Crude fiber	%	17.5	19.2
Ether extract	%	3.1	3.4

Continued

41

Feed name or analyses		Mean As fed	Dry
N-free extract	%	40.9	44.9
Protein (N x 6.25)	%	21.0	23.0
Horses dig prot	%	13.2	14.5
Lignin	%	10.6	11.7
Energy			
Horses	DE kcal/kg	2453.	2690.
Horses	ME kcal/kg	2012.	2206.
Horses	TDN %	56.	61.
Calcium	%	1.26	1.38
Chlorine	%	.26	.28
Iron	%	.060	.060
Magnesium	%	.46	.50
Phosphorus	%	.36	.40
Potassium	%	1.97	2.17
Sodium	%	.12	.13
Sulfur	%	.20	.22
Cobalt	mg/kg	.140	.150
Copper	mg/kg	8.0	8.8
Manganese	mg/kg	120.8	132.5
Zinc	mg/kg	15.5	17.0
Carotene	mg/kg	147.0	161.2
Vitamin A equiv	IU/g	245.0	268.7

42

Feed name or analyses		Mean	
		As fed	Dry

CLOVER, RED. Trifolium pratense

Clover, red, hay, s-c, (1)

Ref no 1-01-415

		As fed	Dry
Dry matter	%	87.7	100.0
Ash	%	6.9	7.9
Crude fiber	%	26.4	30.1
Ether extract	%	2.5	2.9
N-free extract	%	38.8	44.2
Protein (N x 6.25)	%	13.1	14.9
Horses	dig prot %	7.0	8.0
Cellulose	%	22.9	26.1
Lignin	%	12.8	14.6
Energy	GE kcal/kg	3900.	4447.
Horses	DE kcal/kg	1817.	2072.
Horses	ME kcal/kg	1490.	1699.
Horses	TDN %	41.	47.
Calcium	%	1.41	1.61
Chlorine	%	.23	.26
Iron	%	.010	.010
Magnesium	%	.39	.45
Phosphorus	%	.19	.22
Potassium	%	1.54	1.76
			Continued

(1) dry forages and roughages
(2) pasture, range plants, and forages fed green

43

Feed name or analyses		Mean	
		As fed	Dry
Sodium	%	.13	.15
Sulfur	%	.11	.17
Cobalt	mg/kg	.130	.150
Copper	mg/kg	9.8	11.2
Manganese	mg/kg	57.6	65.7
Zinc	mg/kg	15.1	17.2
Carotene	mg/kg	32.3	36.8
Vitamin A equiv	IU/g	53.8	61.3

COCONUT. Cocos nucifera

Coconut, meats, solv-extd grnd, (5)
Solvent extracted coconut meal (AAFCO)
Solvent extracted copra meal (AAFCO)

Ref no 5-01-573

		As fed	Dry
Dry matter	%	92.0	100.0
Ash	%	5.6	6.1
Crude fiber	%	15.0	16.3
Ether extract	%	1.8	2.0
N-free extract	%	48.3	52.5
Protein (N x 6.25)	%	21.3	23.1
Horses	dig prot %	17.2	18.7
Lignin	%	1.0	1.1
			Continued

(3) silages
(4) energy feeds
(5) protein supplements

44

Feed name or analyses		Mean	
		As fed	Dry
Energy			
Horses	DE kcal/kg	3002.	3263.
Horses	ME kcal/kg	2462.	2676.
Horses	TDN %	68.	74.
Calcium	%	.17	.18
Chlorine	%	.03	.03
Phosphorus	%	.61	.66
Riboflavin	mg/kg	13.2	14.3
Thiamine	mg/kg	.9	1.0

CORN. Zea mays

Corn, aerial pt, ensiled, mature, well-eared mn 50 dry matter, (3)

Ref no 3-08-152

		As fed	Dry
Dry matter	%	55.0	100.0
Ash	%	3.0	5.4
Crude fiber	%	12.6	23.0
Ether extract	%	1.6	2.9
N-free extract	%	33.5	60.9
Protein (N x 6.25)	%	4.3	7.8
Horses	dig prot %	2.5	4.5
			Continued

(6) minerals
(7) vitamins
(8) additives

45

TABLE I-1 – COMPOSITION OF SOME COMMON HORSE FEEDS (Continued)

Feed name or analyses		As fed (Mean)	Dry (Mean)
Energy			
Horses	DE kcal/kg	1722.	3130.
Horses	ME kcal/kg	1412.	2567.
Horses	TDN %	39.	71.
Calcium	%	.15	.27
Phosphorus	%	.10	.19

Corn, ears, grnd, (4)
Corn and cob meal (AAFCO)
Ear corn chop (AAFCO)
Ground ear corn (AAFCO)

Ref no 4-02-849

Feed name or analyses		As fed	Dry
Dry matter	%	87.0	100.0
Ash	%	1.6	1.8
Crude fiber	%	8.0	9.2
Ether extract	%	3.2	3.7
N-free extract	%	66.1	76.0
Protein (N x 6.25)	%	8.1	9.3
Horses	dig prot %	4.0	4.6
Energy			
Horses	DE kcal/kg	3452.	3968.
Horses	ME kcal/kg	2831.	3254.
Horses	TDN %	78.	90.
Calcium	%	.04	.05
Iron	%	.007	.008
Magnesium	%	.15	.17
Phosphorus	%	.27	.31
Potassium	%	.53	.61

Continued

46

Feed name or analyses		As fed (Mean)	Dry (Mean)
Cobalt	mg/kg	.300	.300
Copper	mg/kg	7.7	8.8
Manganese	mg/kg	13.0	15.0

Corn, grits by-prod, mn 5 fat, (4)
Hominy feed (AAFCO)
Hominy feed (CFA)

Ref no 4-02-887

Feed name or analyses		As fed	Dry
Dry matter	%	90.6	100.0
Ash	%	2.5	2.8
Crude fiber	%	5.0	5.5
Ether extract	%	6.5	7.2
N-free extract	%	65.9	72.7
Protein (N x 6.25)	%	10.7	11.8
Horses	dig prot %	7.2	7.9
Energy	GE kcal/kg	4275.	4702.
Horses	DE kcal/kg	3795.	4189.
Horses	ME kcal/kg	3112.	3435.
Horses	TDN %	86.	95.
Calcium	%	.05	.06
Iron	%	.006	.007
Magnesium	%	.24	.26
Phosphorus	%	.53	.58
Potassium	%	.67	.74
Sulfur	%	.03	.03
Cobalt	mg/kg	.060	.066
Copper	mg/kg	14.6	16.1
Manganese	mg/kg	14.6	16.1

Continued

47

Feed name or analyses		As fed (Mean)	Dry (Mean)
Carotene	mg/kg	9.2	10.1
Niacin	mg/kg	51.1	56.2
Pantothenic acid	mg/kg	7.5	8.2
Riboflavin	mg/kg	2.0	2.2
Thiamine	mg/kg	7.9	8.7
Vitamin A equiv	IU/g	15.3	16.8

Corn, gluten, wet-mil dehy, (5)
Corn gluten meal (AAFCO)
Corn gluten meal (CFA)

Ref no 5-02-900

Feed name or analyses		As fed	Dry
Dry matter	%	91.0	100.0
Ash	%	2.4	2.6
Crude fiber	%	4.0	4.4
Ether extract	%	2.3	2.5
N-free extract	%	39.5	43.4
Protein (N x 6.25)	%	42.9	47.1
Horses	dig prot %	35.7	39.2
Energy			
Horses	DE kcal/kg	3371.	3704.
Horses	ME kcal/kg	2764.	3037.
Horses	TDN %	76.	84.
Calcium	%	.16	.18
Iron	%	.040	.040
Magnesium	%	.05	.05
Phosphorus	%	.40	.44
Potassium	%	.03	.03
Sodium	%	.10	.10

Continued

48

Feed name or analyses		Mean	
		As fed	Dry
Cobalt	mg/kg	.100	.100
Copper	mg/kg	28.2	31.0
Manganese	mg/kg	7.3	8.0
Choline	mg/kg	330.	363.
Folic acid	mg/kg	.20	.20
Niacin	mg/kg	49.9	54.8
Pantothenic acid	mg/kg	10.3	11.3
Riboflavin	mg/kg	1.5	1.6
Thiamine	mg/kg	.2	.2
Arginine	%	1.40	1.54
Cystine	%	.60	.66
Glycine	%	1.50	1.65
Histidine	%	1.00	1.10
Isoleucine	%	2.30	2.53
Leucine	%	7.60	8.35
Lysine	%	.80	.88
Methionine	%	1.00	1.10
Phenylalanine	%	2.90	3.19
Threonine	%	1.40	1.54
Tryptophan	%	.20	.22
Tyrosine	%	1.00	1.10
Valine	%	2.20	2.42

(1) dry forages and roughages
(2) pasture, range plants, and forages fed green

49

Feed name or analyses		Mean	
		As fed	Dry

Corn, gluten w bran, wet-mill dehy, (5)
Corn gluten feed (AAFCO)
Corn gluten feed (CFA)

Ref no 5-02-903

		As fed	Dry
Dry matter	%	90.0	100.0
Ash	%	6.3	7.0
Crude fiber	%	8.0	8.9
Ether extract	%	2.4	2.7
N-free extract	%	48.1	53.4
Protein (N x 6.25)	%	25.3	28.1
Horses	dig prot %	21.8	24.2
Energy	GE kcal/kg	4041.	4490.
Horses	DE kcal/kg	3254.	3616.
Horses	ME kcal/kg	2668.	2965.
Horses	TDN %	74.	82.
Calcium	%	.46	.51
Iron	%	.050	.060
Magnesium	%	.29	.32
Phosphorus	%	.77	.86
Potassium	%	.60	.67
Sodium	%	.95	1.06
Cobalt	mg/kg	.090	.100
Copper	mg/kg	47.7	53.0
Manganese	mg/kg	23.8	26.4

Continued

(3) silages
(4) energy feeds
(5) protein supplements

50

Feed name or analyses		Mean	
		As fed	Dry
Biotin	mg/kg	.30	.30
Choline	mg/kg	1516.	1684.
Folic acid	mg/kg	.20	.20
Niacin	mg/kg	71.9	79.9
Pantothenic acid	mg/kg	17.2	19.1
Riboflavin	mg/kg	2.4	2.7
Thiamine	mg/kg	2.0	2.2
Arginine	%	.80	.89
Histidine	%	.60	.67
Isoleucine	%	1.20	1.33
Leucine	%	2.60	2.89
Lysine	%	.80	.89
Methionine	%	.30	.33
Phenylalanine	%	.90	1.00
Threonine	%	.80	.89
Tryptophan	%	.20	.22
Tyrosine	%	.90	1.00
Valine	%	1.30	1.44

(6) minerals
(7) vitamins
(8) additives

51

TABLE I-1 – COMPOSITION OF SOME COMMON HORSE FEEDS (Continued)

CORN, DENT YELLOW. Zea mays indentata
Corn, dent yellow, grain, gr 2 US mn 54 wt, (4)

Ref no 4-02-931

Feed name or analyses		Mean As fed	Mean Dry
Dry matter	%	89.0	100.0
Ash	%	1.1	1.2
Crude fiber	%	2.0	2.2
Ether extract	%	3.9	4.4
N-free extract	%	73.1	82.2
Protein (N x 6.25)	%	8.9	10.0
Horses	dig prot %	6.7	7.5
Energy	GE kcal/kg	3918.	4402.
Horses	DE kcal/kg	3571.	4012.
Horses	ME kcal/kg	2928.	3290.
Horses	TDN %	81.	91.
Calcium	%	.02	.02
Phosphorus	%	.31	.35
Carotene	mg/kg	1.8	2.0
Niacin	mg/kg	26.3	29.5
Pantothenic acid	mg/kg	3.9	4.4
Riboflavin	mg/kg	1.3	1.5
Thiamine	mg/kg	3.6	4.0
Vitamin A equiv	IU/g	3.0	3.3
Arginine	%	.45	.51
Cystine	%	.09	.10
Histidine	%	.18	.20
Isoleucine	%	.45	.51
Leucine	%	.99	1.11

Continued

Feed name or analyses		Mean As fed	Mean Dry
Lysine	%	.18	.20
Methionine	%	.09	.10
Phenylalanine	%	.45	.51
Threonine	%	.36	.40
Tryptophan	%	.09	.10
Valine	%	.36	.40

COTTON. Gossypium spp
Cotton, seed w some hulls, mech-extd grnd, mn 41 prot mx 14 fbr mn 2 fat, (5)

Cottonseed meal, 41% protein

Ref no 5-01-617

		As fed	Dry
Dry matter	%	94.0	100.0
Ash	%	6.2	6.6
Crude fiber	%	12.0	12.8
Ether extract	%	4.3	4.6
N-free extract	%	30.4	32.4
Protein (N x 6.25)	%	41.0	43.6
Horses	dig prot %	33.2	35.3
Energy	GE kcal/kg	4600.	4893.
Horses	DE kcal/kg	3233.	3439.
Horses	ME kcal/kg	2651.	2820.
Horses	TDN %	73.	78.
Calcium	%	.16	.17
Iron	%	.030	.032
Magnesium	%	.56	.60

Continued

Feed name or analyses		Mean As fed	Mean Dry
Phosphorus	%	1.20	1.28
Potassium	%	1.40	1.49
Sodium	%	.04	.04
Cobalt	mg/kg	.150	.160
Copper	mg/kg	19.5	20.7
Manganese	mg/kg	21.5	22.9
Choline	mg/kg	2780.	2957.
Folic acid	mg/kg	2.30	2.45
Niacin	mg/kg	39.5	42.0
Pantothenic acid	mg/kg	14.0	14.9
Riboflavin	mg/kg	5.0	5.3
Thiamine	mg/kg	6.5	6.9
Arginine	%	4.25	4.52
Cystine	%	.85	.90
Glycine	%	2.05	2.18
Histidine	%	1.10	1.17
Isoleucine	%	1.60	1.70
Leucine	%	2.50	2.66
Lysine	%	1.70	1.81
Methionine	%	.65	.69
Phenylalanine	%	2.35	2.50
Threonine	%	1.45	1.54
Tryptophan	%	.65	.69
Valine	%	2.05	2.18

Table 1

Feed name or analyses		Mean	
		As fed	Dry
Cotton, seed w some hulls, pre-press solv-extd grnd, 41 prot, (5)			
Cottonseed meal, pre-press solvent extracted, 41% protein			
Ref no 5-07-872			
Dry matter	%	92.5	100.0
Ash	%	6.2	6.7
Crude fiber	%	12.0	13.0
Ether extract	%	1.4	1.5
N-free extract	%	31.9	34.5
Protein (N x 6.25)	%	41.0	44.3
Horses	dig prot %	34.8	35.9
Energy Horses	GE kcal/kg	4200.	4540.
Horses	DE kcal/kg	3018.	3263.
Horses	ME kcal/kg	2475.	2676.
Horses	TDN %	68.	74.
Calcium	%	.16	.17
Iron	%	.030	.032
Magnesium	%	.56	.60
Phosphorus	%	1.20	1.30
Potassium	%	1.40	1.51
Sodium	%	.04	.04
Cobalt	mg/kg	.150	.162
Copper	mg/kg	19.5	21.1

Continued

(1) dry forages and roughages
(2) pasture, range plants, and forages fed green

55

Table 2

Feed name or analyses		Mean	
		As fed	Dry
Manganese	mg/kg	21.5	23.2
Choline	mg/kg	2860.	3092.
Folic acid	mg/kg	2.30	2.49
Niacin	mg/kg	39.5	42.7
Pantothenic acid	mg/kg	14.0	15.1
Riboflavin	mg/kg	5.0	5.4
Thiamine	mg/kg	6.5	7.0
Arginine	%	4.25	4.59
Cystine	%	.85	.92
Glycine	%	2.05	2.22
Histidine	%	1.10	1.19
Isoleucine	%	1.60	1.73
Leucine	%	2.50	2.70
Lysine	%	1.70	1.84
Methionine	%	.65	.70
Phenylalanine	%	2.35	2.54
Threonine	%	1.45	1.57
Tryptophan	%	.65	.70
Valine	%	2.05	2.22

(3) silages
(4) energy feeds
(5) protein supplements

56

Table 3

Feed name or analyses		Mean	
		As fed	Dry
Cotton, seed w some hulls, solv-extd grnd, mn 41 prot mx 14 fbr mn 0.5 fat, (5)			
Cottonseed meal, solvent extracted, 41% protein			
Ref no 5-01-621			
Dry matter	%	91.5	100.0
Ash	%	6.2	6.8
Crude fiber	%	12.0	13.1
Ether extract	%	2.0	2.2
N-free extract	%	30.3	33.1
Protein (N x 6.25)	%	41.0	44.8
Horses	dig prot %	33.2	36.3
Energy Horses	GE kcal/kg	4300.	4700.
Horses	DE kcal/kg	3026.	3307.
Horses	ME kcal/kg	2481.	2712.
Horses	TDN %	69.	75.
Calcium	%	.16	.17
Iron	%	.030	.033
Magnesium	%	.56	.61
Phosphorus	%	1.20	1.31
Potassium	%	1.40	1.53
Sodium	%	.04	.04
Cobalt	mg/kg	.150	.164
Copper	mg/kg	19.5	21.3

Continued

(6) minerals
(7) vitamins
(8) additives

57

TABLE I-1 – COMPOSITION OF SOME COMMON HORSE FEEDS (Continued)

Feed name or analyses		Mean As fed	Dry
Manganese	mg/kg	21.5	23.5
Choline	mg/kg	2860.	3126.
Folic acid	mg/kg	2.30	2.51
Niacin	mg/kg	39.5	43.2
Pantothenic acid	mg/kg	14.0	15.3
Riboflavin	mg/kg	5.0	5.5
Thiamine	mg/kg	6.5	7.1
Arginine	%	4.25	4.64
Cystine	%	.85	.93
Glycine	%	2.05	2.24
Histidine	%	1.10	1.20
Isoleucine	%	1.60	1.75
Leucine	%	2.50	2.73
Lysine	%	1.70	1.86
Methionine	%	.65	.71
Phenylalanine	%	2.35	2.57
Threonine	%	1.45	1.58
Tryptophan	%	.65	.71
Valine	%	2.05	2.24

Cotton, seed wo hulls, pre-press solv-extd grnd, mn 50 prot, (5)
Cottonseed meal, pre-press solvent extracted, 50% protein

Ref no 5-07-874

Feed name or analyses		Mean As fed	Dry
Dry matter	%	92.5	100.0
Ash	%	6.2	6.7
Crude fiber	%	8.5	9.2

Continued

Feed name or analyses		Mean As fed	Dry
Ether extract	%	1.2	1.3
N-free extract	%	26.6	28.8
Protein (N x 6.25)	%	50.0	54.0
Horses	dig prot %	40.4	43.7
Energy			
Horses	DE kcal/kg	3059.	3307.
Horses	ME kcal/kg	2509.	2712.
Horses	TDN %	69.	75.
Calcium	%	.16	.17
Iron	%	.011	.012
Magnesium	%	.46	.50
Phosphorus	%	1.01	1.09
Potassium	%	1.26	1.36
Sodium	%	.05	.05
Cobalt	mg/kg	2.000	2.162
Copper	mg/kg	18.0	19.4
Manganese	mg/kg	22.8	24.6
Zinc	mg/kg	73.3	79.2
Arginine	%	4.75	5.13
Cystine	%	1.00	1.08
Glycine	%	2.35	2.54
Histidine	%	1.25	1.35
Isoleucine	%	1.85	2.00
Leucine	%	2.80	3.03
Lysine	%	2.10	2.27
Methionine	%	.80	.86
Phenylalanine	%	2.75	2.97
Threonine	%	1.70	1.84
Tryptophan	%	.70	.76
Valine	%	2.05	2.22

FLAX. Linum usitatissimum

Flax, seed, mech-extd grnd, mx 0.5 acid insol ash, (5)
Linseed meal (AAFCO)
Linseed meal (CFA)
Linseed oil meal, expeller extracted
Linseed oil meal, hydraulic extracted
Linseed meal, old process

Ref no 5-02-045

Feed name or analyses		Mean As fed	Dry
Dry matter	%	91.0	100.0
Ash	%	5.6	6.2
Crude fiber	%	9.0	9.9
Ether extract	%	5.2	5.7
N-free extract	%	35.8	39.4
Protein (N x 6.25)	%	35.3	38.8
Horses	dig prot %	31.0	34.1
Energy			
Horses	DE kcal/kg	3250.	3571.
Horses	ME kcal/kg	2664.	2928.
Horses	TDN %	74.	81.
Calcium	%	.44	.48
Iron	%	.017	.019
Magnesium	%	.58	.64
Phosphorus	%	.89	.98
Potassium	%	1.24	1.36
Sodium	%	.11	.12

Continued

Feed name or analyses		Mean	
		As fed	Dry
Cobalt	mg/kg	.400	.500
Copper	mg/kg	26.4	29.0
Manganese	mg/kg	39.4	43.3
Carotene	mg/kg	.2	.2
Choline	mg/kg	1863.	2048.
Folic acid	mg/kg	2.90	3.20
Niacin	mg/kg	35.6	39.1
Pantothenic acid	mg/kg	17.8	19.6
Riboflavin	mg/kg	3.5	3.8
Thiamine	mg/kg	5.1	5.6
Vitamin A equiv	IU/g	.3	.3
Methionine	%	.70	.77

Flax, seed, solv-extd grnd, mx 0.5 acid insol ash, (5)

Solvent extracted linseed meal (AAFCO)

Solvent extracted linseed meal (CFA)

Linseed oil meal, solvent extracted

Ref no 5-02-048

Feed name or analyses		Mean	
		As fed	Dry
Dry matter	%	91.0	100.0
Ash	%	5.8	6.4
Crude fiber	%	9.0	9.9
Ether extract	%	1.7	1.9
N-free extract	%	39.3	43.2

(1) dry forages and roughages
(2) pasture, range plants, and
forages fed green

61

Feed name or analyses		Mean	
		As fed	Dry
Protein (N x 6.25)	%	35.1	38.6
Horses	dig prot %	30.9	34.0
Energy			
Horses	DE kcal/kg	3049.	3351.
Horses	ME kcal/kg	2501.	2748.
Horses	TDN %	69.	76.
Calcium	%	.40	.44
Iron	%	.033	.036
Magnesium	%	.60	.66
Phosphorus	%	.83	.91
Potassium	%	1.38	1.52
Sodium	%	.14	.15
Cobalt	mg/kg	.20	.20
Copper	mg/kg	25.7	28.2
Manganese	mg/kg	37.6	41.3
Choline	mg/kg	1225.	1347.
Niacin	mg/kg	30.1	33.1
Riboflavin	mg/kg	2.9	3.2
Thiamine	mg/kg	9.5	10.4

(3) silages
(4) energy feeds
(5) protein supplements

62

Feed name or analyses		Mean	
		As fed	Dry

GRAINS. Scientific name not used

Grains, brewers grains, dehy, mx 3 dried spent hops, (5)

Brewers dried grains (AAFCO)

Brewers dried grains (CFA)

Ref no 5-02-141

Feed name or analyses		Mean	
		As fed	Dry
Dry matter	%	92.0	100.0
Ash	%	3.6	3.9
Crude fiber	%	15.0	16.3
Ether extract	%	6.2	6.7
N-free extract	%	41.4	45.0
Protein (N x 6.25)	%	25.9	28.1
Horses	dig prot %	19.9	21.6
Energy			
Horses	DE kcal/kg	2069.	2249.
Horses	ME kcal/kg	1696.	1844.
Horses	TDN %	47.	51.
Calcium	%	.27	.29
Iron	%	.025	.027
Magnesium	%	.14	.15
Phosphorus	%	.50	.54
Potassium	%	.08	.09

Continued

(6) minerals
(7) vitamins
(8) additives

63

TABLE I-1 — COMPOSITION OF SOME COMMON HORSE FEEDS (Continued)

Feed name or analyses		Mean	
		As fed	Dry
Sodium	%	.26	.28
Cobalt	mg/kg	.100	.100
Copper	mg/kg	21.3	22.2
Manganese	mg/kg	37.6	40.9
Choline	mg/kg	1587.	1725.
Folic acid	mg/kg	.22	.24
Niacin	mg/kg	43.4	47.2
Pantothenic acid	mg/kg	8.6	9.3
Riboflavin	mg/kg	1.5	1.6
Thiamine	mg/kg	.7	.8
Vitamin B6	mg/kg	.66	.72
Arginine	%	1.30	1.41
Histidine	%	.50	.54
Isoleucine	%	1.50	1.63
Leucine	%	2.30	2.50
Lysine	%	.90	.98
Methionine	%	.40	.43
Phenylalanine	%	1.30	1.41
Threonine	%	.90	.98
Tryptophan	%	.40	.43
Tyrosine	%	1.20	1.30
Valine	%	1.60	1.74

Hominy feed - see Corn, grits by-prod

64

LESPEDEZA. Lespedeza spp

Lespedeza, hay, s-c, pre-blm, (1)

Ref no 1-07-954

Feed name or analyses		Mean	
		As fed	Dry
Dry matter	%	92.1	100.0
Ash	%	6.5	7.1
Crude fiber	%	21.8	23.7
Ether extract	%	3.1	3.4
N-free extract	%	44.2	48.0
Protein (N x 6.25)	%	16.4	17.8
Horses	dig prot %	11.4	12.4
Energy			
Horses	DE kcal/kg	2558.	2778.
Horses	ME kcal/kg	2098.	2278.
Horses	TDN %	58.	63.
Calcium	%	1.05	1.14
Phosphorus	%	.24	.26

Lespedeza, hay, s-c, mid-blm, (1)

Ref no 1-02-511

		As fed	Dry
Dry matter	%	93.0	100.0
Ash	%	5.5	5.9
Crude fiber	%	28.6	30.7
Ether extract	%	3.7	4.0
N-free extract	%	40.6	43.7

Continued

65

Feed name or analyses		Mean	
		As fed	Dry
Protein (N x 6.25)	%	14.6	15.7
Horses	dig prot %	9.8	10.5
Energy			
Horses	DE kcal/kg	2337.	2513.
Horses	ME kcal/kg	1917.	2061.
Horses	TDN %	53.	57.
Calcium	%	1.11	1.19
Iron	%	.030	.032
Magnesium	%	.25	.27
Phosphorus	%	.24	.26
Potassium	%	.98	1.05

LIMESTONE. Scientific name not applicable

Limestone, grnd, mn 33 Ca, (6)

Limestone, ground (AAFCO)

Ref no 6-02-632

		As fed	Dry
Dry matter	%	100.0	100.0
Ash	%	95.8	95.8
Calcium	%	33.84	33.84
Iron	%	.330	.330
Phosphorus	%	.02	.02
Sodium	%	.06	.06
Manganese	mg/kg	279.6	279.6

66

NATIVE PLANTS, INTERMOUNTAIN. Scientific name not used

Native plants, Intermountain, hay, s-c, (1)
Meadow hay

Ref no 1-03-181

Feed name or analyses		Mean	
		As fed	Dry
Dry matter	%	92.9	100.0
Ash	%	7.5	8.1
Crude fiber	%	28.0	30.1
Ether extract	%	2.8	3.0
N-free extract	%	46.2	49.7
Protein (N x 6.25)	%	8.4	9.1
Horses dig prot	%	2.7	2.9
Energy			
Horses	DE kcal/kg	1884.	2028.
Horses	ME kcal/kg	1545.	1663.
Horses	TDN %	43.	46.
Calcium	%	.53	.57
Phosphorus	%	.16	.17

NATIVE PLANTS, MIDWEST. Scientific name not used

Native plants, Midwest, hay, s-c, immature, (1)
Prairie hay, immature

Ref no 1-03-183

Feed name or analyses		Mean	
		As fed	Dry
Dry matter	%	89.5	100.0
Ash	%	8.3	9.3
Crude fiber	%	28.4	31.7
Ether extract	%	2.3	2.6
N-free extract	%	42.7	47.7
Protein (N x 6.25)	%	7.8	8.7
Horses dig prot	%	2.1	2.4
Energy			
Horses	DE kcal/kg	2013.	2249.
Horses	ME kcal/kg	1650.	1844.
Horses	TDN %	46.	51.
Calcium	%	.51	.57
Iron	%	.01	.01
Magnesium	%	.22	.24
Phosphorus	%	.17	.19
Potassium	%	.97	1.08

Native plants, Midwest, hay, s-c, mid-blm, (1)
Prairie hay, mid-bloom

Ref no 1-07-956

Feed name or analyses		Mean	
		As fed	Dry
Dry matter	%	91.0	100.0
Ash	%	8.7	9.6
Crude fiber	%	29.2	32.1
Ether extract	%	2.6	2.8
N-free extract	%	43.1	47.4
Protein (N x 6.25)	%	7.4	8.1
Horses dig prot	%	3.7	4.1
Energy			
Horses	DE kcal/kg	2006.	2205.
Horses	ME kcal/kg	1645.	1808.
Horses	TDN %	46.	50.
Calcium	%	.31	.34
Phosphorus	%	.19	.21

(1) dry forages and roughages
(2) pasture, range plants, and forages fed green
67

(3) silages
(4) energy feeds
(5) protein supplements
68

(6) minerals
(7) vitamins
(8) additives
69

TABLE I-1 – COMPOSITION OF SOME COMMON HORSE FEEDS (Continued)

Native plants, Midwest, hay, s-c, full blm, (1)
Prairie hay, full bloom

Ref no 1-03-184

Feed name or analyses		As fed	Dry
Dry matter	%	83.3	100.0
Ash	%	8.5	10.2
Crude fiber	%	27.5	33.0
Ether extract	%	2.7	3.2
N-free extract	%	38.3	46.0
Protein (N x 6.25)	%	6.3	7.6
Horses	dig prot %	1.7	2.1
Energy			
Horses	DE kcal/kg	1873.	2249.
Horses	ME kcal/kg	1536.	1844.
Horses	TDN %	42.	51.

Native plants, Midwest, hay, s-c, late blm, (1)
Prairie hay, late bloom

Ref no 1-07-957

Feed name or analyses		As fed	Dry
Dry matter	%	91.3	100.0
Ash	%	8.6	9.4
Crude fiber	%	29.7	32.5
Ether extract	%	3.0	3.3
N-free extract	%	44.0	48.2
Protein (N x 6.25)	%	6.0	6.6
Horses	dig prot %	2.0	2.2

Continued

70

Feed name or analyses		As fed	Dry
Energy			
Horses	DE kcal/kg	1972.	2160.
Horses	ME kcal/kg	1617.	1771.
Horses	TDN %	45.	49.
Calcium	%	.33	.36
Phosphorus	%	.12	.13

OATS. Avena sativa

Oats, hay, s-c, (1)

Ref no 1-03-280

Feed name or analyses		As fed	Dry
Dry matter	%	88.2	100.0
Ash	%	6.6	7.5
Crude fiber	%	27.3	31.0
Ether extract	%	2.7	3.1
N-free extract	%	43.4	49.2
Protein (N x 6.25)	%	8.1	9.2
Horses	dig prot %	3.9	4.4
Energy			
Horses	DE kcal/kg	2372.	2690.
Horses	ME kcal/kg	1946.	2206.
Horses	TDN %	54.	61.
Calcium	%	.23	.26
Chlorine	%	.46	.52
Iron	%	.04	.05
Magnesium	%	.26	.29
Phosphorus	%	.21	.24
Potassium	%	.85	.97

Continued

71

Feed name or analyses		As fed	Dry
Sodium	%	.15	.17
Cobalt	mg/kg	.06	.07
Copper	mg/kg	3.9	4.4
Manganese	mg/kg	65.7	74.7
Carotene	mg/kg	88.9	101.0
Vitamin A equiv	IU/g	148.2	168.4

Oats, cereal by-prod, mx 4 fbr, (4)
Feeding oat meal (AAFCO)
Oat middlings (CFA)

Ref no 4-03-303

Feed name or analyses		As fed	Dry
Dry matter	%	91.0	100.0
Ash	%	2.3	2.5
Crude fiber	%	4.0	4.4
Ether extract	%	5.8	6.4
N-free extract	%	63.1	69.3
Protein (N x 6.25)	%	15.8	17.4
Horses	dig prot %	10.8	11.9
Energy			
Horses	DE kcal/kg	3691.	4056.
Horses	ME kcal/kg	3027.	3326.
Horses	TDN %	84.	92.
Calcium	%	.08	.09
Iron	%	.038	.042
Phosphorus	%	.49	.54
Manganese	mg/kg	44.0	48.4
Niacin	mg/kg	28.1	30.9
Pantothenic acid	mg/kg	23.1	25.4

Continued

72

Oats, grain, (4) — Ref no 4-03-309

Feed name or analyses		As fed (Mean)	Dry
Riboflavin	mg/kg	1.8	2.0
Thiamine	mg/kg	7.0	7.7
Arginine	%	.70	.77
Histidine	%	.30	.33
Lysine	%	.10	.11
Tyrosine	%	.91	1.00
Dry matter	%	89.0	100.0
Ash	%	3.2	3.6
Crude fiber	%	11.0	12.4
Ether extract	%	4.5	5.1
N-free extract	%	58.5	65.7
Protein (N x 6.25)	%	11.8	13.2
Horses	dig prot %	8.8	9.9
Cellulose	%	16.0	18.0
Lignin	%	8.9	10.0
Energy	GE kcal/kg	4187.	4704.
Horses	DE kcal/kg	2982.	3351.
Horses	ME kcal/kg	2446.	2748.
Horses	TDN %	68.	76.
Calcium	%	.10	.11
Iron	%	.007	.008

Continued

Feed name or analyses		As fed (Mean)	Dry
Magnesium	%	.17	.19
Phosphorus	%	.35	.39
Potassium	%	.37	.42
Sodium	%	.06	.07
Cobalt	mg/kg	.060	.070
Copper	mg/kg	5.9	6.6
Manganese	mg/kg	38.2	42.9
Biotin	mg/kg	.30	.30
Choline	mg/kg	1073.	1206.
Folic acid	mg/kg	.40	.40
Niacin	mg/kg	15.8	17.8
Pantothenic acid	mg/kg	12.9	14.5
Riboflavin	mg/kg	1.6	1.8
Thiamine	mg/kg	6.2	7.0
a-tocopherol	mg/kg	5.9	6.6
Vitamin B6	mg/kg	1.2	1.3
Arginine	%	.71	.80
Cystine	%	.18	.20
Histidine	%	.18	.20
Isoleucine	%	.53	.60
Leucine	%	.89	1.00
Lysine	%	.36	.40
Methionine	%	.18	.20
Phenylalanine	%	.62	.70
Threonine	%	.36	.40
Tryptophan	%	.18	.20

Continued

Feed name or analyses		As fed (Mean)	Dry
Tyrosine	%	.53	.60
Valine	%	.62	.70

Oats, grain, Pacific coast, (4) — Ref no 4-07-999

Feed name or analyses		As fed (Mean)	Dry
Dry matter	%	91.2	100.0
Ash	%	3.7	4.0
Crude fiber	%	11.0	12.1
Ether extract	%	5.4	5.9
N-free extract	%	62.1	68.1
Protein (N x 6.25)	%	9.0	9.9
Horses	dig prot %	6.7	7.4
Energy			
Horses	DE kcal/kg	3096.	3395.
Horses	ME kcal/kg	2539.	2784.
Horses	TDN %	70.	77.
Calcium	%	.09	.10
Phosphorus	%	.33	.36

(1) dry forages and roughages
(2) pasture, range plants, and forages fed green
73

(3) silages
(4) energy feeds
(5) protein supplements
74

(6) minerals
(7) vitamins
(8) additives
75

TABLE I-1 – COMPOSITION OF SOME COMMON HORSE FEEDS (Continued)

Oats, groats, (4)
Oat groats (AAFCO)
Oat groats (CFA)
Hulled oats (CFA)

Ref no 4-03-331

Feed name or analyses		As fed (Mean)	Dry (Mean)
Dry matter	%	91.0	100.0
Ash	%	2.2	2.4
Crude fiber	%	3.0	3.3
Ether extract	%	5.8	6.4
N-free extract	%	63.2	69.5
Protein (N x 6.25)	%	16.7	18.4
Horses dig prot	%	11.7	12.9
Energy			
Horses	DE kcal/kg	3731.	4100.
Horses	ME kcal/kg	3059.	3362.
Horses	TDN %	85.	93.
Calcium	%	.07	.08
Magnesium	%	.09	.10
Phosphorus	%	.43	.47
Potassium	%	.34	.37
Copper	mg/kg	6.4	7.0
Manganese	mg/kg	28.6	31.4
Niacin	mg/kg	8.1	8.9
Pantothenic acid	mg/kg	14.7	16.2
Riboflavin	mg/kg	1.3	1.4
Thiamine	mg/kg	6.8	7.5
Vitamin B$_6$	mg/kg	1.1	1.2

76

ORCHARDGRASS. Dactylis glomerata

Orchardgrass, hay, s-c, (1)

Ref no 1-03-438

Feed name or analyses		As fed (Mean)	Dry (Mean)
Dry matter	%	88.3	100.0
Ash	%	6.7	7.6
Crude fiber	%	30.0	34.0
Ether extract	%	3.0	3.4
N-free extract	%	40.0	45.3
Protein (N x 6.25)	%	8.6	9.7
Horses dig prot	%	5.1	5.8
Cellulose	%	22.1	25.0
Lignin	%	6.7	7.6
Energy			
Horses	GE kcal/kg	4059.	4597.
Horses	DE kcal/kg	2219.	2513.
Horses	ME kcal/kg	1820.	2061.
Horses	TDN %	50.	57.
Calcium	%	.40	.45
Chlorine	%	.36	.41
Iron	%	.01	.01
Magnesium	%	.28	.32
Phosphorus	%	.33	.37
Potassium	%	1.85	2.10
Sulfur	%	.23	.26
Cobalt	mg/kg	.02	.02
Copper	mg/kg	12.1	13.7
Manganese	mg/kg	220.4	249.6

Continued

77

Feed name or analyses		As fed (Mean)	Dry (Mean)
Zinc	mg/kg	16.0	18.1
Carotene	mg/kg	29.6	33.5
Vitamin A equiv	IU/g	49.3	55.8

OYSTERS. Crassostrea spp, Ostrea spp

Oysters, shells, f-grnd, mn 33 Ca, (6)
Oyster shell flour (AAFCO)

Ref no 6-03-481

Feed name or analyses		As fed (Mean)	Dry (Mean)
Dry matter	%	100.0	100.0
Ash	%	80.8	80.8
Protein (N x 6.25)	%	1.0	1.0
Calcium	%	38.05	38.05
Iron	%	.290	.290
Magnesium	%	.30	.30
Phosphorus	%	.07	.07
Potassium	%	.10	.10
Sodium	%	.21	.21
Manganese	mg/kg	133.3	133.3

78

PEANUT. Arachis hypogaea

Peanut, kernels, mech-extd grnd, mx 7 fbr, (5)
Peanut meal (AAFCO)
Peanut meal (CFA)
Peanut oil meal, expeller extracted

Ref no 5-03-649

Feed name or analyses		As fed (Mean)	Dry (Mean)
Dry matter	%	92.0	100.0
Ash	%	5.7	6.2
Crude fiber	%	11.0	12.0
Ether extract	%	5.9	6.4
N-free extract	%	23.6	25.6
Protein (N x 6.25)	%	45.8	49.8
Horses	dig prot %	41.2	44.8
Energy			
Horses	DE kcal/kg	3367.	3660.
Horses	ME kcal/kg	2761.	3001.
Horses	TDN %	76.	83.
Calcium	%	.17	.18
Magnesium	%	.33	.36
Phosphorus	%	.57	.62
Potassium	%	1.15	1.25
Manganese	mg/kg	25.5	27.7

Continued

Feed name or analyses		As fed (Mean)	Dry (Mean)
Choline	mg/kg	1683.	1829.
Niacin	mg/kg	169.0	183.7
Pantothenic acid	mg/kg	48.2	52.3
Riboflavin	mg/kg	5.3	5.8
Thiamine	mg/kg	7.3	7.9
Arginine	%	4.69	5.10
Histidine	%	1.00	1.09
Isoleucine	%	2.00	2.17
Leucine	%	3.10	3.37
Lysine	%	1.30	1.41
Methionine	%	.60	.65
Phenylalanine	%	2.30	2.50
Threonine	%	1.40	1.52
Tryptophan	%	.50	.54
Valine	%	2.20	2.39

Peanut, kernels, solv-extd grnd, mx 7 fbr, (5)
Solvent extracted peanut meal (AAFCO)
Groundnut oil meal, solvent extracted
Peanut oil meal, solvent extracted

Ref no 5-03-650

Feed name or analyses		As fed (Mean)	Dry (Mean)
Dry matter	%	92.0	100.0
Ash	%	4.5	4.9
Crude fiber	%	13.0	14.1

Continued

Feed name or analyses		As fed (Mean)	Dry (Mean)
Ether extract	%	1.2	1.3
N-free extract	%	25.9	28.2
Protein (N x 6.25)	%	47.4	51.5
Horses	dig prot %	42.7	46.4
Energy			
Horses	DE kcal/kg	3123.	3395.
Horses	ME kcal/kg	2561.	2784.
Horses	TDN %	71.	77.
Calcium	%	.20	.22
Magnesium	%	.04	.04
Phosphorus	%	.65	.71
Manganese	mg/kg	29.0	31.5
Choline	mg/kg	2000.	2174.
Niacin	mg/kg	170.1	184.9
Pantothenic acid	mg/kg	53.0	57.6
Riboflavin	mg/kg	11.0	12.0
Thiamine	mg/kg	7.3	7.9
Arginine	%	5.90	6.41
Histidine	%	1.20	1.30
Isoleucine	%	2.00	2.17
Leucine	%	3.70	4.02
Lysine	%	2.30	2.50
Methionine	%	.40	.43
Phenylalanine	%	2.70	2.93
Threonine	%	1.50	1.63
Tryptophan	%	.50	.54

Continued

(1) dry forages and roughages
(2) pasture, range plants, and forages fed green
79

(3) silages
(4) energy feeds
(5) protein supplements
80

(6) minerals
(7) vitamins
(8) additives
81

TABLE I-1 – COMPOSITION OF SOME COMMON HORSE FEEDS (Continued)

Feed name or analyses		As fed (Mean)	Dry (Mean)
Tyrosine	%	1.80	1.96
Valine	%	2.80	3.04

PHOSPHATE, DEFLUORINATED

Phosphate, defluorinated grnd, mn 1 pt F per 100 pt P, (6)
Phosphate, defluorinated (AAFCO)
Defluorinated phosphate (CFA)

Ref no 6-01-780

Feed name or analyses		As fed (Mean)	Dry (Mean)
Dry matter	%	99.8	100.0
Calcium	%	33.00	33.07
Iron	%	.920	.922
Phosphorus	%	18.00	18.04
Potassium	%	.09	.09
Sodium	%	3.95	3.96
Fluorine	mg/kg	1800.00	1803.61

82

RICE. Oryza sativa

Rice, bran w germ, dry-mil, mx 13 fbr CaCO3 declared above 3 mn, (4)
Rice bran (AAFCO)

Ref no 4-03-928

Feed name or analyses		As fed (Mean)	Dry (Mean)
Dry matter	%	91.0	100.0
Ash	%	10.9	12.0
Crude fiber	%	11.0	12.1
Ether extract	%	15.1	16.6
N-free extract	%	40.5	44.5
Protein (N x 6.25)	%	13.5	14.8
Horses	dig prot %	8.7	9.6
Energy			
Horses	DE kcal/kg	2648.	2910.
Horses	ME kcal/kg	2171.	2386.
Horses	TDN %	60.	66.
Calcium	%	.06	.07
Iron	%	.019	.021
Magnesium	%	.95	1.04
Phosphorus	%	1.82	2.00
Potassium	%	1.74	1.91
Copper	mg/kg	13.0	14.3
Manganese	mg/kg	417.8	459.2
Zinc	mg/kg	29.9	32.9
Biotin	mg/kg	4.20	4.60
Choline	mg/kg	1254.	1378.

Continued

83

Feed name or analyses		As fed (Mean)	Dry (Mean)
Niacin	mg/kg	303.2	333.2
Pantothenic acid	mg/kg	23.5	25.8
Riboflavin	mg/kg	2.6	2.9
Thiamine	mg/kg	22.4	24.6
Arginine	%	.50	.55
Cystine	%	.10	.11
Histidine	%	.20	.22
Isoleucine	%	.40	.44
Leucine	%	.60	.66
Lysine	%	.50	.55
Phenylalanine	%	.40	.44
Threonine	%	.40	.44
Tryptophan	%	.10	.11
Valine	%	.60	.66

RYE. Secale cereale

Rye, grain, (4)

Ref no 4-04-047

Feed name or analyses		As fed (Mean)	Dry (Mean)
Dry matter	%	89.0	100.0
Ash	%	1.7	1.9
Crude fiber	%	2.0	2.2
Ether extract	%	1.6	1.8
N-free extract	%	71.8	80.7
Protein (N x 6.25)	%	11.9	13.4
Horses	dig prot %	9.4	10.6

Continued

84

Feed name or analyses		As fed	Dry (Mean)
Energy			
Horses	DE kcal/kg	3336.	3748.
Horses	ME kcal/kg	2735.	3073.
Horses	TDN %	76.	85.
Calcium	%	.06	.07
Iron	%	.008	.009
Magnesium	%	.12	.13
Phosphorus	%	.34	.38
Potassium	%	.46	.52
Sodium	%	.02	.02
Copper	mg/kg	7.8	8.8
Manganese	mg/kg	66.9	75.2
Zinc	mg/kg	30.5	34.3
Biotin	mg/kg	.06	.07
Folic acid	mg/kg	.60	.70
Niacin	mg/kg	1.2	1.3
Pantothenic acid	mg/kg	6.9	7.7
Riboflavin	mg/kg	1.6	1.8
Thiamine	mg/kg	3.9	4.4
a-tocopherol	mg/kg	15.0	17.4
Arginine	%	.53	.60
Cystine	%	.18	.20
Histidine	%	.27	.30
Isoleucine	%	.53	.60
Leucine	%	.71	.80
Lysine	%	.45	.51
Methionine	%	.18	.20

Continued

(1) dry forages and roughages
(2) pasture, range plants, and forages fed green
85

Feed name or analyses		As fed	Dry (Mean)
Phenylalanine	%	.62	.70
Threonine	%	.36	.40
Tryptophan	%	.09	.10
Tyrosine	%	.27	.30
Valine	%	.62	.70

SAFFLOWER. Carthamus tinctorius

Safflower, seed, (4)

Ref no 4-07-958

Feed name or analyses		As fed	Dry (Mean)
Dry matter	%	93.1	100.0
Ash	%	2.9	3.1
Crude fiber	%	26.6	28.6
Ether extract	%	29.8	32.0
N-free extract	%	17.5	18.8
Protein (N x 6.25)	%	16.3	17.5
Horses	dig prot %	13.0	14.0
Energy			
Horses	DE kcal/kg	3653.	3924.
Horses	ME kcal/kg	2996.	3218.
Horses	TDN %	83.	89.

(3) silages
(4) energy feeds
(5) protein supplements
86

Safflower, seed, mech-extd grnd, (5)
Whole pressed safflower seed (AAFCO)
Safflower oil meal, expeller extracted
Safflower oil meal, hydraulic extracted

Ref no 5-04-109

Feed name or analyses		As fed	Dry (Mean)
Dry matter	%	91.0	100.0
Ash	%	3.7	4.1
Crude fiber	%	31.0	34.1
Ether extract	%	6.0	6.6
N-free extract	%	30.5	33.5
Protein (N x 6.25)	%	19.7	21.7
Horses	dig prot %	14.5	15.9
Energy			
Horses	DE kcal/kg	2287.	2513.
Horses	ME kcal/kg	1876.	2061.
Horses	TDN %	52.	57.
Calcium	%	.23	.25
Iron	%	.05	.05
Magnesium	%	.33	.36
Phosphorus	%	.71	.78
Potassium	%	.72	.79
Sodium	%	.05	.05
Copper	mg/kg	9.7	10.7
Manganese	mg/kg	17.8	19.6

Continued

(6) minerals
(7) vitamins
(8) additives
87

TABLE I-1 – COMPOSITION OF SOME COMMON HORSE FEEDS (Continued)

Feed name or analyses		Mean As fed	Dry
Zinc	mg/kg	39.8	43.7
Biotin	mg/kg	1.4	1.5
Folic acid	mg/kg	.44	.48
Niacin	mg/kg	85.8	94.3
Pantothenic acid	mg/kg	4.0	4.4
Riboflavin	mg/kg	18.0	19.8
Arginine	%	1.20	1.32
Cystine	%	.80	.88
Lysine	%	.70	.77
Methionine	%	.40	.44
Tryptophan	%	.30	.33

Safflower, seed, solv-extd grnd, (5)
Solvent extracted whole pressed safflower seed (AAFCO)

Ref no 5-04-110

		As fed	Dry
Dry matter	%	91.8	100.0
Ash	%	4.7	5.1
Crude fiber	%	32.3	35.2
Ether extract	%	3.9	4.2
N-free extract	%	29.6	32.2
Protein (N x 6.25)	%	21.4	23.3
Horses	dig prot %	17.2	18.7
Energy			
Horses	DE kcal/kg	2226.	2425.
Horses	ME kcal/kg	1825.	1988.
Horses	TDN %	50.	55.

Continued

Feed name or analyses		Mean As fed	Dry
Calcium	%	.34	.37
Phosphorus	%	.84	.92

SODIUM PHOSPHATE, MONOBASIC

Sodium, phosphate, monobasic, NaH2PO4·H2O, tech, (6)
Monosodium phosphate (AAFCO)

Ref no 6-04-288

		As fed	Dry
Dry matter	%	96.7	100.0
Ash	%	96.7	100.0
Phosphorus	%	21.80	22.46
Sodium	%	32.3	33.4
	%	120.00	124.10

SODIUM TRIPOLYPHOSPHATE

Sodium, tripolyphosphate, comm, (6)
Sodium tripolyphosphate (AAFCO)

Ref no 6-08-076

		As fed	Dry
Dry matter	%	96.0	100.0
Phosphorus	%	24.94	25.98

Feed name or analyses		Mean As fed	Dry

SORGHUM, GRAIN VARIETY. Sorghum vulgare

Sorghum, grain variety, aerial pt, s-c, (1)
Grain sorghum fodder, sun-cured

Ref no 1-04-372

		As fed	Dry
Dry matter	%	90.3	100.0
Ash	%	8.5	9.4
Crude fiber	%	24.8	27.5
Ether extract	%	1.7	1.9
N-free extract	%	49.0	54.3
Protein (N x 6.25)	%	6.2	6.9
Horses	dig prot %	2.3	2.6
Energy			
Horses	DE kcal/kg	2309.	2557.
Horses	ME kcal/kg	1894.	2097.
Horses	TDN %	52.	58.
Calcium	%	.56	.62
Phosphorus	%	.17	.19

Sorghum, grain variety, aerial pt wo heads, s-c, (1)
Grain sorghum stover, sun-cured

Ref no 1-07-961

		As fed	Dry
Dry matter	%	85.1	100.0
Ash	%	8.2	9.6

Continued

Feed name or analyses		Mean As fed	Dry
Crude fiber	%	27.7	32.6
Ether extract	%	1.8	2.1
N-free extract	%	42.9	50.4
Protein (N x 6.25)	%	4.5	5.3
Horses dig prot	%	1.5	1.8
Energy			
Horses DE kcal/kg		2138.	2513.
Horses ME kcal/kg		1754.	2061.
Horses TDN %		49.	57.
Calcium	%	.34	.40
Phosphorus	%	.09	.11

Continued

Sorghum, grain variety, grain, mn 6 mx 9 prot, (4)

Ref no 4-08-138

Feed name or analyses		Mean As fed	Dry
Dry matter	%	88.0	100.0
Ash	%	2.0	2.3
Crude fiber	%	1.9	2.2
Ether extract	%	2.6	3.0
N-free extract	%	74.4	84.6
Protein (N x 6.25)	%	7.0	7.9
Horses dig prot	%	4.0	4.5

Continued

(1) dry forages and roughages
(2) pasture, range plants, and forages fed green
91

Feed name or analyses		Mean As fed	Dry
Energy			
Horses DE kcal/kg		3142.	3571.
Horses ME kcal/kg		2577.	2928.
Horses TDN %		71.	81.
Alanine	%	.61	.69
Arginine	%	.26	.29
Aspartic acid	%	.48	.54
Cysteine	%	.10	.11
Glutamic acid	%	1.36	1.54
Glycine	%	.26	.29
Histidine	%	.16	.18
Isoleucine	%	.26	.30
Leucine	%	.68	.77
Lysine	%	.18	.20
Methionine	%	.09	.10
Phenylalanine	%	.34	.39
Proline	%	.52	.59
Serine	%	.30	.34
Threonine	%	.23	.26
Tyrosine	%	.14	.16
Valine	%	.35	.40

(3) silages
(4) energy feeds
(5) protein supplements
92

Sorghum, grain variety, grain, mn 9 mx 12 prot, (4)

Ref no 4-08-139

Feed name or analyses		Mean As fed	Dry
Dry matter	%	88.0	100.0
Ash	%	1.9	2.2
Crude fiber	%	2.1	2.4
Ether extract	%	2.6	2.9
N-free extract	%	71.1	80.8
Protein (N x 6.25)	%	10.3	11.7
Horses dig prot	%	5.9	6.7
Lignin	%	1.1	1.3
Energy			
Horses DE kcal/kg		3104.	3527.
Horses ME kcal/kg		2545.	2892.
Horses TDN %		70.	80.
Alanine	%	.97	1.10
Arginine	%	.33	.38
Aspartic acid	%	.70	.79
Cysteine	%	.14	.16
Glutamic acid	%	2.24	2.54
Glycine	%	.32	.37
Histidine	%	.23	.26
Isoleucine	%	.43	.49
Leucine	%	1.41	1.60
Lysine	%	.22	.25

Continued

(6) minerals
(7) vitamins
(8) additives
93

TABLE I-1 — COMPOSITION OF SOME COMMON HORSE FEEDS (Continued)

Feed name or analyses		Mean	
		As fed	Dry
Methionine	%	.13	.15
Phenylalanine	%	.53	.60
Proline	%	.84	.96
Serine	%	.44	.50
Threonine	%	.32	.37
Tyrosine	%	.22	.25
Valine	%	.53	.60

Sorghum, grain variety, grain, mn 12 mx 15 prot, (4)

Ref no 4-08-140

		As fed	Dry
Dry matter	%	88.0	100.0
Ash	%	2.3	2.6
Crude fiber	%	1.8	2.0
Ether extract	%	1.5	1.7
N-free extract	%	71.0	80.7
Protein (N x 6.25)	%	11.4	13.0
Horses	dig prot %	6.5	7.4
Energy			
Horses	DE kcal/kg	3026.	3439.
Horses	ME kcal/kg	2482.	2820.
Horses	TDN %	69.	78.
Alanine	%	1.17	1.33
Arginine	%	.39	.43
Aspartic acid	%	.81	.92
Cysteine	%	.18	.20
Glutamic acid	%	2.59	2.94
Glycine	%	.35	.40
Histidine	%	.26	.29
Continued			

94

Feed name or analyses		Mean	
		As fed	Dry
Isoleucine	%	.49	.56
Leucine	%	1.77	2.01
Lysine	%	.23	.26
Methionine	%	.14	.16
Phenylalanine	%	.62	.70
Proline	%	.97	1.10
Serine	%	.51	.58
Threonine	%	.37	.42
Tyrosine	%	.26	.29
Valine	%	.61	.69

SORGHUM, KAFIR. Sorghum vulgare

Sorghum, kafir, grain, (4)

Ref no 4-04-428

		As fed	Dry
Dry matter	%	90.0	100.0
Ash	%	1.5	1.7
Crude fiber	%	2.0	2.2
Ether extract	%	2.9	3.2
N-free extract	%	71.8	79.8
Protein (N x 6.25)	%	11.8	13.1
Horses	dig prot %	6.8	7.6
Energy			
Horses	DE kcal/kg	2858.	3175.
Horses	ME kcal/kg	2344.	2604.
Horses	TDN %	65.	72.
Calcium	%	.04	.04
Continued			

95

Feed name or analyses		Mean	
		As fed	Dry
Iron	%	.010	.010
Phosphorus	%	.33	.37
Copper	mg/kg	6.3	7.0
Manganese	mg/kg	15.8	17.6
Niacin	mg/kg	36.6	40.7
Pantothenic acid	mg/kg	12.2	13.6
Riboflavin	mg/kg	1.4	1.5
Thiamine	mg/kg	3.8	4.2
Vitamin B6	mg/kg	6.80	7.50
Arginine	%	.36	.40
Histidine	%	.27	.30
Isoleucine	%	.54	.60
Leucine	%	1.62	1.80
Lysine	%	.27	.30
Methionine	%	.18	.20
Phenylalanine	%	.63	.70
Threonine	%	.45	.50
Tryptophan	%	.18	.20
Valine	%	.63	.70

SORGHUM, MILO. Sorghum vulgare

Sorghum, milo, grain, (4)

Ref no 4-04-444

		As fed	Dry
Dry matter	%	89.0	100.0
Ash	%	1.7	1.9
Crude fiber	%	2.0	2.2
Continued			

96

Feed name or analyses		Mean As fed	Dry
Ether extract	%	2.8	3.1
N-free extract	%	71.6	80.4
Protein (N x 6.25)	%	11.0	12.4
Horses	dig prot %	6.3	7.1
Energy	GE kcal/kg	3906.	4389.
Horses	DE kcal/kg	3139.	3527.
Horses	ME kcal/kg	2574.	2892.
Horses	TDN %	71.	80.
Calcium	%	.04	.04
Magnesium	%	.20	.22
Phosphorus	%	.29	.33
Potassium	%	.35	.39
Sodium	%	.01	.01
Cobalt	mg/kg	.100	.100
Copper	mg/kg	14.1	15.8
Manganese	mg/kg	12.9	14.5
Choline	mg/kg	678.	761.
Niacin	mg/kg	42.7	48.0
Pantothenic acid	mg/kg	11.4	12.8
Riboflavin	mg/kg	1.2	1.3
Thiamine	mg/kg	3.9	4.4
Vitamin B_6	mg/kg	4.10	4.60
Arginine	%	.36	.40
Cystine	%	.18	.20
Histidine	%	.27	.30
Isoleucine	%	.53	.60
Leucine	%	1.42	1.60
			Continued

(1) dry forages and roughages
(2) pasture, range plants, and forages fed green
97

Feed name or analyses		Mean As fed	Dry
Lysine	%	.27	.30
Methionine	%	.09	.10
Phenylalanine	%	.45	.51
Threonine	%	.27	.30
Tryptophan	%	.09	.10
Tyrosine	%	.36	.40
Valine	%	.53	.60

SOYBEAN. Glycine max

Soybean, seed, mech-extd grnd, mx 7 fbr, (5)
Soybean meal (AAFCO)
Soybean meal, expeller extracted
Soybean meal, hydraulic extracted
Soybean oil meal, expeller extracted
Soybean oil meal, hydraulic extracted

Ref no 5-04-600

Dry matter	%	90.0	100.0
Ash	%	5.7	6.3
Crude fiber	%	6.0	6.7
Ether extract	%	4.7	5.2
N-free extract	%	29.8	33.1
			Continued

(3) silages
(4) energy feeds
(5) protein supplements
98

Feed name or analyses		Mean As fed	Dry
Protein (N x 6.25)	%	43.8	48.7
Horses	dig prot %	37.3	41.4
Energy	GE kcal/kg	4332.	4813.
Horses	DE kcal/kg	3373.	3748.
Horses	ME kcal/kg	2766.	3073.
Horses	TDN %	76.	85.
Calcium	%	.27	.30
Iron	%	.016	.018
Magnesium	%	.25	.28
Phosphorus	%	.63	.70
Potassium	%	1.71	1.90
Sodium	%	.24	.27
Cobalt	mg/kg	.200	.200
Copper	mg/kg	18.0	20.0
Manganese	mg/kg	32.3	35.9
Biotin	mg/kg	.30	.30
Choline	mg/kg	2673.	2970.
Folic acid	mg/kg	6.60	7.30
Niacin	mg/kg	30.4	33.8
Thiamine	mg/kg	4.0	4.4
Arginine	%	2.60	2.89
Cystine	%	.60	.67
Glycine	%	2.50	2.78
Histidine	%	1.10	1.22
Isoleucine	%	2.80	3.11
Leucine	%	3.60	4.00
Lysine	%	2.70	3.00
			Continued

(6) minerals
(7) vitamins
(8) additives
99

TABLE I-1 – COMPOSITION OF SOME COMMON HORSE FEEDS (Continued)

Feed name or analyses		As fed	Dry
Methionine	%	.80	.89
Phenylalanine	%	2.10	2.33
Threonine	%	1.70	1.89
Tryptophan	%	.60	.67
Tyrosine	%	1.40	1.56
Valine	%	2.20	2.44

Soybean, seed, solv-extd grnd, mx 7 fbr, (5)
Solvent extracted soybean meal (AAFCO)
Soybean meal, solvent extracted
Soybean oil meal, solvent extracted

Ref no 5-04-604

Feed name or analyses		As fed	Dry
Dry matter	%	89.0	100.0
Ash	%	5.8	6.5
Crude fiber	%	6.0	6.7
Ether extract	%	.9	1.0
N-free extract	%	30.5	34.3
Protein (N x 6.25)	%	45.8	51.5
Horses	dig prot %	39.0	43.8
Energy	GE kcal/kg	4198.	4719.
Horses	DE kcal/kg	3178.	3571.
Horses	ME kcal/kg	2606.	2928.
Horses	TDN %	72.	81.
Calcium	%	.32	.36
Iron	%	.012	.013
Magnesium	%	.27	.30
Phosphorus	%	.67	.75
Potassium	%	1.97	2.21

Continued

100

Feed name or analyses		As fed	Dry
Sodium	%	.34	.38
Cobalt	mg/kg	.100	.100
Copper	mg/kg	36.3	40.8
Manganese	mg/kg	27.5	30.9
Choline	mg/kg	2743.	3083.
Folic acid	mg/kg	.70	.80
Niacin	mg/kg	26.8	30.1
Pantothenic acid	mg/kg	14.5	16.3
Riboflavin	mg/kg	3.3	3.7
Thiamine	mg/kg	6.6	7.4
Arginine	%	3.20	3.60
Histidine	%	1.10	1.24
Isoleucine	%	2.50	2.81
Leucine	%	3.40	3.82
Lysine	%	2.90	3.26
Methionine	%	.60	.67
Phenylalanine	%	2.20	2.47
Threonine	%	1.70	1.91
Tryptophan	%	.60	.67
Tyrosine	%	1.40	1.57
Valine	%	2.40	2.70

101

SUGARCANE. Saccharum officinarum

Sugarcane, molasses, dehy, (4)
Cane molasses, dried
Molasses, cane, dried

Ref no 4-04-695

Feed name or analyses		As fed	Dry
		Mean	Mean
Dry matter	%	96.0	100.0
Ash	%	8.0	8.3
Crude fiber	%	5.0	5.2
Ether extract	%	1.0	1.0
N-free extract	%	71.7	74.8
Protein (N x 6.25)	%	10.3	10.7
Horses	dig prot %	7.3	7.6
Energy	GE kcal/kg	3087.	3212.
Horses	DE kcal/kg	3293.	3429.
Horses	ME kcal/kg	2700.	2812.
Horses	TDN %	65.	68.

Sugarcane, molasses, mn 48 invert sugar mn 79.5 degrees brix, (4)
Cane molasses (AAFCO)
Molasses, cane

Ref no 4-04-696

Feed name or analyses		As fed	Dry
Dry matter	%	75.0	100.0
Ash	%	8.1	10.8

Continued

102

Feed name or analyses		As fed	Dry
Ether extract	%	.1	.1
N-free extract	%	63.6	84.8
Protein (N x 6.25)	%	3.2	4.3
Horses	dig prot %	1.8	2.4
Energy	GE kcal/kg	3086.	4114.
Horses	DE kcal/kg	3009.	4012.
Horses	ME kcal/kg	2468.	3290.
Horses	TDN %	68.	91.
Calcium	%	.89	1.19
Iron	%	.019	.025
Magnesium	%	.35	.47
Phosphorus	%	.08	.11
Potassium	%	2.38	3.17
Copper	mg/kg	59.6	79.4
Manganese	mg/kg	42.2	56.3
Choline	mg/kg	876.	1167.
Niacin	mg/kg	34.3	45.7
Pantothenic acid	mg/kg	38.3	51.1
Riboflavin	mg/kg	3.3	4.4
Thiamine	mg/kg	.9	1.2

(1) dry forages and roughages
(2) pasture, range plants, and forages fed green

103

TIMOTHY. Phleum pratense

Timothy, hay, s-c, pre-blm, (1)

Ref no 1-04-881

Feed name or analyses		Mean As fed	Mean Dry
Dry matter	%	88.6	100.0
Ash	%	6.6	7.5
Crude fiber	%	29.1	32.9
Ether extract	%	2.6	3.0
N-free extract	%	39.2	44.3
Protein (N x 6.25)	%	10.9	12.3
Horses	dig prot %	5.8	6.6
Energy	DE kcal/kg	2422.	2734.
Horses	ME kcal/kg	1986.	2242.
Horses	TDN %	55.	62.
Calcium	%	.58	.66
Phosphorus	%	.30	.34

(3) silages
(4) energy feeds
(5) protein supplements

104

Timothy, hay, s-c, early blm, (1)

Ref no 1-04-882

Feed name or analyses		Mean As fed	Mean Dry
Dry matter	%	87.7	100.0
Ash	%	5.4	6.2
Crude fiber	%	29.1	33.2
Ether extract	%	2.3	2.6
N-free extract	%	43.2	49.3
Protein (N x 6.25)	%	7.6	8.7
Horses	dig prot %	4.4	5.0
Energy	GE kcal/kg	3893.	4439.
Horses	DE kcal/kg	2281.	2601.
Horses	ME kcal/kg	1871.	2133.
Horses	TDN %	52.	59.
Calcium	%	.53	.60
Phosphorus	%	.23	.26
Potassium	%	.81	.92

Timothy, hay, s-c, mid-blm, (1)

Ref no 1-04-883

Feed name or analyses		As fed	Dry
Dry matter	%	88.4	100.0
Ash	%	5.1	5.8

Continued

(6) minerals
(7) vitamins
(8) additives

105

TABLE .I-1 – COMPOSITION OF SOME COMMON HORSE FEEDS (Continued)

Feed name or analyses		Mean As fed	Mean Dry
Crude fiber	%	29.6	33.5
Ether extract	%	2.4	2.7
N-free extract	%	43.8	49.5
Protein (N x 6.25)	%	7.5	8.5
Horses dig prot	%	4.1	4.6
Energy GE	kcal/kg	3860.	4366.
Horses DE	kcal/kg	2378.	2690.
Horses ME	kcal/kg	1950.	2206.
Horses TDN	%	54.	61.
Calcium	%	.36	.41
Magnesium	%	.14	.16
Phosphorus	%	.17	.19
Carotene	mg/kg	47.2	53.4
Vitamin A equiv	IU/g	78.7	89.0

Continued

Timothy, hay, s-c, full blm, (1)

Ref no 1-04-884

Feed name or analyses		Mean As fed	Mean Dry
Dry matter	%	86.5	100.0
Ash	%	4.7	5.4
Crude fiber	%	29.3	33.9
Ether extract	%	2.3	2.7
N-free extract	%	43.3	50.1
Protein (N x 6.25)	%	6.8	7.9
Horses dig prot	%	1.4	1.6
Energy			
Horses DE	kcal/kg	1602.	1852.
Horses ME	kcal/kg	1314.	1519.
Horses TDN	%	36.	42.

Feed name or analyses		Mean As fed	Mean Dry
Calcium	%	.30	.35
Chlorine	%	.54	.62
Iron	%	.010	.020
Magnesium	%	.12	.14
Phosphorus	%	.18	.21
Potassium	%	1.45	1.68
Sodium	%	.16	.18
Sulfur	%	.11	.13
Copper	mg/kg	4.2	4.8
Manganese	mg/kg	70.0	80.9

Timothy, hay, s-c, late blm, (1)

Ref no 1-04-885

Feed name or analyses		Mean As fed	Mean Dry
Dry matter	%	88.0	100.0
Ash	%	5.3	6.0
Crude fiber	%	28.5	32.4
Ether extract	%	2.2	2.5
N-free extract	%	44.7	50.8
Protein (N x 6.25)	%	7.3	8.3
Horses dig prot	%	3.6	4.1
Energy			
Horses DE	kcal/kg	2250.	2557.
Horses ME	kcal/kg	1845.	2097.
Horses TDN	%	51.	58.
Calcium	%	.33	.38
Phosphorus	%	.16	.18

TREFOIL, BIRDSFOOT. Lotus corniculatus

Trefoil, birdsfoot, hay, s-c, (1)

Ref no 1-05-044

Feed name or analyses		Mean As fed	Mean Dry
Dry matter	%	91.2	100.0
Ash	%	6.0	6.6
Crude fiber	%	27.0	29.6
Ether extract	%	2.1	2.3
N-free extract	%	41.9	45.9
Protein (N x 6.25)	%	14.2	15.6
Horses dig prot	%	9.8	10.7
Energy			
Horses DE	kcal/kg	2453.	2690.
Horses ME	kcal/kg	2012.	2206.
Horses TDN	%	56.	61.
Calcium	%	1.60	1.75
Phosphorus	%	.20	.22

WHEAT. Triticum spp

Wheat, hay, s-c, (1)

Ref no 1-05-172

Feed name or analyses		Mean As fed	Mean Dry
Dry matter	%	85.9	100.0
Ash	%	5.9	6.9

Continued

Feed name or analyses		Mean	
		As fed	Dry
Crude fiber	%	23.9	27.8
Ether extract	%	1.7	2.0
N-free extract	%	47.9	55.8
Protein (N x 6.25)	%	6.4	7.5
Horses dig prot	%	2.9	3.4
Energy			
Horses	DE kcal/kg	2500.	2910.
Horses	ME kcal/kg	2050.	2386.
Horses	TDN %	57.	66.
Carotene	mg/kg	95.9	111.6
Vitamin A equiv	IU/g	159.9	186.0

Wheat, straw, (1)

Ref no 1-05-175

		As fed	Dry
Dry matter	%	90.1	100.0
Ash	%	7.3	8.1
Crude fiber	%	37.4	41.5
Ether extract	%	1.5	1.7
N-free extract	%	40.6	45.1
Protein (N x 6.25)	%	3.2	3.6
Horses dig prot	%	.4	.4
Cellulose	%	45.1	50.1
Lignin	%	12.3	13.7

Continued

109

Feed name or analyses		Mean	
		As fed	Dry
Energy			
Horses	DE kcal/kg	1906.	2116.
Horses	ME kcal/kg	1563.	1735.
Horses	TDN %	43.	48.
Calcium	%	.15	.17
Chlorine	%	.27	.30
Iron	%	.010	.020
Magnesium	%	.11	.12
Phosphorus	%	.07	.08
Potassium	%	1.00	1.11
Sodium	%	.13	.14
Sulfur	%	.17	.19
Cobalt	mg/kg	.040	.040
Copper	mg/kg	3.0	3.3
Manganese	mg/kg	36.4	40.4
Carotene	mg/kg	2.0	2.2
Vitamin A equiv	IU/g	3.3	3.7

Wheat, bran, dry-mil, (4)
Wheat bran (AAFCO)
Bran (CFA)

Ref no 4-05-190

		As fed	Dry
Dry matter	%	89.0	100.0
Ash	%	6.1	6.9

Continued

110

Feed name or analyses		Mean	
		As fed	Dry
Crude fiber	%	10.0	11.2
Ether extract	%	4.1	4.6
N-free extract	%	52.8	59.3
Protein (N x 6.25)	%	16.0	18.0
Horses dig prot	%	15.4	17.3
Energy			
Horses	GE kcal/kg	4052.	4554.
Horses	DE kcal/kg	3571.	4012.
Horses	ME kcal/kg	2928.	3290.
Horses	TDN %	81.	91.
Calcium	%	.14	.16
Iron	%	.017	.019
Magnesium	%	.55	.62
Phosphorus	%	1.17	1.32
Potassium	%	1.24	1.39
Sodium	%	.06	.07
Cobalt	mg/kg	1.000	1.100
Copper	mg/kg	12.3	13.8
Manganese	mg/kg	115.7	130.0
Choline	mg/kg	988.	1110.
Folic acid	mg/kg	1.80	2.00
Niacin	mg/kg	209.2	235.1
Pantothenic acid	mg/kg	29.0	32.6
Riboflavin	mg/kg	3.1	3.5
Thiamine	mg/kg	7.9	8.9
a-tocopherol	mg/kg	10.8	12.1
Arginine	%	1.00	1.12
Cystine	%	.30	.34

Continued

(1) dry forages and roughages
(2) pasture, range plants, and forages fed green
(3) silages
(4) energy feeds
(5) protein supplements
(6) minerals
(7) vitamins
(8) additives

111

TABLE I-1 – COMPOSITION OF SOME COMMON HORSE FEEDS (Continued)

Feed name or analyses		Mean As fed	Mean Dry
Glycine	%	.90	1.01
Histidine	%	.30	.34
Isoleucine	%	.60	.67
Leucine	%	.90	1.01
Lysine	%	.60	.67
Methionine	%	.10	.11
Phenylalanine	%	.50	.56
Threonine	%	.40	.45
Tryptophan	%	.30	.34
Tyrosine	%	.40	.45
Valine	%	.70	.79

Wheat, flour by-prod, c-sift, mx 7 fbr, (4)
Wheat shorts, mx 7 fbr (AAFCO)
Shorts, mx 8 fbr (CFA)

Ref no 4-05-201

Feed name or analyses		As fed	Dry
Dry matter	%	90.0	100.0
Ash	%	3.9	4.3
Crude fiber	%	5.0	5.6
Ether extract	%	4.2	4.7
N-free extract	%	58.5	65.0
Protein (N x 6.25)	%	18.4	20.4
Horses dig prot	%	13.2	14.7
Energy			
Horses	DE kcal/kg	3413.	3792.
Horses	ME kcal/kg	2798.	3109.
Horses	TDN %	77.	86.
Horses Calcium	%	.11	.12

Continued

112

Feed name or analyses		Mean As fed	Mean Dry
Iron	%	.010	.011
Magnesium	%	.26	.29
Phosphorus	%	.76	.84
Potassium	%	.85	.94
Sodium	%	.07	.08
Cobalt	mg/kg	.100	.100
Copper	mg/kg	9.2	10.3
Manganese	mg/kg	104.5	116.1
Choline	mg/kg	928.	1093.
Niacin	mg/kg	94.6	105.1
Pantothenic acid	mg/kg	17.6	19.6
Riboflavin	mg/kg	2.0	2.2
Thiamine	mg/kg	15.8	17.6
a-tocopherol	mg/kg	29.9	33.2

Wheat, flour by-prod, mx 9.5 fbr, (4)
Wheat middlings (AAFCO)
Wheat standard middlings

Ref no 4-05-205

Feed name or analyses		As fed	Dry
Dry matter	%	90.0	100.0
Ash	%	4.4	4.9
Crude fiber	%	8.0	8.9
Ether extract	%	4.6	5.1
N-free extract	%	55.8	62.0
Protein (N x 6.25)	%	17.2	19.1
Horses dig prot	%	12.2	13.6

Continued

113

Feed name or analyses		Mean As fed	Mean Dry
Energy			
Horses	DE kcal/kg	3294.	3660.
Horses	ME kcal/kg	2701.	3001.
Horses	TDN %	75.	83.
Calcium	%	.15	.16
Iron	%	.010	.010
Magnesium	%	.37	.41
Phosphorus	%	.91	1.01
Potassium	%	.98	1.08
Sodium	%	.22	.24
Cobalt	mg/kg	.100	.100
Copper	mg/kg	22.0	24.4
Manganese	mg/kg	118.4	131.5
Choline	mg/kg	1074.	1193.
Folic acid	mg/kg	.90	1.00
Niacin	mg/kg	98.6	109.5
Pantothenic acid	mg/kg	19.8	22.0
Riboflavin	mg/kg	2.0	2.2
Thiamine	mg/kg	12.8	14.2
Arginine	%	.90	1.00
Cystine	%	.20	.22
Glycine	%	.40	.44
Histidine	%	.40	.44
Isoleucine	%	.80	.88
Leucine	%	1.20	1.33
Lysine	%	.70	.77
Methionine	%	.20	.22
Phenylalanine	%	.70	.77
Threonine	%	.60	.66
Tryptophan	%	.20	.22

Continued

114

Feed name or analyses		Mean	
		As fed	Dry
Tyrosine	%	.40	.44
Valine	%	.80	.88

Wheat, grain, thresher-run, mn 60 wt mx 5 fm, (4)

Ref no 4-08-164 Canada

		As fed	Dry
Dry matter	%	88.0	100.0
Ash	%	1.8	2.0
Crude fiber	%	2.2	2.5
Ether extract	%	1.4	1.6
N-free extract	%	69.1	78.5
Protein (N x 6.25)	%	13.6	15.4
Horses	dig prot %	10.6	12.0
Energy			
Horses	GE kcal/kg	4174.	4743.
Horses	DE kcal/kg	3414.	3880.
Horses	ME kcal/kg	2800.	3182.
Horses	TDN %	77.	88.

Continued

Wheat, grain, Pacific coast, (4)

Ref no 4-08-142

		As fed	Dry
Dry matter	%	89.2	100.0
Ash	%	1.9	2.1

Continued

(1) dry forages and roughages
(2) pasture, range plants, and forages fed green

115

Feed name or analyses		Mean	
		As fed	Dry
Crude fiber	%	2.7	3.0
Ether extract	%	2.0	2.2
N-free extract	%	72.8	81.6
Protein (N x 6.25)	%	9.9	11.1
Horses	dig prot %	7.7	8.6
Energy			
Horses	DE kcal/kg	3461.	3880.
Horses	ME kcal/kg	2838.	3182.
Horses	TDN %	78.	88.
Calcium	%	.12	.14
Phosphorus	%	.30	.34
Niacin	mg/kg	59.1	66.3
Pantothenic acid	mg/kg	11.5	12.9
Riboflavin	mg/kg	1.1	1.2
Thiamine	mg/kg	4.9	5.5

Wheat, grain, (4)

Ref no 4-05-211

		As fed	Dry
Dry matter	%	89.0	100.0
Ash	%	1.6	1.8
Crude fiber	%	3.0	3.4
Ether extract	%	1.7	1.9
N-free extract	%	70.0	78.6

Continued

(3) silages
(4) energy feeds
(5) protein supplements

116

Feed name or analyses		Mean	
		As fed	Dry
Protein (N x 6.25)	%	12.7	14.3
Horses	dig prot %	10.0	11.2
Energy	GE kcal/kg	4001.	4495.
Horses	DE kcal/kg	3453.	3880.
Horses	ME kcal/kg	2832.	3182.
Horses	TDN %	78.	88.
Calcium	%	.05	.06
Iron	%	.005	.006
Magnesium	%	.16	.18
Phosphorus	%	.36	.41
Potassium	%	.52	.58
Sodium	%	.09	.10
Cobalt	mg/kg	.080	.090
Copper	mg/kg	7.2	8.1
Manganese	mg/kg	48.8	54.8
Zinc	mg/kg	13.7	15.4
Biotin	mg/kg	.10	.10
Choline	mg/kg	830.	933.
Folic acid	mg/kg	.40	.40
Niacin	mg/kg	56.6	63.6
Pantothenic acid	mg/kg	12.1	13.6
Riboflavin	mg/kg	1.2	1.3
Thiamine	mg/kg	4.9	5.5
a-tocopherol	mg/kg	15.5	17.4
Arginine	%	.71	.80
Cystine	%	.18	.20
Glycine	%	.89	1.00

Continued

(6) minerals
(7) vitamins
(8) additives

117

TABLE J-1 – COMPOSITION OF SOME COMMON HORSE FEEDS (Continued)

Feed name or analyses		Mean As fed	Dry
Histidine	%	.27	.30
Isoleucine	%	.53	.60
Leucine	%	.89	1.00
Lysine	%	.45	.51
Methionine	%	.18	.20
Phenylalanine	%	.62	.70
Threonine	%	.36	.40
Tryptophan	%	.18	.20
Tyrosine	%	.45	.51
Valine	%	.53	.60

Wheat, germ, grnd, mn 25 prot 7 fat, (5)
Wheat germ meal (AAFCO)
Ref no 5-05-218

Feed name or analyses		Mean As fed	Dry
Dry matter	%	90.0	100.0
Ash	%	4.3	4.8
Crude fiber	%	3.0	3.3
Ether extract	%	10.9	12.1
N-free extract	%	45.6	50.7
Protein (N x 6.25)	%	26.2	29.1
Horses	dig prot %	24.7	27.4
Energy	GE kcal/kg	4206.	4673.
Horses	DE kcal/kg	3770.	4189.
Horses	ME kcal/kg	3092.	3435.
Horses	TDN %	86.	95.
Calcium	%	.07	.08
Iron	%	.011	.012
Phosphorus	%	1.04	1.16
Copper	mg/kg	8.8	9.8
			Continued

118

Feed name or analyses		Mean As fed	Dry
Manganese	mg/kg	134.9	149.9
Choline	mg/kg	3010.	3344.
Folic acid	mg/kg	2.00	2.20
Niacin	mg/kg	47.3	52.6
Pantothenic acid	mg/kg	11.2	12.4
Riboflavin	mg/kg	5.1	5.7
Thiamine	mg/kg	27.9	31.0
α-tocopherol	mg/kg	132.7	147.4
Arginine	%	1.60	1.78
Cystine	%	.50	.56
Histidine	%	.50	.56
Isoleucine	%	1.20	1.33
Leucine	%	1.10	1.22
Lysine	%	1.60	1.78
Methionine	%	.30	.33
Phenylalanine	%	.80	.89
Threonine	%	.80	.89
Tryptophan	%	.30	.33
Valine	%	1.10	1.22

WHEATGRASS, CRESTED. Agropyron cristatum

Wheatgrass, crested, hay, s-c, (1)
Ref no 1-05-418

Feed name or analyses		Mean As fed	Dry
Dry matter	%	92.0	100.0
Ash	%	6.7	7.3
Crude fiber	%	30.0	32.6
			Continued

119

Feed name or analyses		Mean As fed	Dry
Ether extract	%	1.8	2.0
N-free extract	%	43.5	47.3
Protein (N x 6.25)	%	9.9	10.8
Horses	dig prot %	5.8	6.3
Energy			
Horses	DE kcal/kg	2352.	2557.
Horses	ME kcal/kg	1929.	2097.
Horses	TDN %	53.	58.
Calcium	%	.30	.33
Phosphorus	%	.19	.21
Cobalt	mg/kg	.220	.240

Wheatgrass, crested, aerial pt, fresh, immature, (2)
Ref no 2-05-420

Feed name or analyses		Mean As fed	Dry
Dry matter	%	30.8	100.0
Ash	%	3.3	10.6
Crude fiber	%	6.8	22.2
Ether extract	%	1.1	3.6
N-free extract	%	12.3	40.0
Protein (N x 6.25)	%	7.3	23.6
Horses	dig prot %	5.5	18.0
Cellulose	%	10.5	34.1
Lignin	%	1.8	5.9
Energy	GE kcal/kg	1331.	4332.
Horses	DE kcal/kg	1005.	3263.
Horses	ME kcal/kg	824.	2676.
Horses	TDN %	23.	74.
Calcium	%	.14	.46
			Continued

120

Feed name or analyses		Mean	
		As fed	Dry
Tyrosine	%	1.50	1.61
Valine	%	2.30	2.47

YEAST, TORULOPSIS. Torulopsis utilis

Yeast, torulopsis, dehy, mn 40 prot, (7)
Torula dried yeast (AAFCO)

Ref no 7-05-534

Feed name or analyses		Mean	
		As fed	Dry
Dry matter	%	93.0	100.0
Ash	%	7.8	8.4
Crude fiber	%	2.0	2.2
Ether extract	%	2.5	2.7
N-free extract	%	32.4	34.8
Protein (N x 6.25)	%	48.3	51.9
Horses	dig prot %	43.9	47.2
Energy	GE kcal/kg	4433.	4763.
Horses	DE kcal/kg	3280.	3527.
Horses	ME kcal/kg	2690.	2892.
Horses	TDN %	74.	80.
Calcium	%	.57	.61
Iron	%	.010	.010
Magnesium	%	.13	.14
Phosphorus	%	1.68	1.81
			Continued

(6) minerals
(7) vitamins
(8) additives

123

Feed name or analyses		Mean	
		As fed	Dry
Iron	%	.010	.010
Magnesium	%	.23	.25
Phosphorus	%	1.43	1.54
Potassium	%	1.72	1.85
Sodium	%	.07	.08
Cobalt	mg/kg	.200	.200
Copper	mg/kg	33.0	35.5
Manganese	mg/kg	5.7	6.1
Zinc	mg/kg	38.7	41.6
Choline	mg/kg	3885.	4177.
Folic acid	mg/kg	9.70	10.40
Niacin	mg/kg	447.5	481.1
Pantothenic acid	mg/kg	109.8	118.0
Riboflavin	mg/kg	35.0	37.6
Thiamine	mg/kg	91.7	98.6
Vitamin B6	mg/kg	43.30	46.60
Arginine	%	2.20	2.36
Cystine	%	.50	.54
Glycine	%	1.70	1.83
Histidine	%	1.10	1.18
Isoleucine	%	2.10	2.26
Leucine	%	3.20	3.44
Lysine	%	3.00	3.22
Methionine	%	.70	.75
Phenylalanine	%	1.80	1.93
Threonine	%	2.10	2.26
Tryptophan	%	.50	.54
			Continued

(3) silages
(4) energy feeds
(5) protein supplements

122

Feed name or analyses		Mean	
		As fed	Dry
Magnesium	%	.09	.28
Phosphorus	%	.11	.35
Carotene	mg/kg	133.6	433.7
Vitamin A equiv	IU/g	222.7	723.0

YEAST. Saccharomyces cerevisiae

Yeast, brewers saccharomyces, dehy grnd, mn 40 prot, (7)

Brewers dried yeast (AAFCO)

Ref no 7-05-527

Feed name or analyses		Mean	
		As fed	Dry
Dry matter	%	93.0	100.0
Ash	%	6.4	6.9
Crude fiber	%	3.0	3.2
Ether extract	%	1.1	1.2
N-free extract	%	37.9	40.8
Protein (N x 6.25)	%	44.6	47.9
Horses	dig prot %	41.0	44.1
Energy	GE kcal/kg	3958.	4255.
Horses	DE kcal/kg	3198.	3439.
Horses	ME kcal/kg	2623.	2820.
Horses	TDN %	72.	78.
Calcium	%	.13	.14
			Continued

(1) dry forages and roughages
(2) pasture, range plants, and forages fed green

121

TABLE I-1 — COMPOSITION OF SOME COMMON HORSE FEEDS (Continued)

Feed name or analyses		Mean	
		As fed	Dry
Potassium	%	1.88	2.02
Sodium	%	.01	.01
Copper	mg/kg	13.4	14.4
Manganese	mg/kg	12.8	13.7
Zinc	mg/kg	99.2	106.7
Biotin	mg/kg	1.10	1.20
Choline	mg/kg	2911.	3129.
Folic acid	mg/kg	23.30	25.00
Niacin	mg/kg	500.3	537.8
Pantothenic acid	mg/kg	82.9	89.1
Riboflavin	mg/kg	44.4	47.7
Thiamine	mg/kg	6.2	6.7
Vitamin B_6	mg/kg	29.50	31.70
Arginine	%	2.60	2.79
Cystine	%	.60	.65
Glycine	%	2.70	2.90
Histidine	%	1.40	1.51
Isoleucine	%	2.90	3.12
Leucine	%	3.50	3.76
Lysine	%	3.80	4.09
Methionine	%	.80	.86
Phenylalanine	%	3.00	3.23
Threonine	%	2.60	2.80
Tryptophan	%	.50	.54
Tyrosine	%	2.10	2.26
Valine	%	2.90	3.12

Feed name or analyses		Mean		Feed name or analyses		Mean	
		As fed	Dry			As fed	Dry

(1) dry forages and roughages
(2) pasture, range plants, and
forages fed green

(3) silages
(4) energy feeds
(5) protein supplements

(6) minerals
(7) vitamins
(8) additives

1 2 4

1 2 5

1 2 6

II

Animal Units

AN ANIMAL UNIT is a common animal denominator, based on feed consumption. It is assumed that one mature cow or one mature horse represents an animal unit. Compared to the feed consumption of a mature cow or a mature horse, that of other age groups or classes of animals determines the proportion of an animal unit which they represent. For example, it is generally estimated that the ration of one mature cow or one mature horse will feed five "hogs raised to 200 pounds." For this reason, the "animal units/head" in this class and age of animals is 0.2. Table II-1 gives the animal units for different classes and ages of livestock.

Table II-1

ANIMAL UNITS

Type of Livestock	Animal Units per Head
Horses	1
Cows	1
Bulls	1
Young cattle, one to two years old	0.5
Calves	0.25
Colts	0.5
Brood sows or boars	0.4
Hogs raised to 200 pounds	0.2
Ewes or rams	0.14
Lambs	0.07
Chickens (per 100)	1
Chicks raised (per 200)	1

III

Weights and Measures

METRIC AND AVOIRDUPOIS SYSTEMS

FROM TIME TO TIME, stockmen and those who counsel with stockmen have need to refer to such weights and measures as follow on pages 853 through 858.

Length

Unit	Is Equal to	
Metric System		(U.S.)
1 millimicron (mμ)	.000000001 m	.000000039 in.
1 micron (μ)	.000001 m	.000039 in.
1 millimeter (mm)	.001 m	.0394 in.
1 centimeter (cm)	.01 m	.3937 in.
1 decimeter (dm)	.1 m	3.937 in.
1 meter (m)	1 m	39.37 in.; 3.281 ft.; 1.094 yd.
1 hectometer (hm)	100 m	328 ft., 1 in.
1 kilometer (km)	1,000 m	3,280 ft., 10 in.; 0.621 mi.
U.S. System		(Metric)
1 inch (in.)		2.54 cm
1 hand[1]	4 in.	
1 foot (ft.)	12 in.	.305 m
1 yard (yd.)	3 ft.	.914 m
1 fathom (f.)[2]	6.08 ft.	1.829 m
1 rod (rd.), pole, or perch	16½ ft.; 5½ yd.	5.029 m
1 furlong	220 yd.; 40 rd.	201.168 m
1 mile	5,280 ft.; 1,760 yd.; 320 rd.; 8 furlongs	1.609 km
1 knot or nautical mile	6,080 ft.; 1.15 land mi.	
1 league (land)	3 mi. (land)	
1 league (nautical)	3 mi. (nautical)	

[1] Used in measuring height of horses.
[2] Used in measuring depth at sea.

CONVERSIONS

To Change	To	Multiply by
inches	centimeters	2.54
feet	meters	.305
meters	inches	39.37
miles	kilometers	1.609
kilometers	miles	.621

Surface or Area

Unit	Is Equal to	
Metric System		(U. S.)
1 sq. millimeter (mm²)	.000001 m²	.00155 sq. in.
1 sq. centimeter (cm²)	.001 m²	.155 sq. in.
1 sq. decimeter (dm²)	.01 m²	15.50 sq. in.
1 centare (ca)	1 sq. m (m²)	1,550 sq. in.; 10.76 sq. ft.
1 are (a)	100 m²	119.6 sq. yd.
1 hectare (ha)	10,000 m²	2.47 a.
1 sq. kilometer (km²)	1,000,000 m²	.386 sq. mi.
U.S. System		(Metric)
1 sq. inch (sq. in.)	1 in. x 1 in.	
1 sq. foot (sq. ft.)	144 sq. in.	.093 m²
1 sq. yard (sq. yd.)	1,296 sq. in.; 9 sq. ft.	.836 m²
1 sq. rod (sq. rd.)	272.25 sq. ft.; 30.25 sq. yd.	25.29 m²
1 rood	40 sq. rd.	10.117 a.
1 acre (a.)	43,560 sq. ft.; 4,840 sq. yd.; 160 sq. rd.; 4 ros.	4,046.87 m²
1 sq. mile (sq. mi.)	640 a.	2.59 sq. km
1 township	36 sections; 6 mi. sq.	

CONVERSIONS

To Change	To	Multiply by
square inches	square centimeters	6.452
square centimeters	square inches	.155
square yards	square meters	.836
square meters	square yards	1.196

Volume

Unit		Is Equal to		
Liquid and Dry:				
Metric System			(U.S.)	
		(liquid)		(dry)
1 milliliter (ml)	.001 liter	.271 dr. (fl.)		.061 cu. in.
1 centiliter (cl)	.01 liter	.338 oz. (fl.)		.610 cu. in.
1 deciliter (dl)	.1 liter	3.38 ozs. (fl.)		
1 liter (l)	1,000 cc	1.057 qts. (fl.)		.908 qt.
1 hectoliter (hl)	100 liter	26.418 gals.		2.838 bu.
1 kiloliter (kl)	1,000 liter	264.18 gals.		1,308 cu. yd.
U.S. System				
Liquid:		(ounces)	(cu. in.)	(metric)
1 teaspoon (t.)	60 drops	1/6		
1 dessert spoon	2 t.			
1 tablespoon (T.)	3 t.	1/2		
1 gill (gi.)	1/2 c.	4	7.22	118.29 ml
1 cup (c.)	16 t.	8	14.44	236.58 ml
1 pint (pt.)	2 c.	16	28.88	.47 liter
1 quart (qt.)	2 pts.	32	57.75	.95 liter
1 gallon (gal.)	4 qts.	8.34 lbs.	231	3.79 liter
1 barrel	31 1/2 gals.			
1 hogshead	2 bbl.			
Dry:				
1 pint (pt.)	1/2 qt.		33.6	.55 liter
1 quart (qt.)	2 pts.		67.20	1.10 liter
1 peck (pk.)	8 qts.		537.61	8.81 liter
1 bushel (bu.)	4 pks.		2,150.42	35.24 liter
Solid:				
Metric System				
1 cu. millimeter (mm³)	.001 cc			
1 cu. centimeter (cc)	1,000 mm³		.061	
1 cu. decimeter (dm³)	1,000 cc		61.023	
1 cu. meter (m³)	1,000 dm³		1.308 cu. yd.	

(Continued)

Volume (Continued)

Unit	Is Equal to	
U.S. System 1 cu. inch (cu. in.)		16.387 cc
1 board foot (bd. ft.)	144 cu. in.	2,359.8 cc
1 cu. foot (cu. ft.)	1,728 cu. in.	.028 m³
1 cu. yard (cu. yd.)	27 cu. ft.	.765 m³
1 cord	128 cu. ft.	3.625 m³

CONVERSIONS

To Change	To	Multiply by
ounces (fluid)..............	cubic centimeters.........................	29.57
cubic centimeters..........	ounces (fluid)	.034
quarts..........................	liters .....:....................................	.946
liters	quarts...	1.057
cubic inches.................	cubic centimeters.........................	16.387
cubic centimeters..........	cubic inches.................................	.061
cubic yards	cubic meters................................	.765
cubic meters................	cubic yards	1.308

Weight

Unit	Is Equal to	
Metric System		(U.S.)
1 microgram (mcg)	.001 mg	
1 milligram (mg)	.001 g	.015 gr.
1 centigram (cg)	.01 g	.154 gr.
1 decigram (dg)	.1 g	
1 gram (g)	1,000 mg	.035 oz.
1 dekagram (dkg)	10 g	5.643 dr.
1 hectogram (hg)	100 g	3.527 ozs.
1 kilogram (kg)	1,000 g	2.205 lbs.
U.S. System		(metric)
1 grain (gr.)	.037 dr.	64.8 mg; .065 g
1 dram (dr.)	.063 oz.	1.772 g
1 ounce (oz.)	16 dr.	28.35 g
1 pound (lb.)	16 ozs.	453.6 g
1 hundredweight (cwt.)	100 lbs.	
1 ton (tn.)	2,000 lbs.	907.18 kg
1 part per million (ppm.)	1 mcg/g 1 mg/l 1 mg/kg	.454 mg/lb. .907 g/tn. .0001 % .013 oz./gal.
1 per cent (%) (1 part in 100 parts)	10,000 ppm. 10 g/l	1.28 ozs./gal. 8 lbs./100 gals.

CONVERSIONS

To Change	To	Multiply by
grains	milligrams	64.799
ounces (dry)	grams	28.35
pounds (dry)	kilograms	.454
mg/lb.	ppm	2.2
ppm	g/tn.	.908
g/tn.	ppm	1.1
mg/lb.	g/tn.	2
g/tn.	mg/lb.	.5
g/lb.	g/tn.	2,000
g/tn.	g/lb.	.0005
g/tn.	lbs./tn.	.0022
lbs./tn.	g/tn.	453.6
g/tn.	%	.00011
%	g/tn.	9,072

Temperature

One Centigrade (C.) degree is 1/100 the difference between the temperature of melting ice and that of water boiling at standard atmospheric pressure.

One Fahrenheit (F.) degree is 1/180 of the difference between the temperature of melting ice and that of water boiling at standard atmospheric pressure.

To Change	To	Multiply by
Degrees Centigrade	Degrees Fahrenheit	9/5 and add 32
Degrees Fahrenheit	Degrees Centigrade	Subtract 32, then multiply by 5/9

Weights and Measures per Unit

Unit	Is Equal to
Volume per unit area:	
1 l/ha	0.107 gals./a.
1 gal./a.	9.354 l/ha
Weight per unit area:	
1 kg/cm²	14.22 lbs./sq. in.
1 kg/ha	0.892 lb./a.
1 lb./sq. in.	0.0703 kg/cm²
1 lb./a.	1.121 kg/ha
Area per unit weight:	
1 cm²/kg	0.0703 sq. in./lb.
1 sq. in./lb.	14.22 cm²/kg

WEIGHTS AND MEASURES OF COMMON FEEDS

In calculating rations and mixing concentrates, it is usually necessary to use weights rather than measures. However, in practical feeding operations it is often more convenient for the horseman to measure the concentrates. Table III-1 will serve as a guide in feeding by measure.

Table III-1

WEIGHTS AND MEASURES OF COMMON FEEDS

Feed	Approximate Weight	
	(lbs. per quart)	*(lbs. per bushel)*
Alfalfa meal	0.6	19
Barley	1.5	48
Beet pulp (dried)	0.6	19
Brewers grain (dried)	0.6	19
Buckwheat	1.6	50
Buckwheat bran	1.0	29
Corn, cracked	1.6	50
Corn, husked ear	—	70
Corn, shelled	1.8	56
Corn meal	1.6	50
Corn-and-cob meal	1.4	45
Cottonseed meal	1.5	48
Cowpeas	1.9	60
Distillers grain (dried)	0.6	19
Fish meal	1.0	35
Gluten feed	1.3	42
Linseed meal (new process)	0.9	29
Linseed meal (old process)	1.1	35
Meat scrap	1.3	42
Molasses feed	0.8	26
Oat middlings	1.5	48
Oats	1.0	32
Oats, ground	0.7	22
Peanut meal	1.0	32
Rice bran	0.8	26
Rye	1.7	56
Soybeans	1.8	60
Tankage	1.6	51
Velvetbeans, shelled	1.8	60
Wheat	1.9	60
Wheat bran	0.5	16
Wheat middlings, standard	0.8	26
Wheat screenings	1.0	32

IV

Gestation Table

THE HORSEMAN who has information relative to breeding dates can easily estimate parturition dates from Table IV-1.

Table IV-1

GESTATION TABLE — MARE

Date Bred	Date Due, 336 Days	Date Bred	Date Due, 336 Days
Jan. 1	Dec. 3	May 11	April 12
Jan. 6	Dec. 8	May 16	April 17
Jan. 11	Dec. 13	May 21	April 22
Jan. 16	Dec. 18	May 26	April 27
Jan. 21	Dec. 23	May 31	May 2
Jan. 26	Dec. 28	June 5	May 7
Jan. 31	Jan. 2	June 10	May 12
Feb. 5	Jan. 7	June 15	May 17
Feb. 10	Jan. 12	June 20	May 22
Feb. 15	Jan. 17	June 25	May 27
Feb. 20	Jan. 22	June 30	June 1
Feb. 25	Jan. 27	July 5	June 6
Mar. 2	Feb. 1	July 10	June 11
Mar. 7	Feb. 6	July 15	June 16
Mar. 12	Feb. 11	July 20	June 21
Mar. 17	Feb. 16	July 25	June 26
Mar. 22	Feb. 21	July 30	July 1
Mar. 27	Feb. 26	Aug. 4	July 6
April 1	Mar. 3	Aug. 9	July 11
April 6	Mar. 8	Aug. 14	July 16
April 11	Mar. 13	Aug. 19	July 21
April 16	Mar. 18	Aug. 24	July 26
April 21	Mar. 23	Aug. 29	July 31
April 26	Mar. 28	Sept. 3	Aug. 5
May 1	April 2	Sept. 8	Aug. 10
May 6	April 7	Sept. 13	Aug. 15

(Continued)

Table IV-1 (Continued)

Date Bred	Date Due, 336 Days	Date Bred	Date Due, 336 Days
Sept. 18	Aug. 20	Nov. 12	Oct. 14
Sept. 23	Aug. 25	Nov. 17	Oct. 19
Sept. 28	Aug. 30	Nov. 22	Oct. 24
Oct. 3	Sept. 4	Nov. 27	Oct. 29
Oct. 8	Sept. 9	Dec. 2	Nov. 3
Oct. 13	Sept. 14	Dec. 7	Nov. 8
Oct. 18	Sept. 19	Dec. 12	Nov. 13
Oct. 23	Sept. 24	Dec. 17	Nov. 18
Oct. 28	Sept. 29	Dec. 22	Nov. 23
Nov. 2	Oct. 4	Dec. 27	Nov. 28
Nov. 7	Oct. 9		

V

All-Time Top Sales

HORSEMEN AND STUDENTS frequently like to refer to the great sales in history of the many breeds. A summary of some of the record horse sales, both for individual animals and consignments, is presented in Table V-1.

Table V-I
ALL-TIME TOP SALES

Breed	Year of Sale	Identity of Animal	Sex	Price	How Sold	Seller	Purchaser
American Saddle Horse	1947	Beau Fortune	Stallion	$ 50,000	Private Treaty	Teater and Reesler, Skokie, Chicago, Ill.	Crebilly Farm, West Chester, Pa.
	1947	The Invasion	Gelding	23,000	Auction	T. A. Walsh, Jr., Omaha, Neb.	Mrs. Jane Gordon, Malvern, Pa.
	1958	Delightful Society	Mare	30,000	Auction	Louis Greaspoon, St. Louis, Mo.	Donald Decker, Omaha, Neb.
	1960	Stonewall Imperial	Gelding	26,500	Auction	Candy Shaffer Stable	Julianna Schmuts, Louisville, Ky.
	1960	Skyrocket	Stallion	17,000	Auction	Candy Shaffer Stable	F. R. Sullivan, Orange, N.J.
	1962	Legal Tender	Gelding	30,000	Auction	T. N. Wood, Harvey's Lake, Pa.	Crabtree Stables, Simpsonville, Ky.
	1965	Radiation	Mare	40,000	Auction	Tom Moore	Patent Leather Farms, Inc. of Wartrace, Tenn. & Bartow, Fla.
Appaloosa	1960	Hanogie	Mare	6,300	Auction	Carey Appaloosa Ranch, Denver, Colo.	Paul Johnson, Cascade, Colo.
	1961	Top Hat	Stallion	9,000	Auction	Ace Hopper, Plainview, Tex.	W. F. Hicks, Ft. Worth, Tex.
	1961	Tinker Bell Day	Mare	10,000	Private Treaty	Ed Hulseman, Red Bluff, Calif.	W. F. Sandercock, Dixon, Calif.
	1964	Quinta's Flying String	Colt	17,500	Auction	Quinta Dispersal, Napa, Calif.	Myrtle Brown, Arbuckle, Calif.
	1966	Chic Appeal	Stallion	15,500	Auction	Leo Marsters, Payette, Idaho	Dale Rumsey, Phoenix, Ariz.
	1967	Sutter's Show Boy	Stallion	44,000	Auction	Robert Heilmann, Grass Valley, Calif.	Partnership, Fiddlestix Farm, Grass Valley, Calif.
Arabian	1961	Indriffnant	Mare	7,900	Auction	Al-Marah Arabian Horse Farm, Washington 14, D.C.	A. M. Work, Portland, Ore.
Belgian	1917	Farceur	Stallion	47,500	Auction	Wm. Crownover, Hudson, Iowa	C. C. Good, Ogden, Iowa
Clydesdale	1911	Baron of Buchlyvie 11263	Stallion	47,500	Auction	J. Kilpatrick, Craigie Mains, Ayr., Scotland	Wm. Dunlop, Dunure Mains, Ayr., Scotland
Paint Horse	1966	Yellow Mount	Stallion	10,000	Private Treaty	Jack Bruns, Muleshoe, Tex.	Mr. and Mrs. S. H. Williamson, Iowa Park, Tex.
Quarter Horse	1949	Geronimo	Stallion	20,000	Auction	J. R. Bell, Canoga Park, Calif.	A. R. Levis, Henderson, Colo.
	1952	N. R. Paul A P-19	Stallion	30,000	Private Treaty	R. Q. Sutherland, Kansas City, Mo.	Gordon Wheeler, Riverside, Calif.
	1954	Miss Panama	Mare	8,000	Auction	Grace Ranch	Art Pollard

(Continued on next page)

Table V-I (Continued)

Breed	Year of Sale	Identity of Animal	Sex	Price	How Sold	Seller	Purchaser
	1957	Poco Tom	Stallion	10,200	Auction	Volney Hildreth, Fort Worth, Tex.	Waldo Haythorne, Ogallala, Neb.
	1957	Kip Mac	Gelding	5,500	Auction	Volney Hildreth, Fort Worth, Tex.	George Glascock, Cresson, Tex.
	1957	Paulyanna	Mare	10,400	Auction	R. Q. Sutherland, Overland Park, Kan.	J. P. Davidson, Albuquerque, N.M.
	1958	Skipity Scoot	Stallion	12,100	Auction	T. E. Connolly, San Francisco; F. Azevedo, Colsa, Calif.	J. P. Davidson, Albuquerque, N.M.
	1958	Pailalika	Mare	10,200	Auction	Pinehurst Stables, Houston, Tex.	Charles Coates, Chappel Hill, Tex.
	1959	King Clo	Stallion	50,000	Auction	J. O. Hankins, Rocksprings, Tex.	C. E. Boyd, Sweetwater, Tex.
	1960	Go Man Go	Stallion	125,000	Private Treaty	J. B. Ferguson, Wharton, Tex.	F. Vessels, Los Alamitos, Calif. and W. H. Peckham, Richmond, Tex.
	1960	Cee Bars Jr.	Colt	12,000	Auction	John Askow, Fayette, Ark.	Ross Inman, Lamar, Colo.
	1960	Josie's Bar	Mare	37,200	Auction	E. L. Cosselin, Edmond, Okla.	Frank Vessels, Los Alamitos, Calif.
	1961	Vandy II	Stallion	40,000	Auction	Paul Lomax, Skiatook, Okla.	Hadan Livestock Co., Camarillo, Calif.
	1961	Three Deep	Mare	20,000	Auction	Sam Steiger, Prescott, Ariz.	Jay Scott, Littleton, Colo.
	1962	Robin Reed	Stallion	120,000	Private Treaty	Roy D. Barnes, Denver, Colo.	Chapparal Racing Stables, Wildorado, Tex.
	1963	Bar Depth	Stallion	100,000	Private Treaty	Lester Goodson, Houston, Tex.	Truman Johnson, Riverside, Calif.
	1963	Moolah Bar	Mare	45,000	Auction	Mawson Estate, Lompoc, Calif.	Red Bee Ranch, Wichita, Kan.
	1964	Leo Bar	Stallion	60,000	Auction	Lou Kosloff's Flying K Ranch	Don Brokaw, Apple Valley, Calif.
	1964	Scoop Bam	Mare	50,000	Auction	Gill Cattle Co., Tucson, Ariz.	Red Bee Ranch, Wichita, Kansas
	1965	May Moon	Mare	46,000	Auction	Belsby Ranch, Fresno, Calif.	Edd Richards, Dinuba, Calif.
	1966	Rocket Bar	Stallion	400,000	Private Treaty	George Kaufman, Modesto, Calif.	W. H. Peckham, Richmond, & S. F. Henderson, Odessa, Tex.
	1967	Go Josie Go	Mare	66,000	Auction	A. O. Phillips, Plano, Tex.	Burnett Estates, Fort Worth & Clarence Scharbauer Jr., Midland, Tex.
Shetland Pony	1950	Hillswicks Oracle	Stallion	4,300	Auction	Mrs. Volney Diltz, Des Moines, Iowa	W. P. Atkinson, Oklahoma City, Okla.
	1950	Dunrovin Larigo Flame	Mare	1,750	Auction	Gene Lowrey, Nebraska City, Neb.	C. R. Donley, Anadarko, Okla.

(Continued on next page)

Table V-I (Continued)

Breed	Year of Sale	Identity of Animal	Sex	Price	How Sold	Seller	Purchaser
	1953	Little Masterpiece	Stallion	7,500	Auction	V. Diltz, Des Moines, Iowa	Sam Tayloe, Germantown, Tenn.
	1953	C—Jo's Toppy	Mare	6,000	Auction	and P. Carlile, Parny, Okla. Cliff and Jo Teague, Sherman, Tex.	I. B. Greene, Ridgway, Ill.
	1954	Dora's Candy Lue	Mare	10,000	Auction	Vern Brewer, Gainesville, Tex., and R. D. Peterson, Temple-	L. W. Smith, Tulia, Tex.
	1954	Little Masterpiece	Stallion	25,000		ton, Tex.	Don Vestal, Parker, Colo.
	1957	C—Jo's Topper	Stallion	56,000	Auction	C—Jo Pony Farm, Sherman, Tex.	Syndicate of five: Boseman, Loewus, Frey, Casemore, and Blair, from Louisiana
	1957	Dainty Doll	Mare	12,500	Auction	Mrs. E. A. Barnes, Lafayette, Ind.	Clark McKelvee, Euless, Tex.
	1958	Supreme's Bit of Gold	Stallion	85,000	Auction	T. P. Parker, Valley View, Tex.	Happy Valley Pony Farm, Bloom-field, Ia.
	1958	Valley Springs Golden Fleece	Mare	33,000	Auction	Ike Bozeman, Zachary, La.	Paul Loewer, Branch, La.
	1960	Captain Topper	Stallion	56,500	Auction	Vern Brewer, Gainesville, Tex.	Miss Patricia Burton, Dryden, Mich.
Standardbred	1889	Axtell	Stallion	105,000	Private Treaty	C. W. Williams, Independence, Iowa	W. P. Ijame, Terre Haute, Ind., J. W. Conley, Chicago, Ill., and Fred Morgan, Detroit, Mich.
	1890	Director	Stallion	75,000	Private Treaty	Monroe Salisbury, Pleasanton, Calif.	A. H. Moore, Philadelphia, Pa.
	1891	Arion	Stallion	125,000	Private Treaty	Leland Stanford, Palo Alto, Calif.	J. M. Forbes, Milton, Mass.
	1896	Anteeo	Stallion	60,000	Private Treaty	S. A. Brown, Kalamazoo, Mich.	H. S. Henry, Morrisville, Pa.
	1903	Dan Patch	Stallion	60,000	Private Treaty	M. E. Sturgis, New York, N.Y.	M. W. Savage, Minneapolis, Minn.
	1947	Algiers	Stallion	70,000	Auction	E. J. Baker, St. Charles, Ill.	C. F. Gaines, and Mrs. H. W. Nichols, Lexington, Ky.
	1949	Nibble Hanover	Stallion	100,000	Private Treaty	D. W. Bostwick, Shelburne, Vt.	Hanover Shoe Farms, Hanover, Pa.
	1951	Tar Heel	Stallion	125,000	Auction	W. N. Reynolds, Est., Winston Salem, N.C.	Hanover Shoe Farms, Hanover, Pa.

(Continued on next page)

Table V-1 (Continued)

Breed	Year of Sale	Identity of Animal	Sex	Price	How Sold	Seller	Purchaser
	1951	Tar Heel	Stallion	125,000	Private Treaty		Hanover Shoe Farms, Hanover, Pa.
	1955	Adios	Stallion	500,000	Private Treaty		Hanover Shoe Farms, Hanover, Pa.
	1956	Good Time	Stallion	116,000	Private Treaty		Castleton Farm, Lexington, Ky.
	1957	Demon Hanover	Stallion	500,000	Private Treaty	R. Critchfield, Wooster, Ohio	(Syndicate) to be located at Walnut Hall Farm, Conerail, Ky.
	1957	Queen of Diamonds	Mare	30,000	Auction	Wallace McKenzie, Diamond, Ohio	H. Beever, St. Joseph, Mo.
	1958	Adios	Stallion	500,000	Private Treaty	Hanover Shoe Farms, Hanover, Pa.	Syndicate
	1958	Dancer Hanover	Colt	105,000	Private Treaty	Hanover Shoe Farms, Hanover, Pa.	Syndicate headed by S. Danver, New Egypt, N.J.
	1959	Dancer Hanover	Colt	200,000	Private Treaty	Syndicate	Hanover Shoe Farms, Hanover, Pa.
	1960	Adios Butler	Stallion	600,000	Private Treaty	Paige West, Snow Hill, Md.; A. Pellio, Scarsdale, N.Y.	Syndicated owners retained 20 shares
	1960	Mon Mite	Yearling Colt	81,000	Auction	Walnut Hall Farm, Conerail, Ky.	K. D. Owen, R. D. Ricketts, R. Thomas, Houston, Tex.
	1961	Jamin	Stallion	800,000	Private Treaty	Mme. Leon Lory-Roederer, France	Syndicate headed by Stanley Tananbaum, Yonkers Raceway
	1962	Painter	Stallion	130,000	Auction	Hunter Hill Farm, Cambridge City, Ind.	Two Gaits Farm, Castleton Farm, Marson, Indianapolis, Ind.
	1963	Safe Mission	Stallion	52,000	Auction	Almahurst Farm, Lexington, Ky.	Gilberto Melzi, Milan, Italy
	1964	Sprite Rodney	Mare	92,000	Auction	Eaton Ridge Farm, Lexington, Ky.	Hanover Shoe Farm, Hanover, Pa.
	1965	Speedy Streak	Yearling Colt	113,000	Auction	Castleton Farm, Lexington, Ky.	Gainesway Farm, Lexington, Ky.
	1966	Bret Hanover	Stallion	2,000,000	Private Treaty	Richard Downing, Shaker Heights, Ohio	Castleton Farm, Lexington, Ky.
	1966	Brad Hanover	Yearling Colt	100,000	Auction	Hanover Shoe Farm, Hanover, Pa.	Lehigh Stables, New Egypt, N.J.

(Continued on next page)

Table V-I (Continued)

Breed	Year of Sale	Identity of Animal	Sex	Price	How Sold	Seller	Purchaser
Thoroughbred	1912	Rock Sand	Stallion	150,000	Private Treaty	August Belmont II	Syndicate
	1915	Tracery	Stallion	265,000	Private Treaty	August Belmont II	Senor Ungue, Argentina
	1922	Whiskaway	Stallion	125,000	Private Treaty	H. P. Whitney	Charles W. Clarke
	1925	Friar Rock	Stallion	130,000	Private Treaty	J. E. Madden	W. R. Coe
	1927	Hustle On	Colt	70,000	Auction	Himyar Stud	W. R. Coe
	1928	New Broom	Colt	75,000	Auction	Mr. T. J. Regan	Eastland Farm Syndicate
	1943	Pericles	Colt	66,000	Auction	A. B. Hancock	William Helis
	1945	Stardust	Stallion	448,000	Private Treaty	H. R. H. Aga Kahn	Syndicate of English Breeders
		Sayajirao	Colt	117,000	Auction	Sir Eric Ohlson	Maharajah of Baroda
	1946	Bois Roussel	Stallion	320,000	Private Treaty	Peter Beatty	Prince Aly Kahn & Syndicate
	1947	Stepfather	3-yr. Colt	200,000	Auction	Louis B. Mayer	Harry M. Warner
		Honeymoon	Mare in training	135,000	Auction	Louis B. Mayer	Harry M. Warner
		Busher	Mare in training	135,000	Auction	Louis B. Mayer	Harry M. Warner
	1948	The Phoenix	Stallion	640,000	Private Treaty	Frederick Meyer (Ireland)	Syndicate of English Breeders
		Algasir	Gelding in training	106,000	Auction	Est. A. C. Ernst	Mrs. F. Ambrose Clark
		Busher	Mare	150,000	Private Treaty	Louis B. Mayer	Mrs. E. N. Graham
	1949	Nasrullah	Stallion	372,000	Private Treaty	Joseph McGrath	Syndicate
	1951	Say Blue	Mare	72,000	Auction	Coldstream Stud	Henry H. Knight
	1953	Tulyar	Stallion	700,000	Private Treaty	H. R. H. Aga Kahn	Irish National Stud
		Lithe	Mare	85,000	Auction	Hal Price Headley	J. S. Phipps
	1954	Polynesian	Stallion	560,000	Private Treaty	Mrs. P. A. B. Widener, II	Ira Drymon & Syndicate
		Nalur (Nasrullah-Larline B)	Colt	86,000	Private Treaty	Clifford Mooers	F. S. Adams & Syndicate
		Festoon	Mare	105,840	Auction (Newmarket)	Est. Lord Dewar	A. B. Askew
	1955	Nashua	Stallion	1,251,200	Sealed Bid	Est. Wm. Woodward, Jr.	Leslie B. Combs II & Syndicate

(Continued on next page)

Table V-I (Continued)

Breed	Year of Sale	Identity of Animal	Sex	Price	How Sold	Seller	Purchaser
		Tulsan (Nasrullah-In Bloom)	Colt	80,000	Auction	Dr. Zolie Asbury	Forrest H. Lindsay
		No Strings	Mare	60,500	Auction	Henry H. Knight	Mrs. Parker B. Poe
	1956	Swaps (½ int. retained by Ellsworth, then sold in 1957 to Galbreaths)	Stallion	2,000,000	Private Treaty	Rex Ellsworth	Mr. & Mrs. John W. Galbreath
		Rise 'N Shine (Hyperion-Deodora)	Colt	87,000	Auction	Taylor Hardin	Mrs. M. E. Lunan
		Segula	Mare	126,000	Auction	Woolwine Syndicate	Stavros Niarchos
		Sometime Thing (Idun-Royal Charger)	Filly in training	100,000	Auction	A. S. Vanderbilt	Whitney Stone
	1957	Round Table	Stallion	175,000	Private Treaty	A. B. Hancock, Jr.	Travis Kerr
		Law and Order (Nasrullah-In Bloom)	Colt	65,000	Auction	Dr. Eslie Asbury	King Ranch
	1958	Turn-To	Stallion	1,400,000	Private Treaty	Harry F. Cuggenheim	Syndicate
		Gallant Man	Stallion	1,333,333	Private Treaty	Ralph Lowe	Syndicate
		Top Charger (Royal Charger-Popularity)	Colt	65,000	Auction	Spendthrift Farm	Leslie Combs & Mrs. John M. Olin
	1959	Ribot	Stallion	1,350,000	Private Treaty (5-yr. lease)	Razza Dormello-Olgiata	John W. Galbreath
		Royal Dragoon (Royal Charger Grecian Queen)	Colt	80,000	Auction	Leslie Combs II	C. G. Raible
		Globemaster (Heliopolis-No Strings)	Colt	80,000	Auction	James L. Wiley	Penowa Farms
		Highland Fling	Mare	80,000	Auction	Philip Godfrey	Keswick Stable
		(Nashua-Bella Figura)	Filly	59,000	Auction	Leslie Combs II	W. Haggin Perry
	1960	Tom Fool	Stallion	1,750,000	Private Treaty	Greentree Stud	Syndicate
		Bally Ache	Stallion	1,250,000	Private Treaty	Leonard Fruchtmon	Syndicate
		Pashmina (Nashua-Beau Jet)	Colt	75,000	Auction	Leslie Combs II	John M. Olin
		Royal Native	Filly in traning	250,000	Private Treaty	P. L. Grissom	Wm. B. McDonald
		(Royal Charger-Thataway)	Filly	60,000	Auction	Leslie Combs II	Mrs. John M. Olin
	1961	Hasty Road	Stallion	1,330,000	Private Treaty	Hasty House Farm	Syndicate

(Continued on next page)

Table V-I (Continued)

Breed	Year of Sale	Identity of Animal	Sex	Price	How Sold	Seller	Purchaser
		Hail to Reason	Stallion	1,085,000	Private Treaty	H. Jacobs	Syndicate
		Swapson (Swaps-Obedient)	Colt	130,000	Auction	Leslie Combs II	John M. Olin
		Honey's Gem	Mare	137,000	Auction	E. Janss Jr. & Dr. J. K. Robbins	Frank C. Bishop Syndicate
		Firey Angel (Nashua-Beau Jet)	Filly	70,000	Auction	Leslie Combs II	Maine Chance Farm
	1962	Shirley Jones	Mare in training	105,000	Auction	Brae Burn Farm	Mrs. J. O. Burgwin
		Sunset Glow	Mare	60,000	Auction	Est. Ira Drymon	Caper Hill Farm
		Polylady	Filly in training	120,000	Auction	Est. W. Alton Jones	Mrs. John W. Galbreath
		(Swaps-Auld Alliance)	Filly	83,000	Auction	Keswick Stables	Robeby Stable
	1963	(Swaps-Blue Star II)	Colt	85,000	Auction	Stonereath Farm	Penowa Farm
		Flanders Field	Mare	66,000	Auction	Robert Courtney, Agent	Desi Arnaz
		(Nashua-Grecian Queen)	Filly	55,000	Auction	Spendthrift Farm	C. W. Engelhard
	1964	Gun Bow	Stallion	1,000,000	Private Treaty	Gedney Farms	Syndicate
		One Bold Bid (Bold Ruler-Forget Me Not)	Colt	170,000	Auction	Warner L. Jones Jr.	Mrs. Harry W. Morrison
		La Dauphine	Mare	177,000	Auction	Leslie Combs II & John W. Hanes	Charles H. Wacker III
		Treasure Chest	Filly in training	70,000	Auction	Ocala Stud Farm	Dave Shaer
	1965	Tom Rolfe	Stallion	1,600,000	Private Treaty	Raymond Guest	A. B. Hancock Jr. Syndicate
		Package of Prove It, Olden Times, Candy Spots	Stallions	3,750,000	Private Treaty	Rex Ellsworth	Syndicate
		Hail to All	Stallion	1,500,000	Private Treaty	Ben Cohen	Syndicate
		Fleet Nasrullah	Stallion	1,050,000	Private Treaty	E. B. Johnson	Syndicate
		Father's Image	Stallion	1,000,000	Private Treaty	J. M. Olin	Syndicate
		Devil's Tattoo	Colt in training	71,000	Auction	Edith Marienhoff & Judge Louie Bandel	Catherine Tyne Potter
	1966	Graustark	Stallion	2,400,000	Private Treaty	John W. Galbreath	Syndicate
		Kauai King	Stallion	2,160,000	Private Treaty	M. Ford	Syndicate
		Restless Wind	Stallion	1,280,000	Private Treaty	Llangollen Farm	Syndicate
		Royal Gunner	Stallion	1,260,000	Private Treaty	M. Ford	Syndicate
		Creme Dela Creme	Stallion	1,200,000	Private Treaty	Bwamalson Farm	Syndicate
		(Bold Ruler-La Dauphine)	Colt	200,000	Auction	Leslie Combs II	Frank McMahon

(Continued on next page)

Table V-I (Continued)

Breed	Year of Sale	Identity of Animal	Sex	Price	How Sold	Seller	Purchaser
		Berlo	Mare	235,000	Auction	Est. Wm. duPont	John E. duPont
		Admiring	Filly in training	310,000	Auction	Bieber-Jacobs Stable	C. W. Engelhard & Robeby Stable
		(Sailor-Levee)	Filly	177,000	Auction	Morven Stud	C. W. Engelhard
	1967	Buck Passer	Stallion	4,800,000	Private Treaty	Ogden Phipps	Syndicate
		Raise a Native	Stallion	2,625,000	Private Treaty	Harbor View Farm	Syndicate
		(Raise a Native-Gay Hostess)	Colt	250,000	Auction	Leslie Combs II	Frank McMahon
		Quill	Mare	365,000	Auction	John A. Bell, et al.	A. B. Hancock Jr. Agent
		(Bold Ruler-Blue Norther)	Filly	190,000	Auction	Mrs. Wm. R. Hawn	John E. duPont

Table V-2

ALL-TIME TOP CONSIGNMENT SALES

Breed	Year of Sale	Number of Animals	Average Price	Seller
Arabian	1961	36	$ 3,332	Al-Marah Arabian Horse Farm, 7500 River Road, Washington, D.C.
Quarter Horse	1948	34	1,208	Circle JR-Bellwood Ranch, Corona, Calif.
	1951	10	1,477	Grace Ranch, Tucson, Ariz.
	1952	36	1,255	Jinkens Bros., Fort Worth, Tex.
	1954	53	1,635	Three D Stock Farm, Arlington, Tex.
	1955	25	1,358	King Ranch, Kingsville, Tex.
	1956	26	1,598	R. L. Underwood, Wichita Falls, Tex.
	1957	44	3,401	R. Q. Sutherland, Overland Park, Kan.
	1958	29	3,403	Pinehurst Stables, Houston, Tex.
	1959	51	5,806	J. L. Taylor, Chino, Calif.
	1960	66	7,042	E. L. Gosselin (and guests), Edmond, Okla.
	1961	25	4,104	King Ranch, Kingsville, Tex.
Shetland Pony	1953	139	889	Southwestern Shetland Breed, Promotion Sale
	1956	133	1,611	National Breed Promotion Sale
	1957	22	7,935	C. C. Teague Consignment to Perry Carlile Sale, Perry, Okla.
	1958	120	4,935	Lowery Dispersal Sale at Perry Carlile sale, Perry, Okla.
	1960	59	4,345	Vern Brewer Production Sale, Gainesville, Tex.
Standardbred	1952	36 (all ages)	14,850	W. N. Reynolds, Disposal, Harrisburg, Pa.
	1952	15 (yearlings)	6,533	Harrisburg, Pa.
	1956	847	2,376	Harrisburg, Pa.
	1958	867 (yearlings)	2,901	Harrisburg, Pa.
	1959	922	3,498	Standardbred Horse Sales Company
	1960	874	3,851	Harrisburg, Pa.
	1961	794 (all ages)	3,468	Harrisburg, Pa.
		305 (yearlings)	4,888	Tattersalls, Inc., Lexington, Ky.
	1962	722 (all ages)	3,869	Harrisburg, Pa.
		355 (yearlings)	5,439	Tattersalls, Inc., Lexington, Ky.
	1963	707 (all ages)	4,827	Harrisburg, Pa.
		322 (yearlings)	5,988	Tattersalls, Inc., Lexington, Ky.
	1964	947 (all ages)	4,042	Harrisburg, Pa.
		389 (yearlings)	5,851	Tattersalls, Inc., Lexington, Ky.
	1965	602 (all ages)	6,115	Harrisburg, Pa.
		338 (yearlings)	5,545	Tattersalls, Inc., Lexington, Ky.
	1966	854 (all ages)	4,715	Harrisburg, Pa.
		336 (yearlings)	7,546	Tattersalls, Inc., Lexington, Ky.
Thoroughbred	1946	415 (yearlings)	9,912	Keeneland Summer Sales
	1947	60 (race horses)	25,830	Louis B. Mayer (Dispersal)
		436 (yearlings)	6,827	Keeneland Summer Sales
	1949	9 (broodmares)	44,222	Est. Crispin Oglebay
	1950	42 (2-yr.-olds)	14,410	Louis B. Mayer
	1951	48 (broodmares)	20,635	Coldstream Stud
	1952	47 (yearlings)	14,526	Almahurst Farm (Henry H. Knight)
	1953	302 (yearlings)	9,746	Keeneland Summer Sales
	1954	344 (yearlings)	9,940	Keeneland Summer Sales
		20 (broodmares)	26,955	Keeneland Summer Sales
	1955	68 (broodmares)	15,232	Henry H. Knight
		346 (yearlings)	11,174	Keeneland Summer Sales
		55 (weanlings)	6,609	Henry H. Knight
	1956	219 (yearlings)	10,133	Saratoga Yearling Sales
	1957	235 (yearlings)	11,789	Keeneland Summer Sales
	1958	357 (yearlings)	9,615	Keeneland Summer Sales
	1959	303 (yearlings)	11,664	Keeneland Summer Sales
	1960	303 (yearlings)	11,844	Keeneland Summer Sales
	1961	298 (yearlings)	14,177	Keeneland Summer Sales
	1962	273 (yearlings)	12,993	Keeneland Summer Sales
	1963	275 (yearlings)	14,191	Keeneland Summer Sales
	1964	212 (yearlings)	17,763	Saratoga Yearling Sales
	1965	25 (broodmares)	40,615	J. W. Hanes & Leslie Combs II
		282 (yearlings)	17,973	Keeneland Summer Sales
	1966	257 (yearlings)	19,535	Saratoga Yearling Sales
		72 (mixed)	39,842	Foxcatcher Gaines
	1967	255 (yearlings)	22,145	Saratoga Yearling Sales

United States and World Records
for Thoroughbreds

THE U. S. AND WORLD RECORDS for Thoroughbreds at some of the popular American distances are given in Table VI-1.

Table VI-1

UNITED STATES AND WORLD RECORDS FOR THOROUGHBREDS

Distance	Name of Horse	Age of Horse (yrs.)	Weight Carried (lbs.)	Track	Date Record Established	Time	United States and/or World Record
1/4 mile	BOB WADE	4	122	Butte, Montana	1890	:21 1/4	U.S.
	BIG RACKET	4	111	Hippedrome de Las Americas, Mexico City	1945	:20 4/5	World
3/8 mile	KING RHYMER	4	118	Santa Anita, Arcadia, Calif.	1947	:32	U.S. & W.
1/2 mile	BEAU MADISON	2	120	Turf Paradise, Phoenix, Ariz.	1957	:45	World
4 1/2 furlongs¹	THE PIMPERNAL	2	118	Belmont Park, N.Y.	1951	:49 4/5	World
5/8 mile	NANCYCEE	4	113	Turf Paradise, Phoenix, Ariz.	1966	:56 1/5	U.S. & W.
5 1/2 furlongs (straight course)	DELEGATE	7	113	Belmont Park, N.Y.	1951	1:01 3/5	World
5 1/2 furlongs (around 1 turn)	NASHARCO	4	120	Turf Paradise, Phoenix, Ariz.	1966	1:02 1/5	U.S. & W.
3/4 mile (6 furlongs)	ZIP POCKET	2	120	Turf Paradise, Phoenix, Ariz.	1966	1:07 2/5	U.S. & W.
6 1/2 furlongs (straight course)	NATIVE DANCER	2	122	Belmont Park, N.Y.	1952	1:14 2/5	U.S. & W.
6 1/2 furlongs (around 1 turn)	SANDY FLEET	4	122	Longacres, Seattle, Wash.	1966	1:14 2/5	U.S. & W.
7/8 mile	EL DRAG	4	115	Hollywood, Calif.	1955	1:20	U.S. & W.
1 mile	DR. FAGER	4	134	Arlington Park, Chicago	1968	1:32 1/5	U.S. & W.
1 mile-70 yds.	DRILL SITE	5	115	Garden State Park, Cherry Hill, N.J.	1964	1:38 4/5	U.S. & W.
1 1/16 miles	SWAPS	4	130	Hollywood Park, Inglewood, Calif.	1956	1:39	U.S. & W.
1 1/8 miles	BUG BRUSH	4	113	Santa Anita, Calif.	1959	1:46 2/5	U.S. & W.
1 3/16 miles	FLEET BIRD	4	123	Golden Gate, Calif.	1953	1:52 3/5	U.S. & W.
1 1/4 miles	NOOR	5	127	Golden Gate, Calif.	1950	1:58 1/5	U.S. & W.
1 3/8 miles	MAN O'WAR	3	126	Belmont Park, New York	1920	2:14 1/5	U.S. & W.
1 1/2 miles	GALLANT MAN	3	126	Belmont Park, New York	1957	2:26 3/5	U.S. & W.
1 5/8 miles	SWAPS	4	130	Hollywood Park, Calif.	1956	2:38 1/5	U.S.
2 miles	POLAZEL	3		Salisbury, England	1924	3:15	World
2 1/2 miles	MISS CRILLO	6	118	Pimlico, Baltimore, Md.	1948	4:14 1/5	U.S. & W.

¹A furlong is a measure of length equal to an eighth of a mile (or 40 rods, 220 yards, or 201.17 meters).

VII

Leading Money-Winning Thoroughbreds and Standardbreds

THE LEADING MONEY-WINNING THOROUGHBREDS in the U. S. are listed, by rank, in Table VII-1. Similar information for Standardbreds is given in Table VII-2.

Table VII-1

LEADING MONEY-WINNING THOROUGHBREDS

Horse	Total Money Won	Racing Years	Owner
Kelso........................	$1,977,896	1961-66	Mrs. Richard C. duPont
Round Table	1,749,869	1956-59	Travis Kerr
Buckpasser................	1,462,014	1965-67	Ogden Phipps
Nashua......................	1,288,565	1954-56	Belair Stud and Leslie Combs II
Carry Back................	1,241,165	1960-63	J. A. Price
Citation....................	1,085,760	1947-51	Calumet Farm
Native Diver	1,026,500	1961-67	L. K. Shapiro
Swoon's Son	970,605	1955-58	E. G. Drake
Roman Brother..........	943,743	1962-65	Harbor View Farm
Stymie......................	918,485	1943-49	Mrs. Ethel D. Jacobs
T. V. Lark	902,194	1959-62	T. V. Lark Syndicate
Swaps	848,900	1954-56	Rex C. Ellsworth

Table VII-2

LEADING MONEY-WINNING STANDARDBREDS[1]

Horse	Total Money Won	Years Raced
Trotters		
Su Mac Lad	$885,095	1956-65
Speedy Scot	650,909	1962-65
Duke Rodney	639,408	1960-66
Noble Victory...	522,391	1964-66
Armbro Flight	493,602	1964-66
Darn Safe	475,738	1953-63
Dartmouth..	429,397	1963-65
Elaine Rodney...	386,808	1959-65
Tornese	384,104	1955-61
Trader Horn..	370,802	1956-60
Pacers		
Bret Hanover	922,616	1964-66
Cardigan Bay	739,456	1959-66
Henry T. Adios..	706,698	1960-64
Bye Bye Byrd	554,257	1957-61
Irvin Paul..	545,545	1959-66
Adios Butler..	509,844	1958-61
Race Time	486,955	1963-65
Romeo Hanover..	473,931	1965-66
Meadow Skipper...	428,057	1962-65
Overtrick	407,483	1962-64

[1]Data for all Standardbred records in this Appendix provided by Mrs. R. L. Evans, Department Racing Information, The United States Trotting Assn., 750 Michigan Ave., Columbus, Ohio.

VIII

Breed Registry Associations

A BREED REGISTRY ASSOCIATION consists of a group of breeders banded together for the purposes of: (1) recording the lineage of their animals, (2) protecting the purity of the breed, (3) encouraging further improvement of the breed, and (4) promoting interest in the breed. A list of the horse breed registry association is given in Table VIII-1.

Table VIII-1

HORSE BREED REGISTRY ASSOCIATIONS

Class of Animal	Breed	Association	Secretary and Address
Light Horses:	American Albino Horse	American Albino Horse Club, Inc.	Miss Ruth E. White, Box 79, Crabtree, Ore. 97335
	Andalusian	American Andalusian Assn.	Glenn O. Smith, Box 1290, Silver City, N.M. 88061
	American Saddle Horse	American Saddle Horse Breeders' Association	Chas. J. Cronan, Jr., 929 Fourth St., Louisville, Ky. 40203
	Appaloosa	Appaloosa Horse Club, Inc.	George B. Hatley, Box 403, Moscow, Idaho, 83843
	Arabian	Arabian Horse Club Registry of America	Ward B. Howland, One Executive Park, 7801 Belleview Ave., Englewood, Colo. 80110
	Buckskin	American Buckskin Registry Association	Bonnie Trent, Box 772, Anderson, Calif. 96007
	Chickasaw	The Chickasaw Horse Assn., Inc.	Love Valley, N.C. 28677
	Cleveland Bay	Cleveland Bay Association of America	A. Mackay-Smith, White Post, Va. 22663
	Galiceno	Galiceno Horse Breeders' Assn., Inc., The	D. L. Adkens, 708 Peoples Bank Bldg., Tyler, Texas 75701
	Hackney	American Hackney Horse Society	Paul E. Bolton, Jr., 527 Madison Ave., Room 725, New York, N.Y. 10022
	Hungarian Horse	Hungarian Horse Association	Mrs. Margit Sigray Bessenyey, Bitterroot Stock Farm, Hamilton, Mont. 59840

(Continued next page)

Table VIII-1 (Continued)

Class of Animal	Breed	Association	Secretary and Address
	Missouri Foxtrot Horse	Missouri Foxtrot Horse Breed Association	Homer Harley, P.O. Box 637, Ava, Mo. 65608
	Morgan	Morgan Horse Club, Inc.	Seth P. Holcombe, Box 2157, West Hartford, Conn. 06117
	Paint Horse	American Paint Horse Association	Ralph Dye, Box 12487, Fort Worth, Texas 76116
	Palomino	Palomino Horse Association	Mrs. Edna Fagan, Office Mgr., Box 446, Chatsworth, Calif. 91311
		Palomino Horse Breeders of America	Melba Lee Spivey, Box 249, Mineral Wells, Texas 76067
	Paso Fino	American Paso Fino Pleasure Horse Assn., Inc.	Mrs. Rosalie MacWilliam, Arrott Bldg., 401 Wood St., Pittsburgh, Pa. 15222
	Pinto	The Pinto Horse Association of America, Inc.	Mrs. Helen H. Smith, Box 3984, San Diego, Calif. 92103
	Peruvian Paso Horses	American Assn. of Owners & Breeders of Peruvian Paso Horses	Dr. Marguerite Rogers, P.O. Box 371, Calabasas, Calif. 91302
	Quarter Horse	American Quarter Horse Association	Don Jones, Box 200, Amarillo Tex. 79105
	Spanish Mustang	Spanish Mustang Registry, Inc.	Bob Racicot, Box 398, Thompson Falls, Mont. 59873
	Standardbred	United States Trotting Association (Standardbred).	Edward Hackett, Chief Exec. Officer, 750 Michigan Ave., Columbus, Ohio 43215

(Continued next page)

Table VIII-1 (Continued)

Class of Animal	Breed	Association	Secretary and Address
	Tennessee Walking Horse	Tennessee Walking Horse Breeders' and Exhibitors' Association of America	Mrs. Sharon Brandon, Box 286, Lewisburg, Tenn. 37091
	Thoroughbred	The Jockey Club	John F. Kennedy, 300 Park Ave., New York, N.Y. 10022
	Ysabella	Ysabella Saddle Horse Assn., Inc.	L. D. McKinzie, McKinzie Rancho, Route 2, Williamsport, Ind. 47993
Ponies:	Connemara Pony	American Connemara Pony Society	Al Mavis, Pres., Route 2, Rochester, Ill. 62563
	Gotland Horse	American Gotland Horse Association	Mrs. John C. Murdock, 110 East Parkway Columbia, Mo. 65201
	National Appaloosa Pony	National Appaloosa Pony Assn.	112 E. Eighth St., Box 297, Rochester, Ind. 46975
	Pony of the Americas	Pony of the Americas Club, Inc.	L. L. Boomhower, Box 1447, Mason City, Iowa 50401
	Shetland	American Shetland Pony Club	Burton Zuege, Box 2339, West Lafayette, Ind. 47902
	Welsh	Welsh Pony Society of America	Mrs. Sidney S. Swett, 1770 Lancaster Ave., Paoli, Pa. 19301
Draft Horses; Jacks and Jennets:	American Cream Horse	American Cream Horse Association	Mrs. K. B. Topp, Hubbard, Ia. 50122
	Belgian	Belgian Draft Horse Corporation of America	Miss B. A. Schmalzried, 282 S. Wabash St., Wabash, Ind. 46992
	Clydesdale	Clydesdale Breeders' Association of the United States	Chas. W. Willhoit, Pres., Batavia, Ia. 52533

(Continued).

Table VIII-1 (Continued)

Class of Animal	Breed	Association	Secretary and Address
	Percheron	Percheron Horse Association of America	Dale W. Gossett, Route 1, Belmont, Ohio 43718
	Shire	American Shire Horse Association	Ed Henken, Box 88, Lynden, Wash. 98264
	Suffolk	American Suffolk Horse Association, Inc.	Ed Henken, Box 88, Lynden, Wash. 98264
	Jacks and Jennets	Standard Jack and Jennet Registry of America	Mrs. F. C. Johns, Route 7—Todds Road, Lexington, Ky. 40502
Donkeys:	Miniature Donkeys	Miniature Donkey Registry of the United States, Inc.	Daniel Langfeld, President, 1108 Jackson St., Omaha, Neb. 68102
All Horses and Half-Breeds:	Any and all colors and types of horses (including animals not eligible for registry, eligible but not registered, or registered in existing associations) including both light and draft horses.	National Recording Office	Ruth E. White, Box 79, Crabtree, Oregon 97335
	Half-bred Thoroughbreds: Foals by registered Thoroughbred stallions and out of mares not registered in The American (Jockey Club) Stud Book, or in The Arabian Stud Book.	American Remount Assn. (The Half-Thoroughbred Registry)[1]	George Havens, Box 1171, Colorado Springs, Colo. 80901
	Half-bred Arabian: 1. In the Half-Arabian Stud Book:	International Arabian Horse Association	Ralph E. Goodall, Jr., Room 306, 224 E. Olive Ave., Burbank, Calif. 91503

(Continued)

Table VIII-1 (Continued)

Class of Animal	Breed	Association	Secretary and Address
	Foals by registered Arabian stallions and out of mares that are not registered in either The American (Jockey Club) Stud Book or The Arabian Stud Book. 2. In The Anglo-Arab Stud Book: (a) Foals by registered[2] Thoroughbred Stallions and out of registered Arabian mares. (b) Foals by registered Arabian stallions and out of registered Thoroughbred mares. (c) Foals by registered Thoroughbred[2] or Arabian stallions and out of registered Anglo-Arab mares. (d) Foals by registered Anglo-Arab stallions out of registered Thoroughbred, Arabian, or Anglo-Arab mares.		
	Half-bred, grade, and cross-bred horses involving—Morgans, American Saddle Horses, Standardbreds, Hackneys, Tennessee Walking Horses, Quarter Horses.	American Part-Blooded, Horse Registry	J. C. Abbett, Registrar, 4120 S.E. River Drive, Portland, Ore. 97222

[1]Formerly the Half-Bred Stud Book operated by The American Remount Association, but now a privately owned registry. It records only foals sired by registered Thoroughbred stallions and out of mares not registered in The American (Jockey Club) Stud Book, or in The Arabian Stud Book.
[2]Thoroughbred stallions registered in either The American (Jockey Club) Stud Book, the General Stud Book (English) or the French Stud Book are accepted.

IX

Breed Magazines

THE HORSE BREED MAGAZINES publish news items and informative articles of special interest to horsemen. Also, many of them employ field representatives whose chief duty is to assist in the buying and selling of animals.

In the compilation of the list herewith presented (see Table IX-1), no attempt was made to list the general livestock magazines of which there are numerous outstanding ones. Only those magazines which are chiefly devoted to horses are included.

Table IX-1

BREED MAGAZINES

Breed	Publication	Address
General	Chronicle of the Horse, The	Middleburg, Va. 22117
	Hoofs and Horns	1750 Humboldt St., Suite 21, Denver, Colo. 80218
	Horse and Rider	116 E. Badillo, Covina, Ca. 91722
	Horse Lover, The	Box 914, El Cerrito, Ca. 94530
	Horseman	5314 Bingle Rd., Houston, Tex. 77018
	Horseman's Courier, The	57 So. Main St., Fairport, N.Y. 14450
	Horsemen's Advisor, The	624 Payton Ave., Des Moines, Iowa 50315
	Horsemen's Journal	425-13th St. N.W., Washington, D.C. 20004
	Horsemen's Yankee Pedlar	Box 297, N. Wilbraham, Mass. 01067
	Horse Show	527 Madison Ave. New York, N.Y. 10022
	Horse World	Box 588, Lexington, Ky. 40501
	Lariat, The	14239 N.E. Salmon Creek Ave., Vancouver, Wash. 98665
	Maryland Horse, The	Box 4, Timonium, Md. 21093
	National Horseman	933 Baxter Ave., Louisville, Ky. 40204
	Northeast Horseman	Box 47, Hampden Highlands, Maine 04445
	Saddle and Bridle	8011 Clayton Rd., St. Louis, Mo. 63117
	Southern Horseman, The	Box 5735, Meridian, Miss. 39301
	Trail Rider, The	Chatsworth, Ga. 30705
	Turf and Sport Digest	511-513 Oakland Ave., Baltimore, Md. 21212
	Western Horseman	3850 N. Nevada Ave., Colorado Springs, Colo. 80901
	Your Pony	1040 W. James St., Columbus, Wisc. 53925
Appaloosa	Appaloosa News	Box 403, Moscow, Ida. 83843
Arabian	Arabian Horse News	Box 1009, Boulder, Colo. 80302
	Arabian Horse World	23 E. Main St., Springville, N.Y. 14141
Hackney	Hackney Journal, The	Box 29, Columbus, Wisc. 53925
Morgan	Morgan Horse Magazine	Box 149, Leominster, Mass. 01453
Paint	Paint Horse Newsletter, The	Box 12487, Fort Worth, Tex. 76116

(Continued)

Table IX-1 (Continued)

Breed	Publication	Address
Palomino	Palomino Horses	Box 249, Mineral Wells, Tex. 76067
Pinto	Pinto Horse, The	4315 Hilldale Rd., San Diego, Calif. 92116
Pony of Americas	Pony of Americas Club Official Magazine	Box 1447, Mason City, Iowa 50401
Quarter Horse	Quarter Horse Digest Quarter Horse Journal	Gann Valley, S.D. 57341 Box 9105, Amarillo, Tex. 79105
Shetland Pony	American Shetland Pony Journal	Box 2339, W. Lafayette, Ind. 47906
Spanish Mustang	Spanish Mustang News	1037 E. Lehi Rd., Mesa, Ariz. 85201
Standardbred	Harness Horse, The Hoof Beats (U. S. Trotting) Standardbred Horse Review	Telegraph Press Bldg., Harrisburg, Pa. 17101 750 Michigan Ave., Columbus, Ohio 43215 21-300 Kennedy, Desert Hot Springs, Calif. 92240
Tennessee Walk- ing Horse	Voice of the Tennessee Walking Horse	Box 6009, Chattanooga, Tenn. 37401
Thoroughbred	Blood Horse, The Florida Horse, The Thoroughbred of California, The Thoroughbred Record, The Washington Horse, The	Box 4038, Lexington, Ky. 40504 Box 699, Ocala, Fla. 32670 201 Colorado Place, Arcadia, Calif. 91006 Box 580, Lexington, Ky. 40501 13470 Empire Way, Seattle, Wash. 98178
Welsh Pony	Welsh News	1427 Hampshire St., Quincy, Ill. 62301

X

State Colleges of Agriculture

THE HORSEMAN can obtain a list of available bulletins and circulars, and other information regarding livestock, by writing to his State Agricultural College. A list of the State Agricultural Colleges (Land Grant institutions have an *) follows:

State	Address
Alabama	*Auburn University, Auburn.
	Tuskegee Institute, Tuskegee.
Alaska	*University of Alaska, Palmer.
Arizona	*University of Arizona, Tucson.
	Arizona State University, Tempe.
Arkansas	*University of Arkansas, Fayetteville.
	Arkansas State University, State College.
California	*University of California, Davis.
	California State Polytechnic College, San Luis Obispo.
	California State Polytechnic College, Kellogg-Voorhis, Pomona.
	Chico State College, Chico.
	Fresno State College, Fresno.
Colorado	*Colorado State University, Fort Collins.
Connecticut	*University of Connecticut, Storrs.
Delaware	*University of Delaware, Newark.
Florida	*University of Florida, Gainesville
	Florida A & M University, Tallahassee.
Georgia	*University of Georgia, Athens.

State	Address
Hawaii	*University of Hawaii, Honolulu.
Idaho	*University of Idaho, Moscow.
Illinois	*University of Illinois, Urbana.
	Southern Illinois University, Carbondale.
	Illinois Normal University, Normal.
	Western Illinois University, Macomb.
Indiana	*Purdue University, Lafayette.
Iowa	*Iowa State University, Ames.
Kansas	*Kansas State University, Manhattan.
Kentucky	*University of Kentucky, Lexington.
	Berea College, Berea.
	Murray State University, Murray.
	Western Kentucky University, Bowling Green
Louisiana	*Louisiana State University, University Station, Baton Rouge.
	Francis T. Nicholls State College, Thibodaux.
	Grambling College, Grambling.
	McNeese State College, Lake Charles.
	Northeast Louisiana State College, Monroe.
	Northwestern State College of Louisiana, Natchitoches.
	Southeastern Louisiana College, Hammond.
	Southern University and A & M College, Baton Rouge.
	University of Southwestern Louisiana, The, Lafayette.
Maine	*University of Maine, Orono.
Maryland	*University of Maryland, College Park.
Massachusetts	*University of Massachusetts, Amherst.
Michigan	*Michigan State University, East Lansing.
	Michigan Emmanual Missionary College, Berrien Springs.
Minnesota	*University of Minnesota, St. Paul.
Mississippi	*Mississippi State University, State College.
Missouri	*University of Missouri, Columbia.
Montana	*Montana State University, Bozeman.
Nebraska	*University of Nebraska, Lincoln.
Nevada	*University of Nevada, Reno.

State	Address
New Hampshire	*University of New Hampshire, Durham.
New Jersey	*Rutgers, The State University, New Brunswick.
New Mexico	*New Mexico State University, University Park.
New York	*Cornell University, Ithaca.
North Carolina	*North Carolina State University, Raleigh.
	Agricultural and Technical College of North Carolina, Greensboro.
	Pembroke State College, Pembroke.
North Dakota	*North Dakota State University, Fargo.
Ohio	*Ohio State University, Columbus.
Oklahoma	*Oklahoma State University, Stillwater.
	Panhandle A & M College, Goodwell.
Oregon	*Oregon State University, Corvallis.
Pennsylvania	*Pennsylvania State University, Stillwater.
	Delaware Valley College of Science and Agriculture, Doylestown.
Puerto Rico	*University of Puerto Rico, Rio Piedras.
Rhode Island	*University of Rhode Island, Kingston.
South Carolina	*Clemson University, Clemson.
South Dakota	*South Dakota State University, University Station, Brookings.
Tennessee	*University of Tennessee, Knoxville.
	Middle Tennessee State University, Murfreesboro.
	Tennessee A & I State University, Nashville.
	Tennessee Technological University, Cookeville.
Texas	*Texas A & M University, College Station.
	Abilene Christian College, Abilene.
	Prairie View A & M College, Prairie View.
	Sul Ross State College, Alpine.
	Texas A & I University, Kingsville.
	Texas Technological College, Lubbock.
Utah	*Utah State University, Logan.
	Brigham Young University, Provo.
Vermont	*University of Vermont, Burlington.
Virginia	*Virginia Polytechnic Institute, Blacksburg.
	Virginia State College, Petersburg.
Washington	*Washington State University, Pullman.
West Virginia	*West Virginia University, Morgantown.

State	Address
Wisconsin	*University of Wisconsin, Madison.
	Wisconsin State University, River Falls.
Wyoming	*University of Wyoming, Laramie.

IN CANADA

Province	Address
Alberta	University of Alberta, Edmonton.
British Columbia	University of British Columbia, Vancouver.
Manitoba	University of Manitoba, Winnipeg.
New Brunswick	University of New Brunswick, Fredericton.
Nova Scotia	University of Nova Scotia, Truro.
Ontario	University of Guelph, Guelph.
Quebec	Faculty d'Agriculture, University of Laval, Quebec City.
	Macdonald College, St. Anne de Bellevue.
Saskatchewan	University of Saskatchewan, Saskatoon.

XI

Practices and Problems
of Horsemen

IN 1961, the author surveyed,[1] from coast to coast, selected breeders of each of the three breeds that are used for racing; namely, (1) Thoroughbreds, (2) Standardbreds, and (3) Quarter Horses. A total of 74 Thoroughbred questionnaires, 16 Standardbred questionnaires, and 32 Quarter Horse questionnaires were executed and returned (the largest number of questionnaires were forwarded to Thoroughbred breeders).

No claim is made to having sampled, extensively and scientifically,[2] the breeds to which reference is made; also, for this reason, breed comparisons are not valid. Yet, the facts and figures herewith presented are sufficiently reliable and authoritative (1) to reflect trends, and (2) to serve as guideposts. Also, this was the first serious independent study attempting to diagnose the practices and problems of more than one breed, and to propose economies for the light horse industry.

The important thing is that breeders and breed registry associations face up to the facts, whether good or bad, as applied to their favorite breeds, rather than ignore their weaknesses and problems. By facing the facts, they can best correct deficiencies and move ahead.

---

[1]*The Thoroughbred of California*, March, 1961, p. 258.

[2]Actually, this limited survey points up the urgent need for a much more extensive and complete study of this type. A larger sample would (1) alleviate many of the wide fluctuations reported herein, and (2) eliminate the obvious errors in certain averages.

The questionnaire was designed to establish the knowns. Here is what was found.

I. *National Picture; for Registered Thoroughbreds, Standardbreds, and Quarter Horses*[3]

Mares, average—	Thoroughbred	Standardbred	Quarter Horses	All Three Breeds
No. covered (or bred) annually	22,250	8,500	52,800	83,550
No. live foals born, annually	12,223	6,000	37,000	55,223
Per cent foal crop	55	70	70	66
Per cent of foals registered	89	90	90	90
No. foals produced in lifetime of mare	5	8	7	7
Stallions, average—				
No. mares bred to each stallion each year	10	11	12	11
No. years in service	10	15	10	11
No. living stallions	3,000	2,154	5,628	9,792
No. stallions used in service annually	2,000	1,000	4,400	7,400
Average age of horses at death:				
Males	15	20	15	16
Females	14	20	15	15

II. *Farm or Ranch Inventory*

Average per establishment:—				
No. of acres	1,375	2,330	5,243	2,267
No. of horses:				
Stallions	1.6	3.0	2.7	2.1
Mares in production	9.8	23.9	21.6	14.7
Barren mares	4.2	6.7	3.3	4.3
Yearlings (as of Jan. 1, 1961)	7.6	19.4	11.2	10.0
Two-year-olds (as of Jan. 1, 1961)	4.8	4.1	3.8	4.4
Horses in training or racing	7.0	8.0	4.7	6.5
Other (than those listed above)	6.1	2.3	4.7	5.3
Total number of horses	44.4	67.4	50.9	47.3
Estimated current total of gross value of all horses	$243,100	$232,300	$149,000	$216,100
Estimated current total of gross value of farm or ranch	$246,700	$352,640	$216,430	$252,000
Estimated profit or loss in operations:				
In 1960—(+ or —)	+$926	—$3,083	+$17,789	+$4,700
Average per year for past 3 years—(+ or —)	+$2,449	—$5,272	+$19,550	+$5,700
Average % return on investment past 3 years	+0.5	—0.9	+5.3	+1.2

The Farm or Ranch Inventory survey revealed the following pertinent facts:

1. It takes a great deal of capital to be in the horse business.

2. The physical plants are too expensive, perhaps due to location and/or too many elaborate buildings.

3. Most Thoroughbred and Standardbred breeders need a lucrative outside business to support their horses. By contrast, only one Quarter Horse breeder was losing money.

Generally speaking, those engaged in the light horse business might well be admonished to heed the advice of J. Pierpont Morgan,

---

[3]Estimates in this section arrived at through various channels and deductions; not obtained from questionnaire to individual breeders.

who told an inquiring friend, "If you have to ask what it costs to maintain a yacht, you can't afford it."

III. *Production Record (Breeding Animals)*

Mares, Average:	Thoroughbreds	Standardbreds	Quarter Horses	All Three Breeds
1. No. covered (or bred) annually	27.2	96.5	53.9	42.6
2. No. different heats each mare is covered each year	2.1	2.2	2.2	2.1
3. Where mares are taken away for breeding, no. weeks boarded at location of stallion	11.5	14.9	8.1	11.1
4. No. live foals born	13.0	45.7	22.5	19.7
5. Percent foal crop[4]	79.4	76.8	83.7	80.1
6. Percent of foals registered	92.9	97.6	96.0	94.3
7. No. foals produced in lifetime of mare	6.8	9.3	10.0	8.2
Stallions, average:				
1. No. services per conception	3.6	2.7	3.0	3.3
2. No. mares bred to each stallion each year	17.7	35.0	33.5	25.0
3. No. years in service	7.8	11.9	9.9	10.9
Average age of horses at death:				
Males	18.1	22.0	17.0	18.4
Females	18.2	21.2	17.8	18.4

IV. *Management Record (Breeding Animals)*

	Thoroughbreds	Standardbreds	Quarter Horses	All Three Breeds
1. Average cost per year of maintaining an *in-foal* mare (including interest on investment; facilities; feed cost; service cost of stallion; transportation and board if taken away for service; veterinary costs; labor; etc.)	$1,612	$ 1,386	$ 829	$1,391
2. Average cost per year for maintaining a mature *barren* mare, not in production (including interest on investment; facilities; feed cost; service cost of stallion, if any, even if not in-foal; transportation and board if taken away for service; veterinary cost; labor; etc.)	$1,157	$ 945	$ 731	$1,019
3. Average cost of raising a foal from birth to two years of age	$1,657	$ 1,104	$ 829	$1,365
4. Average cost per year for maintaining a mature stallion (including interest on investment; facilities; feed cost; veterinary cost; labor, etc.)	$1,829	$ 2,002	$ 1,271	$1,670
5. Average stallion cost per foal, either (1) in service fees or (2) in prorated cost of own stallion	$ 964	$ 605	$ 383	$ 736
6. Average annual expenditure per breeding animal (old and young) for drugs, vitamins, minerals, and tonics. (These to be over and above regular veterinary services.)	$ 80.50	$ 61.00	$ 61.00	$72.70
7. Average annual cost per head for veterinary service (including drugs and supplies prescribed by the DVM) of breeding animals.	$ 69.40	$112.50	$ 39.40	$66.40

The *Management Record (Breeding Animals)* revealed the high cost of raising an animal to two years of age. Since many mares are barren, their keep must also be charged against the foals that are produced. For the nation as a whole, it costs an average of $5,099,

---

[4]Obviously, the better producers were responding, because, for the U.S. as a whole, a foal crop of less than sixty per cent is secured.

$3,648, and $2,309, respectively, to raise each a Thoroughbred, a Standardbred, and a Quarter Horse to two years of age. In this connection, it is noteworthy that, in 1960, a total of 1,910 U. S. Thoroughbred yearlings sold for an average of $5,258; and of course, these were the absolute tops. Among experienced horsemen, the feeling persists that only five percent of the matings result in profitable yearlings.

V. *Racing Record (Racing Animals)*

	Thoroughbreds	Standardbreds	Quarter Horses	All Three Breeds
1. Average cost per foal of futurity and stakes nominations and eligibilities	$ 153	$ 1,572	$ 1,105	$ 608
2. No. young animals placed in training each year	4.5	8.5	4.1	4.9
3. No. young animals placed in training each year that actually race	4.2	2.6	2.8	3.7
Per cent trained that race	93.03	30.5	68.3	74.6
4. Of animals raced, average —				
(1) no. years of racing	4.0	3.1	2.7	3.5
(2) no. races	50.7	58.4	21.6	42.2
(3) lifetime earnings	$20,260	$24,250	$8,410	$17,320
5. Average annual cost of keeping a horse in training (trainer, feed and feed additives, veterinary service, etc.)	$3,410	$4,146	$ 2,370	$3,210
6. Average annual cost per head for veterinary services (including drugs and supplies prescribed by the DVM) of each animal in training or on the track[5]	$ 122	$ 243	$ 317	$ 191

7. Most common causes for retiring a horse from the track (ranked from top to bottom with most common reason at top[5]):

Thoroughbreds	Standardbreds	Quarter Horses	All Three Breeds
a. Unsoundness, injury or disease	Unsoundness, injury, or disease	Unsoundness, injury, or disease	Unsoundness, injury, or disease
b. Racing or training practices	Racing or training practices	Racing or training practices	Racing or training practices
c. Old age	For breeding purposes	For breeding purposes	For breeding purposes
d. For breeding purposes	Old age	Old age	Old age
e. Bad manners or nervous	Bad manners or nervous	Bad manners or nervous	Bad manners or nervous

The section headed *Racing Record* (*Racing Animals*) shows that the average owner races for glory, or at least reasons other than profit. For an investment of $17,621 ($3,590 to raise an animal to two years of age—and it is reasonable to surmise that it would cost this much or more to purchase a comparable two-year-old, *plus* $14,031 expenses for three and one-half years on the track), lifetime earnings of $17,320[6] are secured, leaving a deficit of $301 for each

---

[5]It is recognized that many of these conditions are temporary in nature, requiring only a short rest and/or treatment; that horses are not "sent home" or permanently retired therefrom. Also, a horse with not enough speed on one track may be a winner on another track where (1) the competition is less keen, or (2) the conditions are more to the liking of the horse.

[6]Or earnings of $4,950 per year. In 1959, 28,623 starters competed for a gross of $92,848,541 in the United States, Canada and Northern Mexico, or an average of $3,244 per starter (from: *The Thoroughbred of California*, Feb., 1961, p. 143).

horse raced. Hirsch Jacobs, one of the most astute observers on the racing scene, and the man who has saddled more winners than anybody else in the history of the sport, estimates that only five percent of Thoroughbred racing stables make money.[7]

VI. *Horsemen's Experiences in Economy*

Without lowering the quality or size of their operations, the respondents reported that the following practices or programs, by rank, were most important (in breeding and racing) as ways of lowering costs:

Operation	Rank	Thoroughbreds	Standardbreds	Quarter Horses	All Three Breeds
Breeding	1	Breeding—24%	Feeding—23%	Breeding—44%	Breeding—30%
	2	Feeding—23%	Health and care—21%	Feeding—17%	Feeding—21%
	3	Health and care—20%	Breeding—20%	Management—13%	Management—18%
	4	Management—19%	Management—16%	Pastures—10%	Health and care—16%
	5	Pastures—8%	Buildings and equipment—12%	Health and care—9%	Pastures—8%
	6	Buildings and equipment—6%	Pastures—8%	Buildings and equipment—7%	Buildings and equipment—7%

Operation	Rank	Thoroughbreds	Standardbreds	Quarter Horses	All Three Breeds
Racing	1	Optimum racing stable—20%	Evaluate stock—21%	Train at home—54%	Optimum racing stable—21%
	2	Optimum training time—13%	Optimum training time—19% Minimum futurity costs—19%	Optimum racing stable—34%	Train at home—15%
	3	Good care—11%	Train at home—17%	Buildings and equipment—12%	Optimum training time—12%
	4	Evaluate stock—10% Claim sound horses—10%	Optimum racing stable—11%		Evaluate stock—10%
	5	Buildings and equipment—8%	Keep horse in its class—9%		Good care—8% Claim sound horses—8% All others—26%

The percentage figures of the "All Three Breeds" column under "Horsemen's Experiences in Economy" are particularly revealing. In the horse production operations, fifty per cent of the horsemen stated that they have effected their greatest economies in breeding and feeding. By categories and rank, the following comments were most frequent:

1. *Breeding:* (a) Use proven stock, and (b) eliminate inferior animals.

---

[7]From: *The Thoroughbred of California*, Feb., 1961, p. 143.

2. *Feeding:* Keep feed costs to a minimum by (a) raising your own feed or purchasing feeds at the right time, and (b) using quality feeds.

3. *Management:* (a) Analyze expenditures, (b) plan well, (c) use a minimum and reliable labor force efficiently, and (d) maintain optimum size operation.

4. *Health and Care:* (a) Maintain constant vigilance, (b) prevent injuries, and (c) have an adequate parasite control program.

5. *Pastures:* (a) Make maximum use of pastures, and (b) have good pastures—not merely gymnasiums for horses.

6. *Buildings and Equipment:* (a) Design for efficiency and saving in labor, (b) use good feeding and watering equipment, and (c) own your own trailers and vans.

Those who race horses effected their greatest economies in the following areas, by rank:

1. *Optimum Racing Stable:* Only a minimum number of top horses in the racing stable should be maintained.

2. *Training at Home:* The general feeling prevailed that this minimized breakdowns and lessened costs.

3. *Optimum Training Time:* Particular emphasis was placed on avoiding unnecessary time in training, but training until fit and ready.

4. *Evaluate Stock:* There was general agreement that too many horsemen waste money by training a horse that simply doesn't have what it takes; you cannot make a winner out of a plow horse.

5. *Good Care:* Of course, the age-old argument continues; owners feel that trainers let them down, while trainers feel that heredity (genetics) is most important.

6. *Claim Sound Horses:* Several stated that they effect economies in racing simply by claiming sound horses only.

Among the respondents' sage advice and pungent statements appearing under "Horsemen's Experiences in Economy" were these:

1. "Feed them like wild animals, rather than like pampered domesticated creatures," and

2. "Don't try to keep up with the monied Joneses."

A

B

U